CULTURE METHODS
FOR
INVERTEBRATE ANIMALS

THE PREPARATION OF THIS COMPENDIUM

WAS MADE POSSIBLE BY A GRANT FROM

THE NATIONAL RESEARCH COUNCIL

CULTURE METHODS FOR INVERTEBRATE ANIMALS

A Compendium prepared cooperatively by
American zoologists under the direction
of a committee from Section F of
the American Association for
the Advancement of Science

PAUL S. GALTSOFF
FRANK E. LUTZ · PAUL S. WELCH
JAMES G. NEEDHAM, *Chairman*

*assisted by many specialists whose names appear
in connection with their respective
contributions to this volume.*

Dover Publications, Inc.

New York, New York

Manufactured in the United States of America

Dover Publications, Inc.
180 Varick Street
New York 14, New York

20878

PREFACE

THIS *book has been prepared as an aid to studies that require living animals in continuous supply. They are needed both for teaching and for research, especially for research in genetics, in parasitology, in experimental zoology, in economic entomology, and in nearly every field of applied biology. They are needed in aviaries, in aquaria, in fish culture experiment stations, and in zoological gardens where they are used as food for carnivorous animals. Such needs have seemed to justify an effort to gather together the experience of many scattered workers and make their useful results more widely available.*

The task of the committee in charge has been a simple one—that of serving as a medium for the exchange of experience by actual workers. So we have announced the undertaking to the zoological public and we have personally invited contributions from those we have known to be keeping cultures of small animals. We have put together with a minimum of editing what they have offered. Our responsibility ends here. The articles bear the names of their contributors. We do not guarantee the methods outlined. Indeed, there are great difficulties in keeping cultures going, and failures will occur betimes even in the hands of careful workers. Constant alertness is required to see that fit conditions are maintained, and a large measure of ingenuity is often necessary to adapt places and circumstances to keeping conditions fit.

Thus this is a compendium in the older sense of that word (con and pendere, weighing together), rather than a digest. Perhaps condensation may be in order later when more animals have been managed successfully and more experience has accumulated. This is only a beginning. The gaps in our knowledge are numerous and very obvious. Comparatively few invertebrate animals have been tried as yet, and very few have been managed with complete success.

These pages will record the experience of those among us who have had some measure of success in rearing various invertebrate animals, and will give the methods they have found most useful. It is to be expected that these methods may be improved by further trial. That economic values and gains to health and comfort will grow out of further work along these lines is altogether probable, for the scientific use of our animal resources has only just begun.

Some very simple procedures are included. We have not forgotten the needs of the high school teacher who is wise enough and diligent enough to teach zoology with the saving grace and with the quickening thrill that comes from the use of living materials.

The Committee wishes to acknowledge the efficient aid of its secretary, Miss Mary E. Davis, who has carried a very large share of the burden of this compilation. The task has been lightened by receipt of many valuable voluntary contributions, and the response from those to whom we have appealed for culture methods has been both prompt and generous.

PAUL S. GALTSOFF
FRANK E. LUTZ
PAUL S. WELCH
JAMES G. NEEDHAM, *Chairman*

TABLE OF CONTENTS

PHYLUM I. PROTOZOA

Class Mastigophora

Class Sarcodina

Contents

Contents

Contents

Contents

Contents

PHYLUM XIV. ARTHROPODA
Class Crustacea

Contents

Class Myriapoda

Class Insecta

Contents

PAGE

Contents

Contents

Contents

Contents

PHYLUM XV. MOLLUSCA
Class Amphineura

Class Gastropoda

Class Pelecypoda

PHYLUM XVI. ECHINODERMATA
Class Asteroidea

Class Ophiuroidea

Class Echinoidea

Class Holothurioidea

PHYLUM XVII. CHORDATA
Class Ascidiacea

CULTURE METHODS

FOR

INVERTEBRATE ANIMALS

CONTRIBUTORS

*This list includes the names of those only who prepared material
especially for publication in this volume. The names of
other authors will be found in the index.*

Ackert, J. E.
Adams, J. Alfred
Andrews, E. A.
Archer, A. F.
Baerg, W. J.
Bahrs, Alice M.
Baker, F. C.
Banta, A. M.
Barker, H. Albert
Beers, C. Dale
Berrill, N. J.
Bess, Henry A.
Blake, Charles H.
Blount, Raymond F.
Bond, R. M.
Bowen, W. B.
Boyd, Mark F.
Brandwein, Paul
Brigham, W. T.
Briscoe, M. S.
Brown, M. G.
Burger, Elizabeth
Butt, F. H.
Butts, H. E.
Cain, T. L., Jr.
Calvert, P. P.
Carmichael, E. B.
Carothers, E. Eleanor
Cederstrom, J. A.
Chandler, Asa C.
Cheatum, Elmer P.
Christenson, Reed O.
Clarke, George L.
Clausen, Lucy W.
Coe, Wesley R.
Coker, R. E.
Conklin, E. G.
Danielson, R. N.
Darby, Hugh H.
Davis, Donald W.
Davis, Mary E.
Davis, W. H.
Dawson, R. W.

DeCoursey, R. M.
Didlake, Mary L.
Dobrovolny, C. G.
Doering, Kathleen C.
Dolley, W. L., Jr.
Federighi, H.
Fenton, F. A.
Ferris, Josephine C.
Finley, Harold E.
Flanders, Stanley E.
Florence, Laura
Fluke, C. L., Jr.
Forbes, W. T. M.
Ford, Norma
Fox, Henry
Fry, Henry J.
Fuller, John L.
Fulton, B. B.
Galtsoff, Paul S.
Garman, Philip
Gerould, J. H.
Giese, A. C.
Gilchrist, F. G.
Graham, S. A.
Grave, Benjamin H.
Grave, Caswell
Grieve, Evelyn G.
Griswold, Grace H.
Guberlet, John E.
Hall, R. P.
Halsey, H. R.
Harris, H. M.
Hart, Josephine F. L.
Hasler, Arthur D.
Hassett, C. C.
Heath, Harold
Hegner, R. W.
Hendee, Esther C.
Hess, Margaret
Hess, Walter N.
Hetherington, Alford
Hicks, C. H.
Hoffmann, C. H.

Hogue, M. J.
Holmquist, A. M.
Hopkins, D. L.
Hough, W. S.
Huff, Clay G.
Hurlbut, H. S.
Hyman, Libbie H.
Jacot, Arthur Paul
Jahn, Theodore L.
Johnson, M. W.
Jones, Edgar P.
Jones, R. M.
Kepner, William A.
King, J. L.
Knowlton, G. F.
Kofoid, Charles A.
Kohls, Glen M.
Kornhauser, S. I.
Krull, Wendell
Larsen, E. J.
La Rue, George R.
LeRay, William
Lindgren, D. L.
Lotze, John C.
Ludwig, Daniel
Lutz, F. E.
MacGinitie, G. E.
MacKay, Donald C. G.
Mann, William M.
Marcovitch, S.
Maxwell, Kenneth E.
McCay, C. M.
McNeil, Ethel
Melampy, R. M.
Melvin, Roy
Menusan, H., Jr.
Miller, E. D.
Minnich, D. E.
Moore, J. Percy
Mote, Don C.
Mulrennan, J. A.
Mundinger, F. G.
Murphy, Helen E.

Myers, Earl H.
Nabours, Robert K.
Needham, J. G.
Needler, Alfreda B.
Novikoff, Alex B.
Nuttycombe, John W.
Pace, D. M.
Packard, Charles Earl
Park, Thomas
Patch, Esther M.
Penn, Amos B. K.
Phillies, George
Prytherch, H. S.
Pyenson, L.
Rawlins, W. A.
Readio, Philip A.
Reynolds, Bruce D.
Rice, N. E.
Richardson, H. H.

Ries, Donald T.
Rogers, J. Speed
Rogick, Mary
Schluchter, Alfred W.
Schread, J. C.
Schwardt, H. H.
Scotland, Minnie B.
Setty, Laurel R.
Shepard, H. H.
Shull, A. F.
Smith, George A.
Smith, Helen B.
Smith, Roger C.
Smith, T. L.
Snider, George G.
Sonneborn, T. M.
Spencer, G. J.
Stirewalt, M. Amelia
Stump, A. B.

Stunkard, H. W.
Sturtevant, A. H.
Tait, John
Taylor, C. V.
Thomas, J. O.
Thomsen, Lillian
Trager, William
Turner, John P.
Vance, A. M.
Vaughan, Thomas W.
Wadley, F. M.
Welch, P. S.
Welsh, John H.
Wheeler, Esther W.
White, G. F.
Whiting, P. W.
Wilson, H. V.
Wray, D. L.
Wulzen, Rosalind

INTRODUCTION

By James G. Needham

THE needs of animals determine all successful rearing practices. Their basic requirements are four: (1) *Food;* (2) *Protection from enemies;* (3) *A suitable physical environment:* these for individual livelihood; and also for the maintenance of successive generations; (4) *Fit conditions for reproduction.*

Culturing animals doubtless began with collecting and caring for living specimens, and the first suggestions for supplying their needs in captivity were gained (as they are still to be gained) by carefully observing them in their natural habitat. There they are seen eating their food, constructing their homes, eluding their enemies, accepting their mates, and rearing their offspring. There is no better way to proceed in the beginning than by imitating natural conditions. Our methods must be adapted to the ways of the animal, for only in a very small measure will it change its ways for ours. Especially in the reproductive habits will it show readiness to go its hereditary way, and stubborn refusal to go any other. We may learn by experiment how best to meet its needs under indoor conditions. It is not so much close imitation of the natural environment, as careful feeding and attention to hygienic needs that make for permanent maintenance. Artificial devices may replace and may even better those found in nature (witness the movable-frame beehive as compared with the hollow tree), but the basic requirements of the animal remain ever the same.

This book is concerned with methods of management of animal cultures under control. In the following pages will be found, first some general suggestions covering the principles of culture management by members of the Committee, followed by more specific and detailed methods for rearing particular groups or species, written by many individual contributors and collaborators. As stated in our call for such materials (*Science* 77:427, 1933), we have sought to obtain for at least one species of each considerable group of invertebrates "a fairly complete account of maintenance requirements, covering collecting methods and devices, cages and breeding quarters, plans for feeding and watering, cleaning and aerating quarters, breeding management, and all else that enters into the maintenance of the species through successive generations." When such an account was not available we have welcomed scraps of information that seemed likely to be helpful toward culture-keeping. The contributed articles vary therefore from mere suggestions as to how to get living specimens, to measured procedures quantitatively determined. We have filled some of the more obvious gaps with abstracts and reprintings (initialed by the editor responsible) from available literature but we have by no means exhausted this source of material.

The contributed articles are arranged as far as possible in systematic order following Pratt's *Manual of the Common Invertebrate Animals* (revision of 1935), with the orders of insects following that of Comstock's *Manual for the Study of Insects* (1926 edition). Material within the insect orders is arranged according to the *N. Y. State List of Insects*.

Since from the nature of the book the different types of procedure are widely scattered through its pages, we have tried to make an index that would serve as a finding list for them, and we recommend that the user consult the index freely.

We have assumed on the part of the reader some acquaintance with general zoology and some knowledge of elementary laboratory technique. Limitations of space have necessitated that we restrict the text rather closely to collecting and culture methods. In doing so we have had to omit some interesting and valuable material, principally introductory remarks, systematic discussion, life history details, and suggestions for the use of the materials in special fields. We have also done some condensing to avoid undesirable duplications, and we hope that in so doing we have not been unfair to any of our helpfully minded collaborators. Papers by members of the scientific staffs of federal departments and bureaus have come to us each bearing a statement that it is offered for publication with the permission of the head of the Department concerned. Receipt of these statements is hereby acknowledged; but the statements themselves are omitted from the text to make room for more useful material.

It is hoped that this compilation on culture methods may stimulate interest in maintaining living animals in biological laboratories and may lead to further development of the proper technique. We will be glad to hear comments from the users of this book upon the usefulness of the methods here offered and to learn of new developments in the use of them; for it seems highly probable that both eliminations and improvements resulting from further trials will make necessary an early revision of this compendium.

General Methods of Collecting, Maintaining, and Rearing Marine Invertebrates in the Laboratory

PAUL S. GALTSOFF, *U. S. Bureau of Fisheries*

COLLECTING

THE selection of the equipment for collecting marine animals is governed by various considerations, of which the character of the bottom, depth of water, number of specimens the investigator desires to obtain, the purpose of collecting, and the animal which he seeks, are of

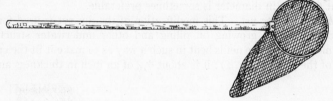

FIG. 1.—The dip net.

paramount importance. The following account describes the instruments which may be needed by an individual collector who desires to bring live material to his laboratory. The description of the method of collecting large numbers of specimens for museums and supply houses, as well as the account of the various oceanographic instruments used in a quantitative study of ocean life are beyond the scope of this book. The reader interested in this matter is referred to such books as: Murray and Hjort (1912); Johnstone (1908); Bulletin No. 85, Oceanography, of the National Research Council (1932); numerous publications of the *Conseil Permanent pour l'Exploration de la Mer; Wissenschaftliche Meeresuntersuchungen* (abt. Helgoland and abt. Kiel), and to the descriptions of equipment given in the reports of various oceanographic expeditions.

The dip net. The dip net (Fig. 1) is the handiest and most indispensable piece of equipment that can be used for many purposes and under a great variety of conditions. It consists of a conical net bag attached to a stout ring made of galvanized iron or preferably of brass and fixed to a wooden handle. The bag usually measures about 1 foot in diameter at the opening and 18 inches in depth. The netting may vary from 1 inch mesh at the top with ½ inch at the bottom for larger specimens, to ¾ of an inch at the top with ⅜ inch mesh at the bottom for smaller forms. For collecting minute organisms a bag made of bolting silk Nos. 12, 16, or 20 may be substituted. The handle is usually from 6 to 7 feet long, but of course may be increased to any desired length.

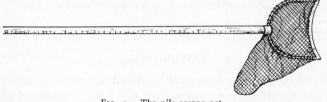

FIG. 2.—The pile scrape net.

For picking up small specimens floating on the water a small dip net about 6 inches in diameter is sometimes preferable.

The pile scrape net. This modification of the dip net is used for collecting organisms growing on piling and other underwater structures. The metal ring of the net is bent in such a way as to make it fit the curvature of the piling (Fig. 2); it is about $\frac{9}{16}$ of an inch in thickness and 12

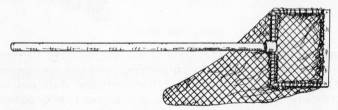

FIG. 3.—The square scrape net.

inches in diameter with the curved scraper 1 inch in width. Attached to this frame is a net 18 inches in depth with the mesh ¾ of an inch at the top and ½ of an inch or less at the bottom. The metal blade which is welded to the lower part of the iron frame works as a cutting knife when the net is pressed against the piling and is pulled up. The length of the handle varies according to local conditions from 6 to 20 feet.

The square scrape net. This type is a modification of the pile scrape net from which it differs only in the shape of the frame, which is not bent (Fig. 3) as it is in the former type, and is provided with a straight cutting blade attached to the base. This net is very useful in collecting organisms growing on walls of various underwater structures such as stone breakwaters and docks. It may be used also for obtaining specimens living on hard or sandy bottoms.

The oyster tongs. Oyster tongs, generally used by fishermen for taking oysters from shallow water, may be used for collecting other bottom animals. This much used implement (Fig. 4) is made of a pair of rakes attached to the lower ends of two long handles fastened together like the blades of shears. The rakes are so fitted together that they rest upon the bottom parallel to each other when the handles are spread. By bringing the handles together the instrument is closed and the teeth of each rake interlock. The rakes are about 14 inches wide with the teeth 3-4 inches long and placed about 1½ inches apart. Oyster tongs are usually available in four sizes, 8, 10, 12, and 16 feet long, although 20 foot handles are sometimes used by the fishermen. Tonging may be efficiently carried out even by an inexperienced collector in water less than 12 feet deep.

FIG. 4.—The oyster tongs.

The digger. The most universal way of obtaining mollusks, worms, and other forms inhabiting muddy bottoms, is with rakes. The simplest type is the ordinary potato digger (Fig. 5) with four to six long thin prongs, and fitted with a handle about 5 feet long. The digger may be conveniently used on the exposed tidal flats. For working under

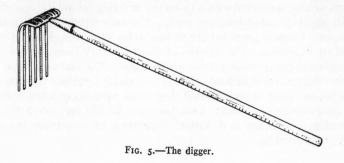

FIG. 5.—The digger.

water the back of the digger is covered with wire netting which holds the animals caught by the prongs. This instrument is commonly used for digging hard clams (Venus) and other mollusks.

The basket rake. By fastening a basket of wire netting to the ordinary garden rake (Fig. 6) a very useful instrument may be made which is

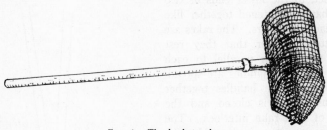

FIG. 6.—The basket rake.

operated either by wading or from a boat. The shape and dimensions of the basket and the mesh of the wire netting vary greatly depending upon the locality and depth of the water in which the implement is to be used. The type of basket rake used for collecting Venus in the deep water of Cape Cod consists of an iron framework forming a curved bowl, the under edge of which is set with 20 steel teeth about $2\frac{1}{2}$ inches in length (Fig. 7). The bowl of the rake, strengthened by side and cross

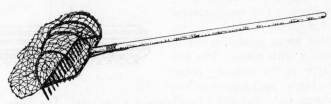

FIG. 7.—The basket rake, Cape Cod type.

pieces of iron, is covered with a twine net dragging behind it. Sometimes teeth about 4 inches long are used. The rake weighs from 15 to 20 pounds. There is great variety in the styles and sizes of basket rakes used by fishermen. The handles of the rakes vary from 23 to 65 feet according to the prevailing depth of the water. The rakes are often provided with several detachable handles of various lengths. Although the handles are made of strong wood they break very easily when operated by inexperienced collectors, since they are flexible and very thin, not exceeding $1\frac{1}{2}$ inches in diameter. Operation of long rakes (65 feet) requires great skill.

The clam hoe and the hooker. These instruments are used for digging in shallow water or on the exposed sand or mud flats. The clam hoe (Fig. 8) has four prongs about 1¼ inches wide and from 12 to 14 inches long, and a strong wooden handle about 4 feet in length. The instrument is suitable for digging in coarse sand or gravel. The hooker

FIG. 8.—The clam hoe.   FIG. 9.—The hooker.

(Fig. 9) used in digging in the hard mud, has four thin, sharp prongs and a short handle.

The shovel. An ordinary steel shovel is a valuable tool for collecting animals living in sand or mud on the beaches or in shallow water.

The dredge. The dredge is the most efficient instrument for collecting bottom dwelling forms regardless of the depth of the water. Dredging at great depths is a difficult operation requiring costly equipment, but dredging in shallow water not exceeding 100 feet, may be carried out from a small boat and does not require special machinery. There are many types and sizes of dredges, ranging from small instruments about 1 foot wide to large commercial oyster dredges several feet wide and having a capacity of over 25 bushels. The description given here refers only to small instruments that may easily be used by the collector of scientific material.

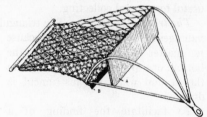

FIG. 10.—The scallop dredge.

The dredge is always made of a rigid iron frame to which a bag made of heavy netting or interwoven chain rings is attached. The most commonly used type is the so-called scraper or scallop dredge (Fig. 10) which consists of a triangular framework with an iron blade (B), 2 inches wide, set at an angle so as to dig into the bottom. On the upper side a raised cross bar connects the two arms. The net with a wooden horizontal bar at the end is fastened to the cross bar and to the top of the blade. Additional weight (A) may be put on the cross bar if it is desired that the instrument cut deeper into the bottom. The dredge shown in figure 10 has a metal sheet (A) which serves the double purpose of providing additional weight and pushing the material scraped by the blade into the bag. The usual dimensions are as follows: arms, 2½ feet; cross bar, 2 feet; blade, 2½ feet long and 2 inches wide. For operating on rough bottoms the blade is set level or even with a slight upward incline, so the dredge will slide over the bottom. A dredge of this type may be made of any size and is very useful for general collecting. For small

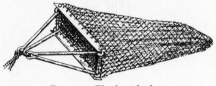

organisms the bags must be made of a fine twine netting or of some other strong, coarse material of the desired mesh.

Instead of a cutting blade the dredge may be provided with a set of teeth. This

Fig. 11.—The box dredge.

type is commonly used for dredging oysters.

The box dredge. The box dredge (Fig. 11) consists of a rectangular iron framework 27 x 12 inches, with two folding arms and two cutting blades, one on each side of the dredge. A bag of coarse netting is attached to the blades. When in operation the two arms are tied together by a piece of string and the drag line is fastened only to one arm. If the dredge is caught under rocks the string breaks and the instrument may be saved by dragging it sidewise by one arm. This small dredge is very useful for general collecting.

The triangular dredge. The triangular dredge (Fig. 12) has some advantages over the other types because no matter which side rests on the bottom one of the blades will cut into the ground when the instrument is dragged.

To facilitate the finding of a dredge in case the drag line snaps, a tail buoy is attached with a length of rope slightly greater than the depth

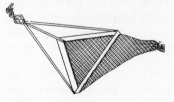

Fig. 12.—The triangular dredge. *After Hagmeier.*

of the water. When the instrument is being dragged slight shocks caused by the impact of the frame with rocks or other objects are conveyed along the rope and are easily noticed by the operator holding it in his hands or only touching it. He can easily feel the change in vibration when the dredge slides over the bottom without cutting into it. In this case more rope should be given out or the speed of the boat reduced.

The material collected in the dredge must be washed free of mud and sorted. For this purpose it is convenient to have a set of sieves with various meshes into which the contents of a dredge is dumped and washed by dipping into the sea. (See p. 534 for drill trap dredge.)

The tangle or mop. This implement (Fig. 13) may easily be made by attaching long loose cotton strands to an iron bar. When trailed along the bottom it captures echinoderms and spiny crustaceans with which it may come in contact. The tangle is widely used in Long Island Sound by the oystermen for removing starfish from their oyster bottoms and is available in various sizes and styles.

The grapple. The grapple (Fig. 14) consists of a number of steel wires passed through a galvanized pipe about one foot long and $1\frac{1}{4}$

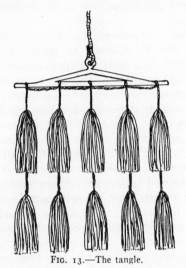

FIG. 13.—The tangle.

FIG. 14.—The grapple.

inches in diameter, the inside of which is filled with lead. The lower ends of the wires are bent back to form hooks, the upper being twisted to make a loop for the attachment of a line. The grapple is very useful for collecting submerged vegetation which may contain rich fauna of crustaceans, worms, Bryozoa, *etc.**

The plankton net. Small organisms suspended in the water are collected by means of a plankton net (Fig. 15) which is towed behind the boat or is allowed to sink and is then slowly hauled up. To avoid backwashing of the material caught in the net the rate of towing or hauling should not exceed 1 meter per second. Plankton nets may be made of various grades of bolting silk depending upon the size of the organisms one is planning to catch. For small planktonic forms No. 20 or 25

*Editor's Note: Lacking a grapple, a substitute for it may be made by coiling a long piece of barbed wire in a circle, fastening it at the overlaps, and attaching a weight at one side and a throwline at the other. This will gather submerged vegetation effectively. J. G. N.

should be used. It is advisable to have the silk part of the net sewn on a canvas collar folded over the metal ring and fastened to it by means of buttons. The lower end of the net is also made of a canvas collar which is slipped over the metal bucket and fastened to it by a clamp ring. The bucket has windows covered with bolting silk and is provided with a stop cock for draining. A small glass bottle or jar may be used instead of a bucket. Nets one foot in diameter are the most convenient ones to handle from a small boat.

The plankton trawl. Planktonic forms living just above the bottom may be collected by means of a plankton net mounted in a horizontal position on a frame attached at right angles to a sheet of galvanized iron. When the plankton trawl (Fig. 16) is dragged it slides over the bottom and catches the organisms which otherwise escape capture. The metal sheet protects the net which does not come in contact with the bottom and therefore may be made of fine bolting silk.

The glass bottomed box. In shallow waters the observation and collection of bottom animals are greatly facilitated by using a water tight box with a pane of plate glass fitted in the bottom. The dimensions and shape may vary to suit individual purposes. The box

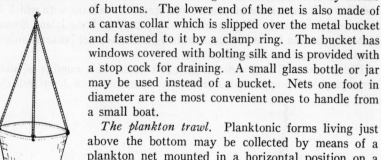

FIG. 15.—The plankton net.

used by the author is 11 inches high with square bottom and top, 9 x 9 and 11 x 11 inches respectively (Fig. 17). It is fastened to a boat by a short line and is placed in the water with the glass side down. It smooths the ruffled surface of the water.

Goggles. Goggles (Fig. 18) are widely used in the Orient by pearl-

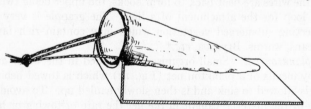

FIG. 16.—The plankton trawl.

oyster fishermen and may be used to aid in the collection and observation of shallow water animals inhabiting the ocean floor. Those with wooden frames are the most convenient for they may be carved to fit the eye-sockets. Condensation of vapor on the inside may be avoided by following the method of the Philippine divers who rub the glass with tobacco soaked in water. Goggles of the type shown may be obtained in Honolulu in almost every store handling fishing tackle and other sporting goods.

The diving helmet. The diving helmet, very useful in warm and clear waters, has become a part of the regular equipment of tropical marine stations. It may not be used by an individual collector, for the operation requires a crew of at least two, and preferably three men to operate the pump and watch the diver. For an untrained person it is inadvisable to descend beyond the 30 foot limit.

Miscellaneous equipment. An experienced collector never forgets a

FIG. 17.—The glass bottomed box.   FIG. 18.—Goggles.

pocket lens of about 8 or 12 power magnification, mounted in a metal frame and suspended from the neck by means of a cord.

For collecting among coral reefs and rocks a good crow bar and cold chisel are indispensable.

Living forms should be placed immediately in a suitable container about ¾ full of seawater. An ordinary milk can, preferably of white porcelain, is very convenient for this purpose. Small organisms may be placed in fruit jars, bottles, or vials. Overcrowding and exposure to direct sunlight should be avoided. All the containers should be kept open as long as possible. In a hot climate keeping the container packed in ice is sometimes necessary if the organisms are in transport for several hours.

MARINE AQUARIA

Aquarium tanks. Various types of aquarium tanks found on the market may be used successfully for keeping live material. A simple water-tight box with an inlet and outlet for seawater may be used for this purpose. A coat of black asphalt paint provides sufficient protection for the wood and is perfectly harmless even to the most delicate forms.* It may be constructed according to the desired size and shape. So-called "white wood" (trade name) untreated in any way but absolutely dry should be used. All wooden parts must be painted separately before they are put together and a second coat of paint (No. 24 Scotch heater, manufactured by Billing and Chapin Co., N. Y.) is applied after the aquarium is assembled. To prevent cracking of the wood, the aquaria must be kept moist all the time. For mounting the glass a type of putty containing no toxic substances and remaining plastic for a long period should be used. Putties that harden quickly should be avoided for they may exert uneven pressure on the glass wall and cause it to crack.**

For more critical experimental work in which a complete elimination of foreign substances is important, only glass containers should be used. All kinds of glassware found on the market may be used for the cultivation of marine forms. Fruit jars, battery jars, precipitating cylinders and more expensive pyrex containers of various shapes and dimensions may be suitable depending upon the requirements of the investigator. If running seawater is not needed small and medium-sized organisms may be kept successfully in ordinary finger bowls, 4 inches in diameter, or in so-called specimen dishes, 7 inches in diameter. These dishes made of heavy glass may be placed one on top of another and are very easy to handle.

For delicate physiological work, as for instance the experiments on fertilization, only the best grade of glass or even quartz should be used. A cheap type of glassware is usually more or less discolored and of uneven thickness. These defects make it unsuitable for photography or for the observation of organisms through a low powered microscope. For these purposes a better type of glassware with parallel walls should be selected. For the cultivation of diatoms, other marine unicellular algae, and flagellates small round flasks are usually used.

Success in cultivating marine organisms depends not so much on the shape and size of the container used as on the cleanliness of the glass. This fact cannot be overemphasized, for many observations have been ruined because of the contamination of the glass by toxic substances the presence of which was not suspected. It is a safe rule in experimenting with living forms never to use glassware which has been previously em-

---

* If it is intended to keep the organisms under observation, a glass walled aquarium should be used.

** The following recipe developed by Prof. Petrunkevitch was found to be excellent: place a portion of spar varnish in a can, stir in screened Portland cement until quite thick. Do not add more cement until the combined mass has stood one or two hours. As the mixture thickens in standing, the consistency should be nearly that of putty. Keep in tightly covered cans.

ployed in the laboratory for some other purpose and may have been in contact with such toxic substances as corrosive sublimate, picric acid, salts of chromic acid, or formalin. There is a considerable difference in the degree of absorption of poisons by glass, corrosive sublimate for instance being the most difficult to remove. When chromium cleaning fluid has been used glassware must be meticulously washed to remove traces of chromium salts. Glassware available in marine laboratories should always be regarded with a certain degree of suspicion because of the impossibility of ascertaining the purposes for which it was previously employed.

New glassware just delivered from the factory need not be washed with cleaning fluid. It should be rinsed in water and, if necessary, washed with "Bon Ami" which is preferable to soaps and soap powders because it is more readily removed. After being used for keeping eggs and larvae the dishes should never be washed directly in freshwater because of the danger of the cytolyzed cells sticking to the glass (Just, 1928). They should be first rinsed with seawater and then washed with freshwater. In drying the glassware, towels coming from the laundry should be avoided because of the alkali present in them. If it is necessary to wipe the glassware, cheesecloth or other soft material washed free from chemicals should be used. Clean dishes should be stacked on filter paper or a clean dry cloth and protected from dust. The practice of placing them upside down on the laboratory table is undesirable because of the possibility of chance contamination. Glassware used in the cultivation of diatoms and other algae should be sterilized in a dry oven ($1\frac{1}{2}$ hours at 160°C).

The use of celluloid. Very often the investigator is confronted with the necessity of making a tank or an apparatus of a special design to be used for a physiological or embryological experiment. The problem is easily solved by using celluloid which is made in sheets about 3 x 5 feet, ranging in thickness from 0.005 to 0.125 inch. The celluloid manufactured by the Dupont Company and other companies producing cellulose by-products may appear in the market under different trade names (pyralin, viscoloid, *etc.*). Clear as well as opaque celluloids and that frosted on one or both sides are available. The thin sheets are almost as transparent as glass but the thicker ones are less clear and have a slightly yellowish hue. Celluloid sheets may be cut by scissors or sawed with a hacksaw. After the edges have been filed and sandpapered the pieces may be stuck together with glue made of a thin solution of celluloid in acetone. This solution dries very quickly and the making of the apparatus presents no difficulty.

Strips and sheets of celluloid may be bent to a desired shape by warming them in hot water. After being cooled they become rigid again.

Celluloid is non-corrosive and apparently insoluble in seawater. It has proved to be the most valuable and indispensable material for the physiological work carried on in the author's laboratory at the U. S. Bureau of Fisheries station at Woods Hole, Mass. (See note 1 on p. 50.)

Seawater supply. Marine biological laboratories are usually provided with running seawater pumped from the sea and stored in tanks. The installation of a satisfactory salt water system is primarily an engineering and architectural problem the discussion of which is beyond the scope of the present book. It suffices to mention here that seawater delivered to the laboratory tables must be pure and should not contain toxic substances. Attempts are always made therefore to avoid its contact with heavy, easily oxidized metals such as iron and copper by using lead, rubber, or rubber-lined steel pipes and nickel or rubber pumps. Many marine laboratories use large capacity bronze pumps which give satisfactory results, for the seawater comes in contact with the metal part of a pump only for a very short time. Celluloid has been recommended for pipe and fittings and is very successfully used by the Biological Station and Aquarium at Helgoland (Hagmeier, 1925). Seawater delivered to a laboratory table through rubber-lined or celluloid pipes seems to be deprived of toxic substances, and may safely be used for physiological experiments and the cultivation of the most delicate marine forms.

The investigator is sometimes confronted with the necessity of conducting his research in a locality remote from a permanent biological station. He can, however, easily provide himself with running seawater by purchasing a small centrifugal pump with an electric motor, a sufficient length of ordinary garden hose and a small tank which should be supported by a platform. A pump delivering 5-10 gallons a minute and two 50-gallon wooden barrels for a storage tank, placed 5-6 feet above ground will provide a sufficient amount of running water for four or five aquaria. One of the barrels may be equipped with a float connected to a switch controlling the operation of the motor so that the pump works only when the water in the barrels reaches a certain low level. The whole equipment may be purchased and assembled for about $60.00.

It has been the author's experience in establishing small temporary laboratories in various localities along the Atlantic and Gulf coasts that ordinary cast iron pumps are preferable to bronze ones. There is but little oxidation of iron when the pump is in operation and consequently water delivered to the laboratory is not toxic. Furthermore, water supplied under similar conditions by bronze pumps proves to be much more harmful to a number of marine forms, such as lamellibranch larvae, that are very sensitive to minute amounts of copper.

A great number of investigators located in inland laboratories are interested in the possibility of maintaining marine forms in a limited amount of seawater, shipped to them from the nearest place on the shore. For this purpose water must be collected from an unpolluted locality, preferably off shore, and stored in a suitable container. Glass bottles are of course ideal but not always practicable for shipping.

If storage in glass containers is desired the ordinary carboys for spring or distilled water may be used. A more practicable and cheaper way is to collect and ship seawater in 25 or 50 gallon paraffined oak barrels. After a few days of storage the organisms present in the water die and the decomposing organic matter depletes the oxygen content of the water, resulting in the accumulation of hydrogen sulphide (H_2S). This, however, does not render the water unsuitable for laboratory use. By aerating the sample for several hours all the hydrogen sulphide is driven out or oxidized and the sulphur is precipitated and may be filtered off. The author's experiments (unpublished data) show that the presence of sulphur is not harmful to many marine invertebrates and that it promotes the growth of Nitzschia cultures.

Seawater in which marine forms have been kept may again be made suitable by filtering it through a layer of gravel and sand and aerating it. Increase in the concentration of salts owing to evaporation may be compensated for by the addition of distilled water, while the deficiency of calcium, phosphates, nitrates, and other salts used up by the organisms is restored by the proper dosage of these respective substances. The simplest way of controlling the concentration of salts consists in marking the level of water in a tank and adding distilled water whenever the level falls because of evaporation. Should a more accurate check be desired the salinity of the water may be determined by titrating the sample with a silver nitrate solution and finding the corresponding concentration in Knudsen's tables. A description of the standard method of salinity determination may be found in Murray and Hjort (1912) and Oxner (1920).

Filtration. Natural seawater may contain large quantities of suspended organic and inorganic matter which must be filtered out before it is supplied to the laboratory table. For this purpose some of the marine laboratories and aquaria have a more or less elaborate system of filters consisting of several layers of gravel and sand through which the water is allowed to pass. The institutions located far from the sea and dependent in their operations upon a more or less limited supply of water, as a rule filter the water as it leaves the aquarium tanks before using it again. In the laboratories located on the seashore the water is pumped directly into tanks in which it remains for a period of time sufficient for the settling of a considerable portion of sediment. The outlet through which the water is drawn from a storage tank is always located several inches above the bottom. A small amount of seawater may be made to last a long time if the investigator regularly filters and aerates it. A very convenient type of filter (Fig. 19) consists of a water-

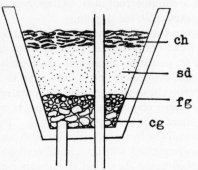

tight wooden box with two pipes passing through its bottom. The long pipe serves as an overflow while filtered water runs through a short pipe after having passed through a layer of charcoal (ch), sand (sd), fine gravel (fg) and coarse gravel (cg). From a reservoir (not shown in the figure) the water is delivered to the aquaria. When in operation the filter is placed below the aquarium from which the water is drawn. (See also p. 540.)

Fig. 19.—Filter for seawater. *After Sachs*. cg, coarse gravel; ch, charcoal; fg, fine gravel; sd, sand.

Sometimes experimental work requires the use of seawater entirely devoid of any suspended matter, either inorganic or organic. It may be obtained by filtering through collodion membranes (ultrafiltration), using fine Berkefeld filters, or by passing through a thick layer of asbestos. Water obtained by the latter method may not be free from bacteria but contains no plankton or micro-plankton. A typical arrangement is shown in figure 20. From a laboratory faucet seawater runs slowly into a large Buchner funnel, the bottom of which is covered with a layer of asbestos (A) about 1 inch thick. A small watch glass is placed on its surface to provide a more uniform distribution of water over the entire area. The funnel is inserted into a neck of a 2 liter vacuum flask connected to a 5 gallon bottle. A glass tube (T) inserted in a stopper of the bottle leads to a suction pump. If neces-

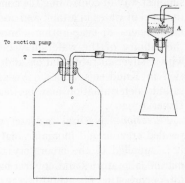

Fig. 20.—Filtering of water through asbestos. A, asbestos; T, glass tube leading to suction pump.

sary, two 5 gallon bottles may be connected in a series. Filtered seawater fills up the flask and gradually is sucked into the bottle. After a few days of operation a compact organic film forms on the surface of the asbestos and filtration becomes much more efficient. The rate of filtration may be regulated by the vacuum produced in the system.

Aeration. The problem of aeration is easily solved in laboratories supplied with compressed air. To avoid possible contamination of water by oil vapors from the pump or by rust which often accumulates in the pipes the air is washed by passing it through a wash bottle filled with water. In most cases the pressure in the compressor is greater than may be used conveniently for aeration. Pressure in the wash bottle, regulated by a number of outlets inserted in the rubber stopper and provided with rubber tubing and screw clamps, may be very accurately adjusted and the system used as a safety valve.

To obtain quick absorption, air blown through water must be delivered in the finest bubbles. This is accomplished by using small blocks made of porous stone (filtros) mounted by means of DeKhotinsky cement at the end of a glass tube. (The blocks are usually available at stores selling aquarium supplies and fishes.) Should less efficient aeration be desired air is blown through a capillary tubing or through a blower (Fig. 21).

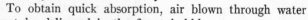

FIG. 21.—The air blower.

In laboratories not equipped with compressed air, aeration may be provided by a small electric pump.*

By means of the following simple devices aeration may be obtained in laboratories not provided with electricity. Two glass cylinders about 8 inches long and 1½ inches wide connected by a long vertical tube are mounted 4 to 5 feet apart on the wall or on a suitable stand (Fig. 22). As the water runs drop by drop through the upper cylinder into a glass tube and fills the lower cylinder, air is sucked through the outlet (A). By regulating the level of the lower outlet (L) a small pressure is produced in the lower cylinder and air is driven through the outlet (C). After being adjusted the cylinders work for a long time without any further attention.

Aeration of the aquarium containing running sea-

FIG. 22.—A simple air pump. A, C, and L, outlets.

* Of the great variety of pumps available on the market the most convenient type for a small laboratory is a model manufactured by Marco Air Product Company, Bloomingfield, N. J. This small and inexpensive instrument is sufficient to aerate 6 or 7 medium-sized tanks. Its operation requires very little attention.

water may be provided efficiently by hanging a loosely fitted glass tube over the faucet and allowing a fine jet of water to strike the surface with

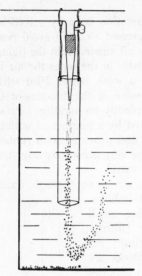

considerable force (Fig. 23). Tiny air bubbles are carried down the entire length of the glass tubing, the lower end of which almost reaches the bottom, and escape through the water, thereby aerating the fluid.

A small but very efficient pump designed by A. E. Hopkins (1934) may be constructed easily from a piece of celluloid. The device consists of a small, motor-driven, centrifugal pump enclosed within a chamber from which it draws water (Fig. 24). The rotor (R) is cut from a piece of celluloid ⅛ inch thick and is mounted on the shaft of ¼ inch glass tubing. The pump receives water through the hole (X) in each side and pumps it out through the tube (O). A larger tube (I) leads from the aquarium into the pump chamber to permit continuous replenishment of the water. The pump is entirely water-lubricated and the only foreign materials used in its construction

FIG. 23.—Aeration by means of a jet of water.

are celluloid, rubber, and glass.

Supersaturation. Not all the forms commonly kept in marine aquaria require aeration. As a matter of fact many of them may be injured or even killed by injudicious aeration. Furthermore, on account of considerable pressure in the seawater pump, water may be supersaturated with air and become decidedly toxic. To avoid injury to the organisms such water must not be delivered directly to the tanks but should be allowed to stand until equilibrium with the atmospheric gases is established. If the water must be

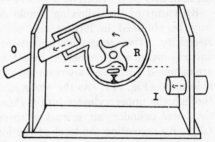

FIG. 24.—The pump for circulation and aeration of water in small aquaria. *After Hopkins.* I, tube leading from aquarium to pump chamber; O, tube for excurrent water; R, rotor; X, hole for incurrent water.

used immediately it should be de-aerated by allowing it to fall on an inclined glass, porcelain, or celluloid plate from which it runs into the aquarium.

Water used in the experiments on fertilization of eggs, development of larvae, *etc.*, should never be taken directly from the laboratory faucet. A suitable container, such as a one or two liter flask, should be filled and set aside for several hours before using to permit the escape of excess of air. For metabolic studies all the micro-organisms suspended in the water must be carefully removed by filtration through a suitable filter and the oxygen content of the sample must be standardized.

Agitation. Agitation of water is essential for maintaining certain forms such as jelly fishes, small crustaceans, larvae of lamellibranch

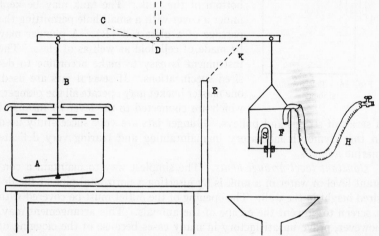

FIG. 25.—The plunger jar. *After E. T. Browne.* A, glass disc or plate; B, glass rod; C, lever; D, axis of lever; E, bar to stop downward motion of bucket; F, bucket; H, flexible hose; K, string; S, siphon.

mollusks, *etc.*, which otherwise settle on the bottom, stick to each other, and die. In the aquaria with running seawater the inlets and outlets may be arranged so as to provide efficient circulation. When the water is not changed for several days or weeks, some method of mechanical agitation is necessary. In a small aquarium this may be accomplished by blowing air through glass tubing lowered to the bottom of the tank. Should aeration not be desired, various kinds of stirring apparatus may be used. There are on the market many types of stirrers, consisting of glass or metal propellers rotated by means of electric motors, which may be adapted to this purpose. The difficulties are that in most cases the stirring devices are designed for use during a limited period of time and are not suitable for long, continuous use. A very simple and practical device which overcomes this difficulty was designed by Browne (1907) and is known as a plunger jar (Fig. 25). It consists of a glass disk or plate (A) suspended from one end of the lever (C), rotating along axis

(D). A bucket (F) with an automatic siphon (S) is suspended from the other end of the lever. The bucket is filled with water delivered through a flexible hose (H). The size of the bucket is so adjusted that when it is almost full it swings down and pulls the plate (A). As soon as the level in the bucket is slightly above the upper level of the siphon the water is emptied through it and the glass plate swings down pulling up the bucket. A bar (E) stops the downward motion of the bucket

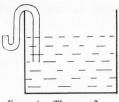

whereas a piece of string (K) prevents the striking of the glass plate (A) against the bottom of the tank. The tank may be kept under a cover with a small hole permitting the passage of a glass rod (B). A plunger may be made of celluloid as well as of glass. The instrument is easy to make according to desired specifications. If several jars are used, one master bucket may operate all the plungers which are connected to the lever by means of

Fig. 26.—The overflow siphon.

a series of strings and pulleys. Plunger jars are very successfully used in the Plymouth laboratory in maintaining and rearing very delicate marine animals.

Constant level arrangements. The simplest way to maintain a constant level of water in a tank is by inserting a horizontal pipe at the desired height in the wall. The opening of the outlet must be covered with a screen to prevent the escape of the animals. This arrangement may, however, prove unsatisfactory in many cases because of the clogging of the screen. Better results are obtained with a vertical overflow pipe passing through the bottom of a tank and protected with a metal screen cylinder extending above the level of the water.

The cylinder is mounted on a tightly fitted cork or rubber stopper with a hole for the passage of a tube. The size of the mesh, of course, depends upon the dimensions of the organisms kept in the tank. The metal screen used for this purpose should not be corrosive in seawater. According to Richards (1933) screens made of pure nickel or of stainless steel are the least toxic.

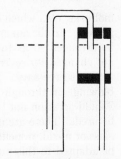

The desired level of running water may be maintained by using an overflow siphon which is made by bending over one arm of a U-shaped glass and placing it in a position shown in figure 26. The controlling level of the siphon may be

Fig. 27.—The overflow siphon. *Adapted from Hagmeier.*

changed easily by attaching a rubber tubing to the short arm and fastening the free end of it at the desired height.

In another type of arrangement (Fig. 27) the outside arm of the siphon is inserted in a small glass cylinder. A glass tube passing through the bottom serves as an overflow controlling the level in the tank. The instrument may easily be made from a large test tube by cutting off its bottom and inserting two rubber stoppers. A hole in the upper stopper serves for the escape of air.

The following arrangement (Fig. 28) permits a careful regulation of the rate of flow of filtered water through a series of culture vessels.

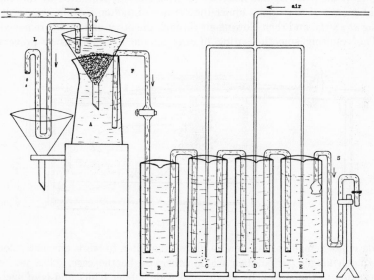

Fig. 28.—The arrangement used in rearing marine larvae. A, reservoir tank; B, C, D, E, culture jars; F, funnel with cotton filter; L, overflow siphon controlling the level of water in the funnel; S, overflow siphon controlling the level in culture jars.

Tall cylindrical jars with wide lips are very convenient for this purpose. To insure a constant flow the water is first filtered through cotton (F) and siphoned from the tank (A), which is always kept full by means of an overflow siphon (L). The first jar (B) serves only as a supply reservoir for the others (C, D, E) which are connected to one another by siphons. The jars are placed on boards of various thicknesses so that in each of them the level of the overflow (the lip of the jar) is gradually increasing from left to right. An automatic siphon (S) controls the level of water in the last jar. By this arrangement water gradually passes from (A) through all other jars and is discharged by the siphon (S). Should the latter become clogged, the water in the first jar rises and overflows before the culture jars, standing slightly above it, become full.

A few organisms may swim back through the siphon connecting the second and the first jar and be lost. The opening of the controlling siphon may be covered with plankton silk or other fine material to prevent the escape of minute organisms. This arrangement has been successfully used by the author in rearing and maintaining small crustaceans, the larvae of mollusks and echinoderms, and small jelly fishes.

Further improvement of this method was made by F. G. Walton Smith whose personal communication reads as follows: "Rapid clogging of the pores of this material (bolting silk) is prevented by dipping the mouth of the siphon under the surface of molten paraffin wax melting at 48° C. and then blowing air through the other end as it is removed. The resulting smooth coating of wax on the fibers seems to prevent

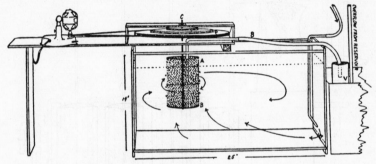

FIG. 29.—The current rotor.

the entanglement of larvae and allows the filter to work efficiently for a much longer period than would otherwise be the case. The net is attached to the siphon by means of a wide rubber band, and is of such a nature that when worked, the openings are just small enough to serve to retain the larvae." Using this technique Dr. Smith had no difficulty in growing oyster larvae at the U. S. Bureau of Fisheries Station at Beaufort, N. C.

Slow exchange of water may be obtained by using the so-called "filtros" block which may be installed as a partition in the aquarium, or by inserting a Berkefeld filter and slowly sucking the water through it. Stone filters become clogged very quickly and require frequent changes.

Current rotor. This instrument is designed to change the water in the aquarium without losing the small organisms living in it. The essential feature of the apparatus (Fig. 29) designed by Galtsoff and Cable (1933) is a cylinder (A) of 60 mesh or finer nickel screen suspended in a tank and rotated by means of an electric motor. Rotation of the cylinder when placed at one end of an oblong aquarium sets up a complex system of currents the direction of which is indicated in the accom-

panying illustration. Strong circular currents are formed in the immediate vicinity of the cylinder, while at the far end the water moves
very gently. There is also a noticeable upward motion from the bottom
of the tank.

The speed of rotation and the corresponding strength of currents may
be regulated by the speed of the motor, controlled through a rheostat,
and by means of a set of pulleys of different diameters. The dimensions
of the cylinder also affect the strength of the current produced and they
therefore should vary according to the size of the aquarium used. The
cylinder shown here is 4 inches in diameter and 6 inches long. About
one inch is left above water. The tank is 25 x 15 x 14 inches. The
bottom of the cylinder (B)
is a celluloid disk. Non-
corrosive material should
also be used for the suspension rod (C) and brace wires
(W). The diameter of the
pulley (P) is 12 inches.

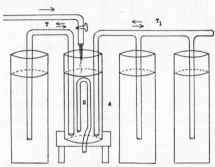

The water may be with-
drawn from the tank through
a siphon (S) the upper end
of which is placed inside the
revolving cylinder. When
the cylinder is in rotation
small organisms are never
actually drawn against its

FIG. 30.—The arrangement imitating tidal
changes. A, controlling jar; S, automatic siphon;
T, T_1, glass tubes connecting the jars.

wall, because the centrifugal force throws them away from it. They
are then caught up in the circular currents and soon find themselves in
quieter waters at the far end of the aquarium. In this manner the
water in the tank may be changed without losing its inhabitants.

When desirable, a constant flow of water may be supplied by placing
the lower end of the overflow siphon (S) in a vessel (V), adjusted so that
the top of it is level with the water in the aquarium. The water is
introduced from a reservoir, in which it is kept at a constant level. If
necessary the water from a laboratory faucet may be filtered through
glass wool to remove sediment and other foreign matter.

Imitation of tidal movement. The arrangement imitating tidal movement of water and permitting attached forms to be subject to rhythmical
changes in hydrostatic pressure consists of a series of tall jars in which
the equilibrium is maintained through a system of tubes (T, T_1) (Fig.
30). An automatic siphon (S) in jar (A) controls the level in all the
jars. After the level in the controlling jar has reached the highest position the water begins to empty through the siphon drawing it from all

the other jars. As soon as the lowest level is reached (determined by the position of the short arm of the siphon) the system begins to fill up and the level in all the jars rises. The rate of flow of water may be regulated to obtain the desired tidal interval. This arrangement was first employed by H. F. Prytherch in a study of the effect of oil pollution on oysters (Galtsoff, Prytherch, *et al.*, 1935). (See note 2 on p. 50.)

Circulation of water in a closed system. Many organisms may be maintained in a limited supply of seawater if the latter is kept in circulation and is systematically filtered. Various simple devices designed

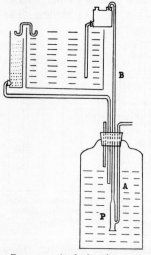

to meet these requirements are based on the use of an air pump. The following is the description of a simple but efficient device (Fig. 31) designed by Burch and Eakin which we copy from *Science* (1934). The pump (P) (Fig. 31) is made from a pyrex glass test-tube, 10 cm. high and 1.5 cm. in diameter. A glass tube (A) 5 mm. in diameter is sealed to the side of the test-tube approximately 2 cm. from the mouth and then bent parallel with the test-tube. A similar glass (B) is sealed to the base of the test-tube. The pump is placed in an inverted position in the reservoir and an exceedingly small air current is permitted to enter the pump through the glass tube (A) at the side. The exact depth at which the pump will give a maximum efficiency may be determined by experimentation; however, the pump should be

FIG. 31.—A device for water circulation. *After Burch and Eakin.* P, pump; A, B, glass tubes.

at least 15 cm. below the water level in the reservoir. (See note on p. 50.)

Another method developed by Cleve (quoted from Hagmeier, 1933) is shown in figure 32. The bottom of a tank is covered with a thick layer of sand (sd) through which water is sucked into a funnel (F) forming the lower end of the siphon, and is emptied into a small tank filled with sand and charcoal (ch). From a filter tank by a similar arrangement of siphon and funnel (F_1) the water enters into a U-shaped glass tube (U). Bubbles of air, blown in at point L gradually push the water into the horizontal tube (T) and back into the tank. By using this arrangement various marine forms may be kept for a very long time in a small amount of seawater.

A similar arrangement for aeration and circulation of water was used by Browne (1907) for the cultivation of hydroids (Fig. 33). Air blown very gently through a tube (A) causes the circulation of water in a small tube (B) in which a portion of a hydroid colony is suspended.

ARTIFICIAL SEAWATER

From a physiological point of view seawater is a well balanced solution of mineral salts, virtually all of them existing in the ionic form. Earlier analyses accounted only for the major salts, ignoring other substances present in extremely small quantities. On the basis of the

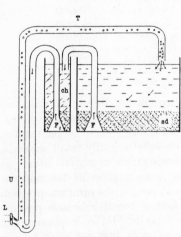

FIG. 32.—The arrangement for filtration and circulation of water. *After Cleve, from Hagmeier.* F, F₁, funnels forming the upper arms of the siphons; sd, sand; ch, charcoal; L, place air is blown in; U, T, return tube.

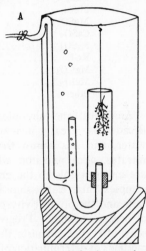

FIG. 33.—A device for aeration and circulation of water in small aquaria. *After Hagmeier.* A, B, tubes.

analyses of the samples collected by the "Challenger," Dittmar gives the following composition of the seawater (quoted from Murray and Hjort, 1912):

TABLE 1. **Composition of seawater** (according to Dittmar).

Grams in 1000 gm. of seawater

NaCl	27.213
MgCl₂	3.807
MgSO₄	1.658
CaSO₄	1.260
K₂SO₄	0.863
CaCO₃	0.123
MgBr₂	0.076

So far as the principal constituents are concerned the composition of seawater salts remains more or less uniform throughout the entire expanse of the ocean, varying only in concentration. This may be seen from Table 2 (quoted from Quinton, 1912) representing the results of the analyses of Forchhammer (1865), Makin (1878), and Dittmar (1884), and expressed as percentage of total solids.

TABLE 2. **Composition of seawater** (percentage of total solids).

	Forchhammer	Makin	Dittmar
NaCl	78.32	76.915	77.758
MgCl$_2$	9.44	11.407	10.878
MgSO$_4$	6.40	4.483	4.323
CaSO$_4$	3.94	4.226	4.070
K$_2$SO$_4$		2.468	2.465
KCl	1.69		
MgCO$_3$			0.290
MgBr$_2$		0.298	0.217
Other	0.21	0.206	

Analytical and physiological work carried out during the last two decades has greatly increased our knowledge of the chemistry of seawater, and has shown that certain substances, such as phosphates, nitrates, silica, and iron, which occur in infinitesimally small amounts, are indispensable to the growth and propagation of marine forms. A complex interrelationship between the concentration of the nutrient salts and the productivity of the sea is at present the principal problem of oceanic biology. Progress in this field of research became possible only after the chemists developed and perfected simple colorometric methods of determination of phosphates, nitrates, iron, and silica.*

According to Thompson and Robinson (1932) the following elements or their compounds (written in the order of their abundance) are determinable in seawater.

TABLE 3. **Approximate composition of seawater with a chlorinity of 19.00%.**

Constituent	Concentration as millimols or milligram atoms per kg. of seawater	Constituent	Concentration as millimols or milligram atoms per kg. of seawater
Chlorine	535.0	Bromine	0.81
Sodium	454.0	Strontium	0.15
Sulphate	82.88	Aluminum	0.07?
Magnesium	52.29	Fluorine	0.043
Calcium	10.19	Silicon	0.04
Potassium	9.6	Boron	0.037
Carbon Dioxide	2.25	Lithium	0.015

*The description of these methods would be out of place in the present book and the readers interested in these are referred to the book of Harvey (1928) and original papers published in the *Journal of the Marine Biological Association of Plymouth* and other oceanographical periodicals.

TABLE 3.—*(continued)*

Nitrate	0.014	Silver	0.0002
Iron	0.0036	Nitrite	0.0001
Manganese	0.003?	Arsenic	0.00004
Phosphorus	0.002	Zinc	0.00003
Copper	0.002	Hydrogen Ion	0.00001
Barium	0.0015	Gold	0.00000025
Iodine	0.00035		

There are, however, a number of elements, such as cobalt, vanadium, lead, nickel, tin, caesium, and rubidium, the presence of which has not yet been detected in seawater but is postulated because they are found in the tissues of marine animals and plants or in the salt deposits left by the evaporation of large quantities of seawater.*

On account of the exceeding complexity of seawater it was only after a great deal of effort that biologists succeeded in elaborating a formula for an artificial solution which possesses the same properties as the ocean water. There exist at present several formulae for the preparation of artificial seawater which may be used in experimentation with marine animals.

For embryological studies on echinoderms Herbst (1903-4) employed the following solution:

NaCl	3.00 gm.
KCl	0.08 gm.
$MgSO_4$	0.66 gm.
$CaCl_2$	0.13 gm.
Dist. water	100 cc.

To this solution 1 cc. of 4.948% $NaHCO_3$ must be added.

In Van't Hoff's formula the principal salts are given in the molecular proportions in which they occur in the sea: namely, 100 NaCl; 7.8 $MgCl_2$; 2.2 KCl; 3.8 $MgSO_4$; and from 1.5 to 2.2 $CaCl_2$. After the $M/1$ solutions of the salts have been mixed in the above mentioned proportions the solution is diluted to the same concentration as that of the seawater in which the animals normally lived. A trace of sodium bicarbonate should be added to bring the pH to 8.0-8.2. Water redistilled from glass must be used. While such a solution would serve for experimental purposes it is not suitable for maintaining the animals over a long period of time. Lacking in phosphates and nitrates, it is obviously unsuitable for the marine algae. A more complex solution prepared according to McClendon's formula answers this purpose.

*For further discussion regarding the composition of the seawater and its significance to the life in the sea the reader is referred to the papers of Quinton (1912), Vernadsky (1923), Thompson and Robinson (1932), and Galtsoff (1932, 1934).

TABLE 4. **Artificial seawater** (according to McClendon).

(All solutions are of M/1 concentrations unless otherwise stated.)

NaCl	483.65 cc.	Na_2SiO_3	0.0025 gm.
KCl	10.23 cc.	$Na_2Si_4O_9$	0.005 cc.
$MgSO_4$	28.55 cc.	H_3PO_4	0.002 cc.
$MgCl_2$	25.16 cc.	H_3BO_3	1.00 cc.
$CaCl_2$	11.00 cc.	Al_2Cl_6	0.01 cc.
NaBr	0.8 cc.	NH_3	0.001 cc.
$NaHCO_3$	2.5 cc.	$LiNO_3$	0.002 cc.
H_2O	373.63 cc.		

It is claimed that even most delicate marine algae will live in this solution for long periods.

For marine forms Penn (1934) recommends the use of the following medium which is based for anions on the analysis of the salt content of the blood of certain organisms and for cations on the buffering properties of salts.

TABLE 5. **Penn's medium for marine forms.**

NaCl	0.1335 N
$CaCl_2$	0.0112 N
KCl	0.0084 N
$NaNO_3$	0.0055 N
$NaHCO_3$	0.0048 N
$MgSO_4$	0.0040 N
KH_2PO_4	0.0005 N
$NaSiO_3$	trace
NH_4NO_3 (For green forms only)	0.0125 N
$FeCl_3$ (For green forms only)	trace

Artificial seawater is regularly used by several marine aquaria in Europe. For example, water in the Berlin aquarium consists primarily of an artificially prepared solution mixed with a small amount of natural seawater. For making up the large quantities of artificial seawater needed for the operation of a public aquarium, a simple procedure must be followed and no attempts made to add all the salts entering into the composition of natural water or to use chemically pure ingredients.

TABLE 6. **Von Flack's formula for making large quantities of artificial seawater.**

Sodium chloride (NaCl)	2815 gm.
Calcium sulphate ($CaSO_4$ $2H_2O$)	172 gm.
Magnesium sulphate ($MgSO_4$ $7H_2O$)	320 gm.
Magnesium chloride ($MgCl_2$ $6H_2O$)	850 gm.
Potassium chloride (KCl)	80 gm.
Magnesium bromide ($MgBr_2$)	10 gm.
Water	100 liters

According to Sachs (1928), elements occurring in small amounts in the sea may be present as impurities in the salts even in excess of their concentration in natural seawater. The two formulae generally used in Germany are given in Tables 6 and 7. Sodium chloride and calcium sulphate are dissolved first in about 30 liters of water. The solution is vigorously shaken and stirred until all the calcium goes into solution, then the other salts are added and the volume is made up to 100 liters. If the water is very hard a smaller amount of calcium sulphate may be used.

TABLE 7. **Schmalz's formula for making larger quantities of artificial seawater.**

Sodium chloride (NaCl) .... 2815 gm.
Potassium chloride (KCl) .... 67 gm.
Magnesium chloride (MgCl$_2$ 6 H$_2$O) .... 551 gm.
Magnesium sulphate (MgSO$_4$ 7 H$_2$O) .... 692 gm.
Calcium chloride (CaCl$_2$ H$_2$O) .... 145 gm.
Water .... 100 liters

First dissolve all the salts excepting calcium chloride; bring up the solution almost to 100 liters; then add calcium chloride and water to make up the volume.

Before using, the newly prepared solution should be tested on sea anemones or other organisms.

METHODS OF SECURING FOOD FOR MARINE INVERTEBRATES

No culture of any organism may be maintained for a long period if proper food is not regularly supplied. In the case of carnivorous animals the problem resolves itself into ascertaining the forms which constitute the principal food of the animal in question and in finding the means of keeping a good supply. Thus many organisms subsisting on animal plankton may be maintained for a long time if an arrangement is possible by which regular plankton samples may be taken and the desired forms obtained. Copepods or other planktonic crustaceans may easily be segregated from the mass of algae and other micro-organisms with which they are closely associated, by pouring the sample of plankton into a crystallizing dish about 10 inches in diameter and from 3 to 4 inches high, the outside wall of which is painted black with the exception of one vertical strip about one inch wide which should remain uncovered. A short time after the dish has been placed on a laboratory table with the open space toward the light, copepods and other crustaceans congregate at the two opposite sides depending upon the phototropic reactions which control their behavior. They may easily be removed with a pipette and fed to the animals in the tanks.

Organisms living on debris, or those which may be fed small pieces of fish or shellfish, may be kept in the laboratory tanks for long periods. Greater difficulty is encountered in keeping alive the plankton-feeding forms. Seawater in laboratory circulation contains but a small number of microscopic algae and may therefore be lacking in essential food elements. On the other hand, it still may contain copepods and other crustaceans which may directly or indirectly be destructive to delicate larvae or other organisms under cultivation. It is therefore advisable to use filtered seawater and to provide food by adding diatoms or other algae. This method requires a constant supply of these forms which must be grown in the laboratory.

Caswell Grave (1902) originated the method of rearing marine larvae by putting them in a balanced aquarium in which the diatoms growing on the bottom furnished an abundant supply of natural food and kept the water pure. This method consists of putting a liter or more of sand dredged from the ocean bottom in an aquarium of seawater and allowing it to stand several days before a window, but protected from direct sunlight. Under these conditions a film of diatoms develops in several days. The larvae, from 12 to 24 hours after fertilization, are placed in an aquarium of fresh water to which a dozen or more pipettefuls of the diatom-stocked surface sand are added. The aquarium is then covered and set before a window. Using this method Grave succeeded in rearing a number of spatangoids and sand-dollars until they had completed their metamorphosis, and in keeping them in a healthy and growing condition for three months thereafter. [See p. 557.] The capacity of the aquarium was 1 liter and the water was changed only twice during this period.

An abundant supply of various diatoms may be raised by using the following method developed by Just (1928). Mud and scrapings from eel grass are placed together with animals and plants in jars containing an equal amount of seawater. The jars are covered and set aside in a subdued light. After a period of putrefaction the culture purifies itself and an abundant growth of diatoms ensues. From this stock culture the diatoms are removed, suspended in filtered seawater and strained through bolting silk. Only the diatoms that have passed through the silk are used for feeding. It is advisable to start several cultures at from 5 to 10 day intervals.

In spite of the fact that a number of marine larvae were successfully reared on diatoms growing in mud or sand cultures both methods suffer from a certain degree of uncertainty. It is impossible to predict what species of diatom will develop and whether similar cultures will always be available. For a more critical work on the physiology of feeding and food requirements, pure cultures should be used. At present cultures of a single species of diatom may be carried on indefinitely under controlled laboratory conditions. The method originated by Miquel (1897) and modified by Allen and Nelson (1910, 1914) consists of adding certain nutrient salts to seawater, sterilizing, and inoculating with a single species of diatom. Two solutions are prepared separately:

TABLE 8. **Preparation of Miquel solution.**

Solution A.

Potassium nitrate .... 20.2 gm.
Distilled water .... 100 cc.

Solution B.

Calcium chloride (CaCl$_2$ 6H$_2$O) .... 4 gm.
Sodium phosphate, secondary,
Crystals (Na$_2$HPO$_4$ 12H$_2$O) .... 4 gm.
Ferric chloride (melted) (FeCl$_3$ 6H$_2$O) .... 2 cc.
Hydrochloric acid (HCl) concentrated............. 2 cc.
Distilled water .... 80 cc.

Dissolve calcium chloride in 40 cc. of distilled water and add the hydrochloric acid. In a separate beaker dissolve the sodium phosphate in 40 cc. of distilled water, add the melted ferric chloride, and slowly mix the two solutions. To prepare Miquel's solution add 2 cc. of solution A and 1 cc. of solution B to one liter of seawater. Sterilize by bringing just to the boiling point. Cool and decant or filter off the slight precipitate, separating the amount obtained into two 1 liter flasks. Shake vigorously to aerate. The prepared medium is poured into sterile, short-necked, wide-mouthed flasks of 125 cc. capacity and is covered with inverted beakers. The flasks should be only about ½ full so that the proportion of air surface to the volume of the liquid is large. The flasks are inoculated by adding 6 to 8 cc. of an old culture of diatoms and are placed in front of a window but are protected from the direct sunlight. They should be shaken at least once a day.

The Miquel's seawater may be modified by adding garden soil extract which is known to have a stimulating effect on the growth of diatoms (Gran, 1931, 1932, 1933). To prepare the extract put 500 grams of garden soil in a flask, add 500 cc. of water and autoclave for 20 minutes at 15 lbs. pressure. Filter, sterilize again, and keep in the refrigerator. Add 1 cc. of soil extract to each liter of prepared Miquel's seawater. Experiments carried out by Gran (1932) at Woods Hole show that the synthetic Ferri-ligno-protein compound of Waksman (1932) which in its chemical characteristics corresponds closely to the "humic" substances of the soil, gives the same stimulating effect on the growth of the plankton diatoms as the soil extract.

Needless to say, in dealing with diatom cultures the same precautions must be taken as are usually observed in bacteriological work. The cultures grow best at about 15° to 16° C.

By using Miquel's seawater Allen and Nelson (1910) were able to obtain persistent cultures of the following species of diatoms: *Asterionella japonica, Biddulphia mobiliensis, B. regia, Chaetoceras densum, C. decipiens, C. constrictum, Cocconeis scutellum, Coscinodiscus excentricus, C. granii, Ditylium brightwellii, Lauderia borealis, Nitzschia closterium, N. closterium forma minutissima, N. seriata, Rhizosolenia stolterfothii, Skeletonema costatum, Streptotheca thamensis*, and *Thalassiosira decipiens*.

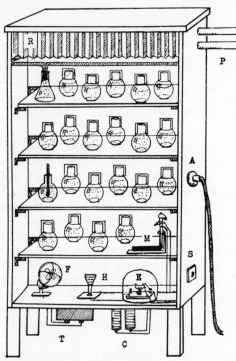

Of all these species the cultivation of *Nitzschia closterium f. minutissima* is more widely practised in many laboratories both in the United States and in Europe than that of any other diatom. This is primarily due to its small size and its ability to remain in suspension for a long period of time, these qualities rendering it very useful as food for small planktonic organisms.

FIG. 34.—The cabinet for diatom cultures. A, air switch; C, dry cells; E, relay; F, fan; H, small heater; M, metastatic temperature controller; P, pipes to refrigeration plant; R, refrigeration unit; S, wall switch; T, transformer.

Light and temperature are the two principal physical factors which govern the rate of propagation of diatoms. The growth of cultures left in the laboratory and subject to rather wide fluctuations in temperature and intensity of illumination are greatly affected by these changes. Temperatures above 22° C. are obviously harmful to a Nitzschia culture and when the summer heat approaches 30°, as happens regularly in the author's laboratory of the U. S. Bureau of Fisheries, they may perish. To avoid this difficulty and to keep the cultures in health, both temperature and illumination should be kept constant.

The following easily constructed arrangement has been successfully used by the author. Culture flasks are kept in a cabinet (Fig. 34), 60″

x 32″ x 11″, with a door (not shown in figure) and back made of double glass panes with a 1 inch air space between them. The cabinet is constructed of wood and insulated with celotex; the inside is painted white. Culture flasks are kept on wire shelves which rest on adjustable metal supports. A clearance of not less than ½ inch between the edges of the shelves and the walls of the cabinet provides for better circulation of air. The upper shelf is occupied by the refrigeration unit (R) separated from the rest of the cabinet by a metal sheet which serves for collecting the condensation water, and also as a protection to the cultures placed just below it against excessive cold. The temperature is regulated by the air switch (A) connected to the electric refrigeration machine (not shown in the diagram). To facilitate circulation of air a small electric fan (F) may be hooked up to the air switch. Experience shows, however, that when the refrigeration unit is in operation there is a sufficient circulation of air inside the box. The temperature differences in the flasks placed on various shelves do not exceed 2° C. and a temperature of from 15° to 16° C. may easily be maintained in the cabinet when the room temperature does not exceed 22° C.

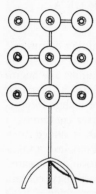

FIG. 35.—The metal stand for illumination of the diatom cabinet.

If necessary the refrigeration unit may be disconnected and a heater, placed on the bottom shelf, turned on. The heating assembly consists of a small heater (H), fan (F), relay (E), and metastatic temperature controller (M).

Equal illumination on both sides of the cabinet is provided by 18 Mazda 25 watt bulbs, mounted on two separate stands (Fig. 35) made of iron pipes and provided with metal reflectors which are placed 3 feet from the glass walls. Under this constant, controlled illumination and temperature, Nitzschia cultures grow better and faster than when kept before the laboratory window.

In a study of the effect of intensity of illumination on the growth of *Biddulphia mobiliensis* and *Carteria sp.*, Schreiber (1927) used the following method (Fig. 36). Cultures kept in the box were

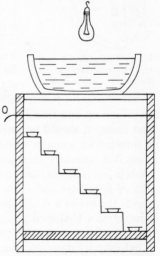

FIG. 36.—The method of growing Nitzschia under artificial illumination. *After Schreiber.* O, screen made of oiled paper.

illuminated from above. To avoid over-heating, light from a 1000 watt gas-filled bulb was passed through a layer of water. A screen (O) made of oiled paper was inserted to provide uniform illumination.

METHODS OF OBTAINING A CULTURE OF A SINGLE SPECIES

Two methods have been employed by Miquel in obtaining cultures of a single species of diatom. The method of isolation consists in picking out an individual cell under the microscope and introducing it into a prepared medium. If the method of subdivision is used, a small quantity of water containing a mixture of various organisms is added to a prepared medium and poured out into a number of tubes. If the operation is repeated many times some of the tubes may contain one unit of diatoms only from which a fresh culture may be made.

Allen and Nelson (1910) proposed the following modifications of this procedure. One or two drops of plankton are added to 250 cc. of a suitable sterile medium and poured into petri dishes. The dishes should be kept under a constant temperature in a subdued light, in a place where they may be examined with a hand lens without moving or disturbing them. In the course of a few days colonies of different species of diatoms will be seen growing at different spots on the bottom. They may

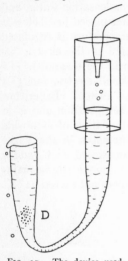

FIG. 37.—The device used for the concentration of diatoms. *After Schreiber.* D, diatoms.

be picked up and transferred to fresh culture media. [See pp. 43, 70.] The isolation should be made as early as possible before all the water is infected by some one organism, either diatom or flagellate. Sometimes it is necessary to repeat the process several times before one succeeds in isolating the desired species. To facilitate the process of elimination of flagellates and other micro-organisms Schreiber (1927) recommends the use of a device shown in figure 37. The principal part of it consists of a U-shaped glass tube, the middle piece of which is drawn into a capillary; one arm is made longer than the other. A diatom culture is fed drop by drop into the long arm from which it flows through the capillary into the short arm. Owing to the higher velocity of the current in the capillary, the diatoms are carried into the left arm and accumulate in the lower part of it. The rate of the flow of water through the apparatus should be adjusted so that the velocity of the vertical current in the left arm is less than the rate of sinking of the diatoms. Free swimming flagellates and organisms lighter than diatoms escape while the latter accumulate in the area (D) just above the mouth of the capillary tubing.

Cultures of a single species of diatom obtained by the method of isolation and subsequent washing usually are contaminated with bacteria, the presence of which apparently does not interfere with the growth of the diatom. Allen designates them as "persistent" cultures, reserving the name "pure" only for bacteria-free cultures of a single diatom species. The elimination of bacteria is a very difficult and time consuming process which consists of repeated washings in sterile media followed by fractional subdivision. Purification of cultures by a method of differential poisoning was attempted by Allen (1914) with only a measure of success. Cultures of *Thalassiosira gravida* were treated by adding 1 mg. of $CuSO_4.5H_2O$ to each 100 cc. After an interval of 12 minutes a fresh medium was inoculated with 1 cc. of the first one. In this way the number of bacteria was materially reduced but complete sterilization was not obtained.

Chlorination produced by electrolysis of water was applied also only with partial success (Allen, 1914). An electric current varying from 1.7 to 1.5 amperes was passed between the two sterile carbon electrodes immersed in seawater. The electrolysis was continued for about 3 minutes; then the water was allowed to stand for one hour. Fifty cc. of chlorinated water were added to an equal amount of sterile medium and the solution was inoculated with a small amount of a Thalassiosira culture. In this way the number of bacteria was materially reduced.

In healthy cultures the presence of bacteria does not interfere with the propagation of the diatom (Nitzschia) but as soon as conditions become unfavorable the bacterial growth is promoted and the diatoms suffer (Galtsoff, *et al.*, 1935). The unhealthy state of such cultures is easily noticeable for the cells stick together forming large clumps which settle on the bottom and which sink almost immediately after stirring. Microscopical examination of a stained preparation showed that every Nitzschia cell was covered with a large number of bacteria closely adhering to its body.

In old cultures Nitzschia has a tendency to develop teratological forms. This condition may be remedied by subculturing and it usually disappears in a short time.

Natural seawater enriched by the addition of nutrient salts appears to be the best medium for the cultivation of diatoms. It is of interest that according to Allen (1914) Thalassiosira failed to grow in artificial seawater to which nitrates, phosphates, and iron were added according to Miquel's method. Excellent results were obtained, however, when less than 1% of natural seawater was added to the culture medium. Artificial seawater used in Allen's experiment comprised only the six principal salts (see Dittmar's analysis of seawater, page 27) and apparently was deficient in some other growth-promoting substance which is present in natural seawater.

Other solutions than that of Miquel have been recommended by several investigators for the cultivation of diatoms and green forms. Schreiber (1927) gives the following formula:

TABLE 9. **Medium for cultivation of diatoms and green forms.**
(Schreiber)

Potassium nitrate (KNO_3) .... 0.2   gm.
Dipotassium hydrogen phosphate (K_2HPO_4) .... 0.1   gm.
Potassium silicate (K_2SiO_3) .... 0.01   gm.
Ferric sulphate ($Fe_2[SO_4]_3$) .... 0.005 gm.
Redistilled water .... 50.00 cc.

This solution is added to 950 cc. of filtered seawater and the medium is sterilized by steam at about 100° C. If during the heating a precipitate (calcium carbonate) is formed, the solution should be allowed to stand several weeks until a sufficient amount of CO_2 has been absorbed from the air and the calcium salts redissolved.

Although diatoms constitute the most essential food element of a great number of plankton-feeding larvae, other food organisms should not be neglected. Mixed cultures of various green flagellates may be obtained from jars in which the algae are allowed to putrify. These cultures once obtained may be carried on for a long time by inoculating Miquel's or other media. Their usefulness in feeding marine larvae should be ascertained, however, by experimentation.

Isolation of a green flagellate and its maintenance in a bacteria-free culture presents less difficulty than does the isolation of a diatom. Using standard bacteriological technique, German investigators succeeded, for instance, in obtaining bacteria-free pure cultures of *Carteria sp.*, a phytomonadine flagellate very common in the North Sea (Schreiber, 1927). The sample of plankton is first centrifuged in sterile seawater and set aside and the Carteriae, which are positively phototropic, are separated from the rest of the planktonic organisms and placed on gelatin or agar plates, from which they are subcultured.

Sperm of marine algae is often used as food for small lamellibranch larvae which are unable to ingest diatoms. At Woods Hole the sperm of Ulva may be obtained during the summer. Freshly collected plants are left exposed overnight on pieces of filter paper. The next morning the leaves are put in a shallow crystallizing dish filled with water and set in a place exposed to strong light. In a short time large masses of green sperm may be pipetted from the side having the greatest illumination.

In order to insure an ample supply of food, the cultivation of diatoms or other algae should be started at least two weeks before the time of the experiment to be conducted with marine larvae. Between the seasons of experimental work with marine larvae, a small number of stock cultures of their food should be maintained in the laboratory.

BIBLIOGRAPHY

ALLEN, E. J. 1914. On the culture of the plankton diatom *Thalassiosira gravida*, Cleve, in artificial seawater. *J. Mar. Biol. Assoc.* 10:417.

ALLEN, E. J., and NELSON, E. W. 1910. On the artificial culture of marine plankton organisms. *Ibid.* N. S. 8:421.

BOND, R. M. 1933. A contribution to the study of the natural food-cycle in aquatic environments. *Bull. Bingham Oceanog. Coll.* 43, Art. 4:1.

BROWNE, E. T. 1898. On keeping Medusae alive in aquarium. *J. Mar. Biol. Assoc.* 5:186.

———— 1907. A new method of growing Hydroids in small aquaria by means of a continuous current tube. *Ibid.* N. S. 8:37.

BURCH, A. B., and EAKIN, R. M. 1934. A device for water circulation. *Science* 80:563.

DITTMAR, W. 1884. "Challenger" reports. Physics and Chemistry 1.

FORCHHAMMER, G. 1865. On the composition of seawater in the different parts of the ocean. *Philos. Trans.* 155.

GALTSOFF, P. S. 1932. The life in the ocean from a biochemical point of view. *J. Wash. Acad. Sci.* 22:246.

———— 1934. The biochemistry of the invertebrates of the sea. *Ecol. Monog.* 4:481.

GALTSOFF, P. S., and CABLE, L. 1933. The current rotor. *Science* 77:242.

GALTSOFF, P. S., PRYTHERCH, H. F., SMITH, R. O., and KOEHRING, V. 1935. The effects of crude oil pollution on oysters in Louisiana waters. *Bull. U. S. Bur. Fish.* 48:143.

GRAN, H. H. 1931. On the conditions for the production of plankton in the sea. *Cons. Perm. Intern. Pour l' Exploration de la Mer. Rapp. et Procès-Verbaux des Reunions.* 75:37.

———— 1932. Phytoplankton methods and problems. *J. du Cons. Intern. Pour l' Exploration de la Mer.* 7:343.

———— 1933. Studies on the biology and chemistry of the Gulf of Maine. *Biol. Bull.* 64:159.

GRAVE, C. 1902. A method of rearing marine larvae. *Science* 15:579.

HAGMEIER, A. 1925. Neue Aquarium-einrichtungen der Staatlichen Bioligischen Anstalt Auf Helgoland. *Intern. Revue d-gesamt Hydrobiol. u. Hydrographie* 12:405.

———— 1933. Die Züchtung verschriedener Wirbelloser Meerestiere *in* Abderhalden's *Handbuch d. Biol. Arbeitsmethoden* Abt. 9 T. 5, 1:465.

HARVEY, H. W. 1928. Biological Chemistry and Physics of the seawater. Cambridge University Press. 194 pp.

HERBST, C. 1903-4. Ueber die zur Entwicklung der Seeigellarven Notwendigen anorganischen Stoffe, ihre Rolle und ihre Vertretbarkeit. *Arch. f. Mech.* 17:306.

HOPKINS, A. E. 1934. A mechanism for the continuous circulation and aeration of water in small aquaria. *Science* 80:383.

JOHNSTONE, J. 1908. Conditions of life in the sea. Cambridge University Press. 332 pp.

JUST, E. E. 1928. Methods of experimental embryology with specific reference to marine invertebrates. *The Collecting Net.* 3:1.

MAKIN, C. J. S. 1878. On the composition of the Atlantic Ocean. *Chem. News* 77:155-156, 171-172.

McCLENDON, J. F. 1917. Physical Chemistry of Vital Phenomena.

MIQUEL, P. 1890-1893. De la culture artificielle des Diatomeès. *Le Diatomiste* 1:73; 93:121; 149:165.

MURRAY, J., and HJORT, J. 1912. The depths of the ocean. Macmillan Co. 821 pp.

OXNER, M. 1920. Manuel Pratique de l'analyse de l'eau de Mer. I. Chlorination par la methode de Knudsen. *Bull. d. 1. Comm. Intern. p. l'explor. Scientifique de la Mer Méditerranée.* 36 pp.

PENN, A. B. K. 1934. Physiological media for fresh water and marine protozoa. *Science* 80:316.

QUINTON, RENE. 1912. L'Eau de Mer Milieu organique. Paris, Masson et Cie. 503 pp.

RICHARDS, O. W. 1933. Toxicity of some metals and Berkefeld filtered seawater to *Mytilus edulis*. *Biol. Bull.* 65:371.

ROGERS, C. G. 1927. Textbook of Comparative Physiology. McGraw Hill Co. 635 pp.

SACHS, W. B. 1928. Meerwasser Aquarium *in* T. Peterfi, *Methoden der Wissenschaftlichen Biologie,* 2:232.

SCHILLER, J. 1933. Ueber kultur und Methoden beim Studium der Meerespflangen *in* Abderhalden's *Handbuch d. Biol. Arbeitsmethoden.* Abt. 9 T. 5, 1:181.

SCHREIBER, E. 1927. Die Reinkultur von marinem Phytoplankton und deren Bedeutung fü die Erforschung der Produktions fähigkeit des Meereswassers. *Wiss. Meeresuntersuchungen* Abt. Helgoland, 16, 10:1.

SCHUBERT, A. 1930. Entwicklung des Nannoplanktons in Rohkulturen mit shebenden Seewasser. *Wiss. Meeresuntersuchungen,* Abt. Helgoland, 18, 2:1.

THOMPSON, T. G., and ROBINSON, R. I. 1932. Chemistry of the Sea. *Bull. Nat. Res. Council* 85, Oceanography, p. 95.

VERNADSKY, W. J. 1923. La Composition chimique de la Matiere vivante et la chimie de l'ecorce terrestre. *Revue General des Sciences Pures et Appliqués,* 34:42.

———— 1924. La matiere vivante et la chimie de la Mer. *Ibid.* 35:5.

———— 1924. La Géochimie, 404 pp. Librairie Felix Alcan, Paris.

WAKSMAN, Ś. S., and IYER, K. R. N. 1932. Synthesis of a humus-nucleus, an important constituent in soils, peats and composts. *J. Wash. Acad. Sci.* 22:41.

COLLECTING AND REARING TERRESTRIAL AND FRESHWATER INVERTEBRATES

F. E. LUTZ, P. S. WELCH, and J. G. NEEDHAM

MUCH that has been stated in the preceding pages by Dr. Galtsoff for marine invertebrates is equally applicable to freshwater forms. It will suffice, therefore, if we merely add some notes and suggestions concerning methods more applicable to inland aquatic, terrestrial, and aerial invertebrates.

COLLECTING AND HANDLING LIVING SPECIMENS

For collecting and transporting the larger inland invertebrates (crayfishes, clams, the larger snails, dragonfly nymphs, diving beetle larvae, *etc.*), the small seines, traps, bait pails, and live boxes of commerce are everywhere available. Also, for getting small animals out of their places of hiding, there are shovels and sifters, rakes and hoes, axes and chisels, *etc.* Some commercial tools especially devised for collecting purposes have been illustrated in the preceding article.

In the following pages we will describe only a few of the most useful and most generally applicable devices for collecting and handling invertebrates. Others will be found in the articles which follow, where their special uses will be indicated. Many others may be found by our readers if they will consult Peterson's *Manual of Entomological Equipment and Methods*, which, although prepared primarily for work on insects, contains much that is equally applicable to the handling of other invertebrates.

FIG. 38.—The apron net.

Aquatic animals. A dip net (Fig. 1) is perhaps the most widely used tool for collecting in freshwater. It must be stout enough to stand hard usage and its mesh must be fine enough to retain the animals desired.

The best single tool for collecting the larger aquatic invertebrate animals is the apron net (Fig. 38). It is so shaped at the front that it may be pushed through beds of weeds or under bottom trash. Its wide-meshed cover allows the animals to enter while keeping out the weeds and coarser trash. A final push through the water lands the catch at the rear where it is easily accessible for picking over by hand.

The smaller animals that are mixed with the trash in the net may best be found by dumping its contents into a white pan of water where they will at once reveal their presence by their activity. They may be taken from the water most easily and without injury on a lifter made from a strip of wire cloth by infolding its edges.

An apron net is equally satisfactory for scraping up and sifting bottom mud and sand to obtain burrowers. It may be used for collecting insects and other animals from among loose stones in rapid streams by setting it edgewise against the bottom facing up stream and stirring the stones above it. The animals that are dislodged by the stirring will be swept by the current into the net. Old leaf drifts caught in the edges of the current may be stirred in the same way to get the animals hiding in them, but more stirring and over-turning of the leaves will be necessary to dislodge them.

The small kitchen strainers for sale in any 10-cent store, if securely attached to handles, are good for dipping small animals from pools.

Small aquatic organisms may sometimes be easily collected and concentrated by the use of the following simple field or laboratory device. Attach a piece of rubber tubing of appropriate size and length to the stem of an ordinary, medium-sized glass funnel. Stretch across the open end of the funnel a piece of India linen, bolting cloth, grit gauze, or similar material, the mesh of which is such that the organism desired will not pass through, and hold in place with a rubber band or cord. Fill a pail with water. Place the funnel, wide end down, in the pail but leave the longer part of the rubber tubing outside the pail, the free end extending below the level of the bottom. Apply momentary suction at the free end of the rubber tubing to convert the latter into a siphon which will drain the water through the gauze-covered funnel to the outside.

By pouring the water containing the desired organisms into the pail the water is gradually eliminated through the funnel but the organisms are retained. This process may be continued until the desired concentration of the organisms in the pail is reached.

A cover of wire cloth of wider mesh may be placed over the pail to exclude from the catch all larger animals and coarser trash.

For collecting plankton a standard plankton net may be used (Fig. 15). If samples for qualitative study only are wanted, a simpler, less expensive, and less cumbersome net is more practical. It may be made by anyone and consists only of a regularly tapered bag of silk bolting cloth attached by a topband to a rather heavy circular rim of non-rusting metal. The bag may be 2 or 2½ feet deep and its bottom should allow easy eversion for the removal of the catch. A cord is attached to the rim for towing.

Removal of the catch in such a net may be facilitated by inserting a vial of appropriate size and shape into a small hole at the end of the bag. Held in place by a rubber band or a stout thread, such a container may be removed easily after the collection is completed.

If made of No. 25 standard silk bolting cloth, the net will retain all but the minutest of the organisms (nannoplankton), but when drawn through the water it will clog quickly, pushing much water aside without straining it. No. 12 cloth, while not retaining things so small, will strain more water and yield a bigger catch of the forms more generally useful in the zoological laboratory.

Small aquatic animals may be taken up on a lifter if not too delicate, but they should not be exposed to the air for any considerable length of time. In general the more delicate among them are better transferred by means of a pipette, without exposure to the air. A hand bulb on a tube may be used for the larger entomostracans.

For isolating single unicellular algae for the production of pure cultures the late Dr. A. Brooker Klugh* devised a plunger pipette that is a great help in picking out cells of the smallest sizes. We copy in full his description and figure of it.

"This instrument (Fig. 39) consists of: (1) a piece of *thin,* soft glass tubing drawn to a capillary tube at one end; (2) a glass plunger drawn from a piece of glass rod to sufficient fineness to fit the capillary tip, and with a flattened knob at the other end; (3) a piece of rubber tubing which is placed so as to project beyond the glass tube.

"In the figure the capillary tube is, for the sake of clearness, shown as relatively coarse, but in practice this tube should have an *inside diameter of 80 micra or less.*

"These parts are so adjusted that the end of the plunger inside the capillary is

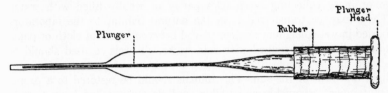

FIG. 39.—The plunger-pipette. *After Klugh.*

about 1 mm. from the end of the capillary, while the knob rests against the rubber. This is accomplished by inserting the plunger (which should be made with the fine-drawn portion longer than required), and cutting off the part which projects through the capillary, then making the fine adjustment by moving the rubber slightly upwards.

"The manner of using this instrument is as follows: A drop or two of water containing some of the organisms it is desired to isolate is placed on a slide, the organism located, and examined with the 4 mm. objective and a x10, or higher, ocular. The desired organism is then located under the 16 mm. or 8 mm. objective. The pipette is held with the thumb and second finger just in front of the rubber, while the plunger-head is pressed with the first finger so that the end of the plunger projects from the tip of the capillary The end of the plunger is brought against the organism and the pressure of the first finger released, when the resiliency of the rubber withdraws the plunger and the organism is drawn into the end of the capillary. (If other organisms, or debris, lie close against the desired organism, they may be knocked away by shooting the plunger in and out by the pressure of the forefinger.) The organism is then transferred in the pipette to a hollow-ground slide containing a drop of the culture medium, and is ejected by a pressure on the plunger-head. It is then examined under high power to see that it is absolutely free from foreign organisms, picked up with the pipette as before, and transferred to the culture-vessel.

"The chief advantages of this instrument are:

"1. The plunger does away with the drawing in of undesirable material by capillarity.

"2. The plunger may be employed to clear other organisms away from the organism to be isolated.

"3. The instrument is quick and certain in operation.

"4. It is easily portable.

"5. It is simple and requires no special attachments.

* *J. Roy. Micr. Soc.* for 1922, p. 267

"6. It is inexpensive, and several can be kept on hand ready for instant use in case of breakages."

A feather, trimmed at tip and edges to the shape and degree of pliancy required, is very useful for holding specimens without injury in any desired position for examination, also, for moving delicate specimens about. Fish culturists have long used a feather for picking over trout eggs on the screens in hatching troughs. For cleaning it is much better than a camel's hair brush. Its hooked barbicels catch and lift the dirt instead of smoothing it down.

Certain aquatic animals suffer greatly when carried to the laboratory in ordinary collecting receptacles partly or wholly filled with water. These may be transferred from the natural habitat to the laboratory buried in wet sphagnum moss or placed between layers of cloth or paper towels thoroughly soaked with cold water. Towels so used should be spread on the bottom of a collecting container and protected from the light and heat of the sun. The animals should be restored to a proper environment as quickly as possible, and closely watched for a time in order that injured specimens may be promptly removed.

Aerial insects. For collecting flying insects an air net is needed. Many kinds will be found advertised in the catalogues of dealers in entomological supplies. The standard insect net is made with a bag of some kind of netting (No. ooo silk-bolting cloth, voile, bobbinet, marquisette, cheesecloth, *etc.*, according to one's choice) 12″ to 18″ in diameter, rounded at the bottom, and a convenient arm-length deep. The bag is attached by a topband to a circular rim of stiff wire, affixed to a light strong handle some three feet long.*

The net must be used with care to avoid injury to delicate specimens, and still greater care must be exercised in handling and carrying and caging them after capture. It is bad treatment of living animals to dump them in numbers into a bare glass or tin container where they cannot get a foothold except by clawing at one another.

For collecting living specimens of leafhoppers, flea beetles, and other small and very agile insects that are prone to jump out of a collecting bottle every time it is opened, Mr. Milton F. Crowell of North East, Pennsylvania,** suggests fastening a small cone of wire cloth, open apex downward, inside the mouth of a collecting vial. The cone serves as a baffle. He uses a 1″ x 3″ shell vial.

"The cone was made by taking a small square of screen and forcing it into the

---

*Directions for making nets and other entomological collecting apparatus may be found in *Elementary Lessons on Insects* by J. G. Needham, pp. 177-184 (C. C. Thomas, Publisher, Springfield, Ill., 1928) and in *Fieldbook of Insects* by Frank E. Lutz, pp. 7-14 and Pl. 3 (G. P. Putnam's Sons, Publisher, New York City, 1935). The latter also gives some information on rearing methods.

**J. Econ. Ent. 21:633, 1928.

opening of the vial by applying pressure to the center of the screen. When the cone was thus shaped, a small hole was cut in its apex. The cone was then placed in the vial again and the corners of the screen trimmed off. The cone can then be forced a little way into the vial, remaining in place by the spring-action of the bent wire against the side of the glass. Care should be taken not to make the cone so small that it will drop out.

Insects that seek the light on emergence from the pupal stage are easily collected in a very simple trap. They are placed in a dark box before emergence. A hole is bored in one side of the box, and the open end of a glass vial is fitted into the hole. Light entering only through this hole attracts the insects to enter the vial, from whence they are easily removed. This is adequate for most minute parasites, but for larger and livelier insects, such as screw-worm flies,* a fruit jar with a cone-shaped baffle guarding against return of the flies to the box, may replace the vial.

For picking up minute beetles by suction Frank J. Psota of Chicago devised an efficient aspirator (Fig. 40) which he has described** as follows:

"The apparatus is shown in the accompanying figures: A, is a cork with center hole; B, a glass tube 4 inches long, 1⅛ inch in diameter, and ⅛ inch thick; C, cork of type similar to A; D, glass tubing bent in S-shape; this curve is very important because it destroys a straight path for insects and dust; E, glass tubing ¼ inch in

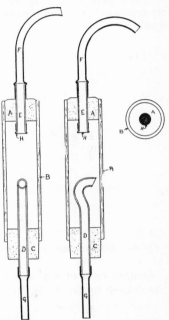

Fig. 40.—A suction-pump collector. *After Psota.* Two longitudinal sections through suction-pump collector and (to the right) a cross-section through the same above the middle, looking upward.

diameter with enlarged edges on both sides of the cork; F, rubber tubing which is of the desired length (usually 20 to 30 inches), with mouthpiece on one end, the other is slipped over the glass near the cork; G, short piece of rubber tubing which prevents

*This is the device used successfully by Mr. D. C. Parmann at the Laboratory of the U. S. Bureau of Entomology at Uvalde, Texas. A rim-capped fruit jar is used, with the center of the cap left out. The rim is fixed inside a large hole bored in the side of the rearing box, and the jar is screwed into it. A cone of wire cloth with an opening at its apex large enough to admit the flies, is so shaped that its base is held firmly between the jar and the screw cap when these are put together, the apex projecting into the jar. Thus the escape of the flies is prevented, until the baffle is removed.

**Ent. News 27:23, 1916.

the glass tube from breaking when insects are collected on or around solid objects and in crevices; H, silk netting which is stretched over the end of the tube and tied with thread sealed with wax in order to prevent it from fraying; this netting prevents the entrance of dust particles into the tube.

"The end of the rubber tube G is placed near the objects desired, such as small beetles, shells, or any small specimens, which are then drawn into the main chamber through the glass tube D, by the suction which is created by a sharp inhalation at the end of the rubber tube F.

"Specimens in the main chamber may be emptied into a cyanide jar by removing the bottom cork C, which is pushed into the tube for only about one-third of its length."

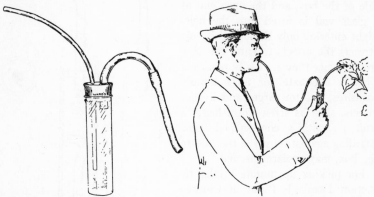

Fig. 41.—Beamer's aspirator. *Courtesy of Ward's Natural Science Establishment, Inc.*

Another form of aspirator (Fig. 41) employing the same principles was devised by Dr. R. H. Beamer of the University of Kansas.

CAGES AND SHELTER

In the maintenance of many kinds of aquatic invertebrates a "rearing raft" may prove to be very useful. A floating raft or platform of appropriate size is anchored in water suitable for the purpose. Suspended beneath this platform are cages so located and so constructed that they maintain the contained animals in approximately the conditions of the native habitat, and make convenient their examination and observation by the investigator.

One of the most generally useful, most easily constructed, and least expensive of cages is the pillow cage (Fig. 42). It is made from a single square of woven wire cloth by doubling and closely folding two opposite edges to form a cylinder, and then in like manner cross-folding the ends. The folds must be crimped tightly and evenly. A square yard of the cloth quartered makes four cages of the size most commonly used for insects. Cages made from small-wire cloth may be folded with the fingers but larger and stronger ones will require a small tinker's folding tongs. A woven edge should form the top, so that there be no wire ends to prick the fingers on opening and closing the cage.

Such a cage is very adaptable. It may be used for carrying home a catch, since its walls afford a foothold, and its crevices at the ends afford hiding places. It may be hung in a tree or buried under trash or immersed in a pond, to hold hibernating animals in safety from their predatory enemies. It may be used for distributing parasitic insects in a grove by placing parasitized pupae within it and hanging it in a tree; the mesh will then have to be of a size to permit the escape of the parasites, while retaining their injurious host insects. When rearing the insects that feed on a growing plant one end may be fitted over a flower pot containing the plant.

FIG. 42.—A pillow cage.

When used as a transformation cage for aquatic insects such as dragonflies, stoneflies, and mayflies, it should be set aslant in the water with only the lower end immersed and plenty of room above for expanding wings. If any adults chance to fall back into the water, the sloping sides will facilitate their crawling out again.

Hollow-ground slides capped with a cover glass are often used as rearing cages for organisms of microscopic size. Dr. Marshall Hertig (*Science* 83: 110, 1936) has suggested a method of making them in any desired shape or size.

"The essential apparatus for turning out these laboratory-made slides is an electric motor (that of an electric fan will serve), a flexible shaft provided with a chuck or "handpiece" into which may be fitted any of the dentist's arsenal of burrs, drills and abrasive devices. Of these the most generally satisfactory for grinding glass are the abrasive wheels, which consist of small disks of carborundum or other material mounted on a mandrel, and which are available in a variety of diameters, thicknesses and degrees of abrasiveness. Abrasive "points," *i.e.*, small carborundum spheres, cones and cylinders, may also be used, but are much less rapid than the abrasive wheels on account of their small diameter and hence low velocity of grinding surface.

"The process of grinding a depression consists merely of placing a drop of water on the slide and applying the abrasive instrument. Very little spattering occurs. The most rapidly ground depression is the slot made by the edge of the carborundum wheel. A cavity of this shape is desirable for elongate specimens. By moving the wheel while grinding, a depression of almost any size and shape may be made, and rotating the slide on a turn-table produces a circular concavity similar to that of the ordinary hollow-ground slide."

CAGE MANAGEMENT

In the maintenance of animal cultures the big factors are food, temperature, humidity, and sanitation.

Feeding and watering. Proper feeding is of first importance in the maintenance of animal cultures. Errors are easily made in both amount and kind of food. The amount should be all that will be completely consumed. Over-feeding is a more common error than under-feeding.

Watering is often as important as feeding, and he who reads the articles that follow will find many ingenious devices for supplying drink while avoiding fatalities from drowning in the pool. For the larger animals commercial chick-watering and rat-watering devices are available. For smaller ones there is such provision as a wide-mouthed bottle filled with water and closed by placing over its mouth a petri dish lined with a sheet of filter paper, the whole then inverted and set on the cage floor. (See p. 433.) Very small insects are supplied both food and drink from open test tubes of capillary smallness filled with liquid and placed where accessible within the cage.

Temperature and humidity. For ordinary rearing work accurately stabilized temperature and humidity are rarely needed, since the animals are well inured to a considerable range of both. But there is much need for the exercise of judgment in the location of cages with respect to both these factors.

Cultures which require a certain uniformity of surrounding temperature may be handled in the following ways if regular temperature control apparatus is not available or is not required. For organisms not requiring light an under-ground cave, a subterranean room, or some similar below-ground space may afford a fairly regular temperature throughout the year. For organisms requiring light, culture jars may be placed in another container through which a stream of water from some constant source is running. Such provision is often very satisfactory providing, of course, that the water passing through this improvised jacket is relatively uniform and of the desired temperature. Workers in lakeside laboratories may sometimes secure the desired uniform temperature by suspending culture containers on ropes hung from a float or buoy in the deep water of a lake. The temperatures at different depths may be determined in advance by the use of an appropriate recording thermometer. Since the deeper waters may change little if at all over the desired period, this method is often a convenient one, and it offers the possibility of selecting temperatures in the vertical temperature gradient.

Modern refrigeration with thermostatic control has made possible the determination of optimum temperature and the limits of tolerance for many species, and has provided the means for maintaining any constant temperature that may be needed for careful experimental work. Insufficient humidity is a most frequent cause of failures of cultures of terrestrial animals. In the following articles will be found many means of adding moisture such as sprinkling, burying in the ground, placing inside the cage water-holding stuffs (filter paper, sphagnum moss, peat, sponges, paper towels, fresh green leaves, *etc.*), conducting water inside by means of wicks, dispersing it from porous earthenware containers by capillarity, allowing evaporation from open pans, spraying it in the cage, *etc.** One of us (Lutz) even in keeping scorpions gives them a shower bath from a bulb spray every day. Although they are desert creatures they normally hide in relatively moist places except at night or when the air outside their hiding places is moist.

On the other hand, too much moisture may be fatal. It frequently brings disaster by favoring the growth of molds.

Sanitation. Keeping cages clean is very important. Sterilization of containers by heat (steam, autoclave, *etc.*) and by chemicals is practiced in many ways, and sterilization of food, drink, and shelters as well. Wooden tubs are prepared for use by charring the interior in a flame. Small containers are closed against infection by sealing the lids with vaseline. Excreta and uneaten food require prompt removal. Cages of certain kinds may be washed, or they may be supplied with removable bottoms, or the floor may be covered with absorbent stuffs like sawdust or sphagnum.

Sick specimens must be isolated to prevent the spread of infection.

Note: The following note concerning Pablum has been sent us by William LeRay and Norma Ford, University of Toronto. "As a food for many invertebrate and vertebrate animals, we are now using a pre-cooked cereal, devised in the Research Laboratories of the Department of Pediatrics, University of Toronto, and sold under the name of Pablum by Mead Johnson & Co., Evansville, Ind.

"Insects which take dry food, such as ants, flour moths, *etc.*, are fond of it; burrowing crayfish grow as rapidly on it as when living outdoors; it is excellent for earthworms, as well as for fish, birds, *etc.* To thrushes this cereal is particularly acceptable.

"Pablum consists of wheatmeal, oatmeal, wheat embryo, yellow cornmeal, powdered beef bone, dried yeast, powdered dehydrated alfalfa leaf, and sodium chloride. It has not only high nutritive value, but also furnishes substantial amounts of vitamins A, B, E, and G, and essential mineral elements, calcium, phosphorous, iron, and copper."

* For chemical methods consult Spencer, Hugh M., Laboratory methods for maintaining constant humidity. *Internat. Critical Tables* 1:67-68, 1926.

ADDENDA

THE progress of technique during the past year has made it desirable to add the following notes. The information they contain is essential, and it brings the methods down to date.

NOTE 1 (supplemental to p. 16)—Extensive use of celluloid in the laboratory may be objectionable on account of its inflammability. To avoid fire hazards a so-called "Plastocele" can be used. This product manufactured by the DuPont Viscoloid Company, Arlington, · N. J., closely resembles celluloid in appearance and general properties but has great advantage over it in being extremely slow burning and difficult to ignite. For dissolving and cementing plastocele a mixture of equal amounts of methyl acetone and methyl cellosolve is used.

P. S. G.

NOTE 2 (supplemental to p. 26)—The operation of the siphon can be greatly improved by blowing a bulb at the end of the upper arm of it and boring a small hole one-half inch above the tip of the lower arm.

P. S. G.

NOTE 3 (supplemental to p. 26)—The water is forced by air bubbles into a Wolff bottle which serves to maintain an even flow into the aquarium. The overflow through the automatic siphon is carried into the top of the gravel and sand filter from which it returns to the reservoir.

P. S. G.

Phylum I

Protozoa, Class *Mastigophora*

GROWTH OF FREE-LIVING PROTOZOA
IN PURE CULTURES

R. P. Hall, *University College, New York University*

INTRODUCTION

THE pure-culture technique offers certain definite advantages in the maintenance of free-living Protozoa in the laboratory. As a dependable source of material for class use, bacteria-free cultures far surpass in value the usual hay infusions. Thus, a number of species of flagellates and ciliates have been maintained in our laboratory over periods ranging from two to six years, with an abundant supply of each type always available. In a suitable medium, bacteria-free cultures remain viable for several months; hence frequent transfers are unnecessary for the maintenance of stock cultures. The technique is simple and requires relatively little equipment and no more than a rudimentary knowledge of bacteriological procedures. Bacteria-free cultures are even more valuable as a source of material for experimental studies. In physiological investigations the advantages of the elimination of bacteria in the precise control of experimental conditions are obvious. Biochemical investigations, impossible a few years ago, may now be carried out on free-living Protozoa with almost the same facility as in the case of bacteria. In short, the establishment of bacteria-free cultures opens to the protozoologist, physiologist, and biochemist a wide field of investigation which promises to add much to our knowledge of the morphology, life history, and metabolism of Protozoa.

Two general methods have been followed in the growth of Protozoa in the absence of other living micro-organisms. In the first, the organisms have been washed free of bacteria and grown in sterile peptone solutions or similar media. In the other method, used particularly for ciliates, the Protozoa have first been freed from bacteria and then placed in suspensions of killed bacteria or other micro-organisms. Ciliates and other Protozoa have also been grown by various workers on single strains of living bacteria, yeasts, algae, and small Protozoa.

Several investigators (Parpart, 1928; Luck and Sheets, 1931; Hetherington, 1934) have described relatively simple methods for washing Protozoa free from bacteria. The method of Parpart, a method which offers few technical difficulties, has been used successfully in our laboratory and elsewhere. In this method it is a comparatively easy matter to free the Protozoa from bacteria, although it is often very difficult to establish thriving cultures of the bacteria-free organisms.

MEDIA FOR CHLOROPHYLL-BEARING FLAGELLATES

For obvious reasons, the chlorophyll-bearing flagellates are more easily established in bacteria-free cultures than is any of the other groups of free-living Protozoa. This is evidenced by the fact that approximately 40 species of green flagellates have been isolated in such cultures, most of the strains being maintained at the present time in the laboratory of Professor E. G. Pringsheim (Pringsheim, 1928a, 1930). The composition of the various media, so far as inorganic constituents are concerned, is based upon past experience in the growth of algae and green flagellates. With the establishment of bacteria-free cultures, peptones or other organic sources of nitrogen have usually been added to the media for the maintenance of rich cultures. Several of the media which have been tried in our laboratory and have given good results with different species of Euglenida and Phytomonadida are listed in Table 1.

TABLE 1. **Media for chlorophyll-bearing flagellates.**

			Media			
Constituents	A	B	C	D	E	F
NH_4NO_3	0.5 gm.		1.0 gm.			
KNO_3		0.5 gm.			0.5 gm.	
Tryptone		2.5 gm.		2.0 gm.	5.0 gm.	
Glycine						1.996 gm.
K_2HPO_4						0.209 gm.
KH_2PO_4	0.5 gm.	0.5 gm.	0.2 gm.	0.25 gm.	0.5 gm.	
$MgSO_4$	0.1 gm.	0.1 gm.	0.2 gm.	0.25 gm.	0.25 gm.	0.048 gm.
NaCl	0.1 gm.	0.1 gm.			0.1 gm.	
KCl			0.2 gm.	0.25 gm.		
$FeCl_3$	Trace	Trace	Trace	Trace		
Sodium acetate		2.5 gm.		2.0 gm		1.48 gm.
Dextrose		2.0 gm.				
Distilled water	1.0 l	1.0 l	1.0 l	1.0 l	0.0 l	1.0 l

Medium A, adjusted to pH 7.0, has given very good results (Loefer, 1934) with *Chlorogonium euchlorum* and *C. elongatum*, and should be equally satisfactory for other species of Chlamydomonadidae. Medium B, at pH 7.0, has supported growth of Chlorogonium and *C. elongatum* (Loefer, 1934) in darkness for more than a year, the flagellates retaining their chlorophyll throughout the period of culture. The same medium has been used for *Haematococcus pluvialis, Colacium vesiculosum,* and five species of Euglena, in the maintenance of stock cultures in light. Medium C at pH 7.0 supports good growth of *Euglena gracilis,* according to the findings of Dusi (1930) and results obtained in our own laboratory. Ammonium phosphate or ammonium sulphate may be substituted for ammonium nitrate. Medium D is the formula used by Lwoff and Lwoff (1929) for *Chlamydomonas agloeformis* and *Haematococcus pluvialis* and by Lwoff and Dusi (1929) for *Euglena gracilis* in darkness, except that Difco tryptone is substituted for the peptone used by the French investigators. In our laboratory, this medium has given excellent results with stock cultures of six species of Euglenida, *Haematococcus pluvialis,* and two species of Chlorogonium. Medium E was used by Jahn (1931) for *Euglena gracilis* and by Hall (1933) for *E. anabaena* and *E. deses.* In addition, the medium is satisfactory for other species of Euglena, and for Haematococcus and Chlorogonium. Growth is less abundant than in media containing sodium acetate, but the cultures remain viable for several months. Medium F, at pH 7.0, supports good growth of *Chlorogonium elongatum, C. euchlorum,* and *Haematococcus pluvialis.* The same medium supports slow growth of the colorless *Chilomonas paramecium,* as reported by Mast and Pace (1933) and confirmed in our laboratory.

In addition to the various liquid media, certain types of solid media have proved useful in our laboratory, particularly for the growth of stock cultures over long periods and also in the preparation of cultures for shipment. In the preparation of a solid medium we have added either Difco dehydrated dextrose-agar or starch agar to one of the media listed above; for a semi-solid medium, one-half or less of the usual amount of dehydrated agar is added to the liquid. Such media may be tubed and then slanted or not, as preferred. Slant or stab cultures may be sealed with melted paraffin, and will usually remain healthy for several months.

MEDIA FOR COLORLESS FLAGELLATES

In general, the addition of peptone in suitable amounts to one of the media (A-F) listed above will provide a satisfactory medium for growth of the colorless Phytomastigophora. The formulae have been varied somewhat by different workers, however, as indicated in Table 2.

Medium G was used by Pringsheim (1921) for growth of *Polytoma uvella,* and good results were obtained also by Lwoff (1932). The same solution, in Pringsheim's laboratory, was made the base of an agar medium which supported good growth of Polytoma. Medium H is a gelatin medium developed by Lwoff (1932) for *Polytoma uvella;* with the omission of gelatin, the same formula gives a very satisfactory liquid medium

TABLE 2. **Media for colorless flagellates.**

	Media			
Constituents	G	H	I	J
Glycine	2.0 gm.			
Peptone		2.0 gm.	10.0 gm.	10.0 gm.
Gelatin	150.0 gm.			
NH_4NO_3			0.5 gm.	
Dextrose	2.0 gm.			
Sodium acetate	2.0 gm.	2.0 gm.	2.0 gm.	
K_2HPO_4	0.2 gm			2.0 gm.
KH_2PO_4		0.25 gm.	1.5 gm.	
K_2CO_3	2.0 gm.			
KCl		0.25 gm.		
$MgSO_4$	0.1 gm.	0.25 gm.	0.25 gm.	
Distilled water	1.0 l	1.0 l	1.0 l	
Tap water				1.0 l

TABLE 3. **Media for ciliates.**

	Media					
Constituents	K	L	M	N	O	P
Peptone	10.0 gm.	10.0 gm.	10-30 gm.		5.0 gm.	
KH_2PO_4			2.0 gm.			
K_2HPO_4						0.02 gm.
Na_2HPO_4	0.01 gm.					
NaCl	0.5 gm.	4.0 gm.			0.003 gm.	0.02 gm.
KCl	0.01 gm.					
$MgSO_4$	0.01 gm.			0.025 gm.	0.0045 gm.	0.02 gm.
$CaCl_2$	0.01 gm			0.001 gm.		
KNO_3				0.5 gm.	0.0013 gm.	
$(NH_4)_2PO_4$				0.05 gm.		
$FeCl_3$				0.001 gm.	0.0002 gm.	
$CaSO_4$					0.015 gm.	
$Ca(NO_3)_2$						0.2 gm.
$FeSO_4$						Trace
Distilled water	1.0 l	1.0 l	1.0 l	1.0 l	1.0 l	1.0 l

for the same species. Lwoff adjusted the pH to 8.0 with K_2CO_3. Medium I was used by Jahn (1933) for the growth of stock and experimental cultures of *Chilomonas paramecium*. Medium J has been used in our laboratory for maintaining stock cultures of *Astasia ocellata* (Jahn strain), *Astasia sp.* (Jahn strain), and *Chilomonas paramecium*.

MEDIA FOR CILIATES

The growth of *Colpidium striatum* and *C. campylum* in various types of media has been investigated by Elliott (1935a), and that of *Glaucoma ficaria* and *G. piriformis* by Johnson (1936). Results obtained by these investigators, as well as our general experience in the maintenance of stock cultures, indicate that simple media, containing one of the Difco peptones (tryptone particularly), are altogether suitable for growth of the four species mentioned. Other investigators have previously used more complex media for Colpidium and Glaucoma, but it seems that, except in special cases, little is to be gained by the use of complex salt solutions in addition to peptone. Occasionally, however, such simple media may fail to support growth of the ciliate; Glaser and Coria (1935) have recently confirmed their earlier reports that a special medium is necessary for growth of Paramecium whereas a relatively simple medium is suitable for Chilodon and Trichoda. Some of the simpler formulae, which have been tried in our laboratory and found satisfactory, are listed in table 3.

Medium K was used by Lwoff (1929) in his earlier work with *Glaucoma piriformis*. Although the medium was very satisfactory, Lwoff later concluded that such a complex medium is unnecessary and accordingly substituted medium L (Lwoff, 1932) in his later investigations. Medium M was used by Elliott (1935, 1935a) for *Colpidium striatum* and *C. campylum*. Difco tryptone was found to be superior to a number of other commercial peptones, although Difco proteose-peptone and neopeptone were fairly satisfactory. Tryptone gave best results with Colpidium in concentrations of 1.0-3.0%. Johnson (1936) has found that a 1.5% tryptone medium is optimal for growth of *Glaucoma ficaria*, while Loefer (1936a) has found it necessary to reduce the concentration to 0.5% for *Paramecium bursaria*. Formula N was devised by Pringsheim (1928) for *P. bursaria*. In Loefer's (1936a) experience, the addition of Difco tryptone (0.5%) or better, Difco proteose-peptone (0.5%), results in a medium very satisfactory for the growth of this ciliate in bacteria-free cultures. Medium O was made up by Loefer (1936a) on the basis of tap water analyses, since it had been found that tap water (New York City) gave excellent results in the cultivation of several species of Protozoa. Either tryptone or proteose-peptone is added to the salt solution in a concentration of 0.5%. Medium P was used for *Paramecium bursaria* by Pringsheim (1928, p. 310); with tryptone or proteose-peptone added, this formula gives a medium satisfactory for growth of the species in bacteria-free culture.

For another medium which has given good results with several bacteria-free strains of ciliates, the reader is referred to the work of Glaser and Coria (1935). Since this medium requires blood serum in its preparation, it will be less generally useful than the simpler media described above, but it should be quite useful in laboratories in which the necessary technical facilities are available.

MEDIA FOR SARCODINA

Acanthamoeba castellanii has been grown by Cailleau (1933) in a liver extract-serum medium sterilized by filtration, and later (1933a) in a peptone medium of the following composition: peanut peptone (Vaillant), 3.0%; sodium chloride, 0.4%; magnesium sulphate, 0.001%; monopotassium phosphate, 0.001%. Other peptones found to be satisfactory were: pancreatic stomach peptone, pancreatic peptone of spleen, and peptic peptone of "delipoïde" liver, all three being Vaillant preparations. With peptone in a concentration of 3.0%, growth of Acanthamoeba was obtained through successive transfers, while low concentrations of peptone were found to be unsatisfactory, as reported previously by Lwoff (1932).

GROWTH OF PROTOZOA ON KILLED MICRO-ORGANISMS

The growth of several species of amoebae on killed bacteria was reported by Tsujitani (1898) and Oehler (1916, 1924, 1924a). Reviews of early and later investigations are to be found in papers by Wülker (1911) and Sandon (1932), respectively. Among the ciliates, *Colpoda steinii* was grown by Oehler (1919) on killed bacteria and yeasts; *Glaucoma scintillans*, on dead bacteria by E. and M. Chatton (1923); *Paramecium caudatum*, on dead yeasts and bacteria by Glaser and Coria (1933); and *Glaucoma ficaria* by Johnson (1936a) on dead bacteria, yeasts, and flagellates. Negative results have been obtained by a number of other workers. The literature has been reviewed by Sandon (1932) and Johnson (1936a).

GROWTH OF PROTOZOA ON SINGLE SPECIES
OF MICRO-ORGANISMS

The maintenance of pure-line cultures of Protozoa on single species of living bacteria, yeasts, or other micro-organisms has been accomplished by a number of investigators, particularly Oehler (1919, 1924, 1924a). More recent investigations include those of Geise and Taylor (1935), Loefer (1936), and Johnson (1936a). The literature has been reviewed by Sandon (1932) and Johnson (1936a). Such methods are much more reliable than the use of the common "infusion" cultures and, while they do not offer the precision of the bacteria-free technique, the procedures are relatively simple and are often worth while in view of the good results obtained.

GROWTH IN RELATION TO pH AND OTHER FACTORS

The observations of a number of workers have shown that the pH of the medium is an important factor influencing the success or failure of bacteria-free cultures of Protozoa. The findings of Dusi (1930a), Jahn (1931), Elliott (1933), Dusi (1933, 1933a), Hall (1933), Loefer

(1935), and Johnson (1936) show that growth of various species of flagellates and ciliates in bacteria-free cultures is influenced to a marked degree by the pH of the medium. The literature on this subject has been reviewed by Loefer (1935). Not only is there a direct relationship between pH and growth in the simpler media, but there are also indirect relationships to be considered. For example, it is known (Elliott, 1935a) that sodium acetate accelerates growth of Colpidium in a medium near pH 7.0, but is decidedly toxic in media below pH 5.5, although the latter pH is near the optimum for growth of the ciliate in acetate-free media. Observations in progress on several species of Euglena indicate that similar relationships hold for the green flagellates. Elliott (1935) has noted a similar relationship between pH of the medium and the accelerating effects of carbohydrates on growth of Colpidium. Near the neutral point, little or no acceleration was observed with certain carbohydrates, whereas in the acid range growth was decidedly stimulated by the same carbohydrates.

The concentration of both organic and inorganic constituents of the medium may also have an important bearing on the maintenance of bacteria-free cultures, as indicated by the observations of Cailleau (1933a), Elliott (1935a), Loefer (1936a), and Johnson (1936). It is known that the addition of various substances—such as dextrose and other carbohydrates, sodium acetate and other salts of the lower fatty acids, yeast extract, etc.—to media listed above will increase the growth of a number of species of Protozoa. Our observations show that the factor of concentrations is important in the determination of such accelerating effects, since an amount in excess of the optimal concentration may even inhibit growth of the Protozoa. This question has been discussed in detail by Loefer (1936a).

REFERENCES

For the culture of many colorless and pale green flagellates see p. 177.
Order Chrysomonadida, Family Ochromonadidae
For the culture of Ochromonas see p. 62.

BIBLIOGRAPHY

CAILLEAU, R.   1933.   Culture d'Acanthamoeba castellani en milieu liquide. *C. R. Soc. Biol.* 113:990.
——— 1933a.   Culture d'Acanthamoeba castellani sur milieu peptoné. Action sur les glucides. *Ibid.* 114:474.
DUSI, H. 1930.   La nutrition autotrophe d'Euglena gracilis Klebs aux dépens de quelques azotés inorganiques. *Ibid.* 104:662.
——— 1930a.   Les limites de la concentration en ions H pour la culture de quelques Euglènes. *Ibid.* 104:734.
——— 1933.   Recherches sur la nutrition de quelques Euglènes.
I. *Euglena gracilis. Ann. Inst. Pasteur* 50:550.
——— 1933a.   Recherches sur la nutrition de quelques Euglènes.

II. *Euglena stellata, klebsii, anabaena, deses* et *pisciformis. Ibid.* 50:840.

ELLIOTT, A. M. 1933. Isolation of *Colpidium striatum* Stokes in bacteria-free cultures and the relation of growth to pH of the medium. *Biol. Bull.* 65:45.

——— 1935. Effects of carbohydrates on growth of Colpidium. *Arch. f. Protist.* 84:156.

——— 1935a. Effects of certain organic acids and protein derivatives on the growth of Colpidium. *Ibid.* 84:472.

GEISE, A. C., and TAYLOR, C. V. 1935. Paramecium for experimental purposes in controlled mass cultures on a single strain of bacteria. *Ibid.* 84:225.

GLASER, R. W. 1932. Cultures of certain Protozoa, bacteria-free. *J. Parasit.* 19:23.

GLASER, R. W., and CORIA, N. A. 1930. Methods for the pure culture of certain Protozoa. *J. Exper. Med.* 51:787.

——— 1933. The culture of *Paramecium caudatum* free from living micro-organisms. *J. Parasit.* 20:33.

——— 1935. The culture and reactions of purified Protozoa. *Amer. J. Hyg.* 21:111.

HALL, R. P. 1933. On the relation of hydrogen-ion concentration to the growth of *Euglena anabaena* var. *minor* and *E. deses. Arch. f. Protist.* 79:239.

HETHERINGTON, A. 1934. The sterilization of Protozoa. *Biol. Bull.* 67:315.

JAHN, T. L. 1931. Studies on the physiology of the euglenoid flagellates. III. The effect of hydrogen-ion concentration on the growth of *Euglena gracilis* Krebs. *Ibid.* 61: 387.

——— 1933. Studies on the oxidation-reduction potential of protozoan cultures. I. The effect of pH on *Chilomonas paramecium. Protoplasma* 20:90.

JOHNSON, D. F. 1936. The isolation of *Glaucoma ficaria* Kahl in bacteria-free cultures, and growth in relation to pH of the medium. *Arch. f. Protist.* 86:263.

——— 1936a. Growth of *Glaucoma ficaria* Kahl in cultures with single species of other micro-organisms. *Ibid.* 86:359.

LOEFER, J. B. 1934. The trophic nature of Chlorogonium and Chilomonas. *Biol. Bull.* 66:1.

——— 1935. Relation of hydrogen-ion concentration to growth of Chilomonas and Chlorogonium. *Arch. f. Protist.* 85:209.

——— 1936. A simple method for the maintenance of pure-line mass cultures of *Paramecium caudatum* on a single species of yeast. *Trans. Amer. Micr. Soc.* 55:255.

——— 1936a. Isolation of a bacteria-free strain of *Paramecium bursaria* and concentration of the medium as a factor in growth. (Submitted for publication.)

LUCK, J. M., and SHEETS, G. 1931. The sterilization of Protozoa. *Arch. f. Protist.* 75:255.

LUCK, J. M., SHEETS, G., and THOMAS, J. O. 1931. The role of bacteria in the nutrition of Protozoa. *Quart. Rev. Biol.* 6:46.

LWOFF, A. 1929. Milieux de culture et d'etretien pour *Glaucoma piriformis* (Cilié). *C. R. Soc. Biol.* 100:635.

——— 1932. Recherches biochimiques sur la nutrition des Protozoaires. Le pouvoir synthese. *Monographies de l'Institut Pasteur* (Paris, Masson et Cie.), 158 pp.

LWOFF, A., and DUSI, H. 1929. Le pouvoir synthèse *d'Euglena gracilis* cultivée a l'obscurité. *C. R. Soc. Biol.* 102:567.

LWOFF, M., and LWOFF, A. 1929. Le pouvoir de synthèse de *Chlamydomonas agloeformis* et *d'Haematococcus pluvialis. Ibid.* 102:569.

MAST, S. O., and PACE, D. M. 1933. Synthesis from inorganic compounds of starch, fats, proteins and protoplasm in the colorless animal, *Chilomonas paramecium. Protoplasma* 20:326.

OEHLER, R. 1916. Amöbenzucht auf reinem Boden. *Arch. f. Protist.* 37:175.

—— 1919. Flagellaten- und Ciliatenzucht auf reinem Boden. *Ibid.* 40:16.

—— 1920. Gereinigte Ciliatenzucht. *Ibid.* 41:34.

—— 1924. Weitere Mitteilungen über gereinigte Amöben- und Ciliatenzucht. *Ibid.* 49:112.

—— 1924a. Gereinigte Zucht von freilebenden Amöben, Flagellaten, und Ciliaten. *Ibid.* 49:287.

PARPART, A. K. 1928. The bacteriological sterilization of Paramecium. *Biol. Bull.* 55:113.

PHELPS, A. 1934. Studies on the nutrition of Paramecium. *Arch. f. Protist.* 82:134.

PRINGSHEIM, E. G. 1921. Zur Physiologie saprophytischer Flagellaten (Polytoma, Astasia und Chilomonas). *Beitr. Allg. Bot.* 2:88.

—— 1928. Physiologische Untersuchungen an *Paramecium bursaria*. *Arch. f. Protist.* 64:289.

—— 1928a. Algenreinkulturen. Eine Liste der Stämme, welche auf Wunsch agbegeben werden. *Ibid.* 63:255.

—— 1930. Neue Chlamydomonaceen, welche in Reinkultur gewonnen wurden. *Ibid.* 69:95.

SANDON, H. 1932. The food of Protozoa. *Publ. Fac. Sci. Egypt* (Cairo, Misr-Sokar Press), 187 pp.

TSUJITANI, J. 1898. Ueber die Reinkultur der Amöben. *Zentralbl. f. Bakt.,* I, 24:666.

WÜLKER, G. 1911. Die Technik der Amobenzuchtung. *Ibid.* 33:314.

Order CRYPTOMONADIDA,

Family CRYPTOMONADIDAE

CULTIVATION OF PROTOZOA

JOHN P. TURNER, *University of Minnesota*

Chilomonas sp. To each 100 cc. of pond water* (previously freed from Protozoa by heating to 70° C.) add 4 grains of wheat. Inoculate with Chilomonas from old culture or from wild stock after isolating them with a fine pipette [see pp. 43, 70]. Within a week the culture should be cloudy with Chilomonas, and this serves as a valuable source of food for many larger forms. Chilomonas may be obtained from almost any pond where there is decomposing vegetation, especially if that be allowed to stand in water in the laboratory for a few days with wheat added.

Amoeba proteus. To each 100 cc. of pond water (previously heated to 70° C. if a "pure" culture is wanted) add 2 grains of wheat and a few drops of Chilomonas culture to serve as food. A day or two later inoculate with the Amoeba (often found on dead lily pads, *etc.*, in shallow water). Keep between 15° and 25° C. for best results, and disturb as little as possible. Cultivate in water less than an inch deep.

* Note: In most parts of the country tap water from city mains will grow Protozoa satisfactorily if allowed to stand for a few days after being drawn. In many cases pond, lake, spring, or stream water is better.

Actinosphaerium eichhorni. To each 100 cc. of pond water add 4 grains of wheat, some Chilomonas and, if available, any other small Protozoa. Inoculate with Actinosphaerium. Culture in a flat, shallow dish. Considerable search of small, permanent ponds may be necessary before Actinosphaerium are found, but by repeated inoculation of a number of rich mixed cultures with each sample taken, one should soon discover them.

Arcella vulgaris. Both wheat and hay infusions are good, but a mixture is best. To 100 cc. of pond water add 2 grains of wheat and ½ gram of hay. Inoculate with Chilomonas if available, although Arcella will grow by feeding merely on the decomposing infusion. After two or three days add Arcella which may be found on the bottom of many old cultures or in the bottom ooze from any shallow pond. Isolate them from the ooze and other Protozoa with a fine pipette [see p. 43] and place them in a watch glass with a drop of water. See that there are no other Protozoa nor worm eggs present that might develop and feed on the Arcella. Then place them in the culture in a shallow dish.

Euplotes patella. To a liter of water add 5 grams of timothy hay, 10 halves of yellow split peas, and 10 grains of wheat. Heat to boiling point and set aside until the next day. Inoculate with Chilomonas which serves as food. In a few days these will be abundant and the culture is ready for the Euplotes. When kept in such medium, Euplotes will multiply to incredible numbers.

Blepharisma sp. Follow directions given for *Euplotes patella* but dilute medium with equal parts of pond water before adding Blepharisma.

Spirostomum ambiguum and *S. teres.* Putrid cultures are best. Rich wheat and hay infusions give excellent results. To each 100 cc. of water add 5 grains of wheat and 5 or 10 2-inch lengths of timothy hay stalks. Inoculate with Chilomonas for food and after a day or two add the Spirostomum. If available, bed the bottom of the dish with old, thoroughly washed sphagnum moss. They should multiply to such numbers as to make large white blotches on the moss.

Stentor coeruleus. Fill a battery jar ½ to ¾ full of a culture of Paramecium prepared as follows: One liter of lake water is brought to a boil and a handful of timothy hay added; as soon as all the hay has been submerged in the boiling water the heat is turned off and, on the following day, the infusion is diluted with an equal portion of lake water and inoculated with the Paramecia. In a week or so the Paramecia are sufficiently abundant. Then add a gram or two of timothy hay and inoculate with Stentor. If kept near a window but not in direct sunlight, the Stentor should become very abundant. With occasional (every 2 or 3 weeks) additions of small amounts of raw, dry hay, rich cultures will last for months.

REFERENCES

For the culture of Chilomonas see also pp. 62, 63, and 136.
For the culture of *Chilomonas paramecium* see pp. 53 and 113.
Order Phytomonadida
For the culture of various members of this order see p. 52.
Family Chlamydomonadidae
For the culture of Chlamydomonas see p. 53.
For the culture of *Haematococcus pluvialis* see p. 53.
For the culture of *Chlorogonium euchlorum* and *C. elongatum* see p. 52.
For the culture of Carteria see pp. 35 and 38.
Family Volvocidae
For the culture of Volvox see references on p. 72.

Family POLYTOMIDAE

POLYTOMA CULTURES*

JOSEPHINE C. FERRIS, *University of Nebraska*

PUT 270 grams of chicken-size bone meal into a muslin bag and tie compactly so that the whole mass is in a firm ball. Cover with water and bring to a boil. Pour off water and allow the bag to cool for 2 hours. Boil 1 gram of ground timothy hay for 10 minutes and allow to cool. Pour cooled hay solution into small battery jar and add enough cold sterilized water to make 1200 cc. Lift cooled bag of bone meal with sterilized forceps into jar and inoculate with Polytoma. Keep at about 17° to 20° C. Every 48 hours repeat the above procedure and use all the scum of the old culture in inoculating the new culture. Such a culture may be maintained many months or even years. Removing the surface film of Polytoma with a sterilized spoon and centrifuging yields concentrated masses of these Protozoa.

REFERENCES

For the culture of Polytoma see also p. 53.
For the culture of *Parapolytoma satura* see pp. 113 and 116.

Order EUGLENOIDIDA, Family EUGLENIDAE

CULTURING EUGLENA PROXIMA

J. A. CEDERSTROM, *University of Minnesota*

Euglena proxima may be cultured very readily for laboratory use in filtered rain water (100 cc.) to which is added 1 cc. of one day old pasturized milk from which the cream has been removed completely. Keep the culture at ordinary room temperatures of from 60° to 68° or

* See Biol. Bull. 63:442, 1932.

70° F. Place the culture near a window; diffused light is quite satisfactory. From three to six weeks are needed for the development of the culture. This time will depend on the density of the population desired. Ordinary half-pint milk bottles make satisfactory containers, and absorbent cotton stoppers, which will admit air, may be used to keep out dust and spores of other forms of life. Good results have been obtained in culturing other species of Euglena in the same manner.

A pure culture of Euglena may be obtained by selecting under the microscope with a fine pipette [see p. 43] individual specimens of the desired species. A clean culture is very valuable and, once it is obtained, it may be perpetuated indefinitely if care is taken to prevent contamination. Obviously, only sterilized pipettes should be used in removing specimens from the culture for class use.

REFERENCES

For the culture of *Euglena spp.* see pp. 53, 63, and 71.
For the culture of *Euglena deses* see p. 53.
For the culture of *Euglena anabaena* see p. 53.

A CULTURE MEDIUM FOR FREE-LIVING FLAGELLATES*

THE following culture method, which has been tried out for two years, may be of use to other laboratories. Whole wheat is weighed into 5 gm. lots, which are then put into large test tubes and 25 cc. of tap water added. These are then plugged with cotton, capped with lead foil, and autoclaved at 15 pounds' pressure for 2 hours, which very thoroughly macerates the wheat. Tap water is again added up to 50 cc., and desired percentages of this fluid are used after shaking. After opening a tube it is necessary to sterilize again in an Arnold sterilizer, as bacterial growth is vigorous in the mixture. However, a tube may be used day after day, if sterilized daily.

Various percentages of this mixture afford a very good medium for many Protozoa. Bacterial feeders such as Chilodon, Paramecium, Oicomonas, and others thrive on it. Ochromonas, Chilomonas, and several of the smaller Euglenas (*E. gracilis* [see also pp. 53 and 82], *E. quartana,* and *E. mutabilis*) have been grown in abundance in various dilutions. There are several species of Amoeba which likewise occur or are capable of being cultured in large numbers. It has proved best, however, for Entosiphon and Peranema. Both of these forms are easily grown in quantities sufficient for classroom use; isolation cultures of the former have been carried over a year on this medium. In general it seems much better than cracked boiled wheat, which is often used.

* Reprinted from *Science* 65: 261, 1927, by JAMES B. LACKEY, *U. S. Public Health Service.*

CULTURE OF SOME FLAGELLATES AND CILIATES

PAUL BRANDWEIN, *Washington Square College, New York University*

Euglena. To 100 cc. of a modified Klebs' solution (Solution B)* in a white glass battery jar add 40 rice grains (boiled 5-10 minutes) and 900 cc. of distilled water. The foregoing medium is allowed to stand for about five days. The jar is then placed in indirect sunlight (the direct rays of the sun should not strike this culture for more than an hour a day), and inoculated with Euglenae three times (10 cc. of a dense Euglena culture) at three day intervals. If an old Euglena culture is available the organisms may be found encysted on the sides of the vessel and it is of great advantage to inoculate the cysts along with the free Euglenae. Starting ten days after the initial inoculation, growth may be accelerated by adding (three times, at weekly intervals), 25 cc. of Solution B and 10 mg. of the tryptophane powder. The further addition of 5 grains of boiled rice each month will serve thereafter to maintain the culture. Large ciliates and rotifers are detrimental.

Another technique, applicable to several Protozoa involves the use of an egg yolk-distilled water medium.

Chilomonas. A thin smooth paste is prepared by grinding 0.5 gm. of the boiled yolk of a fresh hen's egg with a small amount of distilled water. This is added to 500 cc. of distilled water and the mixture, after standing two days, is inoculated with the original Chilomonas culture. If such a culture is not available, spontaneous inoculation will occur if the culture jar is left uncovered, since cysts of Chilomonas seem to be omnipresent.

Paramecium, Colpidium, Colpoda, Euplotes. These ciliates have done well on the egg yolk medium when Chilomonas is provided as prey. Start a Chilomonas culture as previously directed and inoculate with 10 cc. of a culture of the desired ciliate, three times, on the 4th, 6th, and 8th day after starting. Dense maximum growth has usually been obtained in two weeks and subculturing has been necessary about every month.

Didinium. The organism will thrive exceedingly well when introduced into one of the Paramecium cultures described above. As the Paramecium diminishes in one culture a fresh one should be available for inoculation with the Didinium. In fact it is advisable to keep Paramecium cultures in a separate room; otherwise it is difficult to avoid contamination with Didinium.

Vorticella. A modification of the method found useful for Paramecium is necessary here. The medium of ½ gram of mashed hard-boiled egg yolk in 750 cc. of distilled water is permitted to stand for two days; it is then filtered through cotton, 100 cc. of the filtrate are added to a

---

* Modified Klebs' Solution (Solution B): KNO_3 .25 gm., $MgSO_4$ .25 gm., KH_2PO_4 .25 gm., $Ca(NO_3)_2$ 1 gm., Bacto-Tryptophane Broth (powder) .010 gm. (Digestive Ferments Co.), distilled water to make 1000 cc.

finger bowl and the Vorticellae are introduced; great numbers of the animals will be found clinging to the glass surface within two weeks. It is advisable to subculture every three weeks.

Stentor. This organism may be cultured by two methods; namely, that found useful for Amoeba, and that described for Vorticella, except that certain modifications must be made here. The rice-agar with 50 cc. of Solution A [see footnote on p. 73] is permitted to stand for two days in a finger bowl; at this point Chilomonas is added together with as many Stentors as possible. Or, the medium of ½ gram of mashed hard-boiled egg yolk in 750 cc. of distilled water is permitted to stand for three days, filtered, and inoculated with Chilomonas and the Stentors. (About 5 cc. of a heavy Chilomonas culture are necessary for the inoculation in both cases.) It is desirable to subculture every month.

Stylonychia and *Oxytricha.* For these hypotrichs and certain others the presence of Chilomonas seems advantageous. Before introducing the desired ciliate, allow some 30 cc. of Solution A in a rice-agar bowl, inoculated with 10 cc. of a Chilomonas culture [see p. 63] to stand about four days. Swarming cultures have usually been obtained within two weeks.

REFERENCES

For a Phacus-like organism see p. 69.
For the culture of *Colacium vesiculosum* see p. 53.
For Euglenamorpha see p. 69.
Family Astasiidae
For the culture of *Astasia sp. and A. ocellata* see p. 54.
For the culture of Peranema see pp. 62 and 136.
Family Heteronemidae
For the culture of Entosiphon see pp. 62 and 177.

Order PROTOMONADIDA,
Family TRYPANOSOMATIDAE

A SIMPLE METHOD FOR CULTURING TRYPANOSOMA LEWISI

REED O. CHRISTENSON, *University of Minnesota*

IT is not always feasible, on short notice, to obtain living trypanosomes. Laboratory cultures should be established and maintained. This can be done easily by using the following method which we have found both simple and reliable.

Wild rats are caught by setting a number of spring-traps near their holes or runways. The captives are killed and opened. A small amount of blood is taken from the heart, using clean pipettes, and this is dropped into cotton-stoppered vials half full of sterile 0.75% saline solution. The vials are taken to the laboratory, a drop of the fluid placed on a slide, covered, and examined. Under low power (16 mm. objective) the parasites cannot be seen, but if they are present their movements cause violent agitation of the corpuscles, thus enabling a tentative diagnosis to be made. They are readily seen under high power (4 mm. objective) if the light is carefully regulated. About 5 to 10% of the wild rats carry infections.

To establish the strain in laboratory animals the fluid from positive vials is drawn into a clean hypodermic syringe, and intraperitoneal inoculations are made into partly grown laboratory rats, about 0.5 cc. being given each one. Occasionally an animal will be found to be immune. This fact necessitates the infection of several so as not to lose the infection. About seven days later a test is made. The tip of the tail is cut off and a drop of blood allowed to mix with a small drop of saline solution on a slide. It is then covered and examined microscopically.

By the end of the second week the trypanosomes have usually reached their maximum number and have begun to decrease. By the fourth or fifth week (occasionally somewhat longer) they may have disappeared entirely from the blood. Before this time it is necessary to inoculate new, non-immune animals. An infected rat is etherized; the needle of a hypodermic syringe partly filled with saline solution is inserted into the heart; and some blood is drawn out. This is injected directly into the peritoneal cavity of the new animals. By repeating the transfer of infective serum at the proper times the strain may be maintained for indefinite periods.

Occasionally it is desired to keep living trypanosomes for a few days in the serum-saline mixture. This may be accomplished by placing the container in a refrigerator (about 18° C.) where they will live for a week or longer.

REFERENCES

For the culture of Oicomonas see p. 62.
Family Bodonidae
For the culture of Embadomonas see p. 88.

Order POLYMASTIGIDA

NOTES ON CULTURING CERTAIN PROTOZOA AND A SPIROCHAETE FOUND IN MAN

M. J. Hogue, *University of Pennsylvania Medical School*

MEDIA USED

Locke-Egg medium. One hen's egg is thoroughly shaken with glass beads in a flask. Add 200 cc. of Locke solution (sodium chloride 0.9 gm., calcium chloride o.024 gm., potassium chloride o.042 gm., sodium bicarbonate o.02 gm., dextrose o.25 gm.). Heat over a hot water bath for 15 minutes keeping the medium in constant motion by revolving the flask. Filter through cotton with a suction pump. Put about 6 cc. of the filtrate into each test tube. Autoclave the tubes for 20 minutes under 15 pounds' pressure (Hogue, 1921a).

Ovomucoid medium. The white of one hen's egg is thoroughly shaken with glass beads in a glass flask. Add 100 cc. of o.7% sodium chloride solution. Cook this for half an hour over a hot water bath, keeping the contents of the flask in constant motion by revolving the flask. Filter through cotton, using a suction pump. Put about 6 cc. of the filtrate in each test tube. Sometimes one loopful of the egg yolk is added to each test tube. Autoclave the tubes for 20 minutes under 15 pounds' pressure (Hogue, 1921a).

Sodium chloride sheep serum water. To a flask containing 100 cc. of o.85% sodium chloride solution which has been sterilized in the autoclave for 15 minutes at 15 pounds' pressure add 10-15 cc. of sterile sheep serum water. This is prepared by diluting one part of sheep serum with three parts of distilled water and sterilizing in an Arnold steam sterilizer for one hour at 100° C. for three successive days. Pour the sterile sodium chloride sheep serum water into sterile test tubes. It will have a pH of 7-7.4 (Hogue, 1922a).

Sodium chloride pig serum water. This is made in the same way as sheep serum water except that one part of pig serum is diluted with four parts of distilled water. It will have a pH of from 6.8-7.4 (Hogue, 1922a).

Sodium chloride sheep serum water modified. This modification is used for *Trichomonas buccalis.* Take equal amounts of o.85% sterile sodium chloride solution and sterile sheep serum water. Put 5 cc. in a test tube. This has a pH of 7.7. Just before using, add a small amount of saliva taken from a person who is not infected with *T. buccalis* (Hogue, 1926).

Deep cultures. "Deep cultures" are used in order to keep organisms for a long time without transferring them (Hogue, 1922a, 1922b, 1926, 1933). These are made by putting 15 cc. of the culture to be used into 150 mm. test tubes, inoculating them at the bottom of the tube with a long pipette and then covering the medium with a layer of sterile paraffin oil. This prevents evaporation but does not make the cultures anaerobic. Under these conditions the animals do not divide so rapidly and do not form such large quantities of waste products. In these "deep cultures" they live for weeks or months, depending on the species.

Retortamonas intestinalis (Waskia or Embadomonas) grew well on both Locke-egg and ovomucoid, forming cysts in each medium. On the Locke-egg it lived from 3-10 days. One culture lived 17 days on the ovomucoid. The cultures were grown at 35° C. (Hogue, 1921a).

A new variety of Retortamonas found in man grows well on sodium chloride sheep serum water. It has been kept at room temperature (20-33° C.) for over 3 years and has survived one heat wave of 39.5° C. It is transferred every 7 days. "Deep cultures" of it are kept at room temperature. In them the organisms live from 8-9 months. One culture lived over 12 months (Hogue, 1933).

Trichomonas buccalis grew on a sodium chloride sheep serum medium especially rich in sheep serum and containing a small amount of human saliva. On this medium they were cultured for over 7 months. Transfers were made every 2-3 days, though they lived about 5 days on this medium at 30° C. In "deep cultures" they lived from 30-60 days (Hogue, 1926).

Trichomonas hominis grew well on Locke-egg, ovomucoid and sodium chloride sheep serum water. In the early work the first two media were used and the cultures were incubated at 35° C. They lived about 6 days on the Locke-egg and from 6-10 days on the ovomucoid (Hogue, 1921b). In later work sodium chloride sheep serum water has been used. They have been incubated at 36° C. and at room temperature. In "deep cultures" these organisms live from 35-66 days at 35° C. The most favorable pH for rapid multiplication is pH 7.2-8.4 with pH 8 as an optimum. If it is desirable to keep the cultures longer pH 7.2-7.4 is better. Here they divide more slowly (Hogue, 1922a).

Spirochaeta eurygyrata grew well on Locke-egg, ovomucoid, and sodium chloride pig serum water. On ovomucoid and Locke-egg they lived from 8-12 days. The best results were obtained with sodium chloride pig serum water with pH 7. These were incubated at 35° C. In "deep cultures" of sodium chloride pig serum water they lived from 60-90 days. One culture contained active spirochaetes 127 days after inoculation (Hogue, 1922b).

REFERENCES

For the culture of Trichomonas see also pp. 69, 88, and 91.
For the culture of Tritrichomonas see p. 118.
For the culture of Enteromonas see p. 88.
For the culture of Monocercomonas see p. 129.
For the culture of Chilomastix see p. 88.

BIBLIOGRAPHY

HOGUE, M. J. 1921a. *Waskia intestinalis:* Its cultivation and cyst formation. *J. A. M. A.* 77:112.

———— 1921b. The cultivation of *Trichomonas hominis*. *Amer. J. Trop. Med.* 1:211.

———— 1922a. A study of *Trichomonas hominis,* its cultivation, its inoculation into animals, and its staining reaction to vital dyes. *Johns Hopkins Hosp. Bull.* 33:437.

———— 1922b. *Spirochaeta eurygyrata. J. Exper. Med.* 36:617.

———— 1926. Studies on *Trichomonas buccalis. Amer. J. Trop. Med.* 6:75.

———— 1933. A new variety of *Retortamonas (Embadomonas) intestinalis* from man. *Amer. J. Hyg.* 18:433.

FROG AND TOAD TADPOLES AS SOURCES OF INTESTINAL PROTOZOA FOR TEACHING PURPOSES*

R. W. HEGNER, *School of Hygiene and Public Health*

MANY teachers of protozoology and invertebrate zoology use frogs for the purpose of obtaining intestinal Protozoa for class use, but it does not seem to be generally known that the tadpoles of frogs and toads are even more valuable than the adults as sources of material. Unfortunately tadpoles are most abundant late in the spring and in early summer when classes are usually not in session, but two species of frogs that are more or less common throughout the United States pass two or more seasons in the tadpole stage and hence are available in the autumn and, in the southern part of the country, at any time of the year; these are the green frog, *Rana clamitans,* and the bullfrog, *R. catesbiana.* A breeding place once found will serve as a source of supply year after year.

Sample tadpoles should be collected some time before the class meets so as to determine the incidence of infection and numbers present of the various species of Protozoa, since these vary from year to year. The specimens for class use may be collected several days before they are needed but should not be kept more than a week or two since they tend to lose their infections under laboratory conditions. The writer has found dishes about 10 inches in diameter and 3 inches deep containing a quart of tap water to be suitable for about 20 tadpoles each. The dishes should not be covered with glass plates, but the water should be changed every day or two. Tadpoles may be killed very quickly, as adult frogs usually are, by destroying the brain and spinal cord with a heavy needle. The ventral body wall may then be opened from the anterior to the posterior end. The intestine is coiled within the body cavity, being several hundred millimeters in length. The rectum, or posterior portion of the alimentary tract, is tightly coiled and is separated from the intestine by a constriction. The different species of intestinal Protozoa are rather definitely distributed within the intestine and rectum.

* Reprinted from *Science* 56:439, 1922, with slight changes by the author.

The anterior portion of the intestine is inhabited by a flagellate, *Giardia agilis* [see also p. 89]; in various parts of the intestine and rectum *Endamoeba ranarum* may be found; the rectum is the principal habitat of three genera of flagellates, Trichomonas [see p. 67], Hexamitis, and Euglenamorpha, and of several green flagellates resembling members of the genera Euglena and Phacus. To study any of these in the living condition, the part of the digestive tract containing them should be teased out in a drop of 0.7% salt solution and covered with a cover glass. Any of the species mentioned may be found with low magnification, such as obtained with a 16 mm. objective and a number 5 ocular.

Nyctotherus cordiformis is a very large ciliate that is often found in the rectum of tadpoles. It appears to be a scavenger and resembles Paramecium in structure and in its primary life processes. *Opalina ranarum* is also a large ciliate. It and other species of Opalina are frequent inhabitants of the rectum of tadpoles.

Class *Sarcodina*, Order AMOEBAEA, Family

AMOEBIDAE

PROTOZOAN CULTURES*

GEORGE R. LA RUE, *University of Michigan*

NATURAL POND CULTURES

THESE cultures should be made by the methods of Hyman, Jennings, and others. The plant material collected should not be restricted to Ceratophyllum and Elodea, but should include any vegetable matter, *e.g.*, old lily pads and stems, cat-tails (especially if decay has commenced), decaying leaves of trees, grass and sedges, *etc.*, from pools, ponds, marshes, bogs, ditches, and rivers. Chara and clean Spirogyra and the brown mat of algae from the surface of a dam or of stones are of value, if not too much is taken and if to this is added hay or other materials to furnish food for bacteria. Decaying Sphagnum from sphagnum bogs is valuable. Mud or ooze from the bottom of ponds or pools which get the drainage from pastures or barnyards is also good. In collecting this vegetable material always bring some of the water from the same situation. Most Protozoa are sensitive to changes in water. Treated water is particularly bad for some species and should never be used until it has stood for some days in an open vessel or tank.

---

* The beginner would do well to read the article by Hyman (*Trans. Micr. Soc.* 44:216, 1925) to secure some ideas concerning general methods. He should also read other articles, some of which are listed at the end of these directions.

Place natural pond cultures in shallow glass or earthenware dishes and keep covered to prevent evaporation. If pond scums and Euglena are wanted or if these are needed for the food of any desired protozoan, set the cultures in diffuse light, never in direct sunlight. Label each culture. Use one pipette for each culture. This precaution is of great importance in examining the subcultures.

Examination of cultures. At intervals each culture should be examined carefully. In making the examination, take samples of scum, of clear liquid, scrapings from sides of vessel, from the light side and from the dark side, from the vegetation, and from the bottom. These situations may furnish different forms because some forms swim freely while others creep. Some require much oxygen while others can exist on less.

Subcultures. If at any time any culture is yielding a large number of desirable species such as Paramecium, Euglena, Amoeba, *etc.,* subcultures should be made as follows: Clean thoroughly short stender dishes or finger bowls. Place in these filtered cistern or distilled water. Do not use raw tap water. If neither cistern nor distilled water is available, filter some water which has stood for a long time in an aquarium or tank. Such water seems to have lost many of its noxious properties. Place a few straws of clean hay in the water and allow it to stand 36 to 48 hours before the desired Protozoa are placed in it. In place of dry hay, the hay may be boiled in distilled or cistern water and the hay, not the hay water, added to the water in the dish. Boiling the hay will sterilize it so that sterilization of the hay in an autoclave is probably unnecessary. Allow to stand before inoculating. In such cultures bacteria will develop and on these Paramecium and certain other forms feed.

PURE CULTURES

Isolation of particular species is not an entirely simple matter. However, individual Protozoa may frequently be secured by using a mouth pipette. This is a glass tube with a finely drawn tip in one end of a rubber tube 12 to 15 inches long with a short piece of glass tubing to place in the mouth in the other end. Place a small dish of the culture containing the organism sought on the stage of the binocular microscope and put the glass tube in the mouth. When a desired individual is found bring the point of the pipette near it and suck on the tube. With some practice the protozoan may be caught and may be put on a slide in a small drop of water and examined. In this way individual Protozoa may be isolated for the inoculation of cultures and by washing them in one or several changes of water the worker can be reasonably sure that other species are not present.

Amoeba. In culturing Amoeba tap water may be harmful and must not be used. Distilled water is very good. Boil a little hay and add the hay (not water) to distilled water in several short stender dishes (2½ to 4 in. diam.), or finger bowls. Inoculate the cultures with Euglena, diatoms, and other algae, small colorless flagellates, or some small ciliates like Colpidium [see p. 107]. When these cultures are going well inoculate with material containing plenty of good-sized Amoebae. If the food organism is an alga the Amoeba culture must have diffuse light. If ciliates are the food organism darkness will be suitable but not necessary. When such cultures are once established add dry or boiled hay at intervals of a few days to a few weeks and add distilled water to make up for evaporation. Reinoculate cultures if they do not show numbers of good Amoebae.

The following method of culturing large Amoebae has proved very successful. Thoroughly wash and rinse finger bowls and fill ⅔ full of distilled water. Add 6 or 8 grains of rolled wheat, rolled oats, or rice. Rice is best. Label, cover, and mark level of water on label. Inoculate at once with Amoebae from a good culture, taking material from the *bottom of the dish* and examining it to ascertain that Amoebae are actually being taken. At intervals of a week or two fill cultures up to mark, using distilled water. After culture is well established add a few kernels of rice or flakes of wheat or oats occasionally. Removal of a part of the water from time to time and the addition of fresh distilled water stimulates reproduction.

Euglena. Euglena thrives best in water having considerable organic material. For this reason good cultures may be made in manure solutions. Horse or cow manure is boiled in spring water or distilled water. These solutions should be made and allowed to stand 36 to 48 hours and then inoculated with Euglena. Old hay cultures if left in diffuse light almost invariably end in being almost pure cultures of Euglena. In collecting Euglena in nature seek it in barnyard pools, or pasture pools which receive considerable organic material. It may often be found among the algae of ponds even though no green scum is found on the surface. Any green scum on the surface of a pond, or green slime on decaying vegetation in ponds or streams, is almost certain to have large numbers of euglenoid forms in it.

Besides hay and manure solutions, rice in water yields good cultures. In using rice, boil 7 or 8 grains in a pint of distilled water or old water from a tank, put in a broad dish and allow to stand until a bacterial scum has formed. Then inoculate. Euglena cultures come on slowly, and must be started 4 to 8 weeks before they are needed for study. In old cultures Euglenae usually encyst on the surface of the dish, and they may be kept many months in the encysted condition. Covered cultures may be good for months and since they may be revived after encystment takes place by adding fresh manure solution, they serve as admirable sources of material for inoculating new cultures.

Paramecium. Hay cultures are perhaps the most common type but Paramecium will thrive in almost any medium which does not become too sour and which will grow plenty of bacteria. Cracked wheat has been used; also rice, rolled wheat or oats, bread, and malted milk. The latter makes a good bacterial culture; such cultures do not last long but they are easily inoculated into new cultures. If wheat is used, add boiled wheat to distilled water at the rate of 30 or 40 kernels to a gallon of water. Rolled wheat or oats should be used raw, and at the beginning not more than 10 flakes to a pint of water. Bread should be used sparingly.

BIBLIOGRAPHY

DAWSON, J. A. 1928. The culture of large free-living Amoebae. *Amer. Nat.* 62:453.

HYMAN, L. 1925. Methods of securing and cultivating Protozoa. I. General statements and methods. *Trans. Amer. Micr. Soc.* 44:216.

―――― 1931. Methods of securing and cultivating Protozoa. II. Paramecium and other ciliates. *Ibid.* 50:50.

JENNINGS, H. S. 1903. Methods of cultivating Amoeba and other Protozoa for class use. *J. Appl. Micr. and Lab. Methods* 6:2406.

KOFOID, CHARLES A. 1915. A reliable method for obtaining Amoeba for class use. *Trans. Amer. Micr. Soc.* 34:271.

LA RUE, G. R. 1916. Notes on the collection and rearing of Volvox. *Ibid.* 35:151.

―――― 1917. Notes on the culturing of microscopic organisms for the zoological laboratory. *Ibid.* 36:163.

―――― 1917. Further notes on the rearing of Volvox. *Ibid.* 36:271.

SMITH, B. G. 1907. Volvox for laboratory use. *Amer. Nat.* 41:31.

TURTOX SERVICE LEAFLET No. 4. The care of Protozoan cultures in the laboratory. *General Biological Supply Co.*

TURTOX PROTOZOA BOOKLET. *General Biological Supply Co.*

TURTOX BIOLOGY CATALOG and TEACHERS' MANUAL. *General Biological Supply Co.*

WELCH, M. W., 1917. The Growth of Amoeba on a solid medium for class use. *Trans. Amer. Micr. Soc.* 36:21.

CULTURE OF SOME FRESHWATER RHIZOPODA

PAUL BRANDWEIN, *Washington Square College, New York University*

*Amoeba.** The following method has been notable in giving a larger proportion of successful cultures which achieve a very dense maximum growth in 3-4 weeks and do not require subculturing for 8-10 weeks. It

―――――――

*CHALKLEY, H. W., 1930, *Science* 71:441 and PACE, D. M., 1933, *Arch. f. Protist.* 79:133 have previously reported two methods for Amoeba. Our medium differs little from Chalkley's, but the method in its entirety has given better results.

differs from previous methods chiefly in the use of agar* and the slight modification of the salt content of the culture solution.

Prepare finger bowls by covering the bottom with a thin (1-2 mm.) sheet of agar. This is done by pouring a warm, filtered, aqueous 0.75% solution of powdered agar into each bowl. While the agar is still soft imbed 5 rice grains, evenly spaced. The finger bowls and pipettes are previously washed thoroughly in hot water, and the rice heated (10 minutes) in a dry test tube immersed in boiling water—two necessary precautions against contaminating organisms.

About 50 Amoebae, together with 10 cc. of the medium in which they have previously been growing, are introduced into each bowl and then 30 cc. of the general culture solution (Solution A) † are added. Thereafter, every three days, 20 cc. of solution A are added to each bowl until the total volume is 80-90 cc.

When maximum growth has been attained and a culture shows signs of waning, it may be replenished by adding 10 cc. of solution A and 1 rice grain (preheated).

In a day or two after starting a culture the agar layer becomes detached from the bottom of the vessel and the Amoebae grow in layers on its upper and lower surfaces and also on the glass surface.

In about 2 months, it is advisable to subculture by dividing the contents of each bowl, exclusive of the rice-agar, into four parts, pouring each into a freshly prepared finger bowl, and adding an equal quantity of solution A. From here the procedure is the same as before.

If the original source of Amoebae is limited, as is the case when they are collected from the field‡, it is necessary to modify the method slightly, by starting the cultures in Syracuse dishes instead of finger bowls. This apparently gives a better initial concentration of the Amoebae and makes the change of culture conditions less abrupt.

The Syracuse dishes are prepared with an agar film in which 2 rice grains are imbedded. Introduce the available Amoebae with 4 cc. of the water in which they were collected and 4 cc. of solution A. In successful cases there will be a rapid proliferation and when 200-300 animals

---

*The use of an agar layer on the bottom of the dishes was originally suggested by Dr. R. Chambers for the purpose of anchoring the rice grains, about which the Amoebae tend to congregate. Mr. M. Sheib, working for Dr. Chambers, has been very successful with this method. The writer came upon it independently, and is of the opinion that the augmented growth is due to the increased surface available to the Amoebae for securing their prey, although some component, added via the agar, may be involved.

†General culture solution (Solution A)—NaCl 1.20 gms., KCl 0.03 gms., CaCl₂ 0.04 gms., NaHCO₃ 0.02 gms.; phosphate buffer solution having a pH 6.9-7.0, 50 cc.; distilled water to 1000 cc. For use dilute this 1:10. This solution maintains a fairly constant pH of about 7.0 and serves well not only for Amoeba, but also for general use.

‡In ponds from beds of Vaucheria, Hydrodictyon, from the under side of Castalia, Lemna, and Spirodela leaves.

are present, the culture (minus the rice-agar) is added to a rice-agar bowl with 30 cc. of culture solution A. The steps from here are the same as before.

The cultures were maintained at 19-22° C. by stacking the finger bowls in a sheet metal container, placed in a sink through which tap water was kept circulating to the level of the highest finger bowl. Even better growth has been obtained at 17-19° C., but it was easier to maintain the former temperature.

Arcella. The foregoing technique has also been very successful for this organism. In this case, however, temperature control is not necessary.

It is detrimental to have Stentor, Paramecium, large hypotrichs, Philodina, or Stenostomum in cultures of Amoeba or Arcella. A culture in which these organisms have gained ascendance should be discarded and precautions should be taken against contamination of other cultures. Chilomonas and Colpidium while not detrimental in moderate populations, should not be allowed to proliferate to the point where a culture becomes cloudy with them. Mold usually grows on and about the rice and does not seem detrimental although at times it is annoying since it is hard to disentangle the Amoebae from the mycelium.

Actinosphaerium. For this organism best success has been obtained by insuring the presence of Paremecium, Stenostomum, or Philodina, which forms, apparently, serve as prey. To 30 cc. of solution A in a rice-agar bowl add 30 cc. of a dense culture of either of these animals and inoculate with 5-10 Actinosphaeriae. Maintain in diffuse light and replenish with more of the above mentioned organisms as required. Prolific cultures have usually been obtained in about two weeks.

AMOEBA

WILLIAM LeRAY and NORMA FORD, *University of Toronto*

THE fact is not generally appreciated that Amoebae are found in clean water, not foul. Two forms of Amoebae (*A. proteus* type) are used in our department. One of these, an unusually large and active form, possessing many pseudopodia, is found in association with catfish and newts (*Ameiurus nebulosus* and *Triturus viridescens*). Another with fewer pseudopodia and more regular in outline is taken with the Brook Stickleback (*Eucalia inconstans*). The latter form we find the more satisfactory for class work.

The Brook Sticklebacks are collected in the backwash pools of rivers or streams. Two or three of these small fish are placed in a bowl containing 2000 cc. of pond water and fed upon Daphnia or enchytraeid worms. Gradually ooze forms on the bottom of the bowl and in about two weeks this ooze will be found to contain Amoebae.

A culture of Amoebae is then set up in bowls containing 600 cc. of pond water. The bottom of each bowl is sprinkled with exceedingly fine sand which has been carefully washed and sifted through bolting cloth. The individual grains of sand should be scarcely larger, and for the most part smaller, than a single Amoeba. To each bowl is added 6 grains of boiled wheat. (The development of the culture may be hastened by using boiled brown rice in place of the wheat, although the latter culture does not last so long.) Some ooze from the fish bowls is now introduced and the culture kept at about 73° F.

In order that the Amoebae may thrive, fungus must grow on the grains of wheat. If this fails to appear, it may be obtained by adding a bit of dead worm or dead fly from some other culture.

Within twelve days there should be an abundance of the Amoebae. Large numbers may be present as early as six or seven days, and usually so in eight days. A culture lasts about a month, but new ones should be started while the Amoebae are still active and healthy. Old cultures should be made over completely.

The fine sand in the culture is most helpful in picking the Amoebae out of the bowl for microscopic study, since a little sand taken into a pipette will have the organisms attached to it. The sand also forms an excellent support for the coverslip, allowing the Amoebae to move about freely. As part of the habitat of the culture the grains of sand afford a cover under which the organisms can hide. In an undisturbed culture the Amoebae will be found contracted and resting either under the grains or close beside them. If disturbed by jarring or by a beam of light the Amoebae glide or "walk" away from this protecting cover.

REFERENCES

For the culture of Amoeba see also pp. 62, 134, 136, and 177.

STOCK CULTURES OF AMOEBA PROTEUS*

IN the course of experiments it has been necessary to maintain cultures of *Amoeba proteus* in stock. The writer endeavored to find a medium that made requisite a minimum amount of attention. The effort in this direction met with considerable success. In view of the wide use of Amoeba of the proteus type in biological research and elementary instruction in biology, a culture medium that is simple, reproducible, and extremely reliable will be of general interest. The medium used is as follows:

$$NaCl \quad .... 0.1 \ gr.$$
$$KCl \quad .... 0.004 \ gr.$$
$$CaCl_2 \quad .... 0.006 \ gr.$$
$$H_2O \quad .... 1000 \ cc. \ (glass \ distilled)$$

* Reprinted with slight changes from an article in *Science* 71:442, 1930, by H. W. CHALKLEY, *U. S. Public Health Service.*

Two hundred to 250 cc. of this solution is put into a finger bowl or glass crystallizing dish 8 or 10 cm. in diameter and to each of such dishes is added 4 or 5 grains of polished rice (any brand carried at the corner grocery is suitable). The cultures thus prepared are immediately seeded with 50 to 100 Amoebae, covered with glass plates to prevent evaporation and entry of dust, and then left, preferably in a dark cool place, to develop. Such cultures will produce a fine crop in from 2 to 4 weeks and so far in some 30 to 40 cultures the writer has had only one or two failures. Out of five cultures that were set up as a test, three cultures one year old had ample numbers of Amoebae; the other two died out in eleven months.

These five cultures during their existence were deliberately neglected. No detritus was removed. Rice was added only when it was discovered that none was apparent in the culture. Water too was added to compensate for evaporation with no attempt at regularity, say, on the average of once a month. The temperature variation was from 19° to 28° C.

In other words, the cultures were subjected to as careless handling as if in the hands of a somewhat below par student assistant, but they survived.

M. E. D.

REFERENCES

For the culture of *Amoeba proteus* see also p. 59.

THE CULTURE OF
AMOEBA PROTEUS LEIDY *PARTIM* SCHAEFFER

D. L. HOPKINS, *Duke University* and D. M. PACE, *Johns Hopkins University*

THE Amoebae used in the development of the following culture methods correspond to those designated by Schaeffer as *Amoeba proteus* Pallas (Leidy) in 1916 and as *Chaos diffluens* Mueller in 1926. We shall follow Mast and Johnson (1931) and retain the generic name, Amoeba, but shall follow Schaeffer (1916) in separating *Amoeba proteus* (Leidy) into two species, *Amoeba proteus* Leidy *partim* Schaeffer and *Amoeba dubia* Schaeffer. While our experience has been limited to *Amoeba proteus*, it is probable that the culture methods described would also be satisfactory for *Amoeba dubia*.

Collection and culture. *Amoeba proteus* is not found in nature as frequently as are smaller Amoebae. When found it will usually be in ponds or pools where there is neither too great nor too little organic material, where there are no excessively swift currents, and in water that is not too alkaline. If, with a spoon or dipper, surface water containing a considerable amount of organic material is collected, taken to the laboratory, poured into tall slender jars and allowed to settle it will be found that the heavy organic material will settle in a thick layer on the bottom, and that the Amoebae will settle on top of this layer. They then may be removed with a pipette to a shallow dish and examined.

Amoeba proteus collected in this way may be cultured simply by placing a suitable spring or pond water in finger bowls or other shallow dishes to depth of about 2 cm., adding 3 to 4 grains of wheat, or 5 to 6 grains of polished rice, or 5 to 6 one-inch stems of timothy hay, and then inoculating with Amoebae from the collection. The Amoebae in these cultures will become very abundant in from 3 to 4 weeks. It should be noted here that Dawson (1928) gives an elaborate method for obtaining cultures from freshly collected material consisting of a gradual dilution of the collected water with distilled water. This process of dilution in our experience has not been necessary. Cultures obtained from freshly collected material are likely to contain in addition to Amoebae various organisms such as small Crustacea, rotifers, and various Protozoa. Since none of these organisms, except the cryptomonad, Chilomonas, are necessary as food, and since others such as the Crustacea probably feed on the Amoebae; it is well to take steps to eliminate these unnecessary organisms. *A. proteus* feeds on a variety of organisms, but Chilomonas alone is entirely adequate.

Freeing Amoeba cultures of contaminating organisms and establishing clone cultures. Sterilize some spring water by autoclaving for 15 minutes at 15 pounds' pressure, or merely by bringing to a boil. Allow to cool. Place sterile spring water in three or four sterile, chemically clean Syracuse watch glasses, and a finger bowl. The water in the finger bowl should have a depth of about 2 cm. Add to the finger bowl, 3 to 4 grains of wheat, 5 to 6 grains of rice, or 5 to 6 pieces of timothy hay stems about 1 inch long. The wheat, rice, or hay should be autoclaved dry 15 minutes at 15 pounds' pressure, or placed dry in a test tube, then the test tube placed in a beaker of boiling water for about 15 minutes. Now with a sterile capillary pipette and under a binocular microscope, select active Amoebae, pass them one at a time through the dishes of sterile spring water. If it is desired to obtain a clone culture (culture containing Amoebae all of which have descended from a single parent) put only one washed Amoeba into the finger bowl culture. To obtain merely a clean culture it is advisable to put into the finger bowl culture 25 or more Amoebae. Now add to the culture in the finger bowl containing washed Amoebae a drop of culture fluid containing only Chilomonas [see pp. 59 and 63] and bacteria. The best way to do this is to take small drops of the old culture fluid, examine them carefully under high power selecting only those drops which show only Chilomonas and bacteria to be present, rejecting all others. It is best to place these drops each on a small sterile coverslip, and then if the drop is found

satisfactory merely drop the coverslip into the culture bowl. Now cover
the cultures carefully with a glass cover or stack the finger bowls. In
either case be sure that the covers are sterile and chemically clean. It
is always wise to set up several cultures to insure against mishap. If
successful the cultures will become more or less abundant in from four to
six weeks. To subculture proceed as before except that it is not now
necessary to wash the Amoebae, unless observation has shown that they
have become contaminated with undesirable organisms.

The salt content of culture media. While almost any uncontaminated
freshwater will support growth it was found by Pace (1933) during a
detailed study of the relation of salts to growth and reproduction that
a more certain way of obtaining the proper salt concentration for abundant growth and reproduction is by using a synthetic spring water of a
definite composition and concentration determined by experiment to be
optimum for growth and reproduction. The following solutions are
recommended:

	(1)	(2)
Na_2SiO_3	15 mg.	100 mg.
NaCl	12 mg.	12 mg.
Na_2SO_4	6 mg.	6 mg.
$CaCl_2$	6.5 mg.	6.5 mg.
$MgCl_2$	3.5 mg.	3.5 mg.
$FeCl_3$	4 mg.	4 mg.
Dist. Water 1000 cc.		1000 cc.

Sufficient HCl to give a pH of 7.0 to 6.8.

We shall designate (1) as "dilute artificial spring water" and (2) as
"concentrated artificial spring water." The difference between the (1)
and (2) solutions is in the concentration of sodium silicate. The first
solution is recommended when attempting to culture Amoebae recently
collected, since the concentration is nearer that of most natural freshwaters than is the second. However, when Amoebae have been cultured
in a dilute medium they may be transferred to the more concentrated
solution and more rapid growth and reproduction will be obtained. In
fact the second solution is a solution in which optimum growth and
reproduction was found to take place. A concentration between those of
these two solutions in which the sodium silicate is 25 mg. per liter instead of 15 mg. or 100 mg. per liter, results in a much slower rate of
reproduction. No serious difficulty will arise if the total salt concentration of (1) is a little less or that of (2) is a little greater, but the concentration of (1) must not be a little greater, or that of (2) a little less
than that indicated. Reproduction is much better when sodium silicate
is present than when it is replaced by some other salt. Chalkley (1930)
and Hahnert (1932) give salt mixtures which allow good growth and

reproduction, but the "concentrated artificial spring water" just given has proven superior in our experience.

Hydrogen-ion concentration of cultures. *Amoeba proteus* will culture successfully at widely varying hydrogen-ion concentrations. Good cultures have been obtained at pH values anywhere between 4.0 and 8.5. A pH value of 6.6 to 6.8 is generally considered to be optimum. The optimum pH value, however, is probably dependent upon the salt content of the culture. Therefore for ordinary purposes it is unnecessary to take any steps to control the hydrogen-ion concentration of the cultures. The great majority of cultures set up as described above will come to an equilibrium at a favorable hydrogen-ion concentration.

The maintenance of a constant hydrogen-ion concentration for special purposes is rather difficult. The addition of enough buffer salts to maintain a constant pH value brings the total salt concentration to a value too high for growth of the Amoebae. However, Hopkins and Johnson (1928) by a gradual addition of buffer salts were able to adapt the Amoebae to the increased salt concentration so that a constant pH value was maintained, and at the same time Amoebae grew and reproduced. This procedure should be as follows: To a new culture in which Amoebae have begun to grow and reproduce add each day about 0.5 cc. of Clark and Lubb's phosphate buffer of the desired pH value for each 100 cc. of culture fluid until a total of 5 cc. of the buffer has been added for each 100 cc. of culture fluid.

Hopkins (1926) used a feeding method for maintaining a constant hydrogen-ion concentration. Amoeba cultures when first set up as described above first become more acid in reaction and then gradually return to the alkaline side of neutrality. If, when in the return of a culture to alkalinity a given pH value is reached which is desired to be maintained as a constant value, one adds a certain amount of fresh sterilized hay or wheat infusion daily, the acid tendency of the fresh infusion will oppose the alkaline tendency of the culture. By measuring the hydrogen-ion concentration daily and adding fresh infusion accordingly it is possible to maintain the concentration within a range of 0.2 pH units.

Temperature. As long as the temperature in the culture is below 25° C. they remain in good condition. If the temperature is too low growth is retarded. It is necessary to freeze them before they are seriously injured. About 22° C. is perhaps optimum for growth. In summer when room temperature goes above 25° C. it is advisable to keep cultures in a cool basement room or, better, in a cold room where the temperature is maintained at the desired level.

Light. Direct sunlight is injurious. Growth is just as good in absolute darkness as in any light intensity.

Using methods described above the senior author has kept *Amoeba proteus* in continuous culture since 1923, a total of 12 years, and the Amoebae are still in excellent condition.

BIBLIOGRAPHY

CHALKLEY, H. W. 1930. Stock cultures of Amoeba. *Science* 71:442.

DAWSON, J. A. 1928. The culture of large free living Amoebae. *Amer. Nat.* 62: 453

HAHNERT, F. H. 1932. Studies on the chemical needs of *Amoeba proteus:* A culture method. *Biol. Bull.* 62:205.

HOPKINS, D. L. 1926. The effect of certain physical and chemical factors on locomotion and other life processes in *Amoeba proteus. J. Morph. and Physiol.* 45:97.

HOPKINS, D. L., and JOHNSON, P. L. 1928. The culture of *Amoeba proteus* in a known salt solution. *Biol. Bull.* 56:68.

MAST, S. O., and JOHNSON, P. L. 1931. Concerning the scientific name of the common large Amoeba, usually designated as *Amoeba proteus* (Leidy). *Arch. f. Protist.* 75:14.

PACE, D. M. 1933. The relation of inorganic salts to growth and reproduction in *Amoeba proteus. Ibid.* 79:133.

SCHAEFFER, A. A. 1916. Notes on the specific and other characters of *Amoeba proteus* Pallas (Leidy). *A. discoides* spec. nov. and *A. dubia.* spec. nov. *Ibid.* 37:204.

——— 1926. Taxonomy of the Amebas with description of thirty-nine new marine and fresh water species. *Carn. Inst. Wash. Dept. Mar. Biol.* 24: 1.

CULTURING AMOEBA PROTEUS AND A. DUBIA

H. R. HALSEY, *Columbia University*

BOTH *Amoeba proteus* and *A. dubia* are found in freshwater ponds and streams among aquatic plants such as Cabomba or Elodea, or in the debris on the bottom of such bodies of water, particularly among rotten leaves. Large individuals are often found in considerable numbers among Sphagnum.

Place small amounts of such material in finger bowls or large petri dishes, cover with spring water or with water from the source, and add 2 or 3 grains of uncooked rice, or an equal number of one-inch lengths of boiled timothy hay stalks. Do not place too much of the material in a single dish. This results in decay, and in the appearance of large numbers of bacteria which cause the death of any Amoebae that may be present.

Amoebae will appear in considerable numbers in successful cultures within a week or ten days. The decaying organic material is then removed and the Amoebae cultured by the following method. Make a hay infusion of 8 one-inch lengths of timothy hay stalks in 100 cc. of spring water, boil for 10 minutes and allow to stand for 24 hours. At the end of this time add large numbers of small Protozoa such as Colpidium [see pp. 63 and 108] and Chilomonas [see pp. 59 and 63] to the medium. Allow this to stand for two or three days before using. The Amoebae multiply rapidly on this medium so that the bottom of the culture dish is soon covered with them. These cultures should be examined weekly. *Amoeba proteus* and *A. dubia* have been observed to injest 50 to 100 Chilomonas within 24 hours. This results in the rapid disappearance of the food organisms from the culture. If the food organisms become few in number pipette off half of the culture medium and add an equal amount of fresh protozoan hay infusion. At the same time add 2 grains of uncooked rice, boiled wheat, or 4 one-inch lengths of boiled timothy hay stalks per 50 cc. of culture medium.

The Amoebae in such cultures divide rapidly up to 13 divisions per ten day period as judged from organisms kept in isolation. The cultures may be run successfully for as long as six months. They may be kept at room temperature even during the summer months though it is best to use refrigeration if the temperature reaches 90° F. or higher.

Subcultures are made by pipetting half of the material on the bottom of the old culture into a new dish and adding an equal amount of protozoan hay infusion and food material.

This culture method may be varied somewhat, but the following facts should be kept well in mind. Large numbers of bacteria in a culture tend to cause the death of the Amoebae; therefore other Protozoa should be present in the medium. The use of large amounts of organic material such as boiled rice, wheat, or cracked wheat should be avoided. These ferment very readily, causing the death of most of the Amoebae. The depression period observed by many investigators is due to this cause. If the protozoan hay infusion with a small amount of food is used about 90% of the cultures will be successful. This compares with only 50% of bacterial cultures in the author's experience. In the former case there is no depression period, in the latter a depression period of a month is not unusual.

CULTIVATION OF MAYORELLA (AMOEBA) BIGEMMA ON EUGLENA GRACILIS

JOHN C. LOTZE, *Ohio State University*

THE food of *Mayorella bigemma* is listed by Schaeffer (1918) in his original description as "flagellates, ciliates, diatoms, rhizopods, nematodes, vegetal tissue, *etc.*" Botsford (1922) reported the culturing of *Mayorella bigemma* in solutions of beef extract. Taylor (1929) stated that *Mayorella bigemma* may easily be cultivated under the same conditions as *Amoeba proteus*.

In 1929, the author found a few amoebas of this species in an old hay infusion culture of mixed Protozoa. A clone culture was successfully established and maintained with good results by using *Euglena gracilis* as the source of food. The amoebas have been cultured by this method for a period of over four years.

Distilled water, well water, and a synthetic well water were used in the preparation of culture media. Natural well water proved to be the most satisfactory. The source of this water was a well on the campus of Ohio State University. The synthetic well water was more satisfactory than distilled water; however, fair results were obtained with the latter.

Solutions of aminoids* were used in the cultivation of *Euglena gracilis*. A solution of 0.04% aminoids was very satisfactory and had no appreciable effect upon the amoebas introduced into such cultures.

Pyrex Erlenmeyer flasks were used exclusively. The best results were obtained by using 125 cc. flasks with 75 cc. of culture medium. The medium was first made up in a liter flask; then the proper amount was poured into each of the smaller flasks. The flasks were then loosely stoppered with sterile cotton and placed on a hot plate. When the contents just came to a boil, the flasks were removed and allowed to cool. Immediately thereafter, the medium was inoculated with Euglena. This procedure was very effective in eliminating contamination of the cultures by other Protozoa.

Although it was found that the amoebas could be introduced into the cultures with the euglenas, the number of amoebas produced in such cultures was never as great as it was when the euglenas were given a good start beforehand. Satisfactory results were also obtained when amoebas were introduced into Euglena cultures in which the euglenas were passive and many were enveloped in gelatinous sheaths.

A few cultures were maintained for a long period of time by the addition of euglenas previously concentrated with a centrifuge. Food was added only when that of a culture had become scarce. These additions compensated for the loss of water from a culture due to evaporation. One culture has been maintained by this method since the spring of 1929.

Another satisfactory method consisted of adding aminoids to an amoeba culture when the euglenas contained in it had become scarce. An amount of aminoids sufficient to make a 0.04% solution was roughly estimated and added to the culture. An addition of a very large amount of aminoids was always followed by a rapid increase in the number of bacteria in the culture, and finally, the death of the amoebas.

No attempt was made to control the hydrogen-ion concentration in

---

* Either beef or milk aminoids, commercial products of the Arlington Chemical Co., Yonkers, N. Y.

the amoeba-Euglena cultures. The distilled water used had a pH value of 6.0 to 6.2 and synthetic well water made from this was 7.1. The pH of the well water was always about 7.2. A 0.04% solution of aminoids, freshly made up, sterilized by boiling, and thoroughly cooled for an hour or two had a pH of about 6.9 to 7.2. In the course of 3 or 4 weeks the pH of such cultures gradually rose to 8.0 or 8.2 and sometimes to 8.4. This was true regardless of whether they were Euglena or Euglena-amoeba cultures. After the cultures had attained this pH, they maintained it without appreciable fluctuation.

Light conditions favorable for the cultivation of *Euglena gracilis* were not detrimental to the amoebas. All cultures were kept near a north window to protect them from direct sunlight.

The amoebas were easily cultured at ordinary room temperatures. Best results were obtained when the temperature was 75° F. or slightly above. However, cultures were maintained without attention over longer periods of time at lower temperatures.

BIBLIOGRAPHY

BOTSFORD, E. F. 1922. Rhythms in the rate of reproduction of *Amoeba bigemma*. *Proc. Soc. Exper. Biol. and Med.* 19:396.

SCHAEFFER, A, A. 1918. Three new species of amoebas: *Amoeba bigemma* nov. spec., *Pelomyxa lentissima* nov. spec., and *P. schiedti* nov. spec. *Trans. Amer. Micr. Soc.* 37:79.

TAYLOR, M. 1929. Some further observations on *Amoeba proteus*. *Nature* 123:942.

THE CULTURE OF FLABELLULA MIRA

D. L. HOPKINS, *Duke University*, N. E. RICE, *Brenau College*, and
H. E. BUTTS, *Wellesley College*

A MARINE amoeba, *Flabellula mira*, named and described by Schaeffer (1926), has been found only in the waters around Florida. The amoebae used in the development of the following culture methods were collected at Tortugas, Florida, in 1929, and have been maintained in culture at the Duke University Zoological Laboratory since then, making a total of six years in culture.

These amoebae may be collected from their natural habitat easily. With a pipette collect some seawater containing a little seaweed or debris from tidal pools or shallow places over a reef. Bring it into the laboratory, pour into petri dishes, dilute considerably with sterile seawater, and add 6 grains of wheat to each petri dish. In three or four days the amoebae will have become abundant on the bottom of the dish and on the surface film. It is very probable that more than one species of amoebae will be present and will develop in these cultures. There are two or three amoebae of the genus Flabellula from which it is very difficult to distinguish *Flabellula mira*. It is therefore necessary to study them for some time in pedigreed or clone cultures to be sure you have the right species. To obtain these amoebae in clone cultures proceed as follows:

With a sterile capillary pipette pass an amoeba through three or four changes of sterile seawater in sterile depression slides. From the last depression slide transfer it to a small drop of sterile wheat infusion in seawater (prepared by boiling about 30 grains of wheat in 100 cc. of seawater for about two minutes). Now with sterile vaseline seal the coverslip over the depression slide with the drop hanging down from the under side of the coverslip. Prepare several hanging-drop clone cultures in this way. When several amoebae have developed, sterilize the upper surface by washing with absolute alcohol. Allow the alcohol to evaporate completely, break the seal with sterile forceps, remove the coverslip and drop it with the amoeba-side up into sterile seawater in a sterile petri dish. Add 6 grains of wheat sterilized by autoclaving 15 minutes at 15 pounds' pressure. The amoebae will remain attached to the coverslip and thus will easily be found when desired. They will become abundant within a week. If evaporation is prevented, the amoebae will remain viable for weeks. The cultures, however, come to a condition of maximum population in about seven days. They should be subcultured every two weeks.

To subculture the pure clones sterilize wheat, petri dishes, seawater, and inoculating pipettes; place seawater and 6 grains of wheat, in a petri dish; then with the pipette draw some of the amoebae up from the bottom of an old culture and add them to the new culture medium. Growth will proceed as before.

These amoebae feed on bacteria; therefore there is little difficulty in obtaining food organisms. Sufficient bacteria, except in rare cases, are carried with the amoeba to inoculate the new cultures even after four or five washings.

The salt content of cultures. *F. mira* is remarkable in its ability to adapt itself to great variations in the salt content of its medium. It may be cultured readily and indefinitely in the following modification of the artificial seawater of McClendon, Gault, and Mulholland (1917):

Substance	gms.
$CaCl_2$	1.220
$MgCl_2.6H_2O$	5.105
$MgSO_4.7H_2O$	7.035
KCl	0.763
NaCl	28.340
$NaBr.2H_2O$	0.082
$NaHCO_3$	0.210
Distilled water	1000 cc.

Butts (1935) has made a study of the effects of salts on the growth and reproduction of this form. It may be cultured in any concentration from a five-fold dilution to a concentration so high that some of the salts begin to precipitate. The optimum concentration is about 10% distilled water and 90% seawater. The salt ratios may be altered considerably and still the amoebae will grow and reproduce.

The hydrogen-ion concentration. The hydrogen-ion concentration seems to have but little influence on reproduction. It is possible to culture *F. mira* at any concentration between pH 3.0 and 9.0. Reproduction, however, seems to be more rapid in the ranges pH 8.0-9.0, and pH 5.0-7.0, than in the range pH 7.0-8.0. In artificial or natural seawater cultures the hydrogen-ion concentration remains fairly constant, varying within the range pH 8.0 to pH 8.4.

The culture of F. mira on solid media. Rice (1935) has made use of silica gel and Bacto agar plates in culturing *F. mira*. The Bacto agar method may be described as follows: Place 100 gm. wheat in 1000 cc. of artificial seawater and autoclave for 20 minutes at a pressure of 15 pounds and a temperature of 125° C. Strain through a cheesecloth, and then filter through a coarse filter paper. Now add 15 gms. Bacto agar and enough artificial seawater to bring the volume back to 1000 cc. Autoclave again at the same temperature and pressure for 30 to 60 minutes. The resulting agar medium is then tubed, plugged with cotton, sterilized again, and set aside for future use. When ready to culture the amoebae on this medium, melt the agar in a tube, pour into a sterile petri dish, cover, and allow to cool and solidify. Then transfer a small drop of liquid culture medium containing amoebae and associated bacteria to the center of the plate, or scatter small drops about over the entire surface of the plate. The water will be absorbed by the agar and the amoebae and bacteria will grow and develop on the surface. The bacteria and consequently the amoebae will become very abundant and concentrated. Often the amoebae become so thick that they form a sort of epithelial layer over the surface of the agar. To subculture, amoebae and bacteria are transferred with a platinum loop to freshly poured plates.

The culture of F. mira on pure strains of marine bacteria. By the proper bacteriological methods isolate bacteria from good cultures of *F. mira*. Then pour artificial seawater-wheat-extract-agar plates and inoculate only in the center with amoebae and associated bacteria. Now with a platinum loop make a smear of the previously isolated marine bacterium in a circle about 1 cm. from the center inoculated with amoebae. Some of the amoebae in traveling the 1 cm. distance from the point of their inoculation over a sterile surface lose contaminating bacteria so that when they enter the smear of the pure strain of bacteria they are sterile. (Some, however, may carry bacteria even this distance.) They immediately feed on these bacteria and multiply rapidly. As soon as they have become numerous they should be transferred to a new plate and checked by the usual bacteriological methods for contaminations. If contaminants are present, the process should be repeated. *F. mira* may be cultured indefinitely on pure strains of bacteria.

The organic composition of the medium for F. mira. We have used wheat mainly as the original source of organic material. However, a variety of substances are adequate, such as 1% solutions of sucrose, other sugars, or soluble starch; and 0.2% solutions of different amino acids and mixtures of amino acids and sugars in either liquid or solid media made up in artificial seawater.

Light and temperature. *F. mira* may be cultured in any light intensity between bright sunlight and complete darkness and at any temperature between 10° C. and 42° or 43° C., the optimum being between 25° and 35° C.

BIBLIOGRAPHY

BUTTS, H. E. 1935. The effect of certain salts of seawater upon reproduction in the marine amoeba *Flabellula mira* Schaeffer. *Physiol. Zool.*

McCLENDON, J. J., GAULT, C. C., and MULHOLLAND, S. 1917. The hydrogen-ion concentration, CO_2 tension, CO_2 content of seawater. *Carn. Inst. Wash. Dept. Mar. Biol.* 11:21.

RICE, N. W. 1935. The nutrition of *Flabellula mira* Schaeffer. *Arch. f. Protist.* 85:350.

SCHAEFFER, A. A. 1926. Taxonomy of the amoebas with description of thirty-nine new marine and freshwater species. *Carn. Inst. Wash. Dept. Biol.* 24:1.

VALKAMPFIA CALKINSI AND V. PATUXENT*

OYSTERS obtained from markets sometimes yield *Valkampfia calkinsi* and *V. patuxent* from the intestinal tract. These two may be cultured easily on ordinary agar plates, yielding abundant parasitic material. Without considerable familiarity it is almost impossible to distinguish living leucocytes from the parasitic amoebae.

M. E. D.

REFERENCES

For the culture of *Endamoeba blattae* and *E. thomsoni* see p. 128.
For the culture of *Endamoeba ranarum* see p. 69.

NOTES ON VARIOUS MEDIA USED IN THE CULTURE OF INTESTINAL PROTOZOA

CHARLES A. KOFOID and ETHEL McNEIL, *University of California*

IT IS very important to keep in mind that there are two reasons for culturing intestinal Protozoa. The first is to aid the diagnostician in determining their presence or absence in the stool specimen. It is not

* Abstracted from an article in *Science* 78:128, 1933, by C. M. BREDER, JR., *New York Aquarium*, and R. F. NIGRELLI, *New York University*.

necessary in this case to keep the organism in culture over any long period of time.

The second purpose is to preserve a constant supply of culture material over long periods for animal inoculation, metabolism experiments, or immunological studies. Therefore a medium which may be successful for the first purpose may be entirely unsatisfactory for the second. With this in mind we will give a brief discussion of the following media: Boeck and Drbohlav (1925), Dobell and Laidlaw (1926), Kofoid and Wagener (1925), Tanabe and Chiba (1928), Cleveland and Collier (1930), Craig (1930), Deschiens (1930), St. John (1932).

Of these, the first three have been so well tested that there is little need of discussing them further. They are all satisfactory in maintaining cultures over long periods of time. We prefer the L. E. A. medium of Boeck and Drbohlav to their L. E. S. medium. We feel, however, that the growth of Blastocystis and bacteria is less in the L. E. B. medium of Kofoid and Wagener (1925). Particularly is this noticeable in the culture of *Dientamoeba fragilis*. We have found, too, that the optimum pH for Dientamoeba is lower than for *Endamoeba histolytica* (about pH.6.6).

Of the others we have found that St. John's medium is excellent in producing a sudden increase in rate of multiplication and is thus useful for classroom studies as well as for diagnostic purposes. It has also the advantage of being relatively inexpensive and easy to prepare. But we have never been able to keep the amoebae in this medium longer than several weeks.

St. John, 1932.

SLANTS	LIQUID
None	Heart muscle (Bacto Beef Heart Dehydrated) is extracted in a modified Locke's solution by boiling for one hour.

Heart muscle .... 1 gram
Locke's solution * .... 1000 cc.

The extract is filtered through filter paper and autoclaved at 15 lbs. pressure. "Ralston's" whole wheat flour is added.

Craig's media (as he himself states) are primarily to aid the diagnostician, and not for the maintenance of cultures by transfer.

*Locke's solution:

Sodium chloride .... 9.00 gm.
Calcium chloride .... 0.24 gm.
Potassium chloride .... 0.42 gm.
Sodium bicarbonate .... 0.20 gm.
Dextrose .... 2.50 gm.
Distilled water .... 1000 cc.

Craig, 1930.

1	2	3
Inactivated human blood serum ....1 part	Inactivated human blood serum ....1 part	Inactivated human blood serum.....1 part
Locke's solution 7 parts	Ringer's solution 7 parts	0.85% NaCl ....7 parts
Rice starch is added.		

All are sterilized by Berkefeld filtration.

Tanabe's medium is satisfactory for a certain length of time, but as yet does not justify its use in preference to the Boeck-Drbohlav medium or one of its modifications. However, we feel that their effort to simplify the medium is a step in the right direction.

Tanabe and Chiba, 1928.

SLANTS	LIQUID
Agar ....10 grams	5% rabbit serum in Ringer's.
Asparagin .... 1 gram	Rice starch is added.
Ringer's solution ....1000 cc.	

We have not had as much success with Cleveland's liver-infusion-agar medium as was hoped. We agree with him that it seems to be almost specific for *Endamoeba histolytica,* but we find two objections to its use: 1) Blastocystis multiplies very rapidly in it, and, 2) production of gas by bacteria displaces the agar slants to an annoying degree. The first objection seems to us of considerable importance where only fresh smear examinations are made.

Cleveland and Collier, 1930.

SLANTS	LIQUID
Liver Infusion Agar (Digestive Ferments Co.).....30 grams	Horse serum ....1 part
Na₂HPO₄ .... 3 grams	0.8% NaCl ....6 parts
Water ....1000 cc.	
Rice flour is added.	

We have not, as yet, had opportunity to duplicate all details of Deschiens' medium, but it is probable that the results would be somewhat similar to those of Tanabe.

Deschiens, 1930.

SLANTS	LIQUID
Agar .... 20 grams	Locke—Ringer's solution or
NaCl .... 5 grams	Physiological salt solution
Beef extract............... 2-5 grams	
Water ....1000 cc.	

Powdered fish muscle or powdered beef muscle is added to each tube.

Trichomonas, Chilomastix, Enteromonas, and Embadomonas grow well in the L. E. A., L. E. B., or L. E. S. media. Giardia has not as yet been cultured, but recent experiments indicate that some sort of tissue extract in which the oxygen supply is kept constant will eventually be successful.

Miss Bonestell (working in this laboratory) has found that the various species of Trichomonas multiply exceedingly rapidly in rat embryo extract, such as is used for tissue cultures.

BIBLIOGRAPHY

BOECK, W. C., and DRBOHLAV, J. 1925. The cultivation of *Endamoeba histolytica*. *Amer. J. Hyg.* 5:371.
CLEVELAND, L. R., and COLLIER, J. 1930. Various improvements in the cultivation of *Entamoeba histolytica*. *Ibid.* 12:606.
CRAIG, C. F. 1930. The cultivation of *Endamoeba histolytica*. In Hegner and Andrews: Problems and Methods of Research in Protozoology. 532+ ix pp. Macmillan Co., New York.
DESCHIENS, R. 1930. Culture de l'amibe dysenterique et nutrition de cette amibe dans les cultures. *Extrait du 1er Congrés Internat. de Microbiol.*, Paris. pp. 1-4.
DOBELL, C., and LAIDLAW, P. P. 1926. On the cultivation of *Endamoeba histolytica* and some other entozooic amoebae. *Parasit.* 18:283.
KOFOID, C. A., and WAGENER, E. H. 1925. The behavior of *Endamoeba dysenteriae* in mixed cultures of bacteria. *Univ. Calif. Publ. Zool.* 28:127.
KOFOID, C. A., and McNEIL, E. 1931. The advantages of Locke's blood medium in the culture of parasitic Protozoa of the digestive tract. *Amer. J. Hyg.* 15:315.
ST. JOHN, J. H. 1932. A new medium for the culture of *Endamoeba histolytica*. *Amer. J. Trop. Med.* 12:301.
TANABE, M., and CHIBA, E. 1928. A new culture medium for *Endamoeba histolytica*. *Acta Medicinalia in Keijo*, 11:1.

IN VIVO CULTIVATION OF INTESTINAL PROTOZOA IN PARASITE-FREE CHICKS*

ROBERT HEGNER, *School of Hygiene and Public Health*

AS EVERY one who has attempted experiments with animal parasites in laboratory animals knows, one of the greatest difficulties is to secure parasite-free animals for infection purposes. Chicks offer a number of advantages: they may be obtained at any time of the year; they are very inexpensive; they are free from animal parasites when they hatch from the egg; they may be maintained in the laboratory free from animal parasites without difficulty and at low cost; and they may be inoculated very easily *per os* or *per rectum* with material containing animal parasites. It seems evident that greater precautions are necessary to prevent contamination under ordinary laboratory conditions with Coccidia than with Amoebae, flagellates, or ciliates.

Besides being parasite-free and easily maintained in this condition, chicks are favorable for experimental studies because one may obtain

---

* Reprinted from *Science* 69:432, 1929, with slight changes by the author.

samples from the cecum, where intestinal Protozoa seem to be almost entirely localized, without killing the birds or resorting to surgical opera tion. The contents of the cecum are evacuated from time to time and this material may be distinguished easily from the intestinal contents passed in the form of feces. The fecal material is usually compact and dark in color, whereas the cecal contents are more liquid and yellowish in color. The best way to obtain cecal material seems to be to give the chicks fresh food and water early in the morning and then place them under glass dishes on paper towels. Here they may easily be watched until cecal material is passed. Some of the chicks will not evacuate their cecal contents for several hours, but most of them will deposit the desired material within a few minutes.

The method of procedure followed was usually as follows. The Protozoa to be inoculated were obtained either from cultures grown in test tubes or from fecal material. If from the former, a more concentrated inoculum was sometimes prepared by centrifuging the culture medium and pouring off most of the supernatant fluid. If the trophozoites of Protozoa were located in fecal material, this mass was diluted with normal saline solution and passed through cheesecloth to remove all coarse particles that might otherwise clog the passage through the tube used for inoculation. Protozoan cysts may be secured in large numbers by any of the concentration methods devised for this purpose. A simple method is to stir up the infected material in several liters of water in a tall, narrow cylinder; allow the cysts to settle to the bottom, which requires about 30 minutes, then pour off most of the supernatant fluid, fill the cylinder with water, stir thoroughly and allow the cysts to settle again. After this has been repeated several times the cysts are well washed and concentrated.

A 5 cc. Luer syringe to which was attached a rubber catheter shortened to a length of about 10 cm. was used for inoculating material into the chicks. Most of the chicks were about 4 days old, although older birds were used for studies of age resistance. The amount of inoculum depends on the age (size) of the chick. From 2 to 4 cc. of material may be injected into the crop of a 4-day-old chick by lubricating the catheter with vaseline, inserting it down the throat with one hand while the bird is held in the other, and then slowly pushing down the plunger of the syringe. Similarly from 1 to 3 cc. may be injected into the rectum. The catheter should be inserted about 2 or 3 cm. The anal opening should be held closed with the fingers for a few seconds after the catheter is removed. Material injected into the rectum appears to find its way immediately into the cecum.

The results of introducing intestinal Protozoa from man and other animals into chicks have been prepared for publication elsewhere

(Hegner, 1929). They indicate that infections may be set up easily in the cecum with a number of species of Amoebae, flagellates, and ciliates. Some of the infections continued for over 6 months and apparently would have remained indefinitely. Among the Protozoa used were *Trichomonas hominis* from the human intestine and *T. buccalis* from the human mouth. These were maintained in chickens for over 4 months when the experiments were terminated.

One of the most interesting results of the experiments was the discovery that the chick may be used as a sort of *in vivo* test tube for the cultivation of intestinal Protozoa. For example, cecal material from a guinea-fowl which was found by the ordinary smear method to contain a very few trichomonads was injected *per rectum* into chicks. Two days later large numbers of trichomonads, Chilomastix, and Endolimax amoebae were present in cecal material evacuated by the chicks. The trichomonads appeared to belong to two or three different species. On the third day the trophozoites of a large Endamoeba were found.

This work indicates that Protozoa too few in number to be found in smears made from the cecal contents of birds such as guinea-fowls, ducks, and geese grow and multiply so rapidly when inoculated into parasite-free chicks that they may not only be demonstrated without difficulty but may be secured in sufficient numbers to prepare permanent slides for the detailed study of their morphology. Data already obtained by the use of fecal material from other animals inoculated into chicks suggest that this method of cultivating intestinal Protozoa *in vivo* in chicks may be extended to include species from other types of animals, especially mammals.

BIBLIOGRAPHY

HEGNER, R. W. 1929. Transmission of intestinal Protozoa from man and animals to parasite-free fowls. *Amer. J. Hyg.* 9:529.

Order TESTACEA, Family ARCELLIDAE

A METHOD OF CULTURING ARCELLAE

E. D. MILLER, *University of Virginia*

A WHEAT medium has been found to be very well adapted for culturing the Arcellae. This is prepared by bringing 300 cc. of distilled water to a boil and introducing 15 selected grains of wheat, after which the material is set aside to cool. After 24 hours all except 5 grains are removed. The medium is not used for culture purposes for another 24 hours. During the 48 hours sufficient bacteria have accumulated to serve as food material.

There is a tendency toward an over-accumulation of bacteria both in the cultures and in the stock supply. The stock supply may be filtered through several layers of cheesecloth to remove excess bacterial accumulations. The material in the culture dishes may be poured off frequently and some of the filtered material added.

CULTURING ARCELLAE

BRUCE D. REYNOLDS, *University of Virginia*

ARCELLAE may be cultured in a hay infusion as follows:
Place 10 grams of clean timothy hay in a clean pyrex beaker containing 250 cc. of distilled water (pH 6.8). Heat to boiling point and allow to boil slowly for 5 minutes, then strain through two thicknesses of cheesecloth and store in quantities of about 3 cc. in small, sterile, hard glass test tubes. The tubes should then be plugged with cotton and placed in boiling water for 15 minutes. After 2 days they should be subjected again to boiling for the same period of time in order to kill any bacteria which may have escaped the first sterilization by being in the spore stage. The medium in these tubes constitutes the stock solution and will keep for months without deterioration provided evaporation does not take place.

In making up the culture medium take 1 part of the stock solution and add to it 9 parts of distilled water (pH 6.8), giving a 10% hay infusion. After the tube containing some of the stock solution has been opened and a part of its contents used the remainder should be discarded.

Using the medium prepared in the above manner Arcellae may be cultured in hollow-ground slides over a long period of time in a constant medium. The culture medium should be changed every day or two and the depression slides should be kept in a moist chamber placed in subdued light.

REFERENCES

For the culture of Arcellae see also pp. 74 and 134.
For the culture of *Arcella vulgaris* see p. 60.

Family DIFFLUGIIDAE

METHODS OF CULTURING TESTACEA

A. B. STUMP, *University of Virginia*

Difflugia oblonga (*D. pyriformis*), small varieties [see also p. 136]; *D. lobostoma* and *D. constricta*, small varieties; and *Lesquereusia spiralis* may be cultured almost indefinitely by using a number of the green algae for food, such as Spirogyra, Zygnema, Mougeotia, and Oedogonium.

Culturing may be carried on in almost any type of container, though the shallow types usually give best results.

Spring, pond, or tap water may be used, with preference in the order named. The pH should be between 6 and 7.3. If small containers, depression slides, *etc.*, are used over long periods of time, the water must be changed frequently (every 2 to 3 days). Larger cultures in petri dishes may be run a week to 10 days.

Cultures should be kept out of direct sunlight and below 22° C. if possible. Small amounts of fine sand should be provided in cultures of *D. oblonga, D. constricta,* and *D. lobostoma* for shell construction.

Order FORAMINIFERA

CULTURE METHODS FOR MARINE FORAMINIFERA OF THE LITTORAL ZONE

EARL H. MYERS, *Scripps Institution of Oceanography*

ALTHOUGH the Foraminifera are universally distributed in the sea and have been the subject of investigations for more than 200 years, comparatively little is known concerning their methods of reproduction, or of those physiological factors which limit the geographical and bathymetric distribution of these organisms (Myers, 1934). Confusion in the systematic designation of species is frequently due to their changing morphology which is the result of an alternation of generations, growth stages, a response to environmental conditions, or parasitism. In any attempt at a natural classification of these polymorphic forms, it is necessary to recognize their genetic relationship, and, where it is possible, their biological explanation should be determined. The solution of many of these problems can best be approached by means of laboratory cultures. Many species of the littoral zone may be maintained in cultures with a minimum of effort and without the use of running seawater. Therefore, this field of investigation offers a splendid opportunity for original work to anyone who has access to the sea and has acquired a reasonable amount of skill in microscopic technique.

In selecting a problem in this field, time is an important factor to take into consideration, due to the low rate of reproduction in this group as compared to other Protozoa. Growth in the majority of polythalamous species is a discontinuous process, because of an alternation of a vegetative phase with the addition of each newly formed chamber. In small species of Discorbis, where the test is composed of a continuous series of from 14 to 19 graduated chambers, from 3 to 12 hours are required for the addition of each new chamber. Under optimum conditions an individual will mature usually in from 19 to 23 days, and at that time produce from 30 to 40 young by multiple fission. In the larger species of Elphidium, in which the test consists of from 40 to 50 chambers, it is doubful whether more than two generations occur annually. Since the life span determines the frequency with which one might expect to encounter individuals in a state of reproductive activity, it will be less difficult to obtain cytological evidence in support of a proposed life cycle in small quickly maturing species, and a more abundant supply of material will become available in a given time.

The following method of collecting and maintaining these organisms in culture has proven satisfactory for species of Discorbis, Pyrgo, Triloculina, Bulimina, Patellina, Spirillina, and Robulus, and should be satisfactory for small species found within the limits of the intertidal zone.

An abundant supply of living Foraminifera may usually be obtained by washing seaweed or eel grass vigorously between the hands and allowing the organisms, sand grains, and other bits of débris to settle through a piece of bolting cloth into the bottom of a glass vessel. A convenient glass bucket for this purpose is made from a 10- x 14-inch battery jar provided with a rope handle and covered with canvas for protection. The bucket should be equipped with a tubular net 8 inches deep attached to a wooden hoop that will rest on the upper rim of the bucket. The vertical sides of the net should be made of unbleached muslin and the flat bottom of No. oo bolting cloth.

After allowing the organisms about one minute to settle, the water should be decanted. Repeated washing by decantation will free the collection from silt and a considerable amount of organic débris that would decompose later. If several collections are to be made the material must be transferred to another container. A set of glass refrigerating dishes 6 inches in diameter and 2 inches deep that stack one on top of the other is convenient for this purpose. A carrying rack should be provided for the dishes and, where the collecting ground is some distance from the laboratory, it is advisable to control the temperature by packing with ice.

The rate of mortality is high in newly collected material, and we have found at La Jolla that certain species that will survive at room temperature for more than a year do not reproduce until the temperature is lowered to 18° C. or less. Therefore, it is well to sort the material after the Foraminifera have become acclimatized to laboratory conditions.

Crowding of newly collected material should be avoided at all times. Not more than 5 cc. of the washings containing the Foraminifera should be placed in each of a number of 4-inch round-bottomed finger bowls filled with seawater, or about 20 cc. of this material may be added to a 10-inch crystallizing dish. The dishes should be covered to prevent excess evaporation and contamination.

The water should be changed twice a day for the first few days, and after that, once a day for a period of about two weeks. By that time many Foraminifera will have crawled up the sides of the dishes and, if a suitable substrate of diatoms has developed, several species should have become established and reproductive activity begun.

To establish persistent cultures of a single species, dishes should be prepared with a suitable substrate of diatoms before the isolation and transfer of the Foraminifera. Pure cultures of Nitzschia [see p. 34], Navicula, or similar diatoms may be used for this purpose, or substrate material may be used which has been taken from a dish in which the Foraminifera have become established and in which the diatom substrate is thin, uniform, and free from filamentous algae. If the latter method is employed and no new material is added to contaminate the culture, a single species of diatom will usually dominate the substrate in a short time.

The day after a foraminifer has reproduced asexually, the young, which in some species number 200 or more, remain in the vicinity of the parent tests. In establishing subcultures, several thousand individuals may be transferred in a minimum of time by selecting these groups. If this method is employed the age of the organisms will be known and a maximum number of individuals of any stage of development will be available at a given time. A convenient mouth pipette for handling these organisms has been described (Myers, 1933). [see also pp. 43 and 70.]

After the cultures are established, it is advisable to change the water occasionally to compensate for evaporation and to replace nutrient material removed by the organisms. A strong stream of water directed against the sides of a dish by means of a glass syringe equipped with a large rubber bulb will remove accumulated débris and help maintain a thin clean substrate.

Before seawater is added to a culture, the water to be added should be filtered through a porcelain base Berkefeld or a sintered glass filter of suitable porosity. Growth of diatoms may be influenced by controlled illumination. When a subdued north light does not produce a suitable growth, a few drops of a saturated solution of potassium nitrate may be added to each culture or Allen and Nelson's (1910) modification of Miquel's solution may be used. [See p. 33.]

Temperature is a limiting factor in the distribution of species. In cultures of *Patellina corrugata* there is a difference of only 4° to 5° C. between the optimum and the upper thermal limit at which this species can exist. Therefore, in any attempt to culture Foraminifera it is necessary to avoid temperatures above the mean that prevails in the sea during the summer months.

By employing the simple precautions herein described cultures of a number of species of Foraminifera have been maintained for from one to three years, and on several occasions have been sucessfully transported over land a distance of more than 500 miles.

REFERENCES

Order Heliozoa
For the culture of Actinophrys see p. 136.
For the culture of Actinosphaerium see p. 74.
For the culture of *Actinosphaerium eichhorni* see p. 60.

BIBLIOGRAPHY

ALLEN, E. J., and NELSON, E. W. 1910. On the artificial culture of marine plankton organisms. *J. Mar. Biol. Assoc.* 8:421.
MYERS, E. H. 1933. A mouth pipette and containers for smaller organisms. *Science* 77:609.
———— 1934. The life history of *Patellina corrugata,* a foräminifer. *Ibid.* 79:436.

Class *Sporozoa*, Order COCCIDIOMORPHA

MAINTENANCE OF LABORATORY STRAINS OF AVIAN PLASMODIUM AND HAEMOPROTEUS

CLAY G. HUFF, *University of Chicago*

SINCE methods for the growth of avian parasites of the genera Plasmodium· and Haemoproteus in the absence of living cells of their hosts have not been worked out, these forms must be maintained in one of their hosts. While successive generations of Plasmodium from man have been "cultured," this has only been accomplished by the daily addition of fresh erythrocytes, so that, strictly speaking, this amounts to culture *in vivo*. A method of cultivation has not been worked out which is successful in maintaining the strain over long periods of time. The invertebrate hosts of all of the species of avian Plasmodium whose life cycles have been worked out are culicine mosquitoes [See p. 376]. Avian species of Haemoproteus are transmitted by parasitic flies belonging to the Hippoboscidae [See Huff, p. 446].

STRAINS OF AVIAN PLASMODIUM

All strains of avian malaria of the genus Plasmodium may be maintained by inoculating blood from the infected into a normal bird. *P. relictum* and *P. cathemerium* may be easily transmitted from bird to bird by means of various culicine mosquitoes, the best vectors being *Culex pipiens* and *C. fatigans* [see Huff, p. 386]. The mosquitoes must engorge on the infected bird at a time when gametocytes are present in the blood. Their bites are infectious for other birds after 8 to 14 days depending upon the species of the parasite and the temperature of the environment. *Plasmodium circumflexum* does not infect these common mosquitoes but it has been shown by Reichenow (1932) to be transmitted by *Theobaldia annulata*. While several of the species of culicine mosquitoes become infected in small percentages when fed on birds with infections of *Plasmodium elongatum* and *P. rouxi*, no complete transmission has yet been effected by any of them.

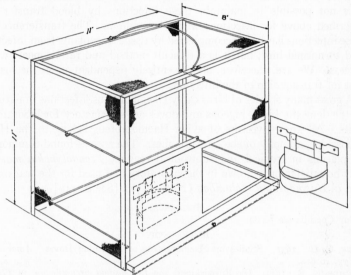

Fig. 43.—Mosquito-proof cage.

Unless there is some special reason why mosquitoes are preferred as the means of transmission, all of these strains may best be maintained in canaries and passed when desired by blood inoculation. Infections produced by any of these species of parasites go through an acute stage which is followed by a latent period of infection of long duration. Spontaneous cure is rare. Therefore, in most cases, the strains may be maintained most easily as latent infections. New infections may be produced in normal birds by inoculating them with blood from the birds with latent infections. A few drops of blood are taken from a leg vein into physiological saline solution (0.85%) and injected by means of a syringe and inoculating needle into a normal bird. This may be done intraperitoneally, intramuscularly, or intravenously. The technique for intravenous inoculation has been described by Taliaferro and Taliaferro (1929). It is to be recommended where heavy infections are desired, and particularly for such species as normally produce light infections (*P. rouxi* and *P. elongatum*).

It is highly desirable to keep all normal and infected birds in screened cages in order to avoid the possibility of mixing infections through the bites of mosquitoes. A cage which has been found to be satisfactory for this purpose is the mosquito-proof, metal cage shown in figure 43.

HAEMOPROTEUS INFECTIONS IN PIGEONS

Since the asexual forms of Haemoproteus do not inhabit the blood, it is not possible to maintain these infections by blood transfer as described above for infections with Plasmodium. The transference of these infections has been accomplished by tissue transplants from infected bird to normal bird, but it is a difficult method and rarely meets with success. We are, therefore, almost entirely dependent upon the insect host for transmission of the infection.

A great many species of birds carry Haemoproteus infections in nature. Of the domestic birds, pigeons and doves are satisfactory for laboratory hosts. All known vectors of avian Haemoproteus belong to the Hippoboscidae, a family of ectoparasitic flies. The species found commonly on pigeons in tropical and subtropical regions, *Pseudolynchia maura*, may be satisfactorily grown in the laboratory and used for the transmission of *Haemoproteus columbae* (Huff, 1932) [See p. 447].

REFERENCES

For Coccidia see p. 89.

BIBLIOGRAPHY

HUFF, C. G. 1932. Studies on Haemoproteus of Mourning Doves. *Amer. J. Hyg.* 16:618.

REICHENOW, E. 1932. Die Entwicklung von *Proteosoma circumflexum* in *Theobaldia annulata* nebst Beobactungen über das verhalten anderer Vogelplasmodien in Mücken. *Jenaische Zeitschr Naturwiss.* 67 Festschr. p. 434.

TALIAFERRO, W. H., and TALIAFERRO, L. G. 1929. Acquired immunity in avian malaria. *J. Prev. Med.* 3:197.

Class *Ciliata*

CULTURE MEDIA FOR OPALINIDAE*

THERE seem to be three major desiderata in culturing Opalinids: (1) To supply predigested food. (2) To avoid free oxygen in the culture fluid. (3) To avoid contamination of the culture medium. None of

* Abstracted from a paper in *Science* 72:561, 1930, by MAYNARD M. METCALF, *Johns Hopkins University*.

the several culture methods that have been suggested since the time of Pütter's first studies provide the first two desiderata mentioned. The third can perhaps be secured by frequent transfer of the animals to new culture fluid. Supplying predigested food or foods may not prove difficult. On the other hand, to keep the culture free of oxygen is not a simple problem. It requires a technique not yet developed, so far as I know, for culturing any protozoan, except such as will thrive *within* an agar or gelatin medium. Frequent changing of cultured opalinids to fresh culture fluid without introduction of considerable oxygen by exposure to the air involves still greater technical difficulty. It could doubtless be done with the aid of a gas mask in an oxygen-free room.

Protoopalinae, when kept in Pütter's or Locke's solution, either with or without bits of the rectal wall of the host, show signs of abnormality within a few hours, often within 4 hours or so. These facts, and the further fact that in this country Protoopalinas are available for study only in a few regions and in the northeastern states not at all, have made me hesitate to attempt to develop a culture medium and culture methods. On the other hand, given a suitable culture medium and procedure, the prompt response by Protoopalina by visible cytological changes under unfavorable conditions might render Protoopalina a peculiarly favorable test animal for studies of protozoan physiology.

REFERENCES

For *Opalina ranarum* see p. 69.

BIBLIOGRAPHY

KONSULOFF, S. 1922, Untersuchungen über Opalina. *Arch. f. Protist.* 44:285.
LARSON and ALLEN, 1928. Further studies on the reaction of Opalina to various laboratory culture media. *Univ. Kansas Sci. Bull.* 18:8.

M. E. D.

Order HOLOTRICHIDA, Family HOLOPHRYIDAE

CULTURE MEDIUM FOR THE CILIATE LACRYMARIA*

MAST, who has had wide experience in collecting Protozoa, says (1911, p. 230): "Lacrymaria is relatively scarce in nature. It is occasionally found in cultures containing decaying aquatic plants but never in great numbers. One rarely finds more than two or three specimens in a drop of solution." No one has succeeded heretofore in cultivating it in the laboratory.

Malted milk in distilled water was prepared in two sets, one of which was boiled and the other not. Both were seeded with Lacrymaria and

* Abstracted from a paper in *Science* 63:212, 1926, by Y. IBARA, *Johns Hopkins University.*

examined from time to time for several weeks. In cultures containing 1-5 mg. of malted milk to 100 cc. of water the Lacrymaria became very abundant and continued to thrive for more than 6 weeks without adding anything to the cultures.

These cultures contained Halteria and another similar organism which was not identified and numerous bacteria. The Lacrymaria were observed to capture Halteria, but they appeared to feed mostly on the other organisms.

BIBLIOGRAPHY

MAST, S. O. 1911. Habits and reactions of the ciliate Lacrymaria. *J. Animal Behav.* 1:229.

M. E. D.

THE CULTURE OF DIDINIUM NASUTUM

C. DALE BEERS, *University of North Carolina*

THE food of *Didinium nasutum* is restricted by the nature of its organs of food capture to a limited number of relatively large ciliates. *Paramecium caudatum* and *P. aurelia* are the forms that are most readily and commonly ingested, though large specimens of Colpoda, Colpidium, and Frontonia are sometimes eaten. Of these food organisms *Paramecium caudatum* is recommended as the most satisfactory. It is easily cultured [See pp. 112—128.] and is wholly adequate to sustain Didinium indefinitely. The culture of Didinium therefore resolves itself into providing the animals with a non-nutrient fluid medium of suitable tonicity and reaction and with an abundance of Paramecia.

The almost complete dependence of Didinium on Paramecium as a source of food means that as a rule Didinium is found in nature only where Paramecium is abundant. Pools and streams that contain a considerable amount of decaying organic matter, including preferably a small amount of sewage, are suitable collecting places. Sediment, submerged decaying leaves, and plant stems should be collected, as well as water from the edges of the pool or stream, for more often Didinium is collected in the encysted condition, the cysts lying free in the sediment or cemented to submerged objects. To this material an equal volume of vigorous Paramecium culture should be added, in order to activate the cysts and to induce the rapid multiplication of active specimens. I have always used timothy hay infusion for growing the Paramecia for Didinium cultures. Cysts will usually activate in hay infusion within a day or two, excystation being induced by the environmental change from freshwater to infusion. The presence of the Paramecia is not a prerequisite to the excystation process; the same result may be obtained with old hay infusion which has never contained Paramecia.

The food supply becomes rapidly depleted in Didinium cultures, since four or five generations are usually produced at room temperature (21° C.) in every 24-hour period, and at least two Paramecia are needed for a single Didinium to attain its full growth prior to division. At higher temperatures the voraciousness and rapidity of reproduction of Didinium are astonishing, in that as many as nine generations may be produced within 24 hours, and the task of supplying Paramecia to large cultures becomes overwhelming.

When Didinia are needed for class use or for research purposes over a period of days or weeks, they are therefore best maintained in small stock cultures, made up, for example, in watch glasses. In the preparation of these cultures chemically clean watch glasses are filled with the desired amount of spring water or pond water (filtered or boiled to remove or kill Entomostraca). Or they may be filled with 0.01% modified Knop solution or with diluted hay infusion from a Paramecium culture. Paramecia are then concentrated with the centrifuge and transferred to the watch glasses, after which a few specimens of Didinium are added. A temperature of about 20° C. is the optimum for the growth of Didinium.

The Paramecia should react normally soon after being transferred to the watch glasses. A medium that is injurious to Paramecium is unsuitable for the growth of Didinium, and, conversely, any fluid medium in which Paramecium exhibits normal behavior and retains its normal cell configuration is usually favorable for Didinium. Occasionally spring water and pond water have a slightly unfavorable hydrogen-ion concentration which needs to be corrected by the addition of about 5 cc. of phosphate buffer mixture of pH 6.8 to each 100 cc. of water. The range of hydrogen-ion concentration which active specimens of Didinium can tolerate is considerable. It varies from pH 5.0 to pH 9.6, but the optimum lies between pH 6.8 and pH 7.2.

Modified Knop solution of suitable concentration (about 0.01%) may be prepared conveniently from the usual three stock solutions: namely, 10% $Ca(NO_3)_2$, 5% KNO_3 and, 5% $MgSO_4$. 7 H_2O. A 1% solution is first made up by adding the following amounts of the stock solutions to 150 cc. distilled water: 10 cc. $Ca(NO_3)_2$, 7.5 cc. KNO_3 and 7.5 cc. $MgSO_4$. Then a 0.01% solution is prepared by adding 1 cc. of the 1% solution to 99 cc. of distilled water. Finally, 5 cc. of $NaOH-KH_2PO_4$ buffer mixture of pH 6.8 is added to each 100 cc. of 0.01% solution.

This solution is often preferable to spring water or pond water for maintaining cultures for experimental purposes, in that its chemical composition is known and constant. It has an added advantage in that it is unfavorable for the growth of bacteria.

Hay infusion, either from a flourishing Paramecium culture or from an old, declining culture, usually has a favorable hydrogen-ion concentration, but it is sometimes too concentrated, and in the preparation of stock cultures it should be diluted with one or two volumes of distilled water.

New stock cultures should be prepared every three or four days. Excessive bacterial activity and an accumulation of metabolic waste are inimical to the growth of Didinium, and may lead to the production of structural abnormalities, or to encystment, conjugation, or death.

Pure lines of Didinium may be maintained with no great difficulty in depression slides kept in moist chambers. The procedure is similar to that employed with stock cultures, but owing to the high rate of reproduction and consequent accumulation of waste, transfers should be made daily to fresh slides.

A seemingly inherent predisposition toward conjugation sometimes leads to difficulty in the culture of pure lines, and a high mortality among exconjugants sometimes leads to the loss of the stock cultures, if conjugation assumes epidemic proportions. Fortunately, the tendency to conjugate may be suppressed in most cases by keeping the cultures at a temperature which never exceeds 21° C. On the other hand, conjugation may often be induced by increasing the temperature from 21° C. to 28° C. Some races rarely conjugate; others conjugate frequently, and it is sometimes advisable to discard the latter. Conjugants are distinctly smaller than vegetative individuals, and the death of the exconjugants is due in some instances to their inability to ingest large Paramecia. A diet of smaller Paramecia may enable them to survive.

Didinium encysts readily as a result of absence of food, accumulation of metabolic waste, or excessive bacterial growth. Of the three factors, absence of food is most effective in inducing encystment, and it is the factor that is most easily controlled experimentally if it is desirable to obtain cysts. Exhaustion of the food supply leads commonly to the encystment of the animals within eight to twelve hours. While the cysts in my experience do not withstand desiccation, they will remain viable for five or six years in water, and it is often convenient to keep Didinium from year to year in the encysted condition. To store cysts for future use, stock cultures may be made up in vials instead of watch glasses. When the Paramecia are all consumed, many of the Didinia will encyst on the sides and bottom of the vial, or on pieces of hay, if these are present. Didinium usually encysts against a solid object, the cysts being cemented to the object by the gelatinous ectocyst. The vials should be only half filled with fluid, so that some air will be present when they are finally stoppered and stored away. The cysts may be activated later by replacing the fluid in the vials with hay infusion from a vigorous Paramecium culture.

All Paramecia used in the culture of Didinium should be well-fed specimens. Much of the difficulty which has been experienced in culturing pure lines of Didinium is the result of feeding the Didinia on underfed Paramecia from an old, declining culture. All attempts to maintain cultures of Didinium on starved, emaciated Paramecia have led without exception in my experience to excessive conjugation, loss of the ability to encyst, reduced division rate, structural abnormalities, and death of the Didinia within two or three weeks at most.

REFERENCES

For the culture of Didinium see also p. 63.
Family Chilodontidae
For the culture of Chilodon see pp. 55 and 62.
For the culture of *Chilodon cucullulus* see p. 104.

Family OPHRYOGLENIDAE

CONTROLLED CULTURES OF FRESHWATER CILIATES

ALFORD HETHERINGTON, *Stanford University*

THE original mass-cultures which provide a varied abundance of ciliates for observation and description prove unsatisfactory for the needs of modern experimentation. Control of culture media has proceeded along two lines, the traditional objective of pure culture (*i.e.*, culture in the absence of other life), and culture on a controlled source of living food. Pure culture is so far successful only for some of the smaller ciliates.

At first sight, culture of the larger ciliates such as *Stentor coeruleus* or *Bursaria truncatella* on pure cultures of, for instance, the small ciliate *Glaucoma pyriformis*, would seem to promise a peculiarly elegant control of these animals which are so easily manipulated with the unaided eye. For very perfect control the food animal could be washed before introduction in known amounts into a simple inorganic medium containing them.

However it turned out that the conditions of survival of the larger free-living ciliates are much more complex than was anticipated, an outcome regretted by those who wish to use them simply as material for physiological investigations, but of interest to those who are concerned with the biology of micro-organisms as such.

PURE CULTURE

Sterilization of Ciliates. A method combining the advantages of migration and of washing was described by Hetherington (1934a). The practice of bacteriological methods is assumed in that which follows.

Glaucoma pyriformis (35-60μ)* grows as vigorously as any ciliate found in freshwaters. [See also p. 54.] It will grow on heavy suspensions of *Bacterium coli,* and is unique in that it adjusts promptly to, and grows vigorously in, sterile 0.5% Difco powdered yeast extract. Individuals are sufficiently large to be counted under the low powers of binocular dissecting microscopes.

Several strains have been described. Lwoff's (1932) and Elliott's (1933) grow on peptone, Butterfield's (1929) grows for several transfers on peptone, but ultimately demands yeast extract, while a strain isolated by Hetherington (1936) shows no growth on peptone. Elliott (1935) observed nutritive differences between peptone-growing strains. Glaser and Coria (1935) isolated strains from hot springs which will tolerate temperatures of 37° C.

Extensive trials of different media (Hetherington, 1936) for *Glaucoma pyriformis* resulted in the following optimum medium:

Yeast Extract, Difco.............................0.5%
Powd. Whole Yeast, Difco   B13412..............0.2%

This is made up in Peters' medium (see p. 000), an inorganic physiological salt solution, and autoclaved at 15 lbs. for 15 minutes. For stock cultures, 125 cc. Erlenmeyer flasks are convenient vessels. Division rates observed were rather constant, varying from 7.97 to 8.03 at 25° C.

Glaucoma scintillans (50-65μ), a typical holotrichous ciliate, was first grown in pure culture by Chatton in 1929, later by Hetherington (1933). [See also p. 56.] Neither investigator achieved dependable growth. Unpublished recent work by the writer resulted in the following medium:

Yeast Extract, Difco.............................0.5%
Powd. Whole Yeast, Difco   B13412..............1.0%

Division rates observed vary from 2 to 2.7 at 25° C.; the ciliates appear normal and well nourished. While these rates are much lower than those resulting from culture on single strains of bacteria, growth in pure culture is now satisfactory for many experimental purposes.

Other freshwater ciliates which have been obtained in pure culture are *Colpoda cucullus, C. steinii, Chilodon cucullulus,* and *Loxocephalus granulosus.* These investigations are reviewed by Hetherington (1934b).

* This ciliate was called Paramecium in the first paper of Peters (1920). Lwoff (1923) first, and Peters (1929) later, called it *Colpidium colpoda.* It was called Colpidium by Butterfield (1929), *Colpidium campylum* by Hetherington (1933) and by Taylor, *et al.* (1933), *Colpidium striatum* by Elliott (1933), and *Saprophilus oviformis* by Glaser and Coria (1935). *Saprophilus oviformis, Glaucoma pyriformis,* and *Colpidium striatum* are probably synonyms (Kahl, personal communication), but *Colpidium campylum* is a common and distinct ciliate which is distinguished by the possession of a conspicuous gullet, inconspicuous oral membranes, and by the fact that it will not grow in pure culture in Difco yeast extract (or peptone, tryptone, or neopeptone, Difco).

Pringsheim (1915) grew *Paramecium bursaria* with its green commensals in an inorganic medium similar to Knop.

In addition, *Paramecium caudatum* may be grown in an enormously complex medium developed by Glaser and Coria (1935). The writer (unpublished work) verified these results using both rabbit and monkey kidney; here again growth is not as vigorous as in the presence of living bacteria. Failure, reported previously (Hetherington, 1934c), was due to the use of a Seitz bacteriological filter rather than a Berkefeld. The filter pads, not the metal of the Seitz filter, contribute a toxic substance to the filtrate.

While it may stretch the definition of pure culture somewhat to include a medium which contains fresh rabbit kidney, these investigations are illuminating, as will be indicated in the next following section.

CULTURE ON SINGLE STRAINS OF BACTERIA

Freshwater ciliates capture and ingest their food, as higher animals do. There is no evidence that they can obtain energy or build protoplasm from simpler nutrients than required by higher organisms.

A division rate of 8.28 may be maintained in the case of *Glaucoma scintillans* on living bacteria in non-nutrient salt solution (25° C.). A small quantity of *Bacillus megatherium,* strain D 20 of the Stanford University Bacteriology Department Collection, having a diameter of about 1 mm., is removed from a 24-hour nutrient plate by means of a platinum needle, put in 0.5 cc. of Peters' medium, together with one Glaucoma. Transfer is made every 24 hours. No difference can be observed between washed and unwashed bacteria.

Turning to larger ciliates, *Colpidium colpoda* (110μ) grows with a division rate of 4.33 (24° C.) on *Aerobacter aerogenes,* strain A 2 Stanford Collection, in the following medium (Hetherington, 1934b):

Peptone, Difco.....................................0.1%
Dextrose, Baker's C. P. powd.....................0.1%

This is made up in Peters' medium, and autoclaved at 15 lbs. pressure for 15 minutes.

Colpidium campylum (50-90μ) has similar nutritive requirements, but is more resistant, and will grow faster in a 0.35% concentration of nutrient. Like *Colpidium colpoda,* it has never been grown in pure culture.

Paramecium caudatum and *P. aurelia* grow luxuriantly in the same system (*Aer. aerogenes* + 0.2% peptone-dextrose), either in tiny isolation volumes or in flasks. This is a more constant medium than the *Pseudomonas ovalis*-powdered lettuce medium reported by Giese and Taylor (1935), which is a technique apparently borrowed from the extensive work of Phelps (1934). It is not clear why Phelps found other particles (lettuce) in addition to living bacteria in nutrient medium necessary for the growth of Paramecium, but it is a general rule that a few drops in an isolation dish is not an ideal volume for developing optimum culture media.

The writer has added sterile Didinium to a culture of *Paramecium caudatum* on *Aer. aerogenes* (= "dreigliedrige Kultur") in liter flasks. The cycles of growth, perfectly visible to the unaided eye, are rather striking, and are duplicated indefinitely with subcultures. Such cultures are easy to maintain; a minute or two for transfer once a month suffices.

In no case has the writer found that a combination of two or more bacteria is better than a suitable single strain for the nutrition of ciliate Protozoa.

Colpidium colpoda, Paramecium caudatum or *P. aurelia, Pleurotricha lanceolata* (Penn, 1935), and *Urocentrum turbo* (Hetherington, 1934b, p. 637), will not grow in an inorganic medium (for instance Peters' medium or spring water) + washed living bacteria. The writer therefore cannot agree with Phelps (1934) that some labile substance in the bacterial cell is destroyed upon killing (regardless of method used— heat, ultraviolet light, HCl, H_2O_2, $(NH_4)_2$ SO_4, and toluene), and that this is the reason pure culture may not be achieved. It would appear rather, since even living bacteria do not suffice when their metabolites are removed, that labile substances pass into the medium which "condition" it in some way, and that these substances must be constantly supplied by metabolizing bacteria. The idea that they are reducing bodies was tested by Hetherington (1934b, p. 636), with negative results. Before growth on dead bacteria may be achieved, unheated liver (Eli Lilly No. 343) and fresh, sterile kidney must be added (Glaser and Coria, 1935). Paramecium may be the simplest type of animal to the taxonomist, but its dietary requirements remind us more of mammals!

Such is the setting for a consideration of the growth requirements of the largest ciliates, which typically eat other Protozoa.

CULTURE ON SINGLE STRAINS OF PROTOZOA

The large and beautiful *Stentor coeruleus* (200-500μ) and *Bursaria truncatella* (300-400μ) are known to eat a variety of foods: bacteria, green and colorless flagellates, diatoms, ciliates, rotifers, and even smaller individuals of their own kind.

Inorganic medium. Of all the physiological media tested, including a variety of spring waters, Peters' medium has proved almost ideal for freshwater ciliates*:

---

*Preparation is described in the author's 1934a work, p. 316.

Ca(HCO$_3$)$_2$ ....0.00055 M.
MgSO$_4$ ....0.00015 M.
KH$_2$PO$_4$ ....0.00030 M.
NaH$_2$PO$_4$ ....0.00015 M.

Since ordinary distilled water is frequently very toxic, it is best to use twice distilled water for preparing Peters' medium.

Glaucoma pyriformis, Colpidium campylum, or *Colpidium colpoda,* carefully washed free of their medium, and added in sufficient amounts (an excess), will support growth of *Stentor coeruleus* in this medium for about four weeks (Hetherington, 1932). After this they degenerate. *Bursaria truncatella* behaves similarly, but degenerates much more promptly. Addition of *Gonium pectorale,* a green form, Chilomonas, a colorless flagellate, and several kinds of washed bacteria, does not alter behavior in the least. *Bursaria truncatella,* in the presence or absence of washed food, dies in physiological medium exactly as described for *Pleurotricha lanceolata* by Penn (1935, p. 126-27).

Accordingly, the present status of our knowledge concerning these ciliates indicates that suitable food + pure physiological medium do not meet their requirements, that certain metabolites of growing bacteria are essential for the continued survival of the larger ciliate Protozoa. Further progress with these animals awaits solution of this problem.

REFERENCES

For the culture of *Glaucoma ficaria* see p. 54.
For the culture of Colpidium see also p. 63.
For the culture of *Colpidium striatum* see p. 54.
For the culture of *Colpidium campylum* see also p. 54.

BIBLIOGRAPHY

BUTTERFIELD, C. T. 1929. A note on the relation between food concentration in liquid media and bacterial growth. *U. S. Pub. Health Repts.* 44:2865.

CHATTON, E., et CHATTON, M. 1929. Les conditions de la conjugaison du *Glaucoma scintillans* en cultures léthobactériennes. Action directe et spécifique de certains agents zygogènes. *C. R. Acad. Sci.* 188:1315.

ELLIOTT, A. M. 1933. Isolation of *Colpidium striatum* Stokes in bacteria-free media. *Biol. Bull.* 65:45.

———— 1935. Effects of carbohydrates on growth of Colpidium. *Arch. f. Protist.* 84:156.

GIESE, A. C., and TAYLOR, C. V. 1935. Paramecia for experimental purposes in controlled mass cultures on a single strain of bacteria. *Ibid.* 84:225.

GLASER, R., and CORIA, N. A. 1935. The culture and reactions of purified Protozoa. *Amer. J. Hyg.* 21:111.

HETHERINGTON, A. 1932. The constant culture of *Stentor coeruleus*. *Arch. f. Protist.* 76:118.

———— 1933. The culture of some holotrichous ciliates. *Ibid.* 80:225.

———— 1934a. The sterilization of Protozoa. *Biol. Bull.* 67:315.

———— 1934b. The rôle of bacteria in the growth of *Colpidium colpoda*. *Physiol. Zool.* 7:618.

—— 1934c. The pure culture of Paramecium. *Science* 79:413.

—— 1936. The precise control of growth in a pure culture of a ciliate, *Glaucoma pyriformis. Biol. Bull.* 71:426.

LWOFF, A. 1923. Sur la nutrition des Infusoires. *C. R. Acad. Sci.* 176:928.

—— 1932. Recherches biochimiques sur la nutrition des Protozoaires. Paris, Masson et Cie.

PENN, A. B. K. 1935. Factors which control encystment in *Pleurotricha lanceolata. Arch. f. Protist.* 84:101.

PETERS, R. A. 1920. Nutrition of the Protozoa: the growth of Paramecium in sterile culture medium. *J. Physiol.* 53:108.

—— 1929. Observation upon the oxygen consumption of *Colpidium colpoda. Ibid.* 68:1.

PHELPS, A. 1934. Studies on the nutrition of Paramecium. *Arch. f. Protist.* 82:134.

PRINGSHEIM, E. G. 1915. Die Kultur von *Paramecium bursaria. Biol. Zentralbl.* 35:375.

TAYLOR, C. V., THOMAS, J. O., and BROWN, M. G. 1933. Studies on Protozoa, IV; Lethal effects of X-radiation of a sterile culture medium for *Colpidium campylum. Physiol. Zool.* 6:467.

CULTIVATION OF COLPIDIUM CAMPYLUM*

T. M. SONNEBORN, *Johns Hopkins University*

USE a basic fluid of spring water in which rye grains, in the concentration of 1.5 gms. per 100 cc., have been boiled for 10 minutes. The fluid is filtered while hot and allowed to stand 1 day exposed to the air. Good mass cultures can be obtained within a day or so by placing 200 cc. of ripe fluid in a finger bowl and inoculating with 10 to 15 cc. of an old culture of *C. campylum.* Such cultures should be renewed every 2 to 6 days.

Isolation cultures under bacteriologically controlled conditions may readily be carried by the following method: Distribute the standard rye infusion as soon as filtered into test tubes, plug with cotton, autoclave, and store till needed. When ready for use, open tube in a flame and inoculate by means of sterile platinum needle with pure cultures of the bacterium, *Achromobacter candicans,* grown on beef-agar slants. Using glassware (petri dishes, columbia dishes, pipettes, *etc.*) previously baked in an oven at 150° C. for an hour, the one-bacterium rye fluid is pipetted into columbia dishes inside of petri dishes and into these dishes sterilized Colpidia are introduced by means of a sterile fine pipette.

Isolation cultures carried with less refined technique, may be maintained by using depression slides containing one drop of one-day-old ripened rye infusion. These should be started with one Colpidium to each drop of culture, and should be renewed daily by transferring one Colpidium to a fresh drop on a fresh slide. A favorable temperature is 22°-23° C.

* Condensed by the author from *Biol. Bull.* 63:187, 1932.

THE CULTURE OF COLPIDIUM CAMPYLUM

C. V. TAYLOR, J. O. THOMAS, and M. G. BROWN, *Stanford University*

THE holotrichous ciliate, *Colpidium campylum*, was obtained originally in an enrichment culture from spinach procured in the vicinity of Monterey Bay, California, and subcultured in a continuously thriving condition in a sterile tap water extract of common commercial yeast.

This extract is prepared in the following manner: 450 grams of a commercial yeast is mixed with 500 cc. of water, kept at 50° C. for 24 hours, then neutralized with NaOH to a pH of 7.0, filtered, and autoclaved.

For cultures the filtrate is diluted ten times with tap water, then apportioned in 5 cc. amounts into test tubes. Sterile technique is used throughout. Each tube is inoculated with approximately 1000 Colpidia. The resulting growth is vigorous and uniform.

Under ordinary laboratory conditions pure strains of this holotrichous ciliate, washed free of bacteria, have thrived vigorously for about two years in this convenient and reproducible medium. The temperature variation was around 20° to 22° C. and the light in the laboratory was a north light.

A CULTURE METHOD FOR COLPODA

M. S. BRISCOE, *Storer College*

FINGER bowls are satisfactory vessels for this culture method. They are first sterilized by exposing them to streaming steam. In this way micro-organisms normally present upon the surfaces of laboratory apparatus are destroyed. Both moist and dry heat were tried but the former is more efficient. If there is no Arnold steam sterilizer in the laboratory the sterilizing process may be accomplished in some similar apparatus. A temperature of 100° C., is sufficient to destroy the majority of micro-organisms that may be present.

With the completion of the sterilizing process, spaghetti, which may be purchased in cans at a grocery store, should be removed from its container. It should be thoroughly washed so as to remove any other substances that may be present. When all of these have been eliminated place some of the spaghetti in a finger bowl and cover it completely with water. Faucet water is satisfactory. Allow it to stand for several days until a scum forms. It is then ready for inoculation with the organisms.

The optimum growth temperature for Colpoda is 70° F. At this temperature the organisms appear normally healthy and grow very rapidly. Increases in temperature do not increase the rate of growth and at sufficiently high temperatures growth ceases. The organisms do not thrive when exposed to intense light such as the direct rays of the sun. Cultures which were not exposed to the air, and hence did not become moldy, continued to thrive for long periods of time.

STOCK CULTURES OF COLPODA*

DURING the course of investigation with Protozoa, a rather convenient and easy method of obtaining and keeping stock cultures of Colpoda was found.

Colpoda, as is well known, usually occur early in soil cultures from which they may be obtained, in the active state, in large numbers. Later in the life of the culture the animals encyst and it is upon this condition that the following method is based.

From a young soil culture active Colpoda are isolated, transferred to Syracuse watch glasses and ordinary hay infusion added. After one or two days the culture fluid in the watch glass is allowed to evaporate slowly by exposure to the air. During this slow evaporation the animals encyst. The dried up culture is left exposed for one or two days, when new hay infusion is added. The animals, having divided within the cysts, revive and are found in greatly increased numbers. This drying process may be repeated until a more or less concentrated culture of organisms is obtained. The concentrated culture of organisms is then pipetted into a petri dish in which a piece of ordinary filter paper, cut so as to exactly cover the bottom of the dish and moistened with hay infusion, is placed. The petri dish is then left uncovered to evaporate slowly. The filter paper, with the encysted organisms on it, when thoroughly dry, may be cut into small pieces and kept indefinitely.

To start fresh cultures, pieces of the filter paper are put into watch glasses or other containers and hay infusion added. In a short time the animals revive and new cultures of the original are thus obtained.

This method of keeping stock cultures seems to be especially adapted for schools and colleges where only a limited amount of time is devoted to the Protozoa and where no time for the ordinary culture preparation work is available.

M. E. D.

REFERENCE

For the culture of Colpoda see also p. 63.

THE CULTURE OF COLPODA CUCULLUS
H. ALBERT BARKER and C. V. TAYLOR, *Stanford University*

Colpoda cucullus may be cultured in finger bowls containing 10-20 cc. of a dilute hay infusion. These infusions, however, are singularly unsuit-

---

* Reprinted with slight changes from an article in *Science* 53:92, 1921, by Joseph H. Bodine, *Iowa State University*.

able as media with which to conduct certain types of experimental investigations because their composition is unknown and uncontrollable and doubtless varies greatly as prepared at different times and places.

For these reasons we have used the reproducible, non-nutritive medium shown in the following table, supplemented by the addition of a pure strain of bacteria for food.

Balanced Physiological Medium
(after Osterhout, 1906)
6% total salt (0.937 M.)

0.937 M.	Parts
NaCl	1,000
$MgCl_2.6H_2O$	78
$MgSO_4.7H_2O$	38
KCl	22
$CaCl_2$	10

This solution is diluted five times to the approximate concentration of pond water, or 0.012% total salt (0.0018 M.). One cc. of M/20 NaH_2PO_4 is added to each 30 cc. of this diluted solution for buffering, and the pH adjusted with suitable quantities of M/20 NaOH.

Colpoda in this medium are fed upon suspensions of a pure culture of the bacterium *Pseudomonas fluorescens*. This bacterium is eminently suitable as a food for Colpoda. When grown in suspensions of it, they appear large and well fed, their division rate is equal to or greater than that in the most favorable hay infusions, they continue normally active, and may be kept indefinitely on this single diet without degeneration.

Pseudomonas fluorescens may be isolated from soils by the use of a liquid enrichment culture in which 2% asparagine serves as the only source of carbon and nitrogen. The bacterium may be isolated and grows rapidly on ordinary yeast—or peptone-glucose-agar plates at 37° C. or below. If inoculated heavily on such plates, the colonies spread out within a few days into a continuous sheet from which masses of bacteria may be removed with a sterile platinum loop in order to be fed to the Protozoa.

The density of the bacterial suspension provided for the Protozoa is difficult to define except as that density in which optimal growth occurs. This most favorable density of bacterial suspension will of course depend in part upon the number of Protozoa inoculated into a given volume of the medium. An approximate idea of a favorable suspension density may be gained from the following illustration: the mass of bacteria which will fill a platinum wire loop 1 mm. in diameter is sufficient to make 6 suspensions of ½ cc. into each of which 20 Colpoda are to be inoculated.

No effort is made to avoid air contaminations of the Pseudomonas suspensions. It was assumed that the suspensions would not be sufficiently nutritive to permit the growth of contaminating micro-organisms. Justification for this may be seen in the fact that molds were never observed to develop during the experiments.

All experiments were carried out in a constant temperature room at 72° F. with north light.

The containers for the culture of Colpoda are watch glasses of about 2 mm. diameter enclosed in petri dishes of suitable size containing in the bottom a small amount of water and so used as moist chambers.

REFERENCES

For the culture of *Colpoda cucullus* see also p. 104.
For the culture of *Colpoda steinii* see pp. 56 and 104.
Family Urocentridae
For the culture of *Urocentrum turbo* see p. 106.

BIBLIOGRAPHY

OSTERHOUT, W. J. V. 1906. Extreme toxicity of sodium chloride and its prevention by other salts. *J. Biol. Chem.* 1:363.

Family PARAMECIIDAE

SOME METHODS FOR THE PURE CULTURE OF PROTOZOA

WILLIAM TRAGER, *Rockefeller Institute for Medical Research*

I. SEPARATION OF THE PROTOZOA FROM OTHER MICRO-ORGANISMS

Migration through Pipettes. The technique developed by Glaser and Coria (1930), and used by them for the separation of certain Protozoa from their contaminating bacteria, depends essentially on the exhibition by the Protozoa of a geotropic response which causes them to swim away from the bacteria through a column of sterile liquid. Two methods for bringing this about are available. In the first, sterile pipettes are used, at least 14 inches long with a $\frac{1}{4}$ inch bore, a tapering point, and a cotton plug at the large end. For negatively geotropic Protozoa such a pipette, by suction through a rubber tube attached to the large end, is filled with sterile tap water to within 2 inches of the top. Then about 2 cc. of a heavy culture of the contaminated Protozoa is carefully sucked up into the pipette, so as to form a layer beneath the sterile water. The tapering end of the pipette is then sealed by heat, care being taken not to permit the formation of air bubbles. The pipette, sealed end down, is set upright in a test tube rack. In from 5 to 30 minutes, negatively geotropic Protozoa will be present at the top of the column of liquid. Even motile bacteria, by their own efforts, can not reach the top in so short a time. Usually, however, one such washing does not free the Protozoa from adherent or ingested bacteria, and in most cases it is necessary to repeat the procedure once or twice, each time sucking up beneath the fresh column of sterile water in a fresh pipette about 2 inches of fluid from the top of the previous pipette. In some cases it is advisable to leave the first or second pipette for 18 to 24 hours to give the surface migrants a chance to evacuate the remains of ingested micro-organisms and to multiply to some extent. This procedure is followed by another rapid washing. Finally a drop of the surface fluid is inoculated into a tube of sterile medium (see Part II). In this manner the ciliates *Trichoda pura*, three strains of the thermal ciliate *Saprophilus oviformis* from Hot Springs, Virginia, a large undetermined ciliate, *Paramecium caudatum* and *P. multimicronucleatum*, and the flagellates *Chilomonas paramecium*, *Parapolytoma satura*, and an undetermined monad from the intestine of the fly, *Lucilia caesar*, were all freed of bacteria, as shown by consistently negative findings in stained films and aerobic and anaerobic cultures on routine laboratory media at both room and incubator temperatures. The upward migration here involved is a genuine geotropic reaction, as it occurs in pipettes held in the dark and in those sealed without any air space at the top.

This same pipette method may be used for positively geotropic Protozoa. The pipette is nearly filled as before with sterile water, the tip is sealed and then a small amount of the contaminated culture is layered on top of the sterile liquid. After a suitable time the end of the pipette is cut off and one or two drops either inoculated into culture medium or placed at the top of another water column for a second washing. In this way an undetermined free-living monad was freed of bacteria after two washings, each consuming about 30 minutes. With either negatively or positively geotropic organisms the addition of killed yeast cells (see Part II) to that part of the water column toward which the Protozoa were to migrate, accelerated their migration.

Migration through V-Tubes. In the second method, V-shaped tubes are used, one arm of the "V" being 12 cm. long with an inside diameter of 28 mm., the other 9 cm. long with an inside diameter of 8 mm. The tube, after sterilization, is filled with 15 cc. of melted semi-solid medium (see Part II). When this has set to a soft gel the contaminated Protozoa are introduced by means of a long fine capillary through the small arm into the bottom of the large one. The tube is permitted to stand for a length of time dependent of the Protozoa concerned, and then samples are taken from the surface of the medium in the large arm. One such treatment frequently suffices. A modification of this technique was used to separate *Spirillum undulans* from other bacteria. A loopful of contaminated culture of the Spirillum was placed on the surface of sterile tap water in the large arm of a V-tube. Five-tenths of a cc. amounts, withdrawn one hour later from the surface of the small arm, gave pure cultures of the Spirillum upon inoculation into suitable media (see also Part III).

II. CULTURE MEDIA FOR CERTAIN BACTERIA-FREE PROTOZOA

"*Basic Medium.*" Among the free-living Protozoa freed of bacteria by any of the above methods some, such as *Trichoda pura*, were able to grow well in simple media such as peptone water. Even such Protozoa, however, grow better in the so-called "basic medium" of Glaser and Coria (1930). This has been recently modified (Glaser and Coria, 1934a) to give more nearly uniform results and is now prepared in the following way: Stock Solution *A* consists of 50 cc. of horse serum in 1000 cc. of well water (or distilled water). This is autoclaved for 30 minutes at 15 lbs. and has a pH of 7.0 without adjustment. Stock solution *B* consists of 50 gms. of timothy hay in 1000 cc. of water. The mixture is infused over night in the refrigerator, filtered through cotton, and the reaction adjusted to pH 7.2-7.4. The stock solutions *A* and *B* are stored separately in a refrigerator and when needed are combined with well water in these proportions:

Solution A   500 cc.
Solution B   250 cc.
Well water   250 cc.

The medium is adjusted to pH 7.2-7.4, tubed in 8 or 10 cc. amounts and autoclaved. This final medium was used only for Protozoa free of other micro-organisms. When heavy initial cultures of unpurified Protozoa are desired 2 cc. of the final medium is added to 20 cc. of the original Protozoa-containing water. To make a solid medium, 1.5 to 2% agar is added. For a semi-solid medium similar to Noguchi's Leptospira medium, 100 cc. of the melted solid medium is diluted with 900 cc. of warm water.

Raw Potato. Some Protozoa, which grew well in basic medium when contaminated with bacteria, did not grow at all in this medium when free of other micro-organisms. Thus a flagellate from the intestine of *Lucilia caesar* would not grow in basic medium except in the presence of living bacteria. The bacteria-free flagellate would not develop on autoclaved potato, but delicate growths of it were obtained in tubes of raw potato under tap water. Such tubes are prepared as follows: Raw potatoes are scrubbed with hot water and partly dried by heat; a part of the surface is washed thoroughly with 70% alcohol and flamed until charred. Cylinders are then cut out with a sterile No. 5 cork borer and put in sterile petri dishes where they are cut into pieces ½ inch long. Each piece is placed in a tube of sterile water. Such tubes are held at room temperature for some time before use, and any showing contamination are discarded.

Special Medium for Paramecia. Two species of Paramecium (*P. caudatum* and *P. multimicronucleatum*) probably furnish the best examples of free-living Protozoa which, when free of other micro-organisms, require a very special complex nutritive medium (Glaser and Coria, 1933, 1934a). Various workers have successfully freed Paramecia of contaminating bacteria, usually by means of the washing of isolated individuals, but the bacteria-free organisms could not be cultured. Such was at first the experience of Glaser and Coria (1930) who used the migration technique to obtain the pure Protozoa. They established a "pure-mixed" culture in basic medium of *Paramecium caudatum* in association with the yeast, *Saccharomyces cervisiae.* Since the yeast is non-motile and heavier than water one can readily take advantage of the negative geotropic migration of the Paramecia to secure pure Protozoa. In practise, the "pure-mixed" culture was centrifuged and washed three times in sterile water. The material so obtained was introduced at the base of a pipette in the manner previously described and the Protozoa permitted to migrate through the column of sterile water. Every day for 5 days material from the top of the pipette was removed and plated on dextrose agar. Only in cultures made on the first day were any yeast colonies obtained, showing that after the first day the yeast cells brought to the surface by the Paramecia had been digested. Upward migration of the Protozoa was complete by the fourth day at a temperature of 20°-22° C. Pure Paramecia obtained in this way were finally cultured in a medium consisting of liver extract, killed yeast, and fresh rabbit kidney. Repeated tests (aerobic and anaerobic cultures in a variety of media at room and incubator temperatures) showed that the cultures so obtained were free of other micro-organisms.

The liver extract consists of a 0.5% solution of Eli Lilly Company's liver extract No. 343 in water. This is filtered through paper and sterilized by filtration through a Berkefeld N filter. This extract has a pH of 6.2 to 6.4 and is placed in 10 cc. amounts in sterile test tubes. Liver extract may also be made in the following way: One hundred grams of finely ground rabbit, beef, or swine liver are infused over night in the refrigerator in 200 cc. of water. The suspension is filtered through cotton, heated over a water bath for about one hour, and then strained through fine gauze, all the fluid being squeezed out of the coagulum. The liquid is further cleared by centrifuging and is then diluted with water to 400 cc. It is warmed to 60° C. and passed successively through sterile Berkefeld V and N candles and then is tubed in 10 cc. amounts. Heat sterilization of the liver extract, either in the autoclave or in the Arnold sterilizer does not give a satisfactory medium.

Dead yeast is prepared from baker's yeast grown for 5 days on dextrose agar in a Blake bottle. The growth is washed off in sterile water, centrifuged, and again washed and centrifuged. The washed yeasts are suspended in 15 cc. of sterile water and this suspension is distributed in 5 cc. amounts to tubes which are then sealed and placed for 30 minutes in a water bath at a temperature of 75° to 80° C. The heated suspensions are tested for sterility on dextrose agar slants. Killed cultures of *Staphylococcus pyogenes aureus* or *albus* may be used instead of the killed yeast.

In the final preparation of the medium, pieces of kidney weighing 0.2 to 0.5 gms. are aseptically removed from a freshly killed rabbit and placed in tubes of liver extract. To each tube is added 0.1 cc. of heat-killed yeast suspension and also some Paramecia from the surface of a migration pipette. An inoculum of about 870 Paramecia was usually used. In such tubes a luxuriant growth of *Paramecium caudatum* is present by the tenth day and successful subcultures are regularly obtained between the seventh and fifteenth day of incubation at room temperatures. Table I shows that the liver extract, killed yeast, and fresh kidney are all essential to the growth of *Paramecium caudatum* in the absence of other micro-organisms. Very similar results have been obtained with the large *Paramecium multimicronucleatum*. By the ordinary migration technique this ciliate was easily freed of all but one contaminant, a small motile bacillus. Further migrations were now performed in sterile water containing a few drops of living yeast cell suspension. The bacillus multiplied very slowly in the water, and the Paramecia fed on the yeast cells. These eventually settled out while the Protozoa swam to the top of the long water column. Such daily migrations were repeated over a period of 6 days and finally a migration in sterile water without yeast cells yielded Protozoa free of other micro-organisms. Such *Paramecium multimicronucleatum* grew in the same medium which was used for *P. caudatum*.

Necessity for a Change of Medium. While both species of Paramecia in their special culture medium, and the flagellate *Parapolytoma satura* on blood agar, seem to grow indefinitely, the other purified Protozoa, when grown continuously in "basic medium" showed a gradually lessening developmental rate and finally died out unless transferred to some other culture medium. Thus after several months in "basic medium," with transfer intervals of 1 to 2 weeks, when the Protozoa had begun to grow less luxuriantly, they were subcultured to potato or carrot water or to basic medium containing sterile rabbit kidney or yeast extract. Such transfers again gave excellent growth, but this again weakened after

TABLE I—**Effect of Liver Extract, Kidney and Yeast on the Growth of Paramecium.**

Medium	Test No.	Degree of growth in days					Transplant
		2	4	6	8	10	
Water+kidney***	1	±***	+	+	+	—	Negative
" "	2	±	+	+	+	—	"
" "	3	±	+	+	+	—	"
Water+kidney+dead yeast	4	±	+	+	+	—	"
" " " "	5	±	+	+	+	—	"
" " " "	6	±	+	+	+	—	"
Water+kidney+living yeast	7	+	++	+++	++++	++++	Positive
" " " "	8	+	++	+++	++++	++++	"
" " " "	9	+	++	+++	++++	++++	"
Lilly's extract+kidney+dead yeast	10	+	++	+++	++++	++++	"
" " " " "	11	+	++	+++	++++	++++	"
" " " " "	12	+	++	+++	++++	++++	"
" " "	13	+	+	+	+	+	Negative
" " "	14	+	+	+	+	+	"
" " "	15	+	+	+	+	+	"
Lilly's extract+dead yeast	16	+	+	+	+	+	"
" " " "	17	+	+	+	+	+	"
" " " "	18	+	+	+	+	+	"
Liver extract+kidney+dead yeast.....	19	+	++	+++	++++	++++	Positive
" " " " "	20	+	++	+++	++++	++++	"
" " " " "	21	+	++	+++	++++	++++	"

*** Water=sterile tap water; kidney=fresh rabbit kidney; Lilly's extract=extract prepared from Eli-Lilly and Company's liver extract No. 343; liver=rabbit liver extract prepared in this laboratory; — = dead; ±=doubtful growth; +=weak growth: ++=fair growth; +++=good growth; ++++=luxuriant growth.

(From Glaser and Coria, 1933)

several months in the new medium, and the Protozoa were then returned to "basic medium" and the whole procedure repeated. Potato or carrot water is prepared by autoclaving 2 gram pieces of the vegetable in tubes with 10 cc. of water. For use, 2 cc. of the liquid so obtained is diluted with 10 cc. of sterile water. Yeast extract is prepared in the following way. Pure cultures of yeast are grown on dextrose agar in Blake bottles for 5 to 7 days at room temperature. The growth is washed and centrifuged three times with 50 cc. of sterile water and 2 cc. of the sedimented cells are then ground for 5 hours in a sterile mechanical grinder consisting of two ground glass tubes one of which, the pestle, fits snugly within the other and is turned by an air turbine motor (see Glaser and Coria 1934a for details). Thirty cc. of sterile water are then added and the mixture stirred for another 20 minutes. This ground yeast suspension is centrifuged 15 minutes to remove the larger particles and is then sterilized completely (*i.e.* freed of intact yeast cells) by filtration through a sterile Berkefeld V filter. Small amounts of such a yeast extract when added to any of the media greatly stimulated the growth of the Protozoa. Extracts filtered through Berkefeld N filters or prepared from yeast killed chemically or by heat did not stimulate. It should be noted that even the best yeast extracts could not be substituted for the intact heat killed yeast cells in the special medium devised for the Paramecia.

III. PARTIAL PURIFICATION OF CULTURES OF
BALANTIDIUM COLI

It has long been realized that bacteria-free cultures of the intestinal protozoan parasites of vertebrates would be extremely useful for the study of the biology and pathogenicity of these organisms. Yet up to the present time no such protozoan has been grown in culture free of bacteria and in most cases it has been impossible even to free the Protozoa of the numerous bacteria which naturally accompany them. Cleveland (1928), however, succeeded in freeing the coprozoic organism, *Tritrichomonas fecalis* of man, from bacteria and was able to grow it on heat-killed bacteria. Glaser and Coria (1934) have recently applied one of their migration techniques to *Balantidium coli* from swine and have been able to free the organism of all bacteria except *Bacillus coli*. Largely as a result of this partial purification, they have been able to maintain this parasitic ciliate in better condition and for a much longer time without subculturing than has heretofore been possible.

They used a liquid medium consisting of 9 cc. of sterile Ringer's (Schumaker, 1931) solution, 0.5 cc. of sterile horse serum, and a sprinkle of rice starch in each tube. Much better results were obtained with a semi-solid medium. This is prepared by adding 25 cc. of 2% standard nutrient agar, 1 gram of sterile rice starch and 12.5 cc. of sterile horse serum to 250 cc. of sterile Ringer's solution warmed to 50° C. The pH of the mixture is adjusted to 7.2 to 7.4 and 15 cc. amounts are transferred aseptically to sterile tubes.

"V" tubes containing 15 cc. of semi-solid medium were inoculated (after being warmed to 37° C.) on the surface of one arm with material scraped from crypts in the mucosa near the ilio-cecal valve of a pig. The Balantidia migrated downwards within 24 to 48 hours at 37° C. and could then be recovered in a sterile pipette inserted through the uninoculated arm of the "V" tube. The semi-solid nature of the medium checked the spread of bacteria, which in a liquid medium would rapidly grow over both arms of the "V" tube. The Balantidia were able to push their way through the gelatinous semi-solid medium and it was found that in such a medium a much higher percentage of positive initial cultures could be obtained than in a liquid medium. Balantidia removed after the final migration were again placed on the surface of one arm of a fresh "V" tube and again permitted to migrate for 24 to 48 hours. This procedure was repeated five times, after which the ciliates were further cultured in ordinary tubes of semi-solid medium. Strains which would not originally grow in the liquid medium could be adapted to this after varying lengths of culture in the semi-solid medium.

These methods failed to free Balantidium of *Bacillus coli* but they did yield cultures which might be regularly transplanted at 8-day intervals and one strain (in liquid medium) which was transferred every 20 days thrived for over 2½ years.

BIBLIOGRAPHY

GLASER, R. W., and CORIA, N. A. 1930. Methods for the pure culture of certain Protozoa. *J. Exper. Med.* 51:787.

———— 1933. The culture of *Paramecium caudatum* free from living microorganisms. *J. Paras.* 20:33.

———— 1934a. The culture and reactions of purified Protozoa. *Amer. J. Hyg.* 21:111.

———— 1934b. The partial purification of *Balantidium coli* from swine. *J. Paras.* 21:190.

CLEVELAND, L. R. 1928. The suitability of various bacteria, molds, yeasts and spirochaetes as food for the flagellate *Tritrichomonas fecalis* of man, *etc.* *Amer. J. Hyg.* 8:990.

SCHUMAKER, E. 1931. The cultivation of *Balantidium coli. Ibid.* 13:281.

THYROID CULTURES OF PARAMECIA*

AT VARIOUS times the writer has had occasion to make some thyroid cultures of *Paramecium caudatum*. It was noted that these animals found this habitat more favorable to existence and reproduction than the ordinary hay infusions.

Such a Paramecium thyroid culture may easily be made by mixing about 2 grams of Armour's Desiccated Sheep Thyroids (U.S.P.) with 2,500 cc. spring water. This mixture should be slightly stirred and allowed to stand exposed to the air for half an hour. Several pipettes full of fluid containing Paramecia are then introduced. If the culture jar is covered with a top and carefully sealed with vaseline an excellent, clear culture will be obtained. After several days it may be noticed that the animals are evenly distributed throughout the liquid, and are not congested about the top of the jar as in ordinary cultures. The cultures usually need but little attention. However, it is sometimes found desirable to add a little fresh water every week or ten days.

M. E. D.

A COMBINED CULTURE METHOD AND INDICATOR FOR PARAMECIUM**

BRAGG AND HULPIEU (1925) describe the effect of a stain obtained from red cabbage leaves as an indicator of the acidity of the food vacuoles of Paramecium. I have been unable to secure similar satisfactory results with the races I am using, but have found that a dilute infusion of red cabbage leaves (about 30 grams to 1 liter of water) is an excellent medium in which the animals reproduce rapidly; at the same

* Reprinted with slight changes from an article in *Science* 58:205, 1923, by WILLIAM L. STRAUS, JR.

**Reprinted with slight changes from an article in *Science* 62:351, 1925, by ROBERT T. HANCE, *University of Pittsburgh.*

time the color of the infusion indicates the chemical condition of the culture. When fresh, the cabbage leaf culture medium is light reddish purple in color, but about 24 hours after being seeded with Paramecium, it turns red, indicating the formation of acid. In four or five days to two weeks, as the Paramecia increase in number, the medium gradually becomes alkaline, as is shown by its change of color to green.

The culture, as far as quantity of Paramecia is concerned, is at its height when it becomes a brilliant green and has lost its early turbidity. The behavior of the cultures may be varied considerably by adding a trace of sodium bicarbonate or a weak acid. In from one to two months, the culture becomes the color of an old hay infusion, fails to react to acids or alkalies and the Paramecia have either wholly or almost wholly died off.

BIBLIOGRAPHY

BRAGG, A. N., and HULPIEU, H. 1925. A method of demonstrating acidity of food vacuoles in Paramecium. *Science* 61:392.

M. E. D.

PARAMECIUM*

WILLIAM LeRAY and NORMA FORD, *University of Toronto*

PARAMECIUM is a form which is easily reared. From the bottom of a permanent pond the foul-smelling debris is taken and kept in a bowl barely covered with water and at a temperature of approximately 73° F. As the debris fouls, the Paramecium become abundant. From time to time (about once a week) a half-inch cube of fish is added to the bowl to maintain a supply of food. Such a culture as this will carry on for months. It is advisable to select a large race and to rear in separate containers. Should some small forms be present in the new bowls they are usually unsuccessful in the competition with the large ones.

A CULTURE MEDIUM FOR PARAMECIUM**

THIS medium has proven very satisfactory for culturing various species of Paramecium in pure line cultures. The main result of the use of the medium is that the organisms do not exhibit a lowering of their normal metabolism after continuous culturing.

* *Editor's Note*: For the technique used by Prof. L. L. Woodruff of Yale University in maintaining his famous pedigreed cultures of Paramecia the reader is referred to the following articles:

WOODRUFF, L. L. 1908. The life cycle of Paramecium when subjected to a varied environment. *Amer. Nat.* 42:520.

—— 1911. Two thousand generations of Paramecium. *Archiv. f. Protist.* 21:263.

—— 1932. *Paramecium aurelia* in pedigreed culture for twenty-five years. *Trans. Amer. Micr. Soc.* 51:196.

WOODRUFF, L. L., and ERDMANN, RHODA. 1914. A normal periodic reorganization process without cell fusion in Paramecium. *J. Exper. Zool.* 17:425.

**Reprinted, with slight changes, from *Science* 75:364, 1932, by LAUREN E. ROSENBERG, *University of California*.

The basic part of the medium is the usual hay infusion of 10 grams of chopped timothy hay boiled for 15 minutes in a liter of well water. This infusion is filtered and sterilized in the Arnold sterilizer at 100° C. one hour a day for 3 days. It is diluted with 9 volumes of sterile well water just before using. Two portions of this infusion are placed in sterile liter flasks with sterile cotton stoppers. One liter is inoculated with *Bacillus subtilus* and the second with *B. coli communis*. A third portion of the medium is made up as follows: Approximately 30 grains of wheat are boiled in a small amount of water for 10 minutes. The wheat grains only are then placed in a third liter flask of sterile well water. The three portions are incubated at 37° C. for 24 hours, and then combined in one large sterile flask. The medium is now ready for use. The culture may be used in almost any size of container, but that used has been the 300 cc. Erlenmeyer flask. These flasks are fitted with cotton stoppers and sterilized. Each flask is filled about ⅔ full of the medium, and different species are transferred to the cultures with sterile pipettes.

The original basic infusion may be made up, sterilized, and stored in a refrigerator until ready for use. Likewise, the medium, made of the three portions, may be stored in a refrigerator for later use.

Sterile precautions are maintained throughout the procedure, but after Paramecium has been transplanted, such strict precautions are no longer necessary. The essential part of the process is to provide a medium rich with a suitable food in which Paramecium will continue to grow normally. With these sterile precautions, other ciliates and flagellates are eliminated. A single organism placed in such a medium will produce a flourishing culture in 7 to 10 days. One should transplant every 2 to 3 weeks. *Paramecium multimicronucleatum, P. bursaria,* and *P. aurelia* have thrived in this medium.

M. E. D.

REFERENCE

For the culture of Paramecium see also pp. 62, 63, 72, 134, 136, and 177.

CULTIVATION OF PARAMECIUM AURELIA AND P. MULTIMICRONUCLEATUM

T. M. SONNEBORN, *Johns Hopkins University*

OF THE many media tried, the most successful is an infusion of 1.5 gms. of desiccated (but not burned), powdered lettuce boiled for 3 minutes in a liter of double distilled water. This infusion is filtered while hot, dispensed into pyrex test tubes or flasks, containing an excess of pure $CaCO_3$ (which adjusts the pH to about 7.2), plugged with cotton, and autoclaved. When ready for use, it is filtered to eliminate the $CaCO_3$ and is inoculated with the bacterium, *Flavobacterium brunneum,* grown on beef-agar slants, and the alga *Stichococcus bacillaris*, grown on 0.05% Benecke's agar slants. The bacterial slants may be used when 1 to 5 days old; the algal slants when 18 to 24 days old. The quantities inoculated into the culture fluid are one 1-mm. loop level full of bacteria and three 2-mm. loops of algae to 20 cc. culture fluid.

Isolation cultures may be carried on depression slides by using two drops of this fluid per depression. Such cultures must be renewed daily by transferring one Paramecium to freshly inoculated fluid on a fresh slide. The optimum temperature is 27°-28° C.

Mass cultures may be carried in cotton-stoppered flasks by using the same fluid. Such cultures must be made frequently to keep the Paramecia in good condition, but the organisms will live for three months or more in a greatly depressed condition without renewal of fluid.

REFERENCES

For the culture of *Paramecium aurelia* see also pp. 105 and 120.
For the culture of *Paramecium multimicronucleatum* see also pp. 113, 115 and 128.
For the culture of *Paramecium bursaria* see pp. 55 and 105.

PARAMECIUM MULTIMICRONUCLEATUM; MASS-CULTURING, MAINTAINING AND REHABILITATING MASS-CULTURES, AND SECURING CONCENTRATIONS

EDGAR P. JONES, *University of Akron and University of Pittsburgh*

MASS-CULTURING

VARIETY in composition is one of the outstanding characteristics of infusions in which Paramecia are to be mass-cultured. There appears to be no single method of successful culturing. In general, *small* quantities of materials, usually organic, must be introduced into water to induce bacterial multiplication. These bacteria are the chief food supply of the Paramecia, at least in the earlier stages of the culture. Liebig's beef extract (Woodruff and Baitsell, 1911), mangle beet water (Glaser and Coria, 1930), sewage (Butterfield, Purdy, and Theriault, 1931), lettuce leaves (Dimitrowa, 1930), wheat (Turtox Leaflet No. 4), bananas (Turtox Leaflet No. 4), timothy hay (Petersen, 1929), Horlick's malted milk (Jennings and Lashley, 1914), gelatin or curd placed under earth, meat, pond lily leaves, red cabbage leaves, and soil are some of the materials which are reported to have been used. Such diverse organic materials may be boiled in water, or they may be allowed to macerate. When the infusion is ready, it may be autoclaved, especially if portions are to be preserved for future use; or it may be used without sterilization.

Slight variations of the above techniques require the introduction of algae (Raffel, 1930), yeast (Lund, 1918), or bacteria (Phelps, 1934) into infusions such as the above. Certain investigators adjust osmotic pressures, pH, or other ionic concentrations by adding salts or other compounds. Such techniques are not essential to the production of excellent mass-cultures of Paramecia, although they will enhance the uniformity of the medium. The present discussion is limited to cultures of *P. multimicronucleatum* grown in infusions prepared by boiling hay or hay-flour combinations in water. The following is a formula which I have employed frequently and successfully:

> 1 gram hay
> 0.1 grams white flour
> 700 cc. distilled water

Stir the flour through the hay. Bring the water to a boil. Add the hay-flour mixture. Boil 10 minutes. Cool. Add distilled water to replace that evaporated. Seed with 200 Paramecia on the second day.

The above formula may be considerably altered, especially in routine work, without materially interfering with the production of a satisfactory population. Permissible variations include the use of hay up to 4 grams if flour be omitted (Jones, 1930); the use of tap or pond water if nontoxic; and variation in the date of seeding and the number of seed Paramecia introduced.

Additions of hay or flour in excess of the amounts stated will produce a hydrogen-ion concentration which will destroy the Paramecia on the fourth or fifth day (Jones, 1930) (pH 4.83 or less). The "seeding" must, under such circumstances be delayed until the pH exceeds 5.0. In the presence of such excesses of food, certain other unidentified split products which result may prove to be toxic, even if the pH be satisfactory. Introduction of excesses of food material must therefore be avoided, either when originally preparing the infusion, or later, if feeding techniques be employed.

Cultures should not be covered if populations of maximum concentration are desired. Non-evaporating cultures made as described above will produce populations of approximately 300 Paramecia per cc. of solution as a maximum, whereas evaporating cultures may eventually yield from 2000 to 4000 per cc.

MAINTAINING AND REHABILITATING MASS-CULTURES

Mass-cultures, especially of the non-evaporating type (in which the cover is placed on the jar, but not screwed down), may be revived by feeding when they approach the point in the cycle of culture conditions at which the Paramecia would normally disappear. When a population of Paramecia is present in a culture it may frequently be increased by the same means. At various times I have with success employed flour, fresh hay infusion, egg, chocolate, peptone solution, or milk as supplemental foods (Jones, 1933). Any simple method of introducing such substances is usually satisfactory if the materials are in a finely divided state or a fluid condition. Flour is introduced by sprinkling approximately ½ gram upon the surface of 700 cc. of infusion in as unlumped a condition as possible, and stirring. A solution of egg may be prepared by breaking an egg into 100 cc. of distilled water in a flask, and shaking with glass beads. Sterile technique may be employed, but I have not observed that it materially alters the end result.

Other investigators report temporary revival of declining cultures secured by introducing sugar (McClendon, 1909), bread (Bauer, 1926), or fresh hay infusion (Kudo, 1931); and the culture has been maintained for a year, in one instance (Kudo, 1934) by occasionally introducing a few grains of wheat and a few pieces of timothy hay.

The degree of success which may be had in maintaining mass-cultures by feeding is indicated by the following preliminary report of the first which I so tested. This was a 700 cc. culture, loosely covered, made in accordance with the formula furnished above. Controls were initiated in similar fashion.

In the controls, which developed and declined in the usual mass-culture fashion, Paramecia could be found for a period of approximately six months. Dense populations were not present after the initial three months. *The fed culture maintained Paramecia for more than twenty months.* It produced a dense population when fed when fourteen months old, although the Paramecium population had dropped almost to zero while the culture had gone unfed over a summer's vacation which had just preceded. The Paramecia eventually disappeared for no known reason, other than that the culture had not been fed for some time.

To further test the potential longevity of Paramecium cultures, fourteen cultures of a capacity of one gallon were prepared. These received infusion of approximately the same composition, and seed in the same ration per volume as described above. They were seeded November 12, 1932.

It became necessary to feed flour to all of these gallon cultures before they were six months old, because, in every culture the Paramecium population had declined almost to extinction. Six cultures now survive (June, 1935). These cultures have been fed repeatedly, usually only when the Paramecium populations were quite low, whereupon they have characteristically produced larger populations. Flour has been most frequently fed, but milk, glucose, albumin, and ethyl alcohol have been used at times. An epidemic of mold which destroyed the Paramecia appeared in practically every culture to which ethyl alcohol was fed.

At the present time, the six of the series which now retain populations

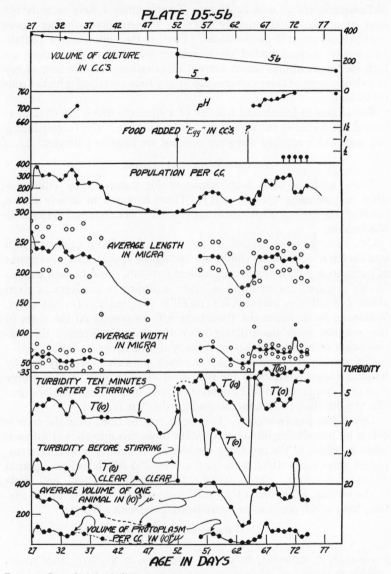

FIG. 44.—Record of the decline of a Paramecium population as well as its later rehabilitation after feeding egg. The abscissa represents time in days, beginning with the 27th day. The Paramecium population was near its maximum. The ordinate presents the following data: volume of infusion; pH; dates when egg was added, with the approximate amounts; *concentration* of Paramecia/cc.; average lengths and widths of 10 living animals, with maxima and minima indicated; turbidity of the culture before stirring (To), and 10 minutes after stirring (Tio); the average volume of single animals in thousands of cubic micra, and the average volume of Paramecium protoplasm maintained per cc. of infusion in millions of cubic micra.

of Paramecia are *30 months of age*. To this group I have recently fed flour at approximately weekly intervals to determine whether dense populations can still be produced. Four of the cultures now contain an average concentration of 300 to 400 per cc. Such concentrations are high for large cultures which are not evaporating. To the best of my knowledge, none of these cultures has at any time contained a higher concentration.

Reductions in length and number of Paramecia which are characteristic of the declining culture are graphed in Fig. 44. The corresponding increases which resulted when egg was fed are likewise indicated.

SECURING CONCENTRATIONS

These methods have been employed for concentrating either rotifers or paramecia (Jones, 1932). There is reason to believe that a considerable variety of protozoans and small metazoans will respond in like fashion.

Concentrations not needed for two days. Distribute cultures which contain Paramecia among containers having the approximate dimensions of quart fruit jars, filling each container half full. Add to each enough freshly prepared, cooled infusion, made according to the formula given above (variation is permissible), to fill it completely. Do not cover. Within 40 to 60 hours the Paramecia will congregate on the sides of the container at or immediately below the surface. Remove the concentration with a pipette having a finely drawn tip and a bulb.

Concentrations for immediate use. Such concentrations may usually be picked up directly from the bottom of an older culture, if a longer pipette is employed. The Paramecia secured by such methods are usually smaller than those concentrated by the first method.

Debris-free concentrations. Paramecia may be freed from the culture debris by introducing into concentration tubes the animals and infusion taken by either of the preceding methods. For this purpose I have employed glass tubes which were 30 cm. long and which had an internal diameter of 8 mm. The organisms, following introduction, will settle to the bottom, after which they will systematically migrate to the surface, from which position they may be removed with a pipette.

BIBLIOGRAPHY

BAUER, FREDERICK. 1926. *Science* 64:362.
BUTTERFIELD, C. T., PURDY, W. C., and THERIAULT, E. J. 1931. *Pub. Health Repts.* 46:393.
DIMITROWA, ARIADNE. 1930. *Arch. f. Protist.* 72:554.
GLASER, R. W., and CORIA, N. A. 1930. *J. Exper. Med.* 51:787.
JENNINGS, H. S., LASHLEY, K. S. 1914. *J. Exper. Zool.* 14:393.
JONES, EDGAR P. 1930. *Biol. Bull.* 59:275.
———— 1932. *Science* 75:52.

——— 1933. *Univ. of Pittsburgh Bull.* 29:141.
KUDO, R. R. 1931. Handbook of Protozoology. Springfield, Ill. C. C. Thomas.
——— 1934. *Turtox News* 12:127.
LUND, BARBARA L. 1918. *Biol. Bull.* 35:211.
McCLENDON, J. F. 1909. *J. Exper. Zool.* 6:265.
PETERSEN, W. A. 1929. *Physiol. Zool.* 2:221.
PHELPS, AUSTIN. 1934. *Arch. f. Protist.* 82:134.
RAFFEL, DANIEL. 1930. *Biol. Bull.* 58:293.
Turtox Service Leaflet No. 4, General Biological Supply House, Chicago, Ill.
WOODRUFF, L. L., and BAITSELL, G. A. 1911. *J. Exper. Zool.* 11:135.

CULTURING PARAMECIUM CAUDATUM IN OAT STRAW INFUSION

GEORGE A. SMITH, *Eugenics Record Office*

AN EXCELLENT medium for culturing *Paramecium caudatum* for a rapid population growth is an oat straw infusion. After having experimented with various types and concentrations of culture media made from timothy hay, oat straw, barley straw, oak leaves, elm leaves, clover, alfalfa, *etc.*, oat straw was found to be the most favorable medium for rapid growth of my strain of Paramecium.

Cut 15 grams of oat straw into short lengths (1-3 cm. long) and place in a quart glass container. Pour 900 cc. of boiling distilled water over the straw. Plug the container with cotton and allow the mixture to cool. Adjust the pH to 7.8 with NaOH. The colorimetric method is sufficiently accurate. Keep the mixture at approximately 25° C. temperature for 48 hours. Shake the culture medium until it is thoroughly mixed; again adjust the pH to 7.8 and the infusion is ready to use. Add approximately 250 Paramecia and in a few days a mass-culture should have developed.

For best results make new culture medium every 48 hours and make new inoculations as often, because usually after 72 hours have elapsed the culture medium begins to deteriorate and is not at its best for optimum growth.

By following the above procedure a number of times a colony of rapidly dividing *Paramecium caudatum* can be developed, each animal dividing at an average rate of once every 8 hours. This is considered optimum growth under these conditions.

For culturing animals for classroom use put two or three dozen grains of oats in 1,000 cc. of water and allow the mixture to stand for three days before inoculating with Paramecia. Within a week a mass-culture of the animals usually develops. It is best to keep the culture covered when it is not in use.

REFERENCE

For the culture of *Paramecium caudatum* see also pp. 56, 105, 113, and 119.

A CULTURE METHOD FOR PARAMECIUM MULTIMI-CRONUCLEATUM AND OXYTRICHA FALLAX

A. C. GIESE, *Stanford University*

BOTH of these may be grown in 0.1% lettuce infusion. The lettuce for this infusion is obtained by drying lettuce leaves in an oven and pulverizing. The proper weight of lettuce is boiled in 0.005 M. KH_2PO_4 solution for 3 minutes, after which the infusion is titrated to a pH of 7.0 with NaOH. The particles of lettuce may be left in or removed. The culture lasts longer if the particles remain. Usually 15 cc. of such an infusion was seeded with 20 to 100 Paramecia or Oxytrichae. It is quite satisfactory for rough work to use tap water instead of the buffer solution.

Order HETEROTRICHIDA
Family PLAGIOTOMIDAE

THE CULTIVATION OF NYCTOTHERUS OVALIS AND ENDAMOEBA BLATTAE*

Nyctotherus ovalis from the hindgut of the cockroach, *Blattella germanica*, may easily be cultured in a modified Smith and Barret (1928) medium. This medium was used by the discoverers for *Endamoeba* (*Entamoeba*) *thomsoni*, and according to Lucas (1928) it is suitable for the cultivation of neither *Endamoeba blattae* nor *N. ovalis*. The medium used by Smith and Barret consists of 19 parts of 0.5% NaCl to 1 part of inactivated human blood serum. By substituting non-inactivated rabbit serum for the human serum a medium is produced in which *N. ovalis* lives and multiplies freely. Dividing forms are common, and occasionally precystic and cystic forms are met with. Three cultures have been maintained for 40 days and at the last examination the organisms were as normal in appearance as those found in their native habitat. Subculturing is done at weekly intervals, and the cultures are maintained at room temperature.

The cultivation of *E. blattae* has been less successful than that of *N. ovalis*. Two cultures out of twelve attempts were maintained for 29 days. At the end of this time the organisms were few in number but entirely normal in appearance and movement. One 2- and one 8-nucleate form were seen, the latter with nuclei of different sizes and evidently precystic. The next examination was negative. This gradual dwindling in number does not necessarily indicate an unfavorable environment, but

* Reprinted with slight changes from an article in *Science* 76:237, 1932, by HARRY E. BALCH, *University of California*.

rather that division is not frequent enough to permit weekly subculturing without gradually diminishing the number of organisms to the point of extinction. Longer intervals between subcultures result in an overgrowth of bacteria and the small flagellate *Monocercomonas orthopterorum*.

REFERENCES

For the culture of Blepharisma see p. 60.
For the culture of *Spirostomum ambiguum* and *S. teres* see p. 60.
For the culture of *Nyctotherus cordiformis* see p. 69.

BIBLIOGRAPHY

LUCAS, C. L. T. 1928. A study of excystation in *Nyctotherus ovalis* with notes on other intestinal Protozoa of the cockroach. *J. Paras.* 14:272.
SMITH, N. M., and BARRET, H. P. 1928. The cultivation of a parasitic Amoeba from the cockroach. *Ibid.* 14:161.

M. E. D.

Family BURSARIIDAE

A METHOD FOR CULTURING BURSARIA TRUNCATELLA*

AMOS B. K. PENN, *Tsing Hua University, Peiping, China*

ADD 1 gram of timothy hay, 1 gram of rye, and 5 grams of fresh cabbage to 600 cc. of spring water. Boil slowly for 5 minutes. Let stand uncovered for 2 days to allow development of bacteria, then remove the cabbage, add 500 cc. spring water, transfer 250 cc. of the solution with corresponding amounts of hay and rye to each of several ½ liter jars and inoculate with Paramecium, Colpidium, and Chilomonas. After 2 or 3 days, *i.e.*, when these organisms have become abundant, inoculate with Bursaria. Cover the jars and keep them in indirect sunlight at room temperature.

If a film of gummy substance has developed on the surface of the infusion, break it. If no gummy substance is present, add some from an old culture.

A culture thus prepared reaches a flourishing condition (10± individuals per cc.) in 2 or 3 days, and continues in this condition for 3 or 4 days. If the infusion is more dilute, the cultures flourish longer, but the Bursaria does not become so abundant.

REFERENCES

For the culture of *Bursaria truncatella* see also p. 103.
For the culture of *Balantidium coli* see p. 118.
Family Stentoridae
For the culture of Stentor see pp. 64 and 134.
For the culture of *Stentor coeruleus* see pp. 60 and 103.
Order Oligotrichida

* Reprinted from *Anat. Rec.* 54:99, 1932, at suggestion of the author.

Family Halteriidae
For the culture of Halteria see pp. 100 and 177.

Order HYPOTRICHIDA
Family OXYTRICHIDAE

UROLEPTUS MOBILIS*

THIS organism, appearing in considerable numbers in an old hay infusion that had been standing for several months, was successfully cultivated and abundant material for study of all the important phases of the life history was secured.

After attempts to cultivate Uroleptus on fresh hay infusion failed, this medium was discarded and boiled flour water, 24 hours old, was substituted. To make this, 150 mg. of white flour is boiled for 10 minutes in 100 cc. of spring water and allowed to stand exposed to the air for 24 hours.

With this medium it was found that the organisms would live and would divide about once in three days. Later, a more satisfactory medium was obtained by mixing 2 parts of the flour water, 2 parts of spring water, and 1 part of old hay infusion. .This improved medium was used for nearly 3 months, the individuals dividing approximately once a day. Finally a still better medium was obtained by boiling 100 mg. of chopped hay with 130 mg. of flour in 100 cc. of spring water for 10 minutes and diluting this, when 24 hours old, with an equal part of fresh spring water. With this medium made fresh every day, the organisms divide from one to three times per day.

As in previous culture work, a single individual is transferred to about 200 mg. of the culture medium contained in a flat, 40-mm. square, ground glass, hollowed dish, 8 mm. in thickness. On the following day the number of individuals is counted and a single individual from these is then isolated and transferred to fresh culture medium made the day before. After an individual is transferred to fresh medium, the remaining individuals are placed in a Syracuse dish containing about 10 cc. of the fresh culture medium. Here they multiply in large numbers, constituting the "stock" material, the source of dividing and conjugating forms.

M. E. D.

REFERENCES

For the culture of Oxytricha see p. 64.
For the culture of *Oxytricha fallax* see p. 128.
For the culture of Stylonychia see p. 64.

* Abstracted from a paper in *J. Exper. Zool.* 27:293, 1919, by GARY N. CALKINS, *Columbia University.*

METHODS FOR CULTURING PLEUROTRICHA*

Amos B. K. Penn, *Tsing Hua University, Peiping, China*

Pleurotricha may be cultured in a hay-rye infusion with Colpidium as food or in a physiological medium with Chlorogonium as food. For experimental work, the latter method is preferred.

A 0.2% hay and 0.2% rye infusion is prepared by boiling in a beaker for 8 minutes 1 gm. of hay and 1 gm. of rye in 600 cc. of spring water. After it has been boiled and cooled, there are about 500 cc. of solution. Then half of the rye grains are removed, leaving the other half with all the hay in the solution. This is then transferred to a battery jar of 1 liter capacity and left for two days, in order to allow bacteria to grow. When the infusion is 2 days old and contains many bacteria, it is inoculated with Colpidium (or Chilomonas). After 24 hours, there are numerous Colpidia present in the infusion. This is then inoculated with Pleurotricha. From time to time rich cultures of Colpidia raised separately [See also p. 51.] are added to the jar as additional food supply.

When doing physiological work where bacteria and organic matter are to be avoided, a physiological medium consisting of all inorganic salts may be prepared according to the formula given below:

$$CaCl_2 \dots\dots 0.0008 \text{ N}$$
$$NaNO_3 \dots\dots 0.0003 \text{ N}$$
$$MgSO_4 \dots\dots 0.0002 \text{ N}$$
$$K_2HPO_4 \dots\dots 0.0001 \text{ N}$$
$$KH_2PO_4 \dots\dots 0.0001 \text{ N}$$
$$NH_4NO_3 \dots\dots 0.0008 \text{ N}$$

In culturing Pleurotricha, Boveri dishes of 50 cm. capacity provided with covers may be used. Place 20 cm. of this medium in each Boveri dish. Add to each dish one pipette of concentrated culture of Chlorogonium, cultivated separately with the same medium. Then transfer one or several pleurotrichs into each dish. Cover and place the cultures in the bright part of the room. Pleurotrichs so cultivated are large and uniform, morphologically and physiologically. They divide four times a day. With this high rate of fission, a single individual may give rise to several hundred individuals in a few days.

References

For the culture of *Pleurotricha lanceolata* see p. 107.
Family Euplotidae
For the culture of Euplotes see p. 63.
For the culture of *Euplotes patella* see p. 60.
For the culture of other hypotrichs see p. 136.

* See also *Arch. f. Protist.* Vol. 84, 1934, and *Science* 80:316, 1934.

STYLONETHES STERKII*

BOTH protective and reproductive cysts of *S. sterkii* remain viable when dried. This discovery made possible a transfer of the new hypotrich from Plymouth, England, to Stanford University, where the strain was continued. The following wheat infusion method of culturing was used exclusively. Twenty grains of wheat were cracked and then boiled in 15 cc. of glass-distilled water for from 3 to 5 minutes. The fluid containing numerous starch grains was used immediately after cooling and was transferred to the culture by means of a pipette having a bore of 1.5 mm.

Experiments have shown that thriving cultures are most easily maintained when complete evaporation of the medium takes place at intervals. Consequently, the organisms were grown in watch glasses holding conveniently about 4 cc. of fluid. These were ordinarily enclosed in petri dishes to prevent evaporation and to facilitate handling, but when mass encystment and complete evaporation of the medium was desired, the cover was removed. Or, the cover may be partly removed so that it protects the watch glass from dust but leaves a wide open gap between the two dishes. Within 8-10 hours, at a temperature varying from 15-22° C., the cultures were completely dried out.

New cultures were started daily when free-swimming individuals were wanted for study. By means of a mouth pipette 20 organisms from a thriving culture were transferred to a watch glass containing 4 cc. of tap water and a drop of fresh wheat infusion. A drop of infusion was added daily to old cultures until protective cysts began to appear (2-4 days). Then they were allowed to dry out. Thus it may be arranged that there are always on hand about as many new cultures as old ones, and a reserve supply of dry cysts. If the study of active organisms is to be suspended for a few days or weeks, it is safe to rely upon the stock of dry cysts to begin new cultures, as was proved by the transfer of cysts in watch glasses from England to California. These cysts were about 3 weeks old when they arrived. Excystment occurred in 3 to 4 hours after distilled water or tap water had been added.

M. E. D.

Order PERITRICHIDA, Family VORTICELLIDAE

A METHOD FOR INDUCING CONJUGATION WITHIN VORTICELLA CULTURES

HAROLD E. FINLEY, *West Virginia State College*

Materials: Columbia culture dishes, depression slides, culture tubes,

* Abstracted from a paper in *J. Mar. Biol. Assoc.* 19:707, 1934, by LAURA GARNJOBST, *Stanford University.*

moist chambers, platinum loop, non-absorbent cotton, alfalfa hay, wheat kernels, glass-distilled water, spring water, La Motte buffer mixtures of known pH, agar-slant cultures of the bacterium *Achromobacter liquefaciens*. From the materials listed above prepare the following:

Standard liquid nutrient: 2 grams alfalfa hay, 3 grams wheat kernels, 100 cc. glass-distilled water. Boil 5 minutes, pour off the liquid, filter it, restore to the original volume (100 cc.) by adding glass-distilled water, sterilize under 15 pounds' steam pressure for 10 minutes.

Activating liquid, solution I: 5 cc. sterile standard liquid nutrient, 10 cc. filtered sterile spring water, 1 loopful *Achromobacter liquefaciens*. Approximate pH value 6.2.

Activating liquid, solution II: Dilute 2 parts of a freshly prepared activating liquid solution I to 50 parts by adding glass-distilled water; to 5 parts of a La Motte buffer mixture of known pH (best results obtained when buffers are in the range pH 6.2 to 6.8 inclusive) add 3 parts of the dilute activating liquid. Thus activating liquids may be prepared in the pH range of the buffers.

Method: Prepare a cyst culture by obtaining 50 or more organisms in a Columbia culture dish; then the glass cover for the dish should be sealed in place with petrolatum and the vessel set aside in a moist chamber until starvation and lack of oxygen induces encystment. Activate the cysts by removing the old culture fluid from the dish containing the cysts; wash cysts in three changes of distilled water and cover them by adding either solution I or solution II. At room temperatures of 20° to 24° C., excystment begins within 30 to 55 minutes after activation. Conjugation begins approximately 14 hours after activation, reaches its maximum intensity at the end of 24 hours and begins to decline at the end of 36 hours. The duration of conjugation epidemics may be prolonged for a variable period of 12 to 36 hours by removing all except a few drops of the liquid from the culture dish and adding fresh activating liquid; best results are obtained when this change is made at the time when the conjugation epidemic begins to subside. The method is invariably successful for *Vorticella microstoma*, *V. convallaria*, and *V. nebulifera* var. *similis*. The excystment technique is a modification of the one described by Barker and Taylor (1933).

REFERENCES

For the culture of Vorticella see also pp. 60, 134, and 136.

BIBLIOGRAPHY

BARKER, H. A., and TAYLOR, C. V. 1933. Studies on the excystment of *Colpoda cucullus*. *Physiol. Zool.* 6:127.
LA MOTTE. 1933. The A. B. C. of pH control. Baltimore.

Miscellaneous Classes and Microbiology

A NOVEL METHOD OF OBTAINING PROTOZOA

W. H. DAVIS, *Massachusetts State College*

FOR years, when I taught zoology, I placed small, green grass culms (in April) in covered jars with wet cotton in the bottom. These remained in an upright position against the glass surface. When Amoeba, Arcella, Stentor, Paramecium, Vorticella, *etc.*, were desired, I scraped dead plant tissue from the surface of the stems or mashed the rotten leaves and incubated 24 hours in a 1% aqueous solution of citric acid.

For the region where this method was developed it did·not fail for five consecutive years to produce the desired results.

PERMANENT CULTURES*

Very frequently instructors are required to keep protozoan cultures over long periods of time. The following method has been used with great success for such cultures as Paramecia, the smaller forms of Amoeba, and certain forms of flagellates.

A large number of hay infusions are started in ordinary drinking-water tumblers, using pond water from different localities. They are then placed in various positions about the room and examined from time to time until the proper culture has been found. When a desired culture is found it should be fed five or six scrapings of dried whole wheat bread. These scrapings are made by taking a scalpel and scraping a crust of bread, care being taken to feed only what the culture will utilize. The glasses are then covered and the process repeated every two weeks or so. Whole wheat bread is far superior to ordinary wheat bread.

Using the above method I have kept ordinary classroom cultures alive for a period of a year. It is also excellent for maintaining such cultures as rotifers and small crustaceans.

FOOD ORGANISMS FOR MARINE AND HALOBIONT ANIMALS

R. M. BOND, *Santa Barbara School, Carpinteria, California*

Dunaliella salina is a large green, yellow, or orange flagellate of world-wide distribution in natural and artificial brines of various compositions. It is most easily obtained from salt-works recovering salt from seawater by solar evaporation. It may sometimes be raised from crude sea-salt, and I once recovered it from seawater from Monterey Bay.

Pure cultures, free of all other organisms, may be grown in any of the

* Reprinted from *Science* 64:362, 1926, by FREDERICK BAUER, *Rhode Island State College.*

ordinary inorganic or organic culture media made up in seawater. Miquel seawater is very satisfactory. [See p. 33.]

D. salina tends to die out in competition with other organisms, except in inorganic media containing 10-20% NaCl. It should, therefore, be kept in a stock culture of Miquel seawater plus 10% NaCl, or in some other equally concentrated medium, and subcultured (if necessary) in a more dilute medium before use.

The cultures should be kept in strong light, though direct sunlight should be avoided in young cultures. The organism can grow throughout a wide temperature range, but 30° C. or just below seems to be optimal.

Dunaliella viridis is always green, and is much smaller than *D. salina*. It seems to do best in a medium of 5-10% salinity. Otherwise, the statements made about *D. salina* hold equally true for this organism.

Platymonas subcordaeformis is a small, green 4-flagellated alga. It is found in saline waters (up to 8-10% salinity) in warm-temperate regions, and is probably of wider range than has been reported. It is frequently found, often in very rich cultures, in spray-pools above tide line on rocks frequented by sea birds. It may sometimes be recovered from seawater.

It grows rapidly and well in seawater (even considerably diluted seawater) to which Miquel's solutions have been added, so that no concentrated stock culture is required.

Light and temperature requirements are as for *Dunaliella salina*.

REFERENCE

For the culture of Ankistrodesmus see p. 227.

WHEAT-GRAIN INFUSION

JOHN W. NUTTYCOMBE, *University of Georgia*

THE culture medium here described has been used constantly for nine years and has proven extremely satisfactory for culturing a wide variety of aquatic invertebrates. Its chief advantages lie in the ease of preparation, wide range of use and the relatively long period of time required for the culture to reach its maximum.

In practice we add 200 or 300 grains of seed wheat to about 250 cc. of spring water in a flask. This is heated over a burner until the water comes to a sharp boil and is then allowed to cool. If it is desired that the cultures reach a maximum more quickly the boiling is continued for several minutes so as to make the contents of the wheat grains more quickly available.

We usually boil spring water to kill the free organisms in it, allow it to cool to room temperature, distribute it in dishes* holding 200 cc. each, and place 3 or 4 grains of the prepared wheat in each dish of water. The dishes are now stacked and allowed to stand 2 or 3 days, during which time enough air is dissolved to make the medium ready for inoculation. If it is desired to immediately inoculate the dishes the water may be artificially aerated.

In general this first inoculation is made with material (bacterial glea, *etc.*) from successful cultures and after considerable growth has set up around the wheat grains (in 3 or 4 days) we subculture into the dish the particular organism desired from the best of the previous cultures.

Initial cultures of an organism are made in the same way except that inoculations are made from the medium in which the organism was collected.

We have made no attempt to control the pH of our cultures within any narrow limits but the range has been between 7.05 and 7.40. Our spring water generally has a pH value of about 7.05, a two-weeks culture about 7.40 and a two-months culture about 7.12. There is some slight seasonal variation in the water which we use.

We have cultured very successfully in this medium the following groups of fresh-water invertebrates:

Protozoa—Several species of Amoeba, Actinophrys, various Difflugia, Chilomonas, Peranema and many other small flagellates, Paramecium, Vorticella, several hypotrichs, and many other Infusoria.

Plathelminthes—Catenula, some 15 species of Stenostomum, Microstomum, and small triclads.

Nemathelminthes—Several species of freshwater nematodes.

Rotifera—Some 20 species.

Annelida—Several species of oligochaetes.

Bryozoa—Plumatella.

Arthropoda—Copepoda, Cladocera, Ostracoda, Hydracarina, mosquito and midge larvae.

We especially recommend this method as a means of maintaining constant supplies of Amoeba for class use. We have for 5 years maintained cultures in the original dishes by simply pouring out the water from each dish every two months and adding fresh water (boiled, cooled, aerated) and 3 or 4 grains of boiled wheat. A sufficient number of Amoebae stick to the bottom of the dish when the water is poured off to seed the culture.

---

* The ice-box dishes (Hazel Atlas Glass Company) which we use for most of our general culture work may be purchased for 10 cents each at any 10-cent store. They have a capacity of 400 cc.; they may be stacked; and they may be obtained in either clear or green glass. These dishes are, for general purposes, quite as satisfactory as the much more expensive pyrex dishes sold for such purposes.

Phylum II

PORIFERA, Class *Noncalcarea*

NOTES ON THE CULTIVATION AND GROWTH OF SPONGES FROM REDUCTION BODIES, DISSOCIATED CELLS, AND LARVAE

H. V. WILSON, *University of North Carolina*

PRODUCTION OF, AND GROWTH OF SPONGES FROM, REDUCTION BODIES

SPONGES (*Stylotella heliophila*) are placed in outside aquaria, concrete or wooden tubs, covered with glass and not in direct sunlight. The sponges should be clean, raised from the bottom on bricks; half a dozen to an aquarium 60 cm. in diameter and 30 cm. deep. The aquarium (tub) is emptied, filled, and flushed for some minutes three times in every twenty-four hours. Reduction begins in a day or two. In the course of two or three weeks gradual death of the tissues coupled with reduction leads to the formation of many small living masses of varying shape lodged on and through the skeletal network of the sponge. In the most striking cases these masses are numerous, more or less spheroidal and small, 1 to 1½ mm. in diameter. Such a dead and macerated sponge body with its contained nodules of brightly colored living tissue suggests a Spongilla full of gemmules. The histological structure of nodules varies with their age, but is very simple, although many details in the process of reduction are unknown.

The reduction bodies have regenerative power. If enclosed in bolting cloth bags and hung in a live box they quickly transform into sponges. Probably with a very excellent water supply the transformation could be induced in the laboratory.

Similar bodies have been produced in the Calcarea (Otto Maas) and in freshwater sponges (K. Müller). (See Wilson, 1907a.)

GROWTH OF SPONGES FROM DISSOCIATED CELLS

A sponge (*Microciona prolifera*) is cut up into small bits about 3 mm. in diameter, which are allowed to fall on a piece of fine bolting cloth supported on the edge of a stender dish and semi-immersed. The cloth is then folded like a bag around the bits of sponge, is partially immersed in a small dish of filtered seawater, and while it is kept closed with the fingers of one hand is repeatedly squeezed between the arms of a small forceps. The pressure and the elastic recoil of the skeleton break up the tissue into its constituent cells and these pass out through the pores of the cloth into the surrounding water. The cells fall to the bottom and may be sown with a pipette on any desirable substratum (slide, cover glass, or oyster shell) immersed in a culture dish of seawater. Or the cells, as pressed out, may be allowed to fall at once on the definitive substratum. The cells attach in the course of an hour or so and the slide or other body may be removed to a fresh dish of water or to a running water aquarium, where it should be raised well above the bottom and protected from the force of the current. Attachment will usually take place by means of coarse reticula which remain permanently attached. Reticular pieces if partially freed from the slide will curl up and form balls, the size of which is under control. Such balls may be transferred to slides in other dishes or in running water aquaria. A convenient vessel to use is a porcelain-lined bucket, in which the slides rest on inverted bottles and are so brought near the surface of the water, the current entering at the bottom. By changing the water two or three times a day, such an arrangement serves in place of a running water aquarium. The balls attach and sponges of desired size may be obtained. The attached reticula or balls metamorphose and in the course of a few days will have transformed into incrusting sponges with functional canal systems. Such cultures are easily kept for long periods of time in small wire gauze cages hung in live boxes. Lobular outgrowths and even embryos have developed in sponges treated in this way.

Modifications in this method of growing sponges have been introduced by J. S. Huxley, K. Müller, P. Galtsoff, M. E. Fauré-Fremiet, M. E. de Laubenfels, J. T. Penney, P. Brien, and others. (See Wilson, 1907 and 1911.)

GROWTH OF SPONGES FROM CILIATED LARVAE

Mycale (Esperella) fibrexilis has embryos during July-August at Woods Hole, Mass. Larvae are liberated, sometimes at once, on placing the sponge in an ordinary 2 gallon glass aquarium jar. Larvae are picked out with a pipette and transferred to culture dishes where they may be kept by changing the water several times a day. They attach in a day or two. They may be made to attach to cover glasses or if they are to be used as section material it is convenient to coat the dish with a thin layer of paraffin and let them attach to this. Little pieces of paraffin with the attached and metamorphosing larvae may then be cut out, fixed (paraffin and sponge), and hardened, the sponge often detaching itself from the paraffin.

Other halichondrine sponges (Lissodendoryx, Microciona) breed during the summer (July-August) at Beaufort, N. C.; Stylotella during October in the same locality. Larvae may be reared in the same way or may be placed in wire gauze cages after attachment and hung in a live box.

In sponges in general, fertilization is internal and the egg develops in the body of the parent to the stage of the ciliated larva. Sponge eggs and embryos are commonly abundant in a breeding sponge and may be seen scattered through the interior with the naked eye. In some marine sponges asexual masses analogous to spongillid gemmules develop likewise in the body of the parent into ciliated larvae. In order to obtain larvae all that is necessary is to place a breeding sponge in an aquarium jar. (See Wilson, 1894.)

GROWTH OF SPONGES FROM FUSION LARVAE

The ciliated larvae of *Lissodendoryx carolinensis* may easily be made to fuse with one another after they have begun to creep over the bottom of the culture dish and are thus approaching the phase in which they attach. It is only necessary to bring them in contact, coaxing them together with needle and pipette in a deep, round watch glass. The compound larva so produced has a feeble locomotory power. Using pairs that are nearly motionless, fusion masses of desired shapes may be produced on cover glasses. Or small excavations may be made in paraffin-coated dishes, and the larvae driven into such holes in large numbers. In this way, cake-like masses may be produced measuring 3-4 mm. in diameter. The smaller compound masses metamorphose without difficulty. The larger in the actual experiments died, sometimes after a partial metamorphosis. (See Wilson, 1907.)

BIBLIOGRAPHY

WILSON, H. V. 1894. Observations on the egg and gemmule development of marine sponges. *J. Morph.* 9:277.

——— 1907. On some phenomena of coalescence and regeneration in sponges. *J. Exper. Zool.* 5:245.

——— 1907a. A new method by which sponges may be artificially reared. *Science* 25:912.

——— 1911. Development of sponges from dissociated tissue cells. *Bull. U. S. Bur. Fish.* 30:1.

Phylum III

COELENTERATA, Class *Hydrozoa*

HYDRAS

LIBBIE H. HYMAN, *New York City*

Collection. Hydras most commonly occur attached to the submerged vegetation, fallen leaves, or other objects in pools, ponds, lakes, and the slow portions of rivers. They are collected from such habitats by gathering a quantity of vegetation and placing it in jars with a relatively small amount of water. As the vegetation begins to decay, the hydras usually come to the top of the jar or the surface film and may be picked out and transferred to suitable containers. One species, *Hydra littoralis*, occurs in enormous numbers on the under surface of stones in streams, spillways, and along shores subject to wave action. When the stones are turned over, this species appears like an orange jelly on the stone. They may be obtained in large numbers by squirting the animals from the stone into a pan by means of a squirter made from an atomizer bulb and a glass tube. Unfortunately this species is not very suitable for laboratory cultivation, but is useful when large numbers are needed for a short time, or when large quantities of hydras are wanted for preservation. Hydras are sometimes found in large numbers attached to the surface film and in such situations are easily gathered. They do not in general live in stagnant water but require rather clean water with adequate oxygen supply.

Laboratory cultivation. The most suitable hydra for laboratory cultivation is the brown hydra, *Pelmatohydra oligactis*, but any of the species which live in standing water may be grown successfully in the laboratory. The species which inhabits moving water, *Hydra littoralis*, mentioned above, may be grown in the laboratory if the water contains a supply of algae or other vegetation to keep up a high oxygen content. The author has not tried bubbling air through a culture of this species but such a procedure would probably be successful. The green hydra, *Chlorohydra viridissima*, is one of the most hardy hydras, very common everywhere, and easy to maintain in the laboratory except for one difficulty. It is difficult to find a food crustacean which is small enough to be ingested by the green hydra. Cultures of the green hydra should be exposed to the light, but for other species a moderate light is best.

The first prerequisite of laboratory cultivation of hydras is suitable water. Hydras should never be put into freshly drawn tap water and in general only natural pond or river water should be used for their culture. If tap water must be used, it must stand for several weeks with growing algae or other aquatic plants in it so that it may become conditioned. The suitability of water for hydras should be tested by placing a few specimens in it. If these expand fully, with tentacles extended to their maximum extent, the water is suitable. In unsuitable water, the column remains contracted and the tentacles fail to expand. The presence of plants is not necessary in a hydra culture except in the case of *Hydra littoralis,* as stated above.

When a suitable water has been found, the hydras are placed in it, and fed daily. At intervals, the accumulation of bottom debris should be removed and small amounts of suitable water may be added from time to time. In general it is desirable that the cultures be covered.

In general hydra cultures succeed better if the temperatures are not too high; 20° C. is a very suitable temperature. The brown hydra, *P. oligactis,* is more susceptible to rise of temperature than any other species and usually dies at 25° C.

The great difficulty in the continuous culture of hydra is the occurrence of the phenomenon of depression. In spite of every care, hydra cultures will pass into this state at intervals and, unless prompt measures are taken, will die out. In depression, column and tentacles fail to expand, the animal ceases to feed, shortens to a stumpy appearance, and finally gradually disintegrates from the tips of the tentacles aborally. Depression is caused by over-feeding, fouling of the water, too high temperatures, and general aging of the culture with accumulation of waste products. The most successful method of reviving the animals from the depressed state is to transfer them to a fresh jar of suitable water. Lowering the temperature is also of assistance.

Sex organs when wanted for class display may be induced in most species of hydra, notably in the brown hydra, by placing the culture in a refrigerator for two or three weeks at a temperature between 10 and 15° C. Such cultures should be fed regularly. In nature most species are found with sex organs in the late fall but the green hydra is said to be sexual in the summer.

Food. Naturally for the continued maintenance of hydra in the laboratory it is necessary to have a food source that is easily cultured. The most suitable animal for this purpose is Daphnia because of its slow movements, weak resistance, and habit of moving about continuously.* Some other cladocerans such as Simocephalus are easily cultivated also but are too strong and powerful for the hydras or else tend to stay on the bottom out of reach. Hydras will not eat ostracods. Oligochaete worms are eagerly accepted but their habits are such that the hydras would seldom have a chance to catch them. The very tiny newly hatched Daphnia in a Daphnia culture may be used as food for *Chlorohydra viridissima;* some small forms such as Ceriodaphnia or the bosminids are suitable and may be grown like Daphnia. [See pp. 207-220.] In case of necessity hydras may be fed on oligochaetes such as naids, tubificids, or enchytraeids, and often these may be purchased from pet shops. It is necessary to cut these up into pieces and to place the pieces in contact with the tentacles with a dropper or forceps; otherwise they fall to the bottom where they are out of reach of the hydras. This method of feeding is very time-consuming, but may be used when it is desired to save valuable experimental material. Experimental material which does not feed well of its own initiative, may often be fed successfully by placing a crushed daphnid, Cyclops, or bit of oligochaete in contact with the tentacles.

Tubificids are easily maintained in the laboratory for food by placing them in containers having two or three inches of pond mud on the bottom. For food, almost any kind of organic material such as boiled lettuce leaves, boiled wheat grains, pieces of bread, or bits of animal flesh, may be added from time to time.

THE CULTURE OF SOME MISCELLANEOUS SMALL INVERTEBRATES

PAUL BRANDWEIN, *Washington Square College, New York University*

Hydra. These animals are maintained in great numbers in balanced aquaria when they are fed constantly with any of the Entomostraca mentioned below.

Plathelminthes. Stenostomum may be cultured using the method used for Paramecium. [See p. 63.] Planaria are usually cultured in enameled pans containing clear pond or spring water; they are fed with boiled egg yolk or fresh liver, care being taken to remove the excess food at the end of a few hours before putrefaction occurs. The Planaria are cut transversely when they reach the size of about 8-12 mm. with a oo cover glass; regeneration occurred rapidly.**

* Editor's Note: William LeRay and Norma Ford, of the University of Toronto, call attention to the fact that in contrast to the grey hydra (*H. vulgaris americana*) the brown species (*Hydra* [=*Pelmatohydra*] *oligactis*) stings its prey only when it needs it for food. Thus in a culture of the brown form the uneaten Daphnia continue to live. The grey hydra on the other hand stings to death any Daphnia which it happens to touch and on the bottom of its culture bowl there will be found a ring of the dead crustaceans. M.E.D.

** This method for Planaria does not differ significantly from the procedure recommended by the commercial houses which supply this organism.

Rotifera. Philodina is easily cultured by either the method of Stylonychia [See p. 64.] or of Paramecium. [See p. 63.]

Entomostraca. Cyclops, Canthocamptus, Diaptomus, Cypris, and Daphnia have been cultured with moderate success by the following method. Two grams of egg yolk, ground into a paste, are added to a gallon jar filled with green pond or aquarium water. This is allowed to stand for about three days and then inoculated with small Protozoa (any species not larger than Colpoda). Next the organism to be cultured is introduced—for Cyclops, Canthocamptus, and Diaptomus a few males and egg-bearing females will suffice, but for Daphnia and Cypris, as many individuals as possible are added. Within a month successful cultures will show organisms in abundance, a condition which will last some 6 weeks.*

Annelida. Microdrilli, such as Nais, Aelosoma, and Dero have responded splendidly to culture in 30 cc. of Solution A (see footnote on p. 73) added to rice-agar as in the case of Amoeba [see p. 72]. The medium in this case, however, should stand for three days before inoculating with the annelids (about 5 will suffice). The number of these organisms can be increased by using larger vessels, *i.e.,* allowing for more fluid and increasing the surface area of the agar.

Class *Scyphozoa*

REARING THE SCYPHISTOMA OF AURELIA IN THE LABORATORY**

F. G. GILCHRIST, *Pomona College*

THE scyphistoma of Aurelia proves to be a very hardy marine form; it may be maintained alive and in fairly active state of budding by keeping it in shallow dishes of seawater (it is well to have the seawater slightly hypotonic) and feeding with ground shrimp or particles of meat. Of course the water should be changed after feeding. The scyphistoma does best with a mixed diet. Scyphistomas have been reared at marine laboratories, using plankton tow (Delap, 1905, 1907) or sea urchin ovaries (Herouard, 1909).

BIBLIOGRAPHY

DELAP. 1905. *Rep. of Sea and Inland Fisheries of Ireland* for 1902 and 1903.
——— 1907. *Ibid.* for 1905.
HEROUARD. 1909. *C. R. Acad. Sci.* Paris, p. 148.

*For Daphnia, the cultures require a temperature of 17-19° C. This was obtained by circulating cold water through a coil of glass tubing (6-8 mm.), set within the gallon jar.

** Editor's Note: For a more complete description of the methods of rearing *Aurelia aurita* and other medusae see Hagmeier, A.: Die Züchtung verschiedener wirbelloser Meerestiere. *In* Abderhalden, 1927-1933: *Handbuch der Biologischen Arbeitsmethoden* Abt. 9, Teil 5:553-562. P. S. G.

Class *Anthozoa*

SAGARTIA LUCIAE

Donald W. Davis, *The College of William and Mary*

Sagartia luciae may be collected at any season from tide pools, piles, rocks, and seaweed within its range—Atlantic coast, Massachusetts to Virginia; also Oakland Harbor, San Francisco Bay. It lives indefinitely in the laboratory with slight care and reproduces freely asexually, but has not been known to reproduce sexually under laboratory conditions. Specimens should be placed in seawater of a depth of one or two inches and exposed to diffuse sunlight. The glass container may well be covered lightly to reduce evaporation and to exclude dust. For the first few days after bringing specimens into the laboratory care should be exercised that the water does not become foul through decomposition of fragments of the specimens, of undigested food that they may eject, or of other organisms that do not survive the change. It is, therefore, advisable to change the water occasionally during the first few days. If economy of the water supply is required, it should be filtered and may then be used over and over.

These anemones thrive in tide pools of a rocky coast and gentleness is not essential. Before long a growth of algae appears on the dish and takes care of the oxygen supply. Probably it provides directly or indirectly for the food requirements of the anemones as well, for specimens thrive without special provision for feeding. They will take minute fragments of fish, crab, or beef. If so fed, only firm fragments, not juicy materials, should be used and the greatest care must be taken that fragments, uninjested or voided after a few minutes or hours, be not left to foul the water.

One other precaution is of much importance. If specimens are left undisturbed, a zoogloea-like coating, probably consisting of slime with imbedded organisms, covers the column and eventually the whole contracted specimen. At intervals of two or three days each such coat should be removed from the dish after being separated from the anemone by means of a gentle stream of water directed at its attachment to the glass. Occasionally rain water should be added to compensate approximately for evaporation.

BIBLIOGRAPHY

Davis, Donald W. 1919. Asexual multiplication and regeneration in *Sagartia luciae* Verrill. *J. Exper. Zool.* 28:161.

REARING CORAL COLONIES FROM CORAL PLANULAE

THOMAS WAYLAND VAUGHAN, *Scripps Institution of Oceanography*

DURING my field work on the corals of Florida and the Bahamas from 1908 to 1915, an endeavor was made to rear coral colonies from planulae in order to ascertain the growth rates of young colonies of the different species. Although the technique used in collecting and rearing planulae and young colonies has been described in a number of publications, all that is essential is contained in those at the end of this note.

The colonies from which it was hoped to obtain planulae were brought from the sea into the laboratory and placed in glass vessels which were deep enough for the specimens to be covered with seawater, but not so deep as to interfere with noticing any planulae that were extruded. Since the water on the parent colonies kept in the laboratory had to be pure, it was necessary to change the water on specimens kept for several days. This was easily done by siphoning the stale water from around the specimens and pouring fresh water into the vessels.

The planulae which were extruded were removed by pipettes and transferred to vessels that contained objects on which it was expected that they would settle.

In my work on the corals of Tortugas, planulae were obtained from five species, as follows: *Astrangia solitaria, Favia fragum, Agaricia purpurea, Porites clavaria, Porites astreoides.* The species with which most success was obtained were *Favia fragum* and *Porites astreoides.* The duration of the free-swimming larval stage is variable both for the same species and for different species. The duration for *Favia fragum* was 6 to 23 days; *Agaricia purpucea,* 11 to 17 days; *Porites clavaria,* 12 to 20 days; *P. astreoides,* 7 or 8 to 22 days.

An effort was made to have the planulae settle on tiles (terra-cotta discs) having a central perforation by which they might be fitted over the heads of iron stakes. The tiles had a diameter of 8 inches and were placed in jars, the inside diameter of which was about 8.25 inches and the depth about 8.5 inches. After the bottom of a jar had been covered with clean sand, a tile was placed in it and the central perforation and the space between the periphery of the tile and the sides of the jar were filled with sand to the level of the upper surface of the tile. As the planulae tend to settle in depressions, it was necessary to fill these spaces. After this preparation, fresh seawater was gently poured in through a funnel until the jar was nearly full. The extruded planulae were pipetted from the vessels containing the parent colonies and placed in the culture jars.

The water in the culture jars must be fresh and pure. It may be changed by one of several devices. In order not to draw off the planulae, which are very small, a bag of fine-mesh bolting cloth must be affixed to any tube used in withdrawing the stale water. One method was to siphon off the stale water with a rubber tube, the end of the tube inserted into the culture jar having been drawn over one end of a glass tube, the other end of which was enveloped in a bolting cloth bag. The table on which the culture jars stood was provided with a gutter into which the water drawn off was discharged, ultimately flowing outside the building through a pipe through the floor. After a jar had been emptied to within an inch of the tile, it was refilled with fresh seawater. This method caused a change in the level of the water, and by the pouring stirred up the unattached planulae.

A second method, which was the one usually employed, was to withdraw the old water by a glass siphon resting on the upper edge of the jar, the siphon having been rendered non-emptying by having its outer end bent upward. The inner end of the siphon was enclosed by a bolting cloth bag. Fresh seawater was added by a siphon extending to the bottom of the culture jar from a supply jar placed at a higher level. By this method a constant level was maintained in the culture jars; the old water was drawn off from the top while the new water was added at the bottom. A third method was to have inside the culture jar a tantalus siphon emptying through the side of the jar near its bottom. Fresh water was siphoned into the culture jar from supply jars placed at a higher level. When the water in a culture jar had reached the level of the upper curvature of the siphon, it began to run out and continued to flow until the level of the open end of the siphon in the jar was reached. The jar was then refilled by the afferent siphon until the level of the upper curvature of the tantalus siphon was again reached, when the water again began to flow out. This method caused a rise and fall in the level of the water. A fourth method was to cut the bottom out of a culture jar and to place the glass collar thus produced over a tile in a jar of larger diameter, the bottom of which had previously been covered with sand to a depth of an inch or slightly more. The tile and its surrounding collar were sunk into the sand until the upper surface of the tile and the upper surface of the sand were level with each other, while the level of the upper edge of the collar remained slightly higher than that of the enclosing jar. Water was siphoned into the collar from supply jars, and filtered through the sand filling the space between the collar and the side of the inclosing jar. When the level of the upper edge of the jar was reached, the water overflowed. This method maintained a constant level of water, drew off old water at the bottom, and added new water at the top.

All four methods were successful, but as the second was somewhat the more convenient it was, as stated above, the one used in most of the experiments.

After the planulae had attached themselves to the terra-cotta discs and had begun to form small colonies, the discs were affixed to the heads of iron stakes driven into the sea bottom at convenient places where the discs would always be submerged at the lowest tides. Through the end of the stake, which extended through the central perforation of the disc, there was a hole in which an iron pin was placed. This pin held the disc firmly on the head of the stake. By this means colonies of both *Favia fragum* and *Porites astreoides* were reared to an age of five years. The diameter of the colonies of *Favia fragum* for colonies five years old ranged from 28.5 to 38 mm., that of the colonies of *Porites astreoides* ranged from 41 to 99.75 mm. The height of the colonies of *Favia fragum* at five years of age ranged from 13.5 to 22 mm., that of colonies of *Porites astreoides* ranged from 18 to 54.4 mm.

BIBLIOGRAPHY

VAUGHAN, T. W. 1910. The recent Madreporaria of southern Florida. *Carnegie Inst. of Washington, Year Book* 9:135.

—— 1911. The Madreporaria and marine bottom deposits of southern Florida. *Ibid.* 10:147.

—— 1919. Corals and the formation of coral reefs. *Smithsonian Inst. Publ.* 2506, Report of 1917:189.

Phylum V

PLATHELMINTHES, Class *Turbellaria*

Order RHABDOCOELIDA, Family CATENULIDAE

CULTURE OF STENOSTOMUM OESOPHAGIUM

MARGARET HESS, *Judson College, Marion, Alabama*

CULTURE medium for *Stenostomum oesophagium* is prepared in the following manner:

Boil 250 cc. of water with 8 to 10 grains of wheat for one minute; allow to stand exposed to the air for 24 hours; remove about two-thirds of the wheat grains and inoculate with a mixed laboratory culture of Protozoa.

Introduce *Stenostomum oesophagium* into this culture 24 hours or more after the addition of the Protozoa. The presence of other Turbellaria, oligochaetes, and small Crustacea has no harmful effect on *Stenostomum oesophagium*.

Varying temperatures have little effect on *Stenostomum oesophagium*, although room temperature has been found the most satisfactory for rapid growth and multiplication. Likewise they are able to withstand variations in hydrogen-ion concentration. The best cultures show a pH range of 5.8 to 7.6.*

CULTIVATION OF STENOSTOMUM INCAUDATUM**

T. M. SONNEBORN, *Johns Hopkins University*

THIS turbellarian may readily be cultivated in mass or in isolation pedigree cultures if fed copious supplies of the ciliate Protozoan, *Colpidium campylum*. The basic medium is prepared by boiling for 10 minutes 15 grams of whole rye grains in one liter of spring water. This infusion is filtered while hot, cooled, inoculated with 1 cc. of a similar

---

*Editor's Note: Concerning two other species of Stenostomum, Jeanette Seeds Carter states (*J. Exper. Zool.* 65:159, 1933) that *S. grande* is naturally cannibalistic and that in *S. tenuicauda* cannibalism is not a normal phenomenon. J. G. N.

** Condensed by the author from: Genetic studies on *Stenostomum incaudatum* (*nov. spec.*). I. The nature and origin of differences among individuals formed during vegetative reproduction. *J. Exper. Zool.* 57:57, 1930. (See pp. 62 and 63.)

1-day old infusion, and allowed to stand at 10° to 14° C. for 1 day. Then the ripened infusion is inoculated with Colpidia, placed in a 9-inch petri dish, and allowed to stand for 4 days. After this time the culture is centrifuged for 30 seconds at 1800 revolutions per minute. The Colpidia form a dense, almost solid mass at the bottom, where they may be separated from the supernatant fluid and the middle layer of debris. The concentrated Colpidia should then be diluted to about 15 cc. with 1-day old rye infusion.

Stenostomum incaudatum may be cultivated in isolation pedigree lines by placing one Stenostomum in a single drop of this fluid on a depression slide. Temperatures of 20° to 26° C. are favorable. The culture fluid should be renewed daily, by transferring one Stenostomum to a fresh slide with fresh, concentrated Colpidium fluid. Mass cultures may be reared in similar rye infusion to which heavy growths of Colpidium have been added. These cultures must be renewed before the supply of Colpidia gets low.

REFERENCES

For the culture of Stenostomum see also pp. 136 and 142.
For the culture of Catenula see p. 136.

Family MICROSTOMIDAE

THE CULTURE OF MICROSTOMUM

M. AMELIA STIREWALT, *University of Virginia*

MICROSTOMUM is particularly sensitive to very small traces of such poisons as are used in chemical reagents. In the selection of glassware to be used in the culture of these animals, therefore, care must be taken that dishes, pipettes, *etc.*, have had no contact with fixing and staining reagents. Petri dishes have proven most successful as aquaria because the large, flat, bottom surface presents ample space for the benthal habits of Microstomum. In these dishes the animals may easily be seen with the naked eye, especially if the culture is placed over a dark background. Both stender dishes and larger culture dishes, however, will serve as aquaria, though the small capacity of the former necessitates frequent change of the culture medium, and the large size of the latter makes close observation of particular animals impossible.

Into the aquarium selected, in the approximate proportion of 9-1, place spring water (from a non-limestone district) and water containing small detritus from the bottom of the stream or pond in which the Microstoma were collected. It is best that no animals be present which can be seen with a magnification of 20. To this medium may then be added such Cladocera as Cypris, Daphnia, and their relatives [see pp. 207-220], and such Copepoda as Cyclops [see p. 227]. Of aerating value are a few branches of Elodea or a small mass of Spirogyra or both. In this culture the Microstoma may then be placed. Microstoma living in the presence of water plants are more active and of larger size than those living in control cultures without these plants. In such a culture the animals may be expected to thrive indefinitely, if at intervals some of the detritus be drawn off with a clean pipette and replaced with fresh water, and if food be supplied regularly.

The food which serves best, in my experience, is the annelid Dero [see p. 143]. Every two or three days the Microstoma should be fed small, freshly cut sections. Enough should be placed in the culture to supply each Microstomum with three or four pieces, for the animals eat voraciously when in a healthy condition. The Dero may be cut easily by means of two small needles used in criss-cross fashion. The pieces should not exceed the size of the Microstoma and must be freshly cut. If the food has been prepared for an hour or more before feeding, the wounded surfaces of the annelid heal, thus cutting off the flow of the fluid by which the Microstoma sense the presence of the food most readily. In such case, or whenever the Microstoma seem insensible to the presence of food, they may find and eat it if several pieces are freshly cut in the culture.

Other conditions being favorable to growth, the size of the Microstoma is directly related to the amount of food consumed. Animals with six zooids often occur in vigorous cultures. On the other hand I have had Microstoma live in favorable cultures for two weeks without feeding. Under such conditions they become progressively smaller until they die from starvation.

The foods eaten by Microstomum under my observation, listed in order of preference, are: Dero, Hydra, liver (tadpole and mammalian), Cypris, Daphnia, Cyclops, Difflugia, Pristina, egg yolk, Stentor, desmids, and Nematodes.

Hydra, as food for Microstomum, deserves special mention. It seems to act as a tonic for animals which are not in good condition as evidenced by their lack of response to food. If, as sometimes occurs, the Microstoma cannot sense food, or refuse it, fragments of hydra, fed in the same way as the annelids, will rejuvenate them.

REFERENCE

For the culture of Microstomum see also p. 136.

GEOCENTROPHORA APPLANATUS

WILLIAM A. KEPNER, *University of Virginia*

THIS member of the group Alloeocoela may be cultured in spring water to every 200 cc. of which 5 cc. of wheat infusion has been added. (Wheat infusion: 10 seeds wheat in 250 cc. spring water. Boiled one minute. Set aside for one week. This infusion may be used thereafter for two months.)

The specimens have been fed with food described by Margaret Sanslow in the *Bull. of Averett College* (Danville, Va.), Vol. 1, No. 4, 1935.* To a small dish containing 205 cc. of water there has been added as much food as will cling to the moist tip of a very small scalpel. This food is cut into very short lengths and then ground in a depression slide with the rounded end of a small glass rod, after which it is placed in the culture dish. The specimens will find this food within fifteen minutes if it is not widely distributed.

Order TRICLADIDA, Family PLANARIIDAE

CULTURE OF PLANARIA [=EUPLANARIA] AGILIS

ROSALIND WULZEN, *Oregon State College* and
ALICE M. BAHRS, *St. Helen's Hall Junior College*

PLANARIA for use in nutrition experiments are collected in the field by placing small lumps of fresh liver in shallow water at the edges of ponds or streams where they are known to be present. They gather on the liver in a short time and may be rinsed off into collecting jars. They should not be crowded in the jars or they will be dead before the laboratory is reached. Likewise, they should not be crowded in the laboratory containers. For stock containers we use white enameled milk pans, because in these the worms may easily be inspected to determine their condition. A city water supply containing chlorine is not to be trusted. For some time it may appear to be harmless but when one observes that the worms are more restless than usual, that is, all the worms in a container are in motion for an extended period of time, one should suspect that the tap water contains too much chlorine. The restless stage is followed by one in which the worms secrete large quantities of mucus and roll away from contact with the container. They gather in writhing masses and will disintegrate if they are not put into

---

*Editor's Note: This food consists of shrimp, corn flakes, shredded wheat, lettuce, spinach, and sea lettuce. These last two ingredients are dried quickly in a flower press. All the materials are separately powdered to medium grains with mortar and pestle and mixed together in amounts such as to provide 50% protein, 31% carbohydrates, 2% fats, 12% minerals, and 5% bulk by volume. M. E. D.

chlorine-free water. We use river or well water collected directly from the source.

After the worms have been distributed in the stock pans they must be treated as though in quarantine for about a month. Every day they must be inspected carefully and any worm showing the slightest irregularity in outline or surface texture must be removed. We have found that the worms come to the laboratory infected with parasitic diseases which develop quickly under the abnormal conditions of a laboratory environment. These diseases are capable of spreading and of annihilating a large part of the stock. If one is to have stock reliable enough for experimentation, all disease must be eliminated, and with care this is easily accomplished. We always boil all water to be used on the worms in order to avoid the introduction of any disease-producing parasite. If at all possible, the water used should be perfectly clear because we have found that even slightly muddy water reacts unfavorably on the worms.

The laboratory routine in the care of the stock is as follows. The worms are washed every other day. This is done by plunging the hand into a lysol solution and then rinsing until no odor of lysol remains, for very slight amounts of lysol are highly poisonous for the worms. Then with the fingers the pan is wiped over its whole surface to loosen the dirty slime which always gathers. The worms settle at once to the bottom and all the water is poured away and replaced by fresh water. If the pan does not appear clean, this is repeated. Once a week the worms are washed into freshly sterilized pans and the dirty pans are thoroughly cleaned and sterilized.

Our stock worms are fed exclusively on raw liver and they continue in vigor and health for an indefinite period of time. The source of the liver must be considered because not all liver has correct nutritional value for the worms. For example, rat liver is poor food while beef liver is almost always excellent. We use liver taken from freshly-killed guinea pigs which are in prime condition. This has been found the best stock feed we have tried because we can control the diet of the animals furnishing the liver, and this is the determining factor in the production of nutritionally correct liver. If the stock is merely being maintained it is sufficient to feed once a week. The feeding is done by placing a small piece of liver in each stock pan. The worms feed readily and the liver is left with them for 3 or 4 hours. It is then removed and the stock pans are thoroughly washed. If one wishes to develop the stock rapidly, the worms should be fed twice a week.

To rear new worms for experimental purposes it is of course only necessary to cut the stock worms into pieces of suitable size and to allow time for regeneration. We always cut off the posterior extremities of the worms, the length of the piece cut off depending upon the size of the worm. We separate these tail pieces into pans by themselves and allow them to stand without feeding for a period of 4 weeks, at which time they have attained the adult shape and are ready for nutritional experiments.

We keep our experimental worms in an incubator with a temperature of 24° C., but the stock and regenerating worms are kept in the laboratory with the heat turned on at night during the cold season. If the worms become thoroughly chilled many or all of them will die. This happens above the freezing point and makes it wisest to keep the stock pans away from cold windows.

PLANARIA

WILLIAM LeRAY and NORMA FORD, *University of Toronto*

FOR eight years a culture of *Planaria* [=*Euplanaria*] *maculata* has been kept under observation and fed very successfully with enchytraeid worms. The animals were collected in a large pond and a selection was made of the individuals which would accept the enchytraeid worms as food.

The planaria are kept in a wooden tub (24 inches in diameter and 11 inches deep), charred on the inside, and are fed about once a week. Approximately 2000 individuals are maintained in this space. When fed, a level teaspoonful of worms is dropped over the bottom of the tub. Several planaria will cluster over each worm and so share the food. The amount of food given is regulated by the growth of the planaria: if they are getting smaller, more enchytraeid worms are offered; if more individuals are needed, additional food will speed up their growth and reproduction.

When large numbers of planaria are needed for class material, we are careful not to disturb the tub for two or three days. A film then forms over the surface of the water. To bring the planaria to the surface, the sides of the tub are tapped with a hammer. Each animal is then picked out with a fine glass rod which is slipped under its dorsal side as it floats ventral side up. The planaria folds its dorsal surface around the rod and it is then dropped quickly into a dish for study. Without the film on the surface of the water the planaria will not stick to the rod.

COLLECTION AND CULTURE OF PLANARIA

GEORGE R. LA RUE, *University of Michigan*

BAITING for planaria by the method described by Hyman (*Trans. Amer. Micr. Soc.* 44:79, 1925) may not always be practicable. Planaria often occur in abundance, sometimes by hundreds, on the lower surface of stones or submerged boards in swiftly flowing water below dams, in the riffles of streams, or on wave-washed shores of lakes. If such waters are not frozen over, collections may often be made in mid-winter. Stones or boards should be removed from the water and the lower surfaces examined for planaria. When found in suitable numbers scrape the worms off into dishes or pails of water, or bring in the small stones with worms adhering.

Planaria may usually be secured in considerable numbers by bringing in masses of submerged vegetation. Cover this material with water, preferably pond water or untreated tap water in large glass jars or aquaria, and allow decay to start. The worms will collect on the surface of the water and on the sides of the vessel. Transfer them to finger bowls or larger vessels of clean water, and keep the dishes in a darkened place.

Feed planaria on tubificid worms, giving only as many tubificids as will be eaten in 3 or 4 hours. Since these worms are completely ingested and live until eaten, the dishes need not be cleaned as frequently as when liver is fed. Dishes should be washed once or twice a week, but soap and other chemicals must be avoided.

REFERENCES

For the culture of planaria see also p. 142.
For the culture of triclads see also p. 136.

PLANARIANS

LIBBIE H. HYMAN, *New York City*

Collection. Different species of planarians live in different sorts of habitats. Some, notably our most common species, *Euplanaria maculata,* live in ponds, lakes, and the slow parts of rivers on the vegetation and on the under surface of stones, leaves, or other objects. They may be obtained by turning over stones and fallen leaves and washing the animals into a pan by means of a strong squirter made of an atomizer bulb and glass tube. Their presence on vegetation may be ascertained by shaking small samples of the vegetation in a vessel of water. If they are present large quantities of the vegetation should be gathered and placed in pans with a small amount of water. As planarians cannot endure stagnant water, they soon come to the top and may be picked off.

Other species, notably the large dark forms such as *Euplanaria agilis* and *E. dorotocephala,* live in springs and spring-fed streams and marshes. Their presence may be discovered by baiting a suspected habitat with a piece of raw meat placed along the edge, not in the current. After 15 or 20 minutes, the piece of meat should be turned over and planarians, if present, will be found attached to the under side. The entire habitat should then be baited with meat. Fresh raw beef is best and should be cut into pieces 1 or 2 inches wide and 2 or 3 inches long. Such pieces should be distributed throughout the edges of the habitat so as to rest partly in the water, partly above the water. At intervals of 15-20 minutes the pieces should be picked up with a long forceps and shaken off into a jar of water. With a few trials of this sort the best spots in the habitat are soon discovered and all of the meat may be moved to such spots. In preparing such collections for transport back to the laboratory, they should be washed free of bits of meat by several rinsings, and the jars filled not more than ¾ full with fresh clean water from their habitat. A depth of not more than an inch of planarians should be allowed to a pint jar. In bringing them in, care must be taken to avoid high temperatures. The jars must not be set on the floor of a car which is apt to become hot from the engine.

Baiting with meat is usually ineffective with pond habitats and commonly succeeds only with species which live in flowing water. Some species, however, even in flowing water, respond poorly to this method and must be picked from stones and water weeds by hand. Among the species which the author has personally seen or knows may be collected successfully by baiting are: *Euplanaria agilis, E. dorotocephala, Fonticola velata,* and *Phagocata gracilis. Euplanaria maculata* and *Procotyla fluviatilis* usually respond poorly to meat baits.

Laboratory maintenance. Planarians of practically any species may be kept successfully in the laboratory in glass or crockery containers or enameled pans. These should be darkened by means of suitable covers. Treated city waters are not very suitable, but most species will live in such water for a considerable time. Spring or well water is desirable.

Those species mentioned above as collectable by baiting with meat are also the ones which may be kept most easily and successfully in the laboratory. They are fed two to three times a week on beef liver (pig liver is not suitable). Before feeding, the water in the pan should be lowered to a depth of several inches. The liver should be cut into long thin strips and disposed over the bottom. The pan is then covered and left undisturbed for 2 or 3 hours, after which the liver is removed, the pans thoroughly rinsed, and filled with fresh water. Even if the animals are not fed, the water should be changed two or three times weekly as planarians are very susceptible to fouling of the water. All food fragments should be carefully removed. *E. dorotocephala, E. agilis,* and *Curtisia foremanii* are very easily kept by this method for long periods of time in the laboratory; *Fonticola velata* and *Phagocata gracilis* may also be maintained on liver, although not so well as the first-named species. In place of liver, pieces of earthworm, clam, *etc.,* may be used; some forms prefer such food. Yolk of egg drawn out with a dropper into a strand on the bottom has been employed successfully.

E. maculata does not feed very well on beef liver and is less easy to maintain in laboratory culture than the preceding species. It is necessary with this species to grind the liver in a meat grinder and wash it thoroughly in running water. Small bits of such washed liver will usually be accepted as food. This species, however, in general prefers pieces of invertebrate flesh or liver or other flesh of tadpoles, fish, *etc.*

Procotyla fluviatilis is the most difficult of our common species to keep under laboratory conditions as it will eat nothing but live prey, such as daphnids, amphipods, and isopods. It will sometimes accept blood clots, but in general it is impractical for laboratory purposes.

Sexual material. Zoologists at times desire sexually mature material for class or experimental purposes. In general those species which reproduce extensively by asexual methods are seldom found in the sexual state; this statement applies to *E. dorotocephala, E. agilis,* and *Fonticola velata.* *E. maculata* and its various varieties are commonly sexual throughout the U. S. in the summer time and numerous egg capsules will be found on the under side of the stones in the habitat of this species. It is a curious fact, however, that *E. maculata* is apparently never sexual in some localities or regions while always sexual in the summer in others. Sexual specimens will continue to lay eggs under laboratory conditions.

Species which do not reproduce asexually are commonly in the sexual state at some definite season of the year. For *Procotyla fluviatilis,* which, owing to its transparency, is our most suitable species for preparing slides showing the reproductive system, the time of sexual maturity extends from September into the winter or even, in some localities, into spring. *Fonticola morgani* (=*Planaria truncata*) is sexual in summer, as is also *Polycelis coronata* of mountain streams of the northwestern U. S.

The only species which may be depended upon to lay egg capsules regularly under laboratory conditions is *Curtisia foremanii* (=*Planaria simplissima*). This species occurs throughout the Atlantic coast states, may easily be cultivated in the laboratory on beef liver, and will lay egg capsules continuously for a long period. The young soon grow up to sexual maturity and also lay in their turn so that a continuous supply of capsules is assured with this species.

Class *Trematoda*

THE PARASITIC FLATWORMS

H. W. STUNKARD, *University College, New York University*

REPORTS on culture methods for different species of parasitic flatworms, similar to those described for free-living invertebrates, can not be made, because at the present time there is no known culture method by means of which a parasitic flatworm may be maintained in artificial media. Attempts to grow the parasites *in vitro* have resulted in failure, largely because there is no adequate knowledge of their metabolic requirements. Their physiology has been studied very little and the factors which determine host-parasite specificity are quite unknown. The basis of the relationship is chemical and the adjustment has developed gradually during a long period of association. Accordingly, the only course of procedure is to maintain these worms in or on appropriate hosts. The life cycles of most species consist of two or more successive generations which may infest different host species. Certain parasites manifest very close host-parasite specificity while other may complete their development in a variety of different hosts. All members of a natural family follow a similar course of development and it has become clearly evident that types of life cycle are closely correlated with phylogenetic and systematic relations of the worms. A brief account is here given of attempts to culture the trematode, *Cryptocotyle lingua,* and the cestode, *Crepidobothrium lönnbergi. C. lingua* was selected because this species manifests little host-parasite specificity, and *C. lönnbergi* because it is relatively common and, being a parasite of cold blooded hosts, may be studied at room temperature.

The writer (1930, 1932) has reported attempts to culture *Cryptocotyle lingua* and *Crepidobothrium lönnbergi.* The metacercariae of *C. lingua* were washed in dilute seawater and placed in an isotonic salt-dextrose medium. As a result of a series of experiments it was determined that a pH of 6.8 is the optimum hydrogen-ion concentration for the survival of the worms. Specimens remained alive in this medium for 12 days, the medium being changed daily. During this time the young worms did not develop; on the contrary they slowly diminished in size and at the end of the experiment were only about ⅔ as large as when removed from their cysts. It seems that the tissue of the body was utilized in metabolism and that the specimens actually starved to death. When kept at 38°, the worms lived only 6 days, but this result is significant, since sexual maturity is attained in the vertebrate host in about 6 days. Keeping the worms under reduced oxygen pressure did not appreciably alter the degree of activity or time of survival. The worms may live for long periods of time in solutions from which the oxygen has been removed.

To supply accessory food substances, veal was digested and the resulting extract was filtered, adjusted to a pH of 7, and sterilized. Various amounts of this material were added to the salt-dextrose solution to form a culture medium. With the addition of protein material, the media rapidly disintegrates as a result of bacterial growth. The worms did not develop at room temperature. In one experiment the worms were put in nutrient fluid for 3 hours in the morning and for 3 hours in the afternoon, and during the remainder of the day were maintained in the salt-dextrose solutions. By this method the young worms were kept alive for 6 days in the incubator and for 14 days at room temperature, but they did not grow and apparently lived no longer in the veal broth than when the products of protein decomposition were absent.

Specimens of *Crepidobothrium lönnbergi* were removed from the intestine of Necturus and washed in sterile Ringer's solution. They were then transferred to a sterile isotonic salt-dextrose solution. The medium was modified by the addition of different amounts of Hottinger broth prepared by the digestion of veal, and a series of cultures were prepared with pH values from 6 to 8. The cultures which varied around pH 7.3 seemed most favorable. The worms were kept in small petri dishes at room temperature and transferred to new media every 12 hours. In one experiment, young specimens were kept alive for 32 days. During this time they increased 3 to 4 times in length and the terminal portion of the strobila became definitely segmented, but the proglottids were abnormal and sterile. Addition to the media of salt extracts of the intestinal mucosa, pancreas, and liver of Necturus, sterilized by filtration, did not appreciably alter the rate of growth or time of survival. The exclusion of free oxygen by anaerobic culture methods did not affect the result. Fresh serum from Necturus was definitely toxic to the worms.

BIBLIOGRAPHY

STUNKARD, H. W. 1930. The life history of *Cryptocotyle lingua,* with notes on the physiology of the Metacercariae. *J. Morph.,* 50:143.
—— 1932. Attempts to grow cestodes *in vitro. J. Paras.* 19:163.

Order MONOPISTHODISCINEA

EPIBDELLA MELLENI

THEODORE LOUIS JAHN, *State University of Iowa*

Occurrence. *Epibdella melleni* is ectoparasitic on the eyes and epidermis and sometimes in the gill and nasal cavities of numerous marine fishes of the order Acanthopteri. It is believed to be a West Indian species, but it now occurs in the New York, Chicago, and Philadelphia public aquariums. A list of susceptible and of non-susceptible fishes was given by Jahn and Kuhn (1932), and this has been checked and extended by Nigrelli and Breder (1934).

Life History. The anatomy of the adult and the complete life history of the species were described by Jahn and Kuhn (1932). The eggs are tetrahedral and are shed singly into the seawater. These may fall free of the fish or may be caught on the gills, scales, *etc.,* by means of filaments and may accumulate in large numbers in the gill and nasal cavities. In 5-8 days ciliated larvae about 225 microns in length are hatched. These swim rapidly, and some eventually become attached to susceptible fishes. Development into the adult is direct.

Collection and culture. Apparently the organisms may be cultured in any balanced or well aerated closed-system aquarium which contains susceptible fishes, and the problem present in the public aquariums mentioned above is how *not* to culture rather than how to culture them. However, after infection an immunity is developed by certain species which makes the continual introduction of new hosts advantageous. This is discussed by Nigrelli and Breder (1934). In mild infections the cornea is attacked and sometimes destroyed. Loss of eyes due to secondary bacterial invaders may follow. In heavy infections the epidermis may be considerably injured, and the scales may be removed from large areas of the body. Over 2,000 worms have been found on the body of a single fish. Severe infections usually result in death of the host. At the New York Aquarium treatment of infected fishes consists of dipping in "sol-argentum" or similar substances or of raising the density of the seawater by addition of salt (Nigrelli, 1932).

In the work of Jahn and Kuhn the adults and the attached larval stages were obtained by scraping mucus from the eyes and body surface of infected fishes with a sharp scalpel. The mucus was transferred to stender dishes. In about 10 minutes the worms became attached to the bottom of the dishes, and the mucus was pipetted off and the seawater renewed. The process of egg laying, and the movements of the digestive system, *etc.*, were observed with a dissecting microscope within a few hours after collection. The eggs were removed immediately after laying and kept in fresh seawater which was changed several times a day until hatching occurred. The free-swimming larvae were isolated with a pipette. In aquarium systems which contain a filter, the eggs and larvae may be found in the filter chambers in considerable numbers.

This species offers a very good source of live demonstration material for the life history of monogenetic trematodes, and the above methods seem advisable for the investigation of any monogenetic life history which is similar to that of Epibdella. The application of these methods to other species should be of special interest, for there are no other life histories known for the order Monopisthodiscinea. The scarcity of observations on the life histories of members of this group is probably due to the scarcity of well kept closed-system salt water aquaria containing susceptible fishes. Under natural conditions, of course, the free-swimming larvae could be collected only rarely in plankton nets, and this material ordinarily would not be sufficient for the study of life histories.

BIBLIOGRAPHY

JAHN, T. L., and KUHN, L. R. 1932. The life history of *Epibdella melleni* Mac-Callum 1927, a monogenetic trematodè parasitic on marine fishes. *Biol. Bull.* 62:89.

NIGRELLI, R. F. 1932. The life-history and control of a destructive fish parasite at the New York Aquarium. *Bull. N. Y. Zool. Soc.* 34:123.

NIGRELLI, R. F., and BREDER, C. M., JR. 1934. The susceptibility and immunity of certain fishes to *Epibdella melleni,* a monogenetic trematode. *J. Parasit.* 20:259.

Class *Cestoidea*

INTERMEDIATE STAGES OF CESTODES

REED O. CHRISTENSON, *University of Minnesota*

THE most available cestode for general laboratory use is *Taenia pisiformis* which occurs in the body cavity, about the mesenteries, or in the liver of native rabbits as a cysticercus, and comes to maturity in the intestinal tract of dogs and related carnivores. By autopsy of a dozen or so cottontail rabbits, ample material may usually be obtained to establish a permanent laboratory supply.

The parasites, in the infective larval stage, appear as small (pea-sized) vesicles enclosing a head and encased in an adventitious connective tissue capsule. Occasionally worm-like motile stages are found free in the body cavity, or the parasites may be seen as regular white blotches in the liver. These are developmental stages and are not suitable for infection.

Encapsulated cysts are fed with meat to tapeworm-free dogs. In about 5 or 6 weeks an examination of the feces will disclose the terminal segments discharged from the worms. These contain ova composed of the hexacanth embryos covered by the striated embryophore as characteristic of the true taeniae. The ova are easily demonstrated by macerating a segment in water, mounting a drop on a slide, covering and studying microscopically. To infect rabbits, the ova are added to a moist bran mash and fed directly to young animals.

When the ova enter the alimentary canal the hexacanths free themselves of their covering, penetrate the host tissues to the blood stream, and are carried to the liver. Here they migrate about in the tissues for a while and by the 24th day have come to the surface where they appear as regularly contoured white blotches. They migrate again, leaving the liver, and come to lie free in the peritoneal cavity as elongate, worm-like bodies. These ultimately assume a spherical shape and become encapsulated, thus reaching the infective stage.

The behavior of the cysticercus upon liberation is of some interest. They may be studied by teasing away the connective tissue capsules, care being taken not to injure the caudal vesicle of the worms, and placing them in warm saline solution. Many of the parasites will evert their heads and crawl about actively in the container, using their hooks and suckers as they would when liberated in the intestine. These specimens make ideal whole mounts either with or without staining.

The behavior of the hexacanth embryo as it leaves its embryophore may be demonstrated by using *Hymenolepis nana* of rats and mice. Terminal segments of the parasite are chilled in a refrigerator (about 20° C.) for a few hours and are then teased apart in a drop of saline on a slide and covered. The slides are gradually warmed to about body temperature and then studied microscopically. This procedure stimulates many of the hexacanths to action and they may be seen jabbing their minute hooklets at the inner membrane of the embryophore. Occasionally they entirely free themselves.

Cysticercoid stages of the smaller cestodes are often difficult to obtain. They may be found in naturally infected intermediate hosts in areas of high frequency of the adult parasite in its primary host. Our method of obtaining these stages is to kill a series of rats from various localities to find the highest incidence and greatest intensity of infection with *Hymenolepis diminuta*. When this is ascertained, beetles (*Tenebrio molitor*) which serve as the common intermediate host are sought and the adults teased apart in a saline filled Syracuse crystal under a binocular dissecting microscope. The cysticercoids fall away from the surrounding tissues and may be identified by their inverted heads, broadly oval bodies, and elongate caudal processes. As high as 20% natural infection has been found in this way, with as many as 28 cysticercoids recovered from a single beetle.

Phylum VI

NEMERTEA

METHODS FOR THE LABORATORY CULTURE OF NEMERTEANS

WESLEY R. COE, *Yale University*

NEMERTEANS are found under extremely diverse environmental conditions. Many species are strictly littoral, living in the mud and sand, or beneath stones between tide-marks, or in shallow water along the seashore. Others are found upon the sea-bottoms at moderate depths. Still others swim freely suspended as bathypelagic organisms 1,000 meters or more beneath the surface of the great oceans, while a few freshwater species are to be found in pools and streams in all temperate and tropical regions or in water-holding leaves of tropical plants. Several species have acquired terrestrial habits, living in moist earth in tropical or semi-tropical lands, whence they have been accidentally transported to greenhouses in all parts of the world.

The nemerteans have a distinct advantage over many other groups of invertebrates for laboratory culture because, although they are essentially carnivorous, the individuals of many of the small littoral species are able to live for a year or more without other food than that which may be obtained from their own tissues. Several of these may reproduce asexually in the meantime, but sexual reproduction does not occur under such conditions.

LITTORAL SPECIES

The slender *Lineus socialis* of the Atlantic coast, or the similar *L. vegetus* of the Pacific coast, found beneath stones between tide-marks, is easiest to culture since it requires only a covered dish of seawater with a bottom layer of pebbles and sand mixed with a little mud, freshly brought from the nemeateans' natural habitat. This material will supply the necessary small Crustacea, nematodes, and other small invertebrates to keep the animals in good condition for a year or two if the water lost by evaporation is replaced from time to time. Asexual reproduction will occur frequently and egg clusters may be deposited in late winter or early spring, but only if the water is kept below 15° C.

For a study of asexual reproduction or regeneration each worm or tiny fragment may be kept in a separate, cork-stoppered, 6- or 8-dram vial containing clean seawater only, changing the water every day or every few days.

The smaller representatives of each of the orders, except the parasitic Bdellonemertea, may be kept in the same manner but somewhat less successfully. The larger forms naturally require vessels with a generous supply of water and a thicker layer of bottom material.

FRESHWATER SPECIES

Species of Prostoma (Stichostemma) are found adhering to the leaves of aquatic plants in pools and quiet streams in nearly all parts of the United States. They thrive in aquaria containing a good growth of vegetation if supplied with minute Crustacea, nematodes, turbellarians, and other small organisms, but the water must be free from bacterial decomposition. The plants will require a thin layer of soil on the bottom of the aquarium. Excessive evaporation is prevented in arid rooms by partially covering the aquarium with a pane of glass. Prostoma thrives best at temperatures of about 20° C. Egg clusters are deposited along the sides of the aquarium at all seasons of the year.

TERRESTRIAL SPECIES

Greenhouses having soil, temperature, and moisture conditions suitable for the cultivation of ferns and moisture-loving tropical plants are suitable for the culture of Geonemertes. The worms are merely allowed to burrow in the moist soil of the pots or boxes containing the plants. They are protandric, with sexual reproduction only. Egg masses are deposited on or near the surface of the soil.

OBTAINING EGGS FOR EXPERIMENTAL PURPOSES

As stated in the preceding sections, the smaller species, such as Lineus and Prostoma, deposit their eggs in gelatinous clusters when the nemerteans are cultured in the laboratory, and in both these genera the eggs develop readily in the jars or aquaria without special precautions. For studies on maturation and fertilization and especially for experimental work where very large numbers of ova are necessary, the larger littoral forms, such as Cerebratulus or Micrura, are easily secured in the breeding season.

A very large female *Cerebratulus lacteus* which occurs in the intertidal zone along the entire Atlantic coast of the United States may produce at one time upwards of fifty million eggs. These are mature in early spring along the Carolina coasts, during May and June in Long Island Sound, in July at Woods Hole, and during July and August in Massachusetts

Bay and on the coast of Maine. Several species of the same genus on the Pacific coast from San Diego to Alaska furnish equally beautiful ova.

The female Cerebratulus may be kept in a vessel of clean seawater for 3 weeks or more, if the water is changed daily and the temperature is held at about 10° C. But the eggs are less suitable for experimental work after the first week. They are spawned spontaneously under such conditions.

To obtain large numbers of ova or young larvae it is necessary to free the eggs from the body. This is best done by taking a small fragment of the body, placing it in a dish of cool seawater and making a longitudinal slit with sharp knife or scissors on the dorsal surface on each side of the median line. The muscular contractions of the fragment will soon force the ripe ova into the water. After a few minutes as many eggs as are wanted are drawn into a pipette and expelled into a dish of clean seawater. They are thereby washed free of most of the body fluids.

The eggs on reaching the water still have the germinal vesicle intact and are not yet ready for normal fertilization. Immediate fertilization usually results in polyspermy. The stimulus of the water soon results in the formation of the first polar spindle which proceeds to the metaphase and then rests. This stage is reached in 10 to 30 minutes after the egg reaches the water, the time depending both on the temperature and on the ripeness of the eggs. The eggs are then ready for fertilization.

To obtain the sperm a small fragment of a male (which may be distinguished from the female by its brighter color) is placed in a dish of clean seawater and a puncture made through the dorsal body wall. The sperm ooze out in a dense mass. A surprisingly minute quantity of this, when expelled from a pipette into a dish containing the ova, will suffice for complete fertilization. If larvae are desired the fertilized eggs must be provided with a generous supply of clean, cool seawater.

REARING LARVAE

Prostoma and other hoplonemerteans develop directly into young worms without the intervention of a free-swimming larval stage such as is characteristic of Cerebratulus. In Lineus an intermediate condition known as the Desor larva occurs. These larvae require no special feeding, but the pilidium larva of Cerebratulus or of Micrura may be reared to the adult form only by the most careful attention.

The difficulty lies in providing suitable nourishment during the 20 or more days which the swimming larva requires before metamorphosis is completed. Small diatoms and other minute algae may be supplied daily, with frequent changes to clean seawater. A more reliable method is to feed regularly from a pure culture of the smallest obtainable diatoms. The temperature of the water should not exceed 20° C.

METHOD FOR STUDIES ON REGENERATION

In nearly all species of nemerteans the body quickly restores a missing posterior extremity. In some forms this ability is limited to the posterior half of the body, but in others the head and a small portion of the foregut region, or even the head alone, without any part of the alimentary canal, can regenerate all the missing parts. Anterior regeneration is usually limited to the head in front of the brain but a few species, particularly those of the genus Lineus, can reproduce the entire body in miniature from any small fragment except the minute piece anterior to the brain. Even a small sector of a fragment, if it contains a tiny piece of the lateral nerve cord, is likewise endowed with the capacity for complete regeneration and reorganization. Curiously enough, individuals of some species live longer in captivity with the head removed than with the entire body intact, for the reason that the decapitated body is less restless.

Operations for regeneration experiments are usually performed without the use of an anesthetic, although the head may be removed if necessary. The worm is placed in a small pool of cool water upon a beeswax plate having a suitable concavity. Under the binocular dissecting microscope the desired cuts may be made with a cutting blade sharply ground from a curved needle. The fragment is then placed in a vessel or vial of clean water.

In some species the fragments are less restless, and consequently regenerate better, if a few bits of shells or small pebbles or sand grains are placed in the vial or dish. This procedure may sometimes make the difference between the success or failure of the experiment. Food may be supplied after the mouth and digestive tract become functional.

Phylum VII

NEMATHELMINTHES, Class *Nematoda*

RECOVERING INFECTIVE NEMATODE LARVAE FROM CULTURES

G. F. WHITE, *U. S. Bureau of Entomology and Plant Quarantine*

THE method outlined here for recovering infective nematode larvae from cultures makes use of the often-observed fact that toward the close of their free-living period the larvae migrate from the medium in which they have been growing. The simple apparatus used traps the migrating larvae in water (White, 1927).

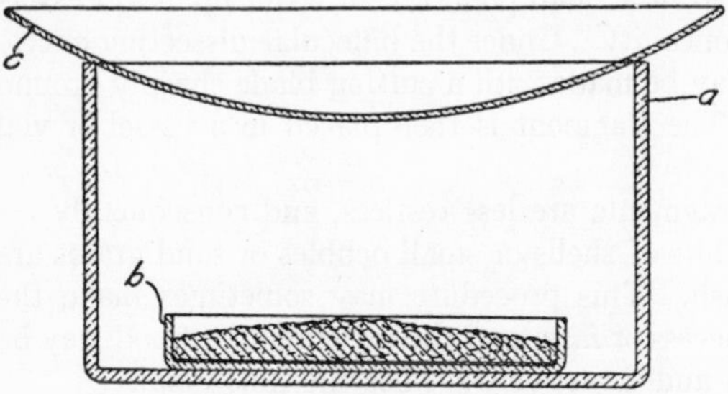

Convenient and sufficient equipment consists of crystallizing dishes 125 to 150 mm. in diameter, watch glasses slightly larger than these dimensions, petri dishes 100 to 125 mm., test tubes 20 by 150 mm., filter papers 9 to 12 cm., a spatula with a 4-inch blade, a test tube rack, a three-quart boiler with cover, animal charcoal, and sterile water. Brief steaming in the covered vessel suffices for the disinfection that is needed.

FIG. 45.—Apparatus used for culturing nematode larvae. a, Crystallizing dish; b, Petri dish with charcoal-feces mixture; c, watch-glass cover. Water surrounds the petri dish equal to about one half its depth.

The charcoal and feces with water added are mixed properly and conveniently in one of the larger watch glasses and transferred to the half of a petri dish, with a moistened filter paper covering the bottom. Sterile water is poured into a crystallizing dish to cover the bottom and into it is placed the half petri dish containing the culture. A watch glass is used as a cover, the apparatus (Fig. 45) after labeling, is placed for incubation preferably where a high humidity may be maintained.

Many of the larvae on approaching the third larval stage migrate from the culture and are trapped in the water surrounding the petri dish. In collecting them the watch glass cover is removed and the half petri dish with the charcoal culture is lifted out, preferably with forceps to avoid infestation. The water containing the larvae is poured from the crystallizing dish into a test tube which is then placed in the rack. The worms soon gravitate to the bottom of the tube, after which the water above may be pipetted off, leaving the larvae concentrated. The apparatus with the charcoal mixture may then be reassembled and steamed.

A number of modifications of the apparatus and the method may be made to meet the worker's special needs. When there is but a small amount of culture it is well to use the half petri dish with the bottom up. A Syracuse watch glass or the top of a Coplin jar serves well in place of the petri dish. Room temperature, especially in summer, may be substituted for the more constant one of an incubator.

A modified form of the apparatus has been used to reduce somewhat the amount of fungous growth in the culture when this seemed desirable. An aluminum pan of the diameter of the crystallizing dish, with the inclined side perforated, is placed beneath the watch glass cover and supported by the edge of the dish. Into the pan is poured a few cc. of an aqueous solution of formalin. A 15% solution has been employed successfully, but the optimum strength should be determined by each worker to meet his own needs.

While using the method one soon learns of its limitations and its advantages. The larvae are recovered from the cultures in relatively clean water. Only infective forms are obtained. A considerable leeway is permitted as to the time larvae may be collected from the apparatus. The first larvae trapped may be poured off, more water added, and the apparatus reassembled for later migrations. Frequently additional ones may be had by transferring the charcoal culture to the Baermann apparatus (Darling, 1911).

The method was found to be convenient and efficient in studies on and in the diagnosis of hookworm and other nematode infestations (Fülleborn, 1921) and in studies on the biology of the causal parasites (Cort, Stoll, and Grant, 1926).

In making studies on the migration of nematode larvae, Looss (1911) trapped them in water but apparently did not employ the observation in devising a routine method for obtaining larvae from cultures.

Among those who have taken advantage of the migrating tendency of larvae in devising methods suitable for their studies is Darling (1911), who used Syracuse watch glasses in the center of which he placed 3 to 5 cc. of stool and added sterile water until the feces were surrounded with fluid. The worms for study were taken from this margin of water. Fülleborn (1921) also made use of this habit, employing agar plates. The charcoal-feces mixture was placed on this medium in the center of the petri dish. The infective larvae migrating from the culture over the agar cause their trails to be inoculated with bacteria. By the growth of these the courses taken by the worms are readily observed.

BIBLIOGRAPHY

CORT, W. W., STOLL, N., and GRANT, J. B. 1926. *Amer. J. Hyg.* Monog. Ser. 7:19.

DARLING, S. T. 1911. Strongyloides infections in man and animals in the Isthmian Canal Zone. *J. Exper. Med.* 14:1.

DOVE, W. E. 1932. Further studies on *Ancylostoma braziliense* and the etiology of creeping eruption. *Amer. J. Hyg.* 15:664.

FÜLLEBORN, F. 1921. Nachweis von Ankylostomum durch Plattenkot-cultur. *Vorl. Mitteilg. Arch. f. Schiffs und Tropenhyg.* pp. 121-123.

LOOSS, A. 1911. The anatomy and life-history of *Anchylostoma duodenale* Dub. *Recds. of Egypt Govt. Sch. of Med.,* Cairo, IV.

WHITE, G. F. 1927. A method for obtaining infective nematode larvae from cultures. *Science* 66:302.

WHITE, G. F., and DOVE, W. E. 1928. The causation of creeping eruption. *J. A. M. A.* 90:1701.

———— 1929. A dermatitis caused by larvae of *Ancylostoma caninum.* *Arch. Dermat. and Syph.* 20:191.

Order HOLOGONIA, Family TRICHINELLIDAE

REARING TRICHINELLA SPIRALIS

REED O. CHRISTENSON, *University of Minnesota*

THE difficulty of isolating developmental stages of *Trichinella spiralis* has restricted its laboratory use often to mere demonstration of the cysts and, more rarely, the adults. It is feasible, however, with a little experience to have on hand for laboratory use ample material of all stages of the parasite in the living condition. The main difficulty lies in obtaining the original infection. Usually a routine examination of wild rats about abattoirs or packing houses will yield material. If this source fails, infected animals may often be obtained from other laboratories.

When trichinosed tissue is obtained a number of animals should be fed to maintain a supply. Rats are ideal, but guinea pigs and rabbits may be used with good results. Cats are more difficult to handle but are ideal animals in which to maintain the infection over long periods of time.

Shortly after the ingestion of infective meat the larvae are liberated from their cysts by the action of the digestive juices. This may be done experimentally by placing infected tissue in an artificial gastric juice composed of water, 1,000 cc.; hydrochloric acid, 10 cc.; scale pepsin (U. S. P.), 2.5 grams; and sodium chloride, 5.0 grams. Small quantities of finely cut meat are stirred up in the mixture and incubated at 38° to 40° C. for 18 hours.

Under natural conditions larvae liberated in the stomach soon make their way to the intestine where they mature in upwards of 48 hours. The isolation of intestinal forms may be achieved with little difficulty.

Nearly grown rats are maintained without food for 48 hours and are then each fed separately a thumb-sized piece of heavily trichinosed tissue. At the desired time (after 48 hours to get early adults) an animal is killed with chloroform and the intestine removed to a stender dish containing warm saline solution. Previous workers have opened the intestine with enterotomy scissors and have searched for the worms in the mucosa. Our method is to cut the intestine, without slitting it, into lengths of about two inches. These are held at one end with forceps and the contents stripped out by compressing a second pair tightly against the intestine near the held end and drawing them downward. The parasites and the slight amount of débris present are caught in a crystal containing saline. The worms may be strained free from the débris using a 40-mesh copper screen, or they may be picked out with a finely drawn pipette. Using this method the author has recovered more than 5,000 adult parasites from a single rat.

It is difficult to obtain larvae from the circulating blood. They are small and considerable quantities of blood must be collected, centrifuged and studied before the larvae are found. Fülleborn accomplished this by centrifuging the blood with a mixture composed of 5% formalin (95 cc.), glacial acetic acid (5 cc.), and concentrated alcoholic gentian violet (2 cc.). The larvae were recovered from the sediment. Using this method Fülleborn isolated larvae from the blood of the ear and heart until the 20th day after infection.

It is quite instructive to present, at least for demonstration, larvae of trichinae migrating between the muscle fibers. By killing heavily infected animals 18 to 20 days after the initial feeding and compressing small bits of diaphragm between glass plates held together by screw clamps, the larvae near the edge of the tissue are forced free and may be studied.

The parasites have come to lie in the muscle in their encysted stage 21 days after infection, and at this point they are again infective. The connective tissue capsule has begun to form and the worms are relatively quiescent. By 35 to 40 days the connective tissue sheath is quite pronounced; this is the best time to obtain encapsulated trichinae.

By maintaining infected animals, rabbits or cats, for three or four years the ultimate calcified stage may be obtained.

Order TELOGONIA, Family ANCYLOSTOMIDAE

THE GROWTH OF HOOKWORM LARVAE ON PURE CULTURES OF BACTERIA*

OVA of the dog hookworm, *Ancylostoma caninum,* have been obtained free from feces and sterilized. These sterile ova have been inoculated onto agar cultures of various bacteria, and the larvae have hatched normally and grown to the infective stage with bacteria as their sole source of food.

The method employed for freeing the ova from the feces consists in thoroughly mixing up about 25 grams of freshly passed feces from a heavily infested dog in 500 cc. of water. The mixture is then washed through a series of copper-wire sieves ranging up to a mesh of 100 wires to the inch. The larger particles in the feces are caught in the sieves but the ova readily pass through with the filtrate. This filtrate is allowed to stand in a large sedimenting cone for about an hour while the ova and heavy débris settle to the bottom. The supernatant fluid is then poured off; the sediment is transferred to a 50 cc. centrifuge tube and repeatedly washed with water, the solid matter being thrown to the bottom each time by centrifuging at a speed of 1,000 revolutions per minute. After the supernatant fluid from the washing has become practically clear, saturated salt solution is poured into the tube and the contents are again centrifuged at the same speed. This time the ova come to the surface and may be collected by removing the surface film with the open end of a piece of large glass tubing. If the material is centrifuged four or five times, a majority of the ova present may be recovered. If much solid material comes to the surface with the ova, it may be necessary to refloat the ova in saturated salt solution a second or even a third time in order to get rid of the foreign material. This method is tedious and time-consuming, but if the feces of a *heavily* infested dog are used, large quantities of ova may be obtained almost entirely free from fecal material.

Ova collected by this method may be sterilized by treatment with a 5% antiformin solution in 10% formalin. From 10 to 50% of the ova remain viable after this treatment. The ova are washed several times with sterile distilled water and are then ready for inoculation onto the agar cultures. During the process of sterilizing and washing, the ova are best kept in a sterile 50 cc. centrifuge tube closed with a cotton plug.

Cultures were made up in 250 cc. Erlenmeyer flasks stoppered with cotton plugs, and consisted of 20 cc. of ordinary bacteriological agar which had been diluted with three parts of water. The flasks were autoclaved and inoculated with bacteria 24 hours before the ova were introduced.

* Reprinted, with slight changes, from *Science* 69:74, 1929, by OLIVER R. McCOY, *School of Hygiene and Public Health.*

Since at ordinary room temperature the ova do not hatch for an additional 36 hours, there was a heavy growth of bacteria in the cultures by the time the larvae were ready to begin feeding. The sterile ova were introduced into the flasks in 1 cc portions of an aqueous suspension, several thousand ova usually being put in each flask.

In experiments so far carried out larvae have grown to the infective stage in the normal period of about 7 days on pure cultures of *Bacillus coli, B. subtilus, B. prodigiosus, B. lactis aerogenes, Staphylococcus aureus, Spirillum metchnikovi, S. rubrum,* and *Micrococcus citreus.* Ova which were put on plain agar without bacteria hatched normally and lived for as long as ten days, but did not grow. If bacteria were then introduced into the flasks, the larvae grew to the infective stage.

Not all bacteria are suitable food for hookworm larvae, since they failed to grow on cultures of *Bacillus pyocyaneus* and *Sarcina lutea,* and growth was very much retarded on cultures of *B. cereus* and *B. megatherium.* Larvae, however, grew normally on a mixed culture of *Bacillus cereus* and *B. coli.*

BIBLIOGRAPHY

Looss, A. 1911. The anatomy and life history of *Anchylostoma duodenale* Dub. Part II. The development in the free state. *Recds. of Egypt Govt. Schl. of Med.* 4:163.

M. E. D.

Family ASCARIDAE

CULTURING EGGS OF THE FOWL NEMATODE, ASCARIDIA LINEATA

J. E. ACKERT, *Kansas State College*

THE eggs may be secured from either live or dead worms, but cultures from live worms are much to be preferred. The anterior end of the worm is excised and the internal organs pressed into a sterile petri dish; the uteri are isolated and transferred to another sterile dish. At various points the uteri are punctured for the liberation of eggs with characteristic light centers which are known to be fertile. The portions of uteri containing fertile eggs are transferred to a final sterile petri dish, and the eggs pressed out and covered with sterile distilled water. To prevent bacterial or fungous growth 4 or 5 drops of 2% formalin are added. The cultures are incubated approximately 3 weeks at 27° to 30° C.

For best results the culture dishes should be opened daily and agitated to facilitate entrance of oxygen. If patches of fungus appear they should be removed. As the eggs usually adhere to the bottom of the dish, the medium must be poured off and a new supply added.

The amount of dilute formalin that may be added to inhibit fungous growth depends upon the permeability of the egg envelopes, which differ in the various species of nematodes.

THE LIFE HISTORY OF THE SWINE KIDNEY WORM*

UNDER laboratory conditions, at a temperature of about 26° to 27° C., the preparasitic stages of the development of *Stephanurus dentatus* were completed in from 5 to 6 days. Eggs obtained from gravid females and cultured in water or on a charcoal and feces mixture hatched in from 24 to 48 hours, and the larvae reached the first lethargus about 24 hours after hatching. The second lethargus was reached about 48 hours later, and the infective stage, that of the third stage larva, was usually attained about 24 hours after the onset of the second lethargus. Low temperatures have been found to retard the development of the eggs and larvae, and at temperatures sufficiently low not only was development arrested but the vitality of the eggs and larvae was destroyed.

When infective larvae of *S. dentatus* were placed on the scarified skin of pigs or when they were injected subcutaneously infection resulted, the course of development being similar to that which followed the administration of larvae by mouth.

Stephanurus has been reared experimentally in guinea pigs in which animals they have been found to attain a considerable growth and development.

M. E. D.

Family OXYURIFORMIDAE

CULTIVATION OF A PARASITIC NEMATODE
WILLIAM TRAGER, *Rockefeller Institute for Medical Research*

THE nematode parasite (*Neoaplectana glaseri*) of the Japanese beetle (*Popillia japonica*) was cultured by Glaser (1931, 1932). Plates of the culture medium are prepared by mixing in a sterile 5½-cm. petri dish about 8 cc. of melted veal infusion agar (pH 7.4) with 2 cc. of a 10% dextrose solution. The surface of the cooled medium is flooded with a concentrated water suspension of a pure culture of baker's yeast and the plate is incubated 24 hours at room temperature. The yeast growth inhibits later bacterial growth and serves as food for the nematodes. These are obtained from diseased Japanese beetle grubs and, after having been sedimented and washed three times in water, are placed on the yeast-culture plate. The culture is incubated at room temperature.

*Abstracted from an article in *Science* 70:613, 1929, by BENJAMIN SCHWARTZ, *U. S. Bureau of Animal Industry*.

The nematodes pass through one generation every 4 or 5 days, and must be subcultured every 2 weeks, by which time most of the yeast in the culture has been consumed.

Most of the nematode strains died out after the seventh or eighth transfer, *i.e.,* after 14 to 16 weeks in culture, during which time from 21 to 32 generations had been produced. The cultures died out because, although the females of the last culture passage were normal in size and shape, their ovaries failed to mature and no young were produced. However, by permitting worms from the sixth transfer to infect Japanese beetle grubs and to go through several generations in their natural hosts, worms could be recovered which could again be grown in culture through 7 or 8 transfers.

Recently (Glaser, unpublished) it has been found possible to culture the worms indefinitely by adding small amounts of powdered ovarian substance to the culture plates.

Free-living soil nematodes do not grow at all under the conditions suitable for Neoaplectana. [See p. 174.]

BIBLIOGRAPHY

GLASER, R. W. 1931. The cultivation of a nematode parasite of an insect. *Science* 73:614.

———— 1932. Studies on *Neoaplectana glaseri,* a nematode parasite of the Japanese beetle (*Popillia japonica*). *N. J. Dept. of Agric.* Circular No. 211.

CULTURING PARASITIC NEMATODE LARVAE FROM SILPHIDS AND RELATED INSECTS

C. G. DOBROVOLNY, *University of Michigan*

THE larvae of these oviparous nematodes are parasitic in the body cavity of silphids and the mature worms are free-living. The worms were successfully reared in cultures.

The larvae were freed from the body cavity of the silphids and cultured in tap water. Most of the worms died in too dilute and in too concentrated cultures. It was further observed that the mortality of larvae cultured in Syracuse watch glasses which were kept full of water was 100%. Best results were obtained by keeping the larvae in culture media of wet sand and macerated beetles.

Family ANGUILLULIDAE

ANGUILLA ACETI*

Anguilla aceti is a very satisfactory subject for type study in biology, zoology, and parasitology classes. It may be procured at any time of

*Abstracted from an article in *Science* 74:390, 1931, by GEORGE ZEBROWSKI, Buck Creek, Indiana.

the year from a corner grocery by asking for bulk cider vinegar. It will live indefinitely in the laboratory if transferred to fresh vinegar every two weeks. Since it is viviparous and transparent, all stages of development may be examined in utero. Anatomical details, such as the alimentary tract, nerve ring, spicules and sperms of male, uterus and uterine development in female, and all young and intermediate stages can be seen with a 4 mm. objective. Placed in a well slide and projected on a daylight screen with a micro-projector, many anatomical features may be shown on the screen under suitable magnification.

M. E. D.

ARTIFICIAL CULTIVATION OF FREE-LIVING NEMATODES*

Asa C. Chandler, *Rice Institute*

THE free-living nematodes of soil and of water may be studied to great advantage by culturing them on ordinary nutrient agar plates. A single isolated adult female of *Rhabditis sp.*, placed on an agar plate with a drop or two of dirty water to supply a bacterial growth, in a period of 5 days will produce thousands of offspring which swarm all over the plate. In 10 days the offspring will number many thousands,—males, females, eggs, and young in all stages of development.

For class demonstration of soil nematodes, a student may place a small quantity of soil, preferably manured soil, in a piece of gauze or in a fine sieve, and wash it in a beaker of warm water; in a few minutes the majority of the nematodes present will have fallen to the bottom of the beaker. If a drop or two of water from the bottom of the beaker is then placed on the surface of a nutrient agar plate, and the plate covered and left at room temperature for from 5 to 10 days, an enormous number of nematodes of several species will usually be found. The majority of the individuals move about on the surface of the agar, but some burrow into it also. The movements on the agar are sufficiently impeded so that they may be watched after the fashion of a slow-moving picture. The swallowing of bacteria and fungus spores, the excretion of waste matter from the anus, and every detail of locomotion may be observed under ideal conditions. Species of Rhabditis and Cephalobus, and others not positively identified, have been cultured in this manner. The method suggests a great range of possibilities in the way of study and experimentation, *e.g.*, on foods, effects of hydrogen-ion concentrations and of chemical substances, resistance to desiccation, tropisms, effects of various modifications in environment on rate of reproduction and development, *etc.* The extremely rapid rate of reproduction and ready inbreeding also suggests possibilities in genetic experiments.

*Recast of article in *Science* 60:203, 1924.

REFERENCES

For the culture of free-living nematodes see also p. 173.
For the culture of fresh water nematodes see p. 136.
For uses of nematodes as food see pp. 162 and 203.

Phylum VIII

TROCHELMINTHES, Class *Rotatoria*

A CULTURE MEDIUM FOR HYDATINA SENTA*

JOSEPHINE C. FERRIS, *University of Nebraska*

BRING to the boiling point in 100 cc. of water 1 gram of urea crystals, 1 gram of dried blood, and 1 gram of dried ox gall. Filter and add 3 cc. of this triple solution to 100 cc. of tap or rain water. This solution is very satisfactory for pedigree cultures of this rotifer in watch glasses if fed on Polytoma cultures. [See p. 61.] If the Polytoma is cultured in a bone meal and hay solution it should be washed at least twice by centrifuging and decanting.

REFERENCES

For the culture of *Hydatina asplanchna* see p. 210.
For the culture of Philodina see p. 143.

Class *Gastrotricha*

METHOD OF CULTIVATION FOR THE GASTROTRICHA

CHARLES EARL PACKARD, *University of Maine*

MANY specimens of *Lepidoderma squamatum* were reared in a 0.1% malted milk solution for a period of 22 months.

One half gram of Horlick's malted milk was dissolved in 500 cc. of clear water from a spring-fed river tributary, usually unfiltered, and boiled for 5 minutes. This was left exposed for 24 hours before being used. Sometimes the solution was filtered, though usually not. Animals were raised in rectangular, covered refrigeration dishes in quantity lots and in depression slides singly or in mass. In most cases *Lepidoderma squamatum* adapted itself readily. When once a culture was started, a small amount of fresh solution was added daily to keep up a supply of animals. Excess fluid was drawn off to prevent overflowing.

Lepidoderma concinnum, and a species of Chaetonotus, a genus characterized by cuticular spines, were also raised in the same medium for several weeks, adaptation being less easily accomplished with these forms.

*See *Biol. Bull.* 63:442, 1932.

They survived and reproduced in small numbers, however. Small amoebae, some Heliozoa, many tiny colorless and pale green flagellates, Entosiphon, Halteria, and several types of rotifers thrived at certain periods. Malted milk as a successful medium for the growth of Paramecium is mentioned by Pixell-Goodrich in Lee (1928).

BIBLIOGRAPHY

LEE, A. BOLLES. 1928. The Microtomist's Vade-Mecum, 9th ed. p. 411.

Phylum IX

Bryozoa, Class *Ectoprocta*

BUGULA FLABELLATA AND B. TURRITA

Benjamin H. Grave, *De Pauw University*

THE breeding season of these Bryozoa at Woods Hole, Mass., extends from June 1 or June 15 to Nov. 1.

The complete life history of *Bugula flabellata* is readily observed because of the ease with which larvae are obtained and kept under laboratory conditions until colonies of several individuals are established. The larvae, which resemble the trochophores of annelids, are given off by the parent colonies at dawn. To obtain them in abundance sexually mature colonies should be collected late in the afternoon and placed in dishes of seawater. These are left over night near a window. Larvae issue from the colonies early in the morning and continue to be liberated from 5 to 10 A.M. They promptly swim to the lighted side of the dish, where they may be taken in a pipette and transferred to fresh dishes of seawater for study. Finger bowls or stender dishes are recommended for the purpose.

At first the larvae, as indicated above, are strongly and positively heliotropic but later a change occurs and they become negative in their response to light. Still later they make permanent attachment to the walls of the dish and proceed to develop into colonies. The larva requires no food because it has no digestive tract, but as soon as attachment occurs the containing dish should be placed in running seawater to secure aeration and food for the developing colony.

The swimming period of the larva is about six hours in duration. The first individual of the colony becomes a complete feeding polypide within two days and a colony of eight is established in one week if conditions are favorable. The colonies under natural conditions bud rapidly and become sexually mature in 1 month. They continue to grow for approximately three months which is the approximate duration of life of colonies established early in the summer. Colonies established late in the summer live over winter.

The rate of growth of colonies may be observed under natural conditions from the establishment of the colony to maturity by placing wooden floats in the region where the species occurs normally. Wooden crosses measuring three or four feet in length have proved excellent for the purpose (Fig. 46). They were tied to a dock and allowed to float on the surface. So constructed they do not turn over in storms and thousands of colonies soon appear on their lower surfaces; from these samples may be taken for study from day to day. Sexually mature colonies which liberate great numbers of larvae daily may be grown in this way.

Bugula turrita has the same life history but it grows in somewhat different situations. The larvae show interesting structural differences, especially in the presence of visible pigmented eye spots, but they respond

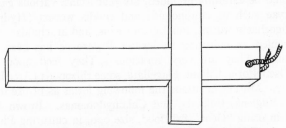

Fig. 46.—Type of wooden cross used to grow colonies of *Bugula flabellata* and other sessile organisms, such as barnacles, ascidians, and hydroids. (Construction: spruce or pine, 2 x 4; three feet long with cross bar 1 x 6, two and one half feet long, sunk flush with the surface.)

to the same treatment, their behavior being the same in all respects. The larvae of *B. turrita* may be liberated in the afternoon.*

CULTURING FRESHWATER BRYOZOA

MARY ROGICK, *College of New Rochelle*

FRESHWATER Bryozoa are among the most common of aquatic invertebrates. Ponds, rivers, streams, lakes, harbors, bays, and quarries abound with specimens. Bryozoa may readily be collected throughout the spring, summer, and fall in either one or two of the following stages: colony, statoblast, or hibernaculum. Hibernacula are produced by colonies of Pottsiella and Paludicella while statoblasts are produced by the Plumatellas, Cristatella, Pectinatella, Lophopodella, Lophopus, and Fredericella. Houghton and Marcus admit the possibility of over-wintering in the case of Fredericella and Lophopus under favorable conditions.

Collection of Bryozoan forms is simple. Floating statoblasts may be obtained by skimming over the surface of the water with a silken dip-net.

* A more complete account of the behavior of the larva and the rate of growth of the colony may be found in *J. Morph.* 49:355, 1930.

Attached or enclosed statoblasts, hibernacula, and colonies may be obtained by scraping with a scalpel or sharpened spatula the under side of rocks, lily pads, submerged objects such as boards and rubbish, floating objects such as sticks and logs, leafy aquatic vegetation such as Vallisneria, Elodea, Potamogeton, Ceratophyllum, Myriophyllum, or Scirpus, and by scraping shells of Unionidae, Astacus (Abricossoff, 1925) and certain tortoises (Annandale, 1912). Records exist for Bryozoans from various depths. Hand collecting is resorted to in the shallows, but at depths beyond three feet the use of double rakes or dredge is necessary.

Some of the enemies of Bryozoa which may occur in the collections and which should be carefully excluded, are planarians, various gastropods, insect larvae such as chironomids and caddis worms (Hydropsyche, *et al.*), oligochaete worms, small crustaceans, and arachnids.

The problem of culturing freshwater Bryozoans has been a rather difficult one. They are very voracious. They feed upon diatoms, desmids, Oscillatoria, Ciliata, Flagellata, some rhizopods (Arcella), small rotifers, *etc.* Marcus mentions the following forms as of use in feeding Bryozoa: Euglena, Colpoda, and Chlamydomonas. Brown has been successful in using "Geha" fish food, size 000, in culturing Plumatella, keeping the colonies alive and reproducing for four weeks.

In culturing Bryozoa shallow dishes or finger bowls should be used if one wishes to observe the organisms very frequently. In larger aquaria they may not be easily examined. The water in the finger bowls should be replaced every 2 or 3 days with fresh pond water or with tempered tap water. The following diets were tried out on *Lophopodella carteri* and found to be unsuccessful: Paramecia, Euglenae, green algae, dried and powdered Elodea, Vallisneria, algae, malted milk, nutritive broth (dehydrated), and fish food (not powdered). As a last resort, greenhouse water which contained a great amount of organic debris or detritus was tried. This was collected from around the stems and bases of large aquatic plants which had been planted in the greenhouse tanks. Some of the mud and decaying vegetation at the base of the plants was included. Planaria, chironomids and other offenders were removed from the culture as far as possible. The debris was removed and new material added every two or three days. This proved to be an ideal medium for rearing colonies. Lophopodella colonies collected in Lake Erie in August and September, 1932, and cared for in the laboratory released statoblasts in October and November. These statoblasts hatched in November, December, January, and February, giving rise to small colonies. These new colonies gave rise to statoblasts in March and April. Some of these statoblasts germinated in April (1933). The culture dishes were kept in the laboratory under ordinary room conditions of light and temperature (approximately 22° C.).

Frequently in some of the cultures there appeared a gelatinous coating over the bottom of the dish, covering the colonies. If this were not removed, the colonies would die from suffocation, lack of food, *etc.* This scum occurred more frequently in flat stender dishes than in finger bowls and Pyrex glassware. When such a condition occurs, the Bryozoa must be transferred to another dish, the scum must be removed from them with dissecting needles, scalpel, or other suitable instrument. They should then be placed in a sterilized finger bowl in fresh pond water.

Lophopodella will tolerate stagnant and polluted water to a surprising extent. A number of colonies were placed in an aquarium with two large stones which had a small amount of dirt and algae on them, some broken lily pads, and a small amount of Elodea, to which was added lake water (about 5 gallons). At the end of ten days, the water was a cloudy yellow in color, turbid, and gave off a very bad odor. The colonies however were in excellent condition. Pectinatella, Cristatella, and some of the other Bryozoans could not tolerate such conditions so well.

BIBLIOGRAPHY

ABRICOSSOFF, G. G. 1925. The materials for the fauna of the Bryozoa of the government of Moscow. *Arb. Biol. Sta. Kossino*, Lief. 2:81.

ANNANDALE, N. 1912. Fauna Symbiotica Indica, No. 3. Polyzoa associated with certain Gangetic tortoises. *Rec. Ind. Mus.* 7:147.

BROOKS, C. M. 1929. Notes on the statoblasts and polypids of *Pectinatella magnifica*. *Proc. Acad. Nat. Sci. Phila.* 81:427.

BROWN, C. J. D. 1933. A limnological study of certain fresh-water Polyzoa, *etc. Trans. Amer. Micr. Soc.* 52:271.

———— 1934. Internal budding: with suggestions for a laboratory study of fresh-water Polyzoa. *Ibid.* 53:425.

DAVENPORT, C. B. 1904. Report on the fresh-water Bryozoa of the United States. *Proc. U. S. Nat. Mus.*, 27:211.

HARMER, S. F. 1913. Polyzoa of Waterworks. *Proc. Zool. Soc. London*, pp. 426.

———— 1931. Recent work on Polyzoa. *Proc. Linn. Soc. London*, Session 143, part VIII, p. 113.

HENCHMAN, A. P. and DAVENPORT, C. B. 1913. Clonal variation in Pectinatella. *Amer. Nat.* 47:361.

HOUGHTON, W. 1860. Note on Fredericella, etc. *Ann. Mag. Nat. Hist.* (3) 6:389.

KRAEPELIN, K. 1885. Die Fauna der Hamburger Wasserleitung. *Abh. Naturwiss. Ver. Hamburg*, 9.

MARCUS, E. 1925. Bryozoa in P. Schulze's *Biologie der Tiere Deutschlands*. Lief. 14, Teil 47, pp. 1-46.

———— 1934. Uber *Lophopus crystallinus* (Pall.). *Zool. Jahrb., Abt. Anat. Ont. Tiere*, 58:501.

ROGICK, M. D. 1934. Studies on fresh-water Bryozoa, I. *Trans. Amer. Micr. Soc.* 53:416.

SCHODDUYN, R. 1923. Matériaux pour servir a l'Etude biologique des Cours d'eau de Flandre Française. *Ann. biol. lac.* 12:121.

TANNER, V. M. 1932. Ecological and distributional notes on fresh-water sponges and Bryozoa of Utah. *Utah Acad. Sci.* 9:113.

WILLIAMS, S. R. 1921. Concerning "larval" colonies of Pectinatella. *Ohio J. Sci.* 21:123.

Phylum XIII

ANNELIDA, Class *Polychaeta*

Order POLYCHAETA ERRANTIA, Family NEREIDAE

NEREIS LIMBATA

BENJAMIN H. GRAVE, *De Pauw University*

Nereis limbata, which occurs abundantly in Eel Pond at Woods Hole, is the one species in this vicinity which is known to have a distinct and unmistakable lunar periodicity in spawning. Eggs may usually be had in great abundance roughly from the full moon until new moon during all of the summer months and not to any considerable extent at any other time.

The eggs and spermatozoa are extruded at night from 9 to 10 P.M. as the sexually mature worms swim at the surface of the sea. As the males and females come into contact with each other they are stimulated to expel their gametes vigorously. The stimulus, however, is chiefly chemical rather than physical. At this time in the month the body cavities of the worms are distended with eggs or spermatozoa and after they are expelled nothing but the ghost of a worm remains.

METHOD OF COLLECTING

A small dip net and a lantern or flashlight are needed in collecting. The worms are attracted to light and may be dipped up and placed in suitable dishes of seawater. Females should be kept separate from males, otherwise they spawn at once.

METHOD OF SECURING EGGS

Select a distended female, place her in a clean dish of seawater, and with scissors cut across her body to allow the eggs to escape. In the same way cut a male in two in a dish containing 25 or 50 cc. of seawater. After washing the eggs once or twice by pouring off the water and re-filling the dish with fresh seawater, add three or four drops of spermatozoa and agitate gently. Within five minutes after insemination the eggs extrude a jelly in which they lie embedded. The eggs are thus readily fertilized artificially and development proceeds. Usually 100% of the eggs cleave and, barring accidents, nearly all develop into normal embryos.

CARE OF CLEAVING EGGS

The cleaving eggs require no further attention except that the water should be changed several times during the next 12 or 15 hours. In the meantime the eggs cleave and acquire cilia. After 24 hours the embryos may be separated from the jelly and transferred to a clean dish of seawater either by pouring or by using a wide-mouthed pipette. Care should be exercised to get rid of all decaying organic matter as soon as possible, and this must be accomplished within 36 hours after insemination or before. Cleaving eggs that are allowed to develop without frequent change of water usually develop abnormally or die.

SCHEDULE OF DEVELOPMENT

The embryo becomes an early gastrula 12 or 15 hours after fertilization, with the four large macromeres constituting the principal part of the endoderm. It is ciliated and rotates in the jelly. It is a late gastrula after 24 to 30 hours, the rate of development depending upon the temperature. Between 36 and 48 hours the larva is a trochophore, at first spherical but later somewhat elongated. On the third day the first three segments of the worm body are completed and no additional segments are added for several days although the embryo increases in size. It is possible to keep the embryos until other segments grow but to do so requires special feeding methods. The Nereis larva is unusually hardy and easily cared for. The trochophores and early segmented larvae are active swimmers but as the ciliary mechanism becomes inadequate they depend more and more upon wiggling and creeping.

CARE OF LARVAE

The egg of Nereis is large and well supplied with yolk and oil so that the larvae require no feeding during the first five or even seven days of development. They are easily cared for because after two days they have a tendency to settle to the bottom on one side of the dish and may be transferred to a clean dish of seawater with a wide-mouthed pipette. This should be done once per day or more frequently in hot weather. After five days they may be fed upon diatoms but if it is desired to keep them for several weeks it is best to transfer them to a large cylindrical balanced aquarium, containing a dense culture of developing diatoms which adhere to its sides. E. E. Just reared Nereis megalops to maturity in such a jar of diatoms. The original stock of diatoms came from the Fisheries Laboratory at Beaufort, N. C.

BIBLIOGRAPHY

LILLIE, F. R., and JUST, E. E.   1913.   Breeding habits of *Nereis limbata* at Woods Hole, Mass. *Biol. Bull.* 24:147.

JUST, E. E.   1922.   On rearing sexually mature Platynereis megalops from eggs. *Amer. Nat.* 56:471.

WILSON, E. B.   1892.   Cell lineage of Nereis. *J. Morph.* 6:361.

A METHOD FOR REARING NEREIS AGASSIZI AND N. PROCERA

JOHN E. GUBERLET, *University of Washington*

THE writer has reared two species of Nereis to sexual maturity in the laboratory by the use of the following method. One species, *Nereis agassizi,* was reared to sexual maturity during each of two consecutive years and in the third attempt the larvae were maintained for a period of nearly 14 months but due to unfortunate circumstances did not reach sexual maturity. A second species, *Nereis procera,* was successively cultured in the laboratory for a year. At the end of that period the worms had reached sexual maturity.

While the worms are "swarming" at the surface in their seasonal spawning it is a comparatively easy matter to capture both males and females. Better results may be obtained if the males and females are kept separate during capture and transfer to the laboratory. They should spawn in separate dishes in sufficient seawater to keep them well covered and to maintain a fairly even temperature. A small amount of water containing spermatozoa is added to the eggs and thoroughly mixed. Care should be taken not to use too great excess of spermatozoa. The dish containing the fertilized eggs should be allowed to stand for a few minutes and then be emptied into a larger container (battery-jar) containing 2 or 3 liters of seawater. This jar is placed in running water or in a suitable location to maintain a fairly constant temperature. The degree of temperature best suited to a particular species would seem to be that of the environment from which the adult worms were taken. After the eggs have settled to the bottom, as much of the water as possible should be siphoned off to remove the excessive spermatozoa from the culture and fresh seawater should be added. Polar bodies begin to appear after 1 to 1½ hours and cleavage starts after 2½ hours. The cleavage rate is usually fairly rapid and movement of the larvae begins in 12 to 15 hours. The trochophore stage is reached in about 36 to 48 hours and larvae with three pairs of setigerous appendages appear in between 3 and 4 days.

It is highly important that the temperature be kept constant. The water should be changed daily and agitated at least once each day to provide aeration. When the larvae have developed setigerous appendages they will soon be provided with jaws and are then ready to begin feeding. The larvae will consume very readily small diatoms which are then added to the culture. For this purpose it was found that species of Navicula and Nitzschia [See p. 34.] were of suitable size. They were eaten in large quantities. The larvae grow rapidly and when they have developed 6 or 8 segments they form mucous tubes within which they hide themselves. When the larvae reach an age and size having 10 or 12 segments they will consume other food in addition to diatoms. At this time Ulva and brown kelp, such as Nereocystis, may be added to the diet. At this time they may consume other small worms and any material that they can devour. The worms extend themselves almost their entire length from their tubes and reach for food.

After the young worms develop tubes it is not necessary to change the water so frequently. A change every 2 or 3 days is sufficient, and at a later date, once a week will suffice, provided there is plenty of green vegetation in the water.

Several important factors must be kept in mind: 1) there must not by overcrowding of organisms; 2) fresh water must be provided to allow for a sufficient supply of oxygen; 3) care must be taken to prevent contamination; 4) the temperature must be kept within a limited range; and 5) a sufficient quantity of suitable food must be provided at all times.

Order POLYCHAETA SEDENTARIA

Family SERPULIDAE

HYDROIDES HEXAGONUS

BENJAMIN H. GRAVE, *De Pauw University*

Hydroides hexagonus, a serpulid worm, secretes a calcareous tube which adheres firmly to shells of mollusks, stones, and wooden structures. The breeding season at Woods Hole opens between June 10 and June 15 and closes between October 15 and November 1.

METHOD OF OBTAINING EGGS AND SPERMATOZOA

To obtain eggs or sperm it is advisable to remove the worms from their calcareous tubes and place them in stender dishes or Syracuse watch crystals filled with seawater, one worm per dish. When so treated they always spawn immediately if they are sexually mature. The sexes are separate and the gametes, whether eggs or spermatozoa, are carried free in the coelomic cavities from which they are extruded through nephridiopores located along the sides of the body. During the early part of the breeding season over 50% of the spawned eggs are immature and undersize. Later on they are nearly all mature and fertilizable. Maturation does not take place until the spermatozoon enters the egg, the germinal vesicle being indistinctly visible through the yolk.

EMBRYOLOGY

It is desirable to delay insemination of the eggs for half an hour after spawning has occurred because the spermatozoa are quite immobile when first extruded. Under the stimulus of seawater they gradually become activated but are relatively inactive at best. After allowing time for activation, remove the eggs by means of a pipette to a fresh dish of seawater and add four or five drops of sperm.

After fertilization the eggs develop within ten hours into actively swimming gastrulae and therefore rise from the bottom. They may now be poured into a clean dish, thus discarding the eggs which failed to develop.

Within 24 hours the embryos have become transparent trochophore larvae which continue to swim actively. They remain in the trochophore stage of development for 10 days or two weeks showing little external change except a slight slender outgrowth at the posterior end which constitutes the beginning of the worm body. They feed readily upon diatoms by means of a ciliary mechanism and may be kept indefinitely under laboratory conditions.

Because they at no time settle to the bottom, it is difficult to keep the water changed but they remain in good condition if poured daily into clean dishes discarding the bottom layers. They have a tendency to collect at one side of the dish and may be transferred to clean dishes of seawater by means of a pipette, but this method involves the loss of many embryos. Zeleny (1906) has reared them to metamorphosis in aquarium jars.

POST EMBRYONIC DEVELOPMENT

The trochophore finally develops a slender worm body, settles permanently, and secretes a calcareous tube. By placing mollusk shells or stones in a cage and sinking them in shallow water which is known to contain breeding Hydroides worms it is possible to secure many young worms and study their further development. Studies of this character carried on at Woods Hole for several years have shown that they become sexually mature in seven or eight weeks before they are half grown. They become fully grown in two years. Most of the worms ordinarily collected are only one year old and it is likely that many if not most of them die during the second year.

The shell of an average-sized worm after one year's growth, measures 65 or 70 mm. in length and 3 or 4 mm. in widest diameter. The largest worms may reach 120 mm. in length and 5 mm. in greatest diameter.

BIBLIOGRAPHY

GRAVE, B. H. 1933. Rate of growth, age at sexual maturity and duration of life of certain sessile organisms at Woods Hole, Massachusetts. *Biol. Bull.* 65:380.

HATSCHECK, B. 1885. Entwicklung der Trochophora von *Eupomatus uncinatus* (*Serpula uncinata*). *Arch. Zool. Inst. Wien.* 6.

SHEARER, C. 1911. On the development and structure of the trochophore of *Hydroides uncinatus. Quart. J. Micr. Sci.* 56:543.

ZELENY, C. 1906. The rearing of serpulid larvae. *Biol. Bull.* 8:308.

Family SABELLARIIDAE

SABELLARIA VULGARIS

ALEX B. NOVIKOFF, *Brooklyn College*

Sabellaria vulgaris is a sedentary polychaete found along the Atlantic coast from North Carolina to Cape Cod (Pratt, 1935). The observations recorded here are based on experiments with worms dredged from a depth of sixty to eighty feet in the waters of Tarpaulin Cove in Vineyard Sound, near Woods Hole, Massachusetts.* The animals are abundant and are easily collected in this rather limited area.

The worms live within sand tubes which they build on stones, empty sanddollar and oyster shells, and occasionally on Bryozoa nodules and Limulus shells. Males and females are about equal in number in the collections. The sexes can be recognized externally only in those fully mature animals which contain a large number of either eggs or sperm. The abdominal segments, which are greatly distended, are dense white in the male and a decided pink in the female. The eggs or sperm are shed almost immediately after the animals are removed from their tubes. The number of gametes shed is greatest from those animals which have a pronounced color in the abdominal segments, but even animals which show neither the distinct white nor pink color may shed abundantly.

Animals collected throughout the greater part of the summer showed no apparent differences in the condition of their gametes. Eggs from worms dredged at irregular intervals during the periods, August 22 to September 7, 1934 and June 24 to September 9, 1935, developed normally in more than ninety-five per cent of the cases.** The same high percentage of normal development usually followed from eggs of animals that had been kept in aquaria with running seawater for as long as nine weeks.

*This work was carried on at the Marine Biological Laboratory, Woods Hole, Massachusetts.

** Verrill (1874, p. 317) states that "eggs are laid in May and June," and Waterman (1934, p. 98) says that "the normal shedding time of May and June is followed by a second but shorter period extending from about August first to fifteenth."

OBTAINING EGGS AND SPERM

Uninjured animals are most easily obtained using the following procedure: (1) remove the sand tube from the shell or rock, (2) break away enough of the tube to make the head and tail visible within, (3) carefully force the animal from the tube by inserting a blunt probe into the head end of the tube.

The sex of the animal removed from the tube is ascertained, if the color of the abdominal segments is not definitely white or pink, by placing it in a few drops of seawater until it begins to shed. The sperm usually pour out of the male in dense white clouds. The masses of eggs shed by the female break up in the water into small groups. The male is placed into four drops of seawater until it has completed shedding. The female is placed into a finger bowl containing about 200 cc. of clear seawater. After it has shed for a few seconds, it is moved to a new position in the finger bowl and allowed to shed in that place for the desired length of time, depending on the number and kind of eggs desired. The first eggs to be shed are not generally used because of the possibility of their having been on the surface of the animal while exposed to the air.

When preparing the eggs for fertilization, it is best to allow them to remain in the seawater for about fifteen minutes. Towards the end of that time, the sperm suspension is prepared. One drop of the sperm shed into the four drops of seawater is diluted with four drops of seawater, and one drop of this diluted suspension is then added to a finger bowl of seawater (about 260 cc.). The eggs are drawn up with a narrow medicine dropper and transferred into this suspension.*

The original sperm suspension (made by allowing the male to shed in four drops of seawater) may still be used after three to four hours and longer if evaporation of the water is prevented. The eggs may be fertilized immediately after shedding, but it is best to allow them to remain in the water for about fifteen minutes before they are fertilized, if eggs of the same stage of development are desired.

EARLY DEVELOPMENT

Just after being shed, the egg is very irregular in shape and contains a large clear germinal vesicle. A few minutes later, the egg begins to round out, a clearly visible membrane is raised from the surface, and the large germinal vesicle breaks down to form a spindle which extends across not quite half the diameter of the egg. The average diameter of the

---

* This procedure is quite different from that of Waterman (1934) who placed the male and female together in a finger bowl of seawater. The method used by me has the following advantages: 1—The eggs obtained are more nearly alike with respect to the stage of development. 2—The eggs are obtained free from the debris which clings to the bodies of the animals. 3—The use of the small quantity of sperm gives higher percentages of normal development. Polyspermy, which might otherwise be encountered, is avoided.

rounded egg is fifty-six micra; the membrane, usually wrinkled, is about twelve micra from the egg surface. Fine protoplasmic processes are seen to extend from the egg surface as the membrane is raised. The elevation of the membrane is apparently due to the swelling of a rather dense jelly situated between the egg surface and the membrane. This jelly is ordinarily invisible but it can be demonstrated by removing the outer membrane (see p. 190) and placing the eggs in a dense suspension of Chinese ink.

The process of fertilization has been described by Waterman (1934) and will be further discussed by me in a future publication. The sperm attaches to the egg within the first minute after mixing the eggs and sperm, but the exceedingly large fertilization cone may not be completely retracted for a period of twelve to fourteen minutes. Some time during the course of sperm entry, the protoplasmic processes are withdrawn into the egg. The egg is too opaque to allow for the direct observation of any internal processes other than those connected with the spindle area.

Preceding the formation of the first and second polar bodies there is a distinct flattening of the egg at the region where the polar bodies will be extruded. The first polar body separates at about nineteen to twenty-three minutes after fertilization; the second comes off nine to eleven minutes later. At fifty to fifty-five minutes after fertilization, a large anti-polar lobe is formed and the cell divides into two (sixty-five to seventy minutes). After the division the polar lobe goes into the CD cell. Ten to fifteen minutes later, a smaller lobe is given off at the anti-polar end of the CD cell and the second cleavage occurs. At the completion of the division the lobe flows into the D cell. The first set of micromeres, which are only slightly smaller than the basal cells, comes off in the usual dexiotropic fashion. During the course of this division a third lobe forms in the D cell. The later cleavage has not yet been described.

At five and a half hours, the developing embryo begins to move about by means of cilia and at eight hours the apical tuft and prototroch are well formed. The larvae live fairly well on a diet of the diatom Nitzschia. One larva was raised, without much care, to the beginning of metamorphosis (seven weeks) at which time it was fixed. Wilson (1929) has given a detailed description of the larvae of the British Sabellarians with which those of *Sabellaria vulgaris* agree very closely.

The exact time relations in development and the effect of change of temperature on such relations have not been studied. The schedule of events as given above is only approximate for room temperatures varying from nineteen to twenty-five degrees C.

REMOVAL OF OUTER MEMBRANE

The outer membrane of the egg may be removed by following a slight modification of a procedure described by Hatt (1932). Two solutions. A and B, are prepared as follows:

Solution A.—A given volume of a solution of 1 gm. of $Na_2 CO_3$ in 1000 gm. of isotonic NaCl (or KCl). This gives a solution with pH 9.6.

Solution B.—0.45 cc. of 1.0 N HCl are added to 100 cc. of isotonic NaCl (or KCl). This solution has enough HCl so that when an equal amount of the solution is added to a given amount of Solution A the resulting mixture is at the pH of seawater (8.2).

The eggs are placed in a Syracuse dish and as much of the seawater as possible withdrawn, without injury to the eggs. A small amount (three to four cc.) of Solution A is poured on them and the dish rotated. After about one minute, the eggs are allowed to settle and the solution withdrawn. Now a carefully measured amount (five cc.) of Solution A is pipetted into the dish. The eggs clump into large masses, but as the membranes dissolve the eggs separate and the masses break up. The disappearance of the egg membranes may be followed under the microscope. When they have disappeared from most of the eggs (about five minutes) five cc. of Solution B is quickly added. The force of the stream from the pipette is sufficient to mix the solutions. After the eggs have again settled, they are transferred to fresh seawater in Syracuse dishes. The bottoms of the dishes have been previously coated with a thin layer of agar to prevent the adhesion of the eggs to the glass surface.

This treatment removes the outer membrane but the jelly still remains about the egg.

BIBLIOGRAPHY*

DEHORNE, A. 1910a. La division longitudinale des chromosomes dans la spermatogenese de *Sabellaria spinulosa*. *Compt. Rend. Acad. Sci.* 150:1195.

———— 1910b. Le valeur des anses pachytenes et le mecanisme de la reduction chez *Sabellaria spinulosa*. *Ibid.* 150:1625.

———— 1911. Recherches sur la division de la cellule. II. Homeotypie et Heterotypie chez les Annelides polychaetes et les Trematodes. *Arch. de Zool. Exp.* S. 9, 1:1.

———— 1913. Nouvelles recherches sur les mitoses de maturation de *Sabellaria spinulosa*. *Compt. Rend. Acad. Sci.* 156:485.

FAURE-FREMIET, E. 1924. L'oeuf de *Sabellaria alveolata* L. *Arch. d'Anat. Micr.* 20:211.

*The literature on the European species of this genus is included in the bibliography. I will shortly publish accounts of (1) the details of fertilization, (2) the later cleavage, and (3) the results of experiments with centrifugation and isolation and transplantation of blastomeres.

HARRIS, E. J. 1935. Studies on living protoplasm. I. Streaming movements in the protoplasm of the egg of *Sabellaria alveolata* L. *J. Exper. Biol.* 12:65.

HATT, P. 1922. La fusion experimentale d'oeuf de *Sabellaria alveolata* L. et leur developpement. *Arch. de Biol.* 42:303.

———— 1932. Essais Experimentaux sur les Localizations Germinales dans l'oeuf d'un Annelide, *Sabellaria alveolata* L. *Arch. d'Anat. Micr.* 28:81.

PRATT, H. S. 1935. Manual of the Common Invertebrate Animals.

VERRILL, A. E. and SMITH, S. I. 1874. Report upon the Invertebrate Animals of Vineyard Sound and Adjacent Waters.

WATERMAN, A. J. 1934. Observations on reproduction, prematuration, and fertilization in *Sabellaria vulgaris*. *Biol. Bull.* 67:97.

WILSON, D. P. 1929. Larvae of the British Sabellarians. *J. Mar. Biol. Assoc.* 30:221.

Class *Oligochaeta*, Family ENCHYTRAEIDAE

CULTIVATION OF ENCHYTRAEUS ALBIDUS

RAYMOND F. BLOUNT, *University of Minnesota Medical School*

SUCCESS in the cultivation of *Enchytraeus albidus* is largely dependent upon constant care and attention to small details in the condition of the culture. The principal things to be considered in this are the medium, moisture, and food.

A dishpan is very satisfactory for a container although a tight wooden box may be used. The latter is not so satisfactory since air and moisture exchange at the sides and bottom make regulation difficult. In any case the use of several small cultures rather than a large one is advisable. There should be a cover to lessen evaporation. In addition to this the surface of the medium may be partially covered by small pieces of slate or stones, or glass jar covers.

The medium is a light loam soil of such a character that it does not easily harden when dry, while on the other hand it should not be sandy. It should not be too great in quantity, as the worms should congregate in masses for breeding. A depth of 2 or 3 inches is best, for if too shallow it is difficult to regulate the moisture.

The culture should be kept in a place where the temperature is such that multiplication is encouraged, but relatively low. The range is wide but the optimum is probably around 20° C.

There should be sufficient moisture to allow free motility of the worms but not enough to bring them to the surface except as they may travel on the under side of pieces of slate or stone resting on the surface of the dirt. They are visible here if glass is used for this purpose. They should not congregate in this position however. In a rich culture the movement of the worms is audible. The addition of water is by sprinkling rather than by pouring and should be frequent and light.

A laundry sprinkler in the neck of a bottle is useful. The regulation of moisture may be aided by removing the cover for a time as necessary. The surface of the earth should be level and pressed down, not too firmly, to leave no lumps above to dry or mold. The fragments of slate or stone on the surface aid greatly in producing an optimal condition beneath. There should be no collection of water in the bottom of the pan. If this occurs it is best to tip the pan up, with something under one edge, to allow the water to drain to one side so that the greater part of the pan may dry. If excessive water is present the earth should be held in place and the pan drained on its side.

The food should be placed where the worms are found as they have usually congregated in favorable localities. However some should be scattered throughout to reach those worms which are dispersed in the culture. It is best to place the food in small masses as the cocoons are deposited on these and the young may be securely attached to them. Cereals, such as oatmeal, are convenient foods. Pieces of boiled potatoes with the skins attached are also excellent. Bread or other materials may be used. It is best to vary the diet. The amount should be such as to be consumed within a reasonable time, frequent rather than large feedings being needed.

Mold may often be present but does not seem to interfere if the food masses are not large. Removal of surface growth and taking the cover off to allow short drying periods will help keep it in check. A culture which attracts Drosophila is often in optimal condition and a few of these flies are usually present. However a souring culture is to be strictly avoided.

In starting a culture the worms should be placed in only a few places rather than scattered throughout the dirt, and food placed with them. Breeding is facilitated if large numbers of worms are together. Since a culture usually presents cycles of abundance and scarcity of worms it is advisable to have several cultures if a constant supply of worms is needed.

In securing worms for use, masses of them may be removed with forceps and placed in water. If small worms are desired it is best to remove also some dirt and food. At times they may be secured by washing the under side of the slate or stones on the surface. Repeated decanting of the water and the addition of more will wash most of the light dirt away and the worms may be transferred with wide-mouthed pipettes through several wash waters to clean them.

It should be emphasized again that constant daily attention to the cultures is essential.

LABORATORY CULTURE OF ENCHYTRAEUS

VICTOR LOOSANOFF, *U. S. Bureau of Fisheries*

THESE small Oligochaetae are extensively used for feeding small fish and amphibians kept under laboratory conditions. Since it is comparatively easy to grow them and because they are excellent food for lower vertebrates, it is desirable to maintain an abundant supply in each laboratory where work on fish or Amphibia is carried on.

To grow Enchytraeus collect rich, dark garden soil and place in a large dish pan. Pulverize a few milk crackers or dry pieces of bread, and mix this powder with the soil, which has previously been rendered moist. After three or four days seed the soil with Enchytraeus taken from another culture or obtained from a biological supply house. Add more cracker powder. The soil must always be kept moist but not wet. It has been observed by the writer that the best growth of worms is obtained if the culture is kept at a temperature of about 20° C. The culture must be kept covered with a lid but not too tightly, allowing free access of air. Addition of small quantities of crushed bone powder helps to keep the culture in good condition. Crushed crackers or bread crumbs should be added to the soil every 4-6 days.

ENCHYTRAEID WORMS

WILLIAM LERAY and NORMA FORD, *University of Toronto*

A SPECIES of enchytraeid worm, which is used in our department, was originally obtained from a dealer. These worms are kept in boxes $1\frac{1}{2}$ x 2 feet in size, over the bottom of which is spread 4 inches of rich soil, consisting largely of decayed leaves. The worms are fed on white bread soaked in milk, buried in furrows across the box. A temperature of about 60° F. is desirable, although some strains of this worm will withstand higher temperatures.

Enchytraeid worms are used to feed a great variety of animals, including leeches, crayfish, *etc.*

REFERENCES

For the culture of *Enchytraeus albidus* see also p. 196.
For the culture of several species of Oligochaetes see p. 136.
Family Aelosomatidae
For the culture of Aelosoma see p. 143.
Family Naididae
For the culture of Nais see p. 143.
For the culture of Dero see p. 143.

Family TUBIFICIDAE

TUBIFICIDAE

George R. La Rue, *University of Michigan*

OLIGOCHAETE worms of the family Tubificidae form an excellent food for many kinds of laboratory animals including planaria, leeches, dragonfly and damselfly nymphs, aquatic beetle larvae, and many fishes. A star-nosed mole kept in the laboratory ate them voraciously. The ease with which these worms may be collected in quantity and kept for months in the laboratory, and the avidity with which they are eaten, make them important laboratory animals.

Tubificidae occur in a considerable variety of freshwater habitats. They may be found most readily and most abundantly in the mud, or in muddy borders, of streams or ponds where considerable organic matter is undergoing decay. When in shallow water they may often be seen with their tails waving in the water, their heads buried in the mud. The location of tubificids in soft muddy borders of streams or ponds may often be determined by noting numerous small casts on the surface. When their presence is suspected take up a small quantity of mud on a trowel and examine it for worms. If they are abundant determine how deeply they are embedded in the mud, then scrape or scoop up the layer of mud containing them with trowels or small shovels and put in 10- or 12-quart pails.

At the laboratory put the contents of a 12-quart pail in a shallow galvanized pan measuring about 15 x 12 x 3 inches deep. Set the pan on a drain table in a cool room and allow a very small stream of water from a faucet to flow continuously through a rubber tube into the pan. The worms will come to the surface in a few hours. During the night small masses of worms tend to migrate out of the pan and onto the drain table if the pan is overcrowded. These may be used for feeding purposes until the stock is reduced.

If the mud rises in the pan because of the formation of gas, prick holes in it and press it down.

In quiet rivers receiving sewage or in ponds to which manure has been added to increase productivity of fish food, tubificids often collect in masses as large as a man's fist, or larger, at the surface, either on or near the decaying material and frequently near the margin or even upon the muddy border. They occur when the water is warm and disappear when it gets cold in the fall. Such worm masses are collected with a large tea strainer, dipper, or long-handled fine-meshed dip net. In the laboratory they may be put with mud and decaying vegetable matter, or with manure, potato, or other food material free from mud.

To feed tubificids the following materials have been used: fresh horse manure, baked potatoes cut in halves, boiled potatoes, butts from head lettuce, masses of bran, and bread. Press food down into the mud. The horse manure and bran should be buried in the mud.

The worms are removed in small masses by means of a pair of forceps. Wash them to remove mud before feeding them to other animals.

REFERENCE

For the culture of Tubificidae see also p. 142.

Family LUMBRICIDAE

EARTHWORMS

WALTER N. HESS, *Hamilton College*

SINCE living earthworms are useful in the laboratory for demonstrating behavior, and since freshly killed earthworms are far superior to preserved specimens for the study of certain organ systems, especially the digestive, circulatory and excretory systems, many laboratories need a supply of living worms for mid-winter use. Brief consideration will be given to the culturing of three species.

Specimens of *Lumbricus terrestris,* the common earthworm of the United States, must be gathered at night and preferably between 10:00 and 12:00 o'clock during or following a drizzling, warm rain when the ground is thoroughly soaked. The worms come to the surface of the ground in large numbers at such times and may be captured easily with the assistance of a strong flash light or an acetylene lantern. The best collecting grounds are closely cut lawns where the soil is rich.

When the worms have been collected they may be left for the remainder of the night in a cool place in a pail containing a small quantity of freshly cut grass. The next morning the worms should be carefully sorted, and all injured or abnormal specimens should be removed. If they are washed and placed, a few at a time, in a dish of water those that are injured may easily be detected.

Earthworms feed very largely on dead and decaying leaves and, like chickens, they digest their food better if there is a certain amount of grit in their diets. We have obtained best results by keeping earthworms in large boxes filled about 12 inches deep with approximately equal parts of old leaves and leaf loam gathered in the woods. Under no conditions should heavy clay soil be used. The worms need no other food, as they feed on the dead leaves. The material should be kept moist but not saturated with water. Unless extreme care was exercised in removing all injured worms, the boxes should be inspected after a week and all dead and dying worms removed. Should it happen that the worms are not keeping well those that are healthy should be removed and placed in a fresh box of leaves and loam.

Earthworms also keep well in very light, loamy soil. If this is used it is often advisable to feed the worms. Bread crumbs or corn meal make excellent food. The food should be moistened with water, spread sparingly over the top of the soil every 2 or 3 weeks and covered with about an inch of loam. Feed sparingly and not too often or the food will spoil and the worms may die.

Avoid trying to keep too many worms in one box. A cubic foot of culture material, after it has settled, will be sufficient for about 50 worms. Cover the boxes with panes of glass and keep cool. Temperatures above 60° F. usually prove fatal.

While cocoons of this earthworm are not easily obtainable, a few of them may usually be found by carefully sorting over the loamy material in the boxes after the worms have been stored in it for a month or so. The young worms emerge from the cocoons in a few weeks and thrive under the same treatment as that given the adults.

The fecal earthworm, *Eisenia* [=*Allolobophora*] *foetida,* which is much hardier than *Lumbricus terrestris,* and which is rather extensively used for experimental purposes, keeps very well in partly rotten cow and horse manure. The worms may usually be found here in abundance. They copulate and form large numbers of cocoons in the laboratory, if kept in containers supplied with this material.

The small‧white earthworm, *Enchytraeus albidus,* lives well in the laboratory. In addition to being an excellent food for small fish and Amphibia it may be narcotized with chloretone and used to demonstrate many annelid structures with the aid of a binocular microscope. Keep in boxes filled with black loam and feed sparingly with bread soaked in milk or water. After each feeding the food should be covered with about an inch of loam. The material should be kept moist but not soaked. The worms prefer temperatures around 55°-60° F. Higher temperatures should be avoided.

REFERENCE

For the feeding of earthworms see also note on p. 49.

CULTURE OF ALLOLOBOPHORA
R. N. DANIELSON, *University of Minnesota*

Allolobophora sp. has been cultured through an adaptation of an old fisherman's trick. Worms collected in the fall were placed in a mixture of black soil and leaf mold in a covered, galvanized iron can, such as a garbage can. Through the winter, the contents of the can were kept moist but not wet, and additions of spent coffee grounds were made at intervals of a month or so. Excessive moisture was corrected by leaving the cover slightly raised. The culture has lived through the three summer months without any attention, but was rather weak in the fall.*

Class *Gephyrea*

CULTURING LARVAE OF URECHIS CAUPO

G. E. MacGinitie, *California Institute of Technology*

THE larvae of the echiuroid, *Urechis caupo*, may be successfully reared by the method given below. This method has also been used to rear the larvae of the phoronid, *Phoronopsis viridis*, the polychaete, *Halosydna brevisetosa*, the tectibranch mollusk, *Tethys californicus*, and sand dollars and sea urchins. No doubt it will serve as a method for rearing many others as yet untried. The following materials will be required: Syracuse watch glasses; finger bowls with glass covers; seawater, preferably filtered not long before use; pipettes or medicine droppers with the small end pulled out to ½ or ⅓ of its original opening; at least two pipettes more finely drawn out with which to tap the animals for eggs and sperm, and a diatom culture.

COLLECTING THE ANIMALS

Urechis caupo inhabits the salt water estuaries of the west coast from San Diego northward. They build elongated U-shaped burrows with two openings to the surface of the mud. These openings are on an average about 30 inches apart, and the burrow itself is from 12 to 16 inches deep. Although the mud flats of estuaries are perforated with the openings of burrows of a great variety of animals, each and every opening in some way gives a clue to the underground inhabitant that made it.

*Editor's Note: Mr. Ralph W. Moltke of 106 Broadway, Peoria, Illinois, issues a small bulletin on permanent-bed culture of *Allolobophora* [=*Eisenia*] *foetida* that he sells to fishermen and to dealers in baits for fishing. It contains detailed practical instructions. With his permission we summarize here the main features of his plan.

1. Select a shady place in well-drained soil for a bed, say 3 x 6 feet.

2. Dig out a foot or more of soil and fill with well rotted manure.

3. Wet it down thoroughly and introduce the worms by distributing them over the surface.

4. Cover them with a sprinkling of dirt and allow them time to burrow.

5. Add some pieces of hard stale bread soaked in water and cover these with dirt.

6. Feed the worms once a week by spreading over the surface of the dirt corn meal, old bread, or vegetable refuse from the kitchen, covering this with dirt each time and adding a layer of straw or gunny-sacking to retain the moisture. Sprinkle the bed with water whenever it shows signs of getting dry.

7. Remove worms for use by turning over surface layer with a hand digging-fork, digging in a new place each time.

J. G. N.

The burrows of Urechis may be distinguished in the following manner:

The opening of the burrow varies somewhat in size according to the size of the animal within, but is always smaller than the deeper portions. The diameter of the opening varies from the size of a lead pencil to some twice that size, and is always well smoothed and has a somewhat slick appearance due to the mucus secreted by the animal, and which holds the sand and mud in place. At one or the other of the openings castings usually will be found. These castings are of equal length and smoothly rounded at each end. A casting of average size will be about 1 mm. in diameter and 1 cm. in length.

Since Urechis is one of the few animals which has two openings to its burrow, one may feel quite sure that it is a burrow of this animal, if, after locating two openings about 30 inches apart, one steps quickly on one hole, or jabs a shovel handle into it, and the water squirts out the other hole. This also locates the animal underground in so far as it must be somewhere between the two openings. This test may not be repeated, for, after being disturbed, Urechis will tightly block the burrow.

In bringing living specimens of Urechis to the laboratory it is necessary that they be kept cool to prevent harm both to the animals themselves and to the sex products that they contain. If they are to be transported for any distance the container in which they are carried should be packed in ice. By using ice I have transported them a distance of 250 miles without ill results. Males and females should be segregated by testing, and kept in separate aquaria so that when used in the future the particular sex needed may be known readily.

MAINTENANCE IN THE LABORATORY

If the animals are to be used for only a short period of time they may be left in the bottom of an aquarium with a good supply of running salt water. However, if they are to be kept for longer periods of time it is much better to keep them in glass tubes. These tubes may be bent U-shaped to simulate their natural burrows, in which case the animals may be kept for years. But even straight tubes in which they may be confined by corking the ends with single-holed corks will keep the animals in good shape for a much longer period than usually will be the case when they are kept free in the aquarium. In the U-shaped tube they will feed and carry on all the activities of their natural habitat. In general they will not feed in a straight tube, although an occasional individual may do so. The glass tubing in which they are confined should be of ample dimensions, as when one is handling the worms they lose their respiratory water and may be confined in a space much smaller than they actually require. Especially in the southern limits of their range Urechis is often spawned out in summer, so that in order to insure material to cover this period it is necessary to collect the animals in May and keep them for rather long periods of time in the manner just described.

FERTILIZING THE EGGS

Eggs or sperm may be removed from any of the six gonopores, which lie in three pairs just posterior to the oral setae, by inserting into one of these pores a finely drawn out pipette, which, of course, has been fire-ended. Use one pipette for males and another for females to avoid premature fertilization. Four or five hundred eggs should be placed in a finger bowl and covered with ¾ inch of filtered seawater, and then fertilized by the introduction of sperm, at the same time mixing well by squirting water in and out of the pipette. A minimum amount of sperm for insuring fertilization should be used, as polyspermic conditions and abnormal larvae nearly always result from an excess of sperm.

CARE OF THE LARVAE

These fertilized eggs should be covered and left to develop to the trochophore stage, or from 18 to 24 hours. Then it is advisable to take from these larvae those which are actively swimming near the surface and distribute them to several finger bowls with approximately 50 to each bowl. Remove any abnormal larvae whenever any are observed. Put glass covers on the finger bowls and set them in a cool place. From this time on the larvae should be carefully inspected and fed each day, and changed to fresh filtered seawater about once each week.

The above directions may need to be modified somewhat for the larvae of other animals.

It should be remembered that the length of the larval stage before metamorphosis is not a criterion of what it would be under natural conditions for obvious reasons. Since feeding must be carefully done to prevent fouling, it is probable that the amount of food is quite different from that of the open ocean. When raised in the above manner Urechis larvae usually require from 40 to 60 days before they metamorphose into burrowing worms.

DIATOM CULTURES

We have used several diatom cultures in the feeding of marine larvae, but we are unable to give a technical name for any of the species used. The first culture I used was one which I believe originally came from the Plymouth Marine Laboratory, and which was already at the Hopkins Marine Station of Stanford University when I first went there. Later I cultured a single-celled green alga which grows quite abundantly on the wet sand of the beaches. Later still a splendid form was cultured from the diatoms of the ocean here at our laboratory. In addition to this another culture was sent to me by Dr. S. C. Brooks a year ago from Woods Hole. Of these cultures the most suitable for food for growing larvae are the first and third, as these are small in size and stay in suspension.

FEEDING

Because it is impracticable to know the concentration of the diatoms within any culture, and because of the varying ability of the animals to use certain amounts of the diatoms as they grow, and also because the number of larvae in the dishes varies somewhat, it is impossible to state definitely what amount of diatom culture should be given to the feeding larvae each day.

Only that amount of diatoms should be fed to the larvae each day that they will clean up well by feeding time on the following day. Due to the transparency of the trochophores it is a simple matter to ascertain if they are feeding well, for the ingested diatoms may be seen massed within the gut.

Be sure, however, that the amount of material is sufficient to last until the time of the next feeding. An average feeding from an average diatom culture at the beginning of the feeding stage would be about ½ cc. to each finger bowl containing 50 larvae. It is better to feed less than may actually be used in the beginning, and increase this amount until the correct amount is known.

SUMMARIZED DIRECTIONS

A number of important factors to be considered are given below, and if these are carefully observed I think successful results would be quite certain with any free-swimming marine larva that is fairly hardy.

1. The seawater should be carefully filtered to remove all planktonic organisms, and unless one is quite certain of the non-toxic condition of the salt water pipe installation of the laboratory, the seawater should be carried in from the outside in a clean glass container.

2. The temperature should be kept as low as possible, preferably at or below that of the outside ocean water. Guard against any sudden change of temperature.

3. Not more than 50 to 75 larvae should be kept in a finger bowl at the beginning, and this number should be reduced to 25 or 30 after feeding has become well established and growth has commenced.

4. Do not put more than three-fourths inch of water in each finger bowl, as more increases the ratio of volume to surface and hence allows less oxygenation.

5. A good diatom culture for feeding is necessary. The diatom should

be quite small and should be one which will stay in suspension.

6. Each day, and this is most important, the bowls should be carefully inspected to note:

a. Are the larvae quite active?

b. Are they feeding?

c. Is the diatom culture well under control by the feeding larvae?

Perhaps nothing will insure failure more surely than feeding too much diatom culture, or allowing the culture to reproduce in the finger bowls. A sufficient amount of it should be fed once each day so that upon inspection the following day at feeding time practically all has been used by the larvae as food.

7. If there are signs of any fouling, or if the diatoms become too numerous, the larvae should immediately be taken out with a small pipette and transferred to a clean bowl with freshly filtered seawater.

8. Each day, just after feeding, gently aerate the water in each bowl with three or four pipettefuls of water from the same bowl. Better still, just before feeding carefully remove three or four pipettefuls of water from each bowl, feed the larvae, and then squirt three or four pipettefuls of freshly filtered seawater into each bowl. Either of these methods serves to aerate the water and to distribute the diatoms throughout the water in the bowls.

BIBLIOGRAPHY

FISHER, W. K., and MACGINITIE, G. E. 1928. A New Echiuroid Worm from California. *Ann. and Mag. Nat. Hist.* 1:199.

———— 1928. Natural History of an Echiuroid Worm. *Ibid.* 1:204.

Class *Hirudinea*

LABORATORY CARE OF LEECHES

J. PERCY MOORE, *University of Pennsylvania*

BESIDES serving for problems peculiarly their own, leeches offer suitable subjects for the study of certain general problems of physiology and behavior and some of them provide beautiful material for embryology, both observational and experimental. For the latter purposes common species of the Glossiphonidae, such as *Glossiphonia complanata*, *Helobdella stagnalis*, and *Placobdella parasitica*, are to be recommended, as the eggs and embryos are carried in large numbers by the female parent either in delicate capsules or uninclosed.

Except for certain of the fish leeches (Ichthyobdellidae) culture is simple and easy. Many of them will live under almost anerobic conditions and the sanguivorous species especially will thrive for a long time on a single meal of blood, or even without feeding at all. I have kept

Macrobdella decora in perfectly good condition without food for as long as 14 months. Most of them require little space and they are resistant to a wide range of temperatures, especially at the lower ordinary registers. But cleanliness is requisite as most species soon succumb to foul or over-heated water. They are also extremely sensitive to many mineral and organic poisons and even minute traces of copper sulphate, calcium chloride, chloroform, nicotine, *etc.*, may be quickly fatal if the leeches cannot escape.

The fish leeches (Ichthyobdellidae) are mostly marine and have been little cultured. Some of them have been kept in the aquaria at Naples and Plymouth where their natural hosts are available. The freshwater *Piscicola* and related genera may be kept in aquaria, either balanced or with running water, with sunfish, goldfish, or other small fishes as hosts. They will attach their egg capsules to aquatic plants, to stones, or to the glass. They are sometimes exceedingly numerous and harmful in the artificial ponds and tanks of trout and other fish hatcheries.

But most useful are the common species of Glossiphonidae. The smaller species may be kept indefinitely, preferably in a moderately cool and light place out of direct sunlight, in finger bowls or small crystallizing dishes, with a few sprigs of Elodea or similar aquatic plants. A few living water snails, such as Physa or Lymnaea, should be added from time to time for food. Pond or spring water should be used, as tap water is frequently chlorinated or otherwise treated and as a consequence is likely to be injurious. Any dead or dying leeches or snails and their feces should be removed promptly. The water should be changed if it shows any indications of contamination. This is easily done as the leeches usually cling firmly to the sides of the vessel. If, in order to stimulate the growth of the plants, it is desired to place the dishes at a window admitting some sunlight, a few pieces of shale, clam shell, or dead leaves should be added to afford concealment and protection. Twenty or thirty of such small species as *Helobdella stagnalis* or *H. lineata* (*fusca*) or half as many *Glossiphonia complanata* will thrive in a finger bowl, exchange spermatophores and produce fertile eggs in abundance throughout spring and summer. The young are easily raised but care should be taken to avoid overcrowding or undue disturbance as they often die if detached from the mother before most of the yolk is absorbed. After the young become free it is best to remove them to a separate dish. Should it be desired to keep large numbers of these leeches, small balanced aquaria with a bottom layer of sandy soil and with plants with ensheathing leaf stalks, like Sagittaria, in addition to Elodea or Myriophyllum, and a supply of snails will serve admirably.

The larger glossiphonids (*Placobdella parasitica, P. rugosa, P. multi-lineata, P. montifera, etc.*) may be kept indefinitely in finger bowls or other flat glass or clay dishes but only 2 or 3 to 5 or 6, according to size, should be placed in a vessel. Most of these normally feed on the blood of snapping or other water turtles (the last named species on frogs and toads) and a supply of these animals should be available. A meal at intervals of a month or two is sufficient, and it is better to prevent the leeches from becoming too heavily gorged. A meal of blood in early spring is usually followed closely by egg-laying, and often reproduction may be initiated during the winter by placing the leeches in a moderately warm room and permitting them to feed on a turtle or frog.

The Erpobdellidae (various species of Erpobdella, Dina, and Nephelopsis) are equally easy to keep if certain precautions are taken. As they are much more active than most of the Glossiphonidae, they require more spacious quarters and the vessels should be securely covered to prevent them from escaping, particularly at night. These leeches are largely nocturnal, predacious and incline to be amphibious. Consequently they often leave the water at night in search of earthworms and similar food. They are also scavengers and will feed on dead or wounded fish, frogs, *etc.* In confinement they are best fed with small earthworms, the larger aquatic Oligochaeta, insect larvae, or finely chopped fresh meat. Plants are usually unnecessary for leeches of this group, but the water should be kept clean, especially after feeding. Plenty of small pieces of stone, bits of bark, and dead leaves should be provided as places of concealment and for the attachment of egg capsules, which are flat, purse-shaped structures, each containing several eggs attached by a flat side to any firm substratum. Egg capsules are produced in great numbers during the spring and summer.

The true blood sucking and medicinal leeches and the related so-called horse leeches, belong to the family Hirudidae. These include the largest of our freshwater leeches. During the middle decades of the last century when leeches were employed medicinally in great numbers they were extensively cultivated in so-called leech farms, especially in France.*

On a small scale these leeches may be raised in tanks or aquaria or even in earthenware jars. The Indian medicinal leech (Hirudinaria) is cultured largely in this way, the reproducing leeches being placed in a jar containing some wet clay, the egg capsules removed daily and placed in moist clay cups until the young hatch when they are transferred to water and after a time cautiously fed. Our American leeches of this type (Macrobdella, Philobdella) are best kept in low-sided aquaria or tanks with a sloping bank of sandy earth at one end and shallow water at the other. A cover of thick moss on the earth is desirable, as well as some

---

* The technique of leech culture was elaborately described in many books published mostly in France, of which Ebrard—Novelle Monographie des Sangsues Medicinales, 1857, is a good example.

stones or pieces of wood under which the leeches may hide. No aquatic plants are required as these leeches spend much of their time hanging from the sides of the vessel above the water and exposed to the air. A small number may be kept alive indefinitely in a glass or crockery jar with a small amount of water and some Sphagnum moss. The leeches of these genera and especially Philobdella, are less strictly sanguivorous than Hirudo, *etc.*, and add to their normal diet frogs' eggs, aquatic larvae, Oligochaetes, *etc.* A meal of blood about every six months is sufficient. This may be taken from frogs or small fishes, but mammalian blood is better as being greater in amount and percentage of solid matter. Care should be taken to avoid overfeeding, which checks breeding. The egg capsules are deposited in the earth just above the water level and are best slit open with fine scissors to secure the eggs. Our largest leeches belonging to the genus Haemopis are more strictly predacious and often wander at night a considerable distance from the water in search of food. One subspecies has become practically terrestrial, living in garden soil and feeding upon earthworms which are the best food for all species in confinement, although they also eat insect larvae, smaller leeches, snails, and almost any animals of suitable size. Except for feeding, culture methods are similar to those recommended for Macrobdella. All leeches of this family are given to wandering, and the vessels should be securely covered, preferably with fine fly screen.

Phylum XIV

Arthropoda, Class *Crustacea*

Subclass *Entomostraca*, Order branchiopoda

A METHOD FOR REARING ARTEMIA SALINA

R. M. Bond, *Santa Barbara School, Carpinteria, California*

Artemia salina is an anostracan phyllopod crustacean about 12 mm. in length. This genus with practically world-wide distribution may be divided into several forms, some of which are parthenogenetic. The taxonomy of the genus is at present in a confused state. The form found in North America is sexual, and occurs naturally in Epsom Lake, Washington; in certain natural salterns along the California coast from San Francisco southward; in Mono Lake, California; in Little Soda Lake, San Luis Obispo County, California; in Great Salt Lake; and probably elsewhere. It has also appeared in numerous man-made salterns, especially where salt is extracted from seawater by solar evaporation.

Resting eggs float in brine and do not hatch until after drying. They are carried by the wind to the lee side of the saltern and are there piled (mixed with debris) in windrows. They may be collected with a shovel and buckets. Artemia eggs mixed with salt, *etc.*, may be obtained from dealers in tropical fish, from the Leslie Salt Company, Redwood City, California, and from San Francisco Aquarium Society, at a price of about $0.50 an ounce. The dried eggs remain viable for several years.

For physiological experiments, or for other purposes, it is often desirable to separate the eggs as completely as possible from foreign matter. This may be conveniently done as follows: Dry the eggs in air and sift through a 10-mesh sieve; suspend in 10-20 volumes of 15% NaCl in a large separatory funnel, and shake well. Heavy substances will settle and salts will dissolve. The brine should be changed about twice a day till it remains clear (about 6 changes, and the final washing should be drained off as completely as possible. The eggs should then be washed in the funnel with distilled water, caught on a 100-mesh sieve, allowed to drain for an hour, spread out, dried in a current of air at 25-30° C. till thoroughly dry (about 30 hours), and then put through a 50-mesh sieve, through which they will just pass. In the distilled water some eggs will sink and some will float. The former are nearly 100% viable. A majority of the floaters will also hatch, but the percentage of viability will be smaller.

For transportation, young Artemia must be placed in open containers, since they are very susceptible to accumulated CO_2.

The hatching medium may be almost any salt solution not containing much potassium, and ranging in concentration from about 0.1% to 6%. Natural or artificial seawater is as good as anything. After hatching, the nauplii may be transferred directly into more concentrated solutions, but in the higher concentrations the mortality may be great unless the change is made gradually, either by stages or by evaporation. Older animals are much less resistant than nauplii, and are killed by large changes in concentration of the medium, unless the changes are very gradual. When a culture is established it is continued by viviparous reproduction. The first batch of eggs produced by the females usually go at once to the nauplius stage in the brood pouch and then escape. Subsequent batches of eggs from the same females are resting eggs and must be dried before hatching. Under most favorable conditions, a generation takes about 3 weeks.

It is possible to raise the animals in a wide variety of salt mixtures, from about 4% to concentration, always provided that the concentration of potassium is not too high in proportion to other salts present. For getting the animals to reproduce as rapidly and as vigorously as possible, I have found nothing better than seawater with 5 to 8 gm. NaCl per 100 cc. added. Artificial aeration of cultures in unfavorable media is helpful.

For food, particulate matter is required. Ordinary yeast is excellent and convenient. It should be suspended in enough freshwater to make up for evaporation and floated on the salt medium. For starting cultures, however, and for unfavorable media, a rich culture of a one-celled green alga such as *Dunaliella salina, D. viridis,* or *Platymonas subcordaeformis* will be found very helpful. [For culture see p. 134.] Food should be added in small quantities every day or two.

The optimum temperature is about 30° C., but Artemia will live at temperatures as low as 10° and as high as 37°.

REFERENCE

For the culture of Artemia see also p. 215.

Families SIDIDAE and DAPHNIIDAE

CULTURE OF CLADOCERA

A. M. BANTA, *Brown University*

THESE small animals are useful as food for cultures of hydra, young and older aquarium fish, and larval salamanders. More directly as scientific material, they are very useful for laboratory teaching and for research purposes.

They provide a favorable laboratory type for illustration of the structure of an entomostracan for which, because of their transparency, they may readily be used alive to demonstrate most of the morphological structures and in addition several physiological activities (respiration feeding and egestion, circulation, reproduction). They are also advantageous for the study of animal behavior, adjustment to environment adjustment to the annual seasonal cycle, *etc*. They are unexcelled for the study of parthenogenetic reproduction and the environmental control of sex of offspring.

As material for physiological studies or experimentation a clone of cladocerans provides the almost unique advantage of genetic uniformity, which is practically guaranteed by their diploid parthenogenetic reproduction.

For studies in the genetics of a pure line or clone they are probably unequalled among metazoans. Also, thanks to the technique developed by Miss Thelma R. Wood, they may be used for studies of genetics in sexual reproduction, an essential supplement to the analysis of the genetics of the clone.

Live animals with which to start cultures may ordinarily be obtained from small ponds or lakes during the open season and frequently through the ice in winter. *Daphnia longispina* and the species of Simocephalus may be secured in moderate numbers in many sections the year round. Simocephalus also occurs occasionally in dense vegetation in relatively quiet portions of freshwater streams. *Daphnia pulex* is frequently abundant especially in spring and early summer in clear and often in rather dirty pond water. The species of Moina are found in late spring and summer in pig-lot or stable-yard puddles and in other situations where the content of organic matter in the water is high.

The essential food of most Cladocera is bacteria or single-celled, *not* filamentous, algae. For *Daphnia magna,* algae are sometimes more advantageous than bacteria although usually *D. magna* does very well in manure culture medium. But for the other species of Daphnia, for Simocephalus, and some of the Sididae, bacteria seem equally good or better. For Moina, bacteria of the colon group (which generally prevail in manure solutions) seem to be best; and *live* bacteria appear to be essential (Stuart, McPherson, and Cooper, 1931).

The manure solution or "stable tea" to be described below has, in the writer's experience, proven a most satisfactory culture medium. It would be misleading, however, to encourage the worker to think that this culture medium is infallible and that every make-up of medium is equally good. It is, however, a highly successful method.

The manure solution or stable tea medium may be made up in accordance with either of the following formulae in battery jars 9 inches in diameter by 12 inches high or in stone jars or enameled containers approximately that size. Galvanized or copper containers are to be avoided for handling the pond water inasmuch as zinc and copper are extremely toxic to Cladocera.

	Formula I.	Garden soil	2 lb.
		Horse manure	6 oz.
		Pond water	2½ gal.

The ingredients should be placed in the container in the order named. The container may be kept in a cool place or surrounded by running water to keep the temperature 15° to 18° C. After 60 to 72 hours (or 48 hours if the temperature has been higher) the floating manure, if any, is removed and the super-natant liquid strained through a silk bolting cloth (about 130 meshes per inch) or other similarly porous, smooth-threaded cloth. With the final liter or so of the liquid a quantity of silt is placed within the straining cloth and enough silt is worked through by active stirring or gently rubbing through the cloth to produce in settling a layer of sediment 1 or 2 mm. thick on the bottom of the jar. This strained liquid constitutes the stock medium. It requires dilution with pond water before being used as culture medium. The proper dilution may vary between 1 part of the stock medium to 2 to 4 parts of pond water, depending upon the density in appearance of the liquid. The pond water used both in making up the stock medium and in the dilution of it is strained or filtered to avoid contamination with "wild" Cladocera and copepods.*

The horse manure may be obtained from a stable and allowed to age for a week or ten days before use. Fresh manure, dry or moldy manure, or manure more than a month old is ordinarily to be avoided. It is convenient to keep a small supply covered over in a wooden box or cardboard carton, which may be kept outdoors (but sheltered from rain) or in a basement location. The stock medium in process of ripening and the

---

*Tap water has frequently been used after it has stood in an aquarium containing some fine sand or silt for at least a week or ten days. But it is questionable if tap water which has been heavily chlorinated or subjected to other extreme measures to render it potable may be so readily "conditioned" and thus rendered suitable for such use.

culture medium in use are practically odorless and may be kept in the laboratory.

The soil to be used handles better if it is of somewhat sandy nature and of not too fine a texture. The main difficulty with soil of very fine particles is the slowness with which the silt becomes settled and thus leaves the medium transparent—but slightly reddish brown in color.

The culture medium must be well stirred while being dipped out into the culture containers (which are not covered or stoppered) in order that some of the silt may be in each individual culture. Immediately after straining or within two days thereafter the stock medium is at its best. It is ordinarily nearly spent after 5 to 7 days. It has been found that the numbers of bacteria rapidly decrease after about the third day following straining. Presumably the accumulation of by-products of bacterial growth and decrease in numbers of bacteria both contribute to render the older solution less effective as a culture medium.

The second formula for making up the manure solution medium produces a much more concentrated stock medium.

Formula II. Garden soil 2 lb.
Horse manure 12 oz.
Pond water 5 qt.

The handling of this make-up differs from that of Formula I only in that the dilution of the resulting stock medium in preparation for use as culture medium is much greater, ranging from 1 part of the strained medium with 4 to 10 parts of pond water. The writer prefers to use the first formula. Several workers prefer and have excellent results with the second formula.

The stable tea has been used and found effective by the writer in open cultures (not covered or stoppered) in quantities from 25 cc. to 10 liters. We have made few attempts at rearing mass-cultures of Cladocera. Manure solution culture medium may readily be used for mass-cultures if every few days it is renewed or strengthened by the addition of small quantities of manure (preferably tied up in cloth bags and submerged). Others have with good results occasionally thrown a dead guinea pig or other small animal into a tank in which an abundance of a culture of Cladocera is on the decline. A more precise method for such situations as large laboratory tanks or outdoor tanks is the use of manure or the employment of Dr. Embody's soy bean meal [see p. 218] or W. A. Chipman's (1934) cotton seed meal [see p. 212] culture methods. In all of these methods the essential feature is the provision of decaying organic matter upon which the proper bacteria may develop and continue to be present in amply large numbers.

The beginner with the manure solution medium might best first employ approximately the minimum dilutions suggested above and gradually increase the strength of the medium. Medium that is unnecessarily weak will give rise to small clutches of young—fewer than 8 per first clutch for Daphnia or Simocephalus or fewer than 12 for Moina. First clutches of 10 to 18 Daphnia or Simocephalus or of 15 to 25 for Moina are to be expected under approximately optimal cultural conditions. Over-dilution is also indicated by too little apparent density of the medium. In 200 cc. large-mouthed, tall salts bottles it should be moderately opaque grayish brown when first placed in the bottles and be fairly clear of suspended matter and of a light amber color after two days in the bottles. Over-strong medium is indicated if it appears too dense or (other conditions being normal) if a considerable percentage of newly transferred animals die, if the development is retarded and clutches of young are small and are produced irregularly, if embryos die in the mother's brood chamber, or (Moina) if first clutches are large but many of the mothers die after their young are released. A little experience will dictate the amount of dilution to be employed. Two successive make-ups may require somewhat different dilutions. The worker must decide by inspection when the dilution is sufficient.

In the writer's laboratory this medium has proven eminently satisfactory when made up with pond water and with horse manure in the proper condition; when the medium has been used with some of the silt; and when it is properly diluted, over-strong medium being especially avoided. This medium has been used by us primarily for rearing to maturity or longer, without change of medium, cladocerans in 200 cc. bottles (half filled) in pedigree cultures of several species and many different clones of Cladocera. Excellent reproducing specimens for laboratory use may be reared from young in 6 to 8 days with 2 to 4 per bottle.

Dr. D. D. Whitney has used a similar stable tea medium for rearing *Hydatina asplanchna* and other rotifers. In all probability this medium may prove useful for other aquatics (*e.g.*, mosquito larvae, *etc.*) which may be fed primarily upon bacteria and which flourish in natural waters containing considerable organic matter.

BIBLIOGRAPHY

CHIPMAN, W. A., JR. 1934. A new culture method for Cladocerans. *Science* 79:59.

STUART, C. A., McPHERSON, MAURITA, and COOPER, H. J. 1931. Studies on bacteriologically sterile *Moina macrocopa* and their food requirements. *Physiol. Zool.* 4:87.

A NOTE ON BANTA'S CULTURE MEDIUM

GEORGE G. SNIDER, *University of Cincinnati*

A. M. BANTA (1921)* introduced a culture medium for cladocerans which has been, and still is, extensively used.
The following modifications of Banta's medium have been used by the
writer and found to yield even better results than those obtained from the
original directions. First, the manure is collected in a relatively fresh
state and permitted to dry thoroughly. It is then added (8 ozs.) to the
garden soil in finely divided form as described. Second, after the animals
have been in the diluted culture medium (each animal in 100 cc. solution)
4 days, 12-15 cc. strained undiluted medium are added. In the case of
Daphnia magna this culture medium usually results in animals producing from 15-20 or more young in their first broods.

CLADOCERA CULTURE

HAROLD HEATH, *Hopkins Marine Station*

THE equipment used in the culturing of Cladocera comprises three
aquaria each with a capacity of 16 gallons. After two of these have
been filled with water a thin layer of sand is spread over the bottom,
and a few aquatic plants are anchored under small stones. At this stage,
a cloth sack, containing approximately 8 ounces of sheep manure, is
suspended in each aquarium, and the culture is allowed to stand for
3 or 4 weeks. Some investigators, I understand, add lettuce leaves from
time to time, but so far as my experience goes the ordinary decomposition
of the aquatic plants affords, with the fertilizer, a sufficient pabulum for
the bacteria and other unicellular organisms which soon appear. Into
this mixture a stock of Cladocera is now introduced, and where the
manure is renewed each month or so the culture usually flourishes for
months, in several instances for more than a year.

To safeguard against accidents or an unaccountable disappearance of
the crustaceans it has been our custom to keep in reserve a third
aquarium cultured according to the foregoing method but without Cladocera. Also in our series approximately ⅓ of each aquarium was
shaded—though this may not be necessary—and the tank was kept in
sunlight where the diurnal temperature ranged from 54° to 74° F.
during the year.

Furthermore, in this region (Monterey Co., Calif.) it is necessary
to place a screen over the aquaria to prevent the entry of two types of
insects, mosquitoes and back-swimmers (*Notonecta sp.*). The first
named organisms probably do not interfere with the Crustacea, although
it is reasonable to presume that they do diminish the food supply. The

*A convenient culture medium for Daphnids. *Science* 53:557, 1921.

back-swimmers, on the other hand, destroyed several colonies before the trouble was discovered.

In conclusion it may be added that no particular attention has been paid to the pH of the water, nor to the contained salts. In some instances the water was drawn from the municipal mains which in turn are supplied from numerous mountain streams. At other times pond water was employed. So far as could be detected no differences existed in the growth rate of these two types of cultures.

Such, in brief, has been my experience in culturing Cladocera, for which credit is due to several investigators in other parts of the country, whose verbal or written statements have been followed in large measure.

A NEW CULTURE MEDIUM FOR CLADOCERANS*

IN recent investigations in this laboratory it has been necessary to use numbers of cladocerans. In order to raise these animals in quantities and under controlled conditions various culture media have been reviewed and tested. Most of the existing media call for manure to supply the organic matter, but as manure is so variable the substitution of materials of more constant composition was tried. Wiebe (1930) has pointed out that soy bean meal is superior to manure for plankton production in pond fertilization, and more recently the U. S. Bureau of Fisheries has found cotton seed meal quite, if not more, desirable for this purpose. It seemed logical, therefore, to substitute cotton seed meal for manure in cladoceran culture media. This change produced a very satisfactory culture medium, having several advantages over the manure infusions as suggested by Banta (1921). [See p. 208.]

Pond water was filtered through coarse filter paper and added to a mixture of fine garden soil and cotton seed meal (commercial cotton seed meal, as used in dairy feeds), in the proportions of 1 liter of filtered water to 90 grams of garden soil and 17 grams of cotton seed meal. After a thorough stirring, the mixture was set aside at room temperature in large Erlenmeyer flasks for five days. During this period the mixture fermented and produced considerable gas. At the end of five days the supernatant fluid was decanted and then strained through muslin. Analyses showed that the strained fluid contained an almost pure culture of *B. coli*. The strained fluid was diluted with filtered pond water before using and re-strained through muslin whenever bacterial masses developed. The pH of the final diluted product was adjusted to 7.2 by the addition of sodium carbonate.

In strong concentration of this medium bacterial masses formed which

---

*Reprinted, with slight changes, from an article in *Science* 79:59, 1934, by WALTER A. CHIPMAN, JR., *U. S. Bureau of Fisheries*.

interfered with the free movement of the Daphnia and often resulted in their death, but by a dilution of 1 part of the strained fluid as decanted from the original mixture with 100 parts of filtered pond water a medium was obtained which remained clear and in which Daphnia grew rapidly and produced normal clones. It has been found desirable to renew the media in which the cultures of animals are growing from time to time, *i.e.*, at periods of a week or more, but the addition of more bacteria to the cotton seed medium, as suggested for manure infusions by Stuart and Banta, has not been found necessary. Fresh stock supplies of the cotton seed mixture have been prepared each week, a small amount of an old mixture being added each time to insure inoculation with the original bacteria.

REFERENCES

For the culture of Cladocera see also p. 136.

BIBLIOGRAPHY

BANTA, A. M. 1921. *Science* 53:557.
STUART, C. A., and BANTA, A. M. 1931. *Physiol. Zool.* 4:72.
WIEBE, A. H. 1930. *Bull. U. S. Bur. Fish.* 46:137.

M. E. D.

A CULTURE MEDIUM FOR DAPHNIA*

FLEISCHMANN'S yeast has been fed to a mass culture of *Daphnia magna* with striking results, reproduction and growth being markedly more rapid, and population more dense than with any of the usual media.

About ¼ of a fresh yeast cake is mixed into a uniform suspension with from 50 to 100 cc. of water, and poured into the aquarium, which contains from 60 to 70 liters of water. The feeding is repeated every 5 or 6 days. It is necessary to have a stream of air bubbling through the medium at all times, or the yeast may prove lethal, probably by giving off CO_2.

The method has not been tried on other species of Cladocera, except *Moina affinis*, with which it was equally successful, nor has it been tried with few animals in small containers, but it is so successful in the mass culture that it seems wise to make the food material known. It should be particularly useful in physiological work, in which the usual manure infusion may be a source of large quantities of unknown solutes. It should also be valuable in raising Daphnia in large numbers as food for other organisms.

M. E. D.

*Reprinted, with slight changes, from *Science* 79:60, 1934, by R. M. BOND, *Santa Barbara School, Carpinteria, California.*

METHODS FOR CULTURING DAPHNIA

ARTHUR D. HASLER, *U. S. Bureau of Fisheries*

1. *Algae Method.* a. Run tap water into battery jars or butter tubs and allow to stand for 24 hrs. for the purpose of getting rid of air bubbles; otherwise the water-fleas adhere to these and are carried to the surface where they soon perish.

b. Add sufficient algae to tinge the water slightly green and inoculate with Daphnia.

c. The alga *Coccomyxa simplex* may be cultured in large quantities by a method developed by H. Schomer. When the culture is at its peak it is centrifuged with a Birge-Juday centrifuge and it is this centrifugate that is added to the Daphnia culture. The algae may be grown in battery jars. The Schomer medium consists of:

$$KH_2PO_4 \quad 2.7 \text{ gm. per liter}$$
$$MgSO_4 \quad 4.9 \text{ gm. per liter}$$
$$Ca(NO_3)_2 \quad 4.7 \text{ gm. per liter}$$

This method surpasses any I have tried in bringing about maximum rate of reproduction.

2. *Yeast Method* (Modified from Bond's). a. Same as (a) above.

b. Make a thick suspension of moist Star or Fleischmann's yeast in a flask by shaking chunks vigorously until a suspension forms; then add the suspension to the culture until the water is slightly milky. When the water-fleas have cleared it, add the same amount again. Water should be completely changed once a month and the crop seined often to prevent crowding. Aeration is not necessary, but the maximum reproductive rate is reached with aeration. Stirring once a day is sufficient to keep the culture going satisfactorily.

c. Augmenting the yeast diet with the algae as described above is recommended. If the cultures are in good light, algae generally grow on the sides. They may be scraped off the walls with a razor blade and then broken up by stirring. These serve well to augment the yeast diet. One may also add about a teaspoonful of dry sheep manure per 4 gal. every two weeks. The addition of these substances gives *D. magna,* for example, the natural red color, whereas if they are raised on yeast alone their color is almost white.

3. *Banta's Method.* [See p. 208.] This method gives very satisfactory results. I raised Daphnia for 9 months in total darkness, using culture water made according to his directions.

4. *Sheep Manure method.* a. Let water stand in suitable containers 24 hours.

b. To every gallon of water, add 1 teaspoonful of dry sheep manure,

0.5 gm. of acid phosphate and a liter of aqueous soil filtrate (water that has been allowed to filter through rich garden soil).

c. Allow mixture to stand for a day and inoculate with Daphnia.

5. *Aquarium water method.* Aquaria that have become very green with a phytoplankton growth furnish a very convenient culture medium for Daphnia. Just remove the fish or transfer the water to another container and inoculate with Daphnia. This method was recommended to a tropical fish fancier who was having trouble with "green aquaria." He removed the fish, then inoculated with Daphnia; after the Daphnia had multiplied sufficiently to "clear" the aquaria, the fish were put back and had a real feast!

20° C. is a satisfactory temperature at which to keep these cultures.

Artemia may also be raised by any of these culture methods. I have kept individual Artemias living for 4 months by using algae. The salt content must be regulated (2 teaspoonfuls to ½ pint of water).

If it is desired to cease the Daphnia cultures during vacation periods, it is only necessary to chill or "crowd" the cultures and thus produce ephippial eggs. These may be collected and stored. To hatch them, place outside a window for two weeks of October weather so that they freeze and thaw several times, then place in water to hatch. They may also be artificially frozen in a refrigerator; 8 thaws and freezes give the maximum yield.

BIBLIOGRAPHY

BANTA, A. M. 1921. A convenient culture medium for daphnids. *Science* 53:557.

BAUER, V. 1921. Wie ernähren sich die Wasserflöhe. *Allg. Fisch. Zeit. Jahrg.* 46:30.

GEYER, HANS. 1909. Einige Bemerkungen u. die Zucht von Daphnia. *Wochenschrift Aquar.-Terrar. Kde. Jahrg.* 26:32.

KNÖRRICH, FRIEDR. WILH. 1901. Studien ueber die Ernaehrungsbedingungen einiger fuer die Fischproduction wichtiger Microorganismen des Süsswassers. *Forsch. Ber. biol. Stat. Blön.* 8:1.

DAPHNIA CULTURE

ALFRED W. SCHLUCHTER, *Dearborn, Michigan*

THE writer has used several methods which seem to work fairly well. The first is a method similar to that described by Mr. Walter Chipman.* [See p. 212]. A wheat bran fermentation was used here, instead of cotton seed meal. This was made as follows: About 20 grams of wheat bran was added to 3 liters of water and allowed to ferment for about one week in a moderately warm place. If the Daphnia culture was to be carried out in the open where plenty of sunlight was present, this culture medium was diluted to about 1 to 100 parts of water and then ¼ to ½

Science 79:59, 1934.

gram each of sodium chloride and calcium sulfate per liter of water were added. This solution was stocked with Daphnia. More infusion was added later as needed.

Experiments have shown that sunlight is important in the propagation of Daphnia and many methods which are successful in strong sunlight will not work when sunlight is completely absent.

The second method was found best and most desirable for indoor propagation since sunlight is not necessary. It depends essentially on a combination of bran infusion and liver. Although the latter may be used alone, experiments indicate that a combination of the two may be more desirable than either alone.

Ten grams of wheat bran were added to 1500 cc. of water and fermented a week, as before. The supernatant fluid was poured off and discarded; only the bran residue was used. This was then added to a shallow tank of about 100 liters' capacity, salt and calcium sulfate being added as before. The liver was heated as rapidly as possible until the proteins were coagulated. It was then cut in slices about 1 mm. thick and of these slices about 0.1 to 0.05 grams per liter of water were added to the tank containing the bran infusion. If too much bran infusion or liver was added, Daphnia came to the top because of lack of oxygen. It was then necessary to replace some of the old with fresh water.

After the liver is heated it may be dried by keeping in a cool place and then used as required. It has been observed that such liver slices in contact with the water will tend to become moldy in the absence of a sufficient number of Daphnia, but if enough Daphnia are present the mold will disappear. Nearly all of this work was done with *Daphnia magna*, although the above methods were found to apply to several other Cladocerans as well.

PROPAGATING DAPHNIA AND OTHER FORAGE ORGANISMS INTENSIVELY IN SMALL PONDS*

FOR the first few years we tried to keep cultures going continuously throughout the summer in the same pond, merely adding from time to time a definite amount of fertilizer. The result was that very successful cultures were maintained during May and part of June which always ran out in July but seemed to come back in late September and October.

The most important causes for the diminishing supply seemed to be the population density, the accumulation of waste products not only from the Daphnia themselves but from micro-organisms also present, predatory enemies of Daphnia, and probably water temperatures somewhat above

---

*Abstracted from an article in *Trans. Amer. Fish. Soc.* 64:205, 1934, by G. C. EMBODY, *Cornell University*, and W. O. SADLER, *Mississippi College*.

82° F. All of these factors have been mentioned before by various investigators, especially by Dr. A. M. Banta and his associates. All of the above mentioned factors except predatory enemies favor the production of so-called winter eggs, which is usually an indication that the culture is on the wane.

In order to have strong cultures at all seasons it becomes necessary to keep the individual Daphnia in the active condition of producing asexual or so-called summer eggs only, which demands the elimination of the inhibitive factors just mentioned.

A too dense population, of course, is easily reduced by using the Daphnia. The excessive accumulation of waste matter is corrected by a change of water in the pond. Predatory enemies are controlled partly by sterilizing the pond bottom and sides immediately before starting a culture and later by spraying the surface with some non-toxic animal oil, such as herring oil, salmon oil, or cod-liver oil. The water temperature cannot be controlled and, consequently, where it ranges above 82° F. for any length of time it may be difficult or impossible to produce cultures of *Daphnia magna.*

A population density reaches the maximum under the experimental conditions maintained in our ponds in from 16 to 26 days with the water temperature varying between 70° and 80° F. Consequently cultures are permitted to develop for 21 days, when they are fed to the fish and an entirely new culture with fresh water is started. The schedule of operations is as follows:

First day—Pond is drained, bottom and sides thoroughly disinfected with a strong solution of chlorinated lime, allowed to stand 6 hours; then refilled, fertilized, and stocked with large Daphnia from an active culture.

Fifth to seventh day—Second fertilization.

Tenth to fourteenth day—Third fertilization.

Twenty-first day—Drawing the pond and using the Daphnia.

In general this routine was continued through several summers from May to October and when a proper amount and kind of fertilizer was administered, the results were consistently good.

Although we have tried to maintain pure cultures of Daphnia, other organisms have naturally appeared and multiplied. Some of these are desirable food animals but others are predators.

Several little hard-shelled ostracods have appeared in considerable numbers, especially late in the culture period. We believe there is some connection between their abundance and a decline in the production of Daphnia, without as yet having direct evidence that they actually prey upon living Daphnia. Disinfection of the pond does not entirely eliminate them but nevertheless helps to keep them under control.

Midges of the genus Chironomus are attracted to the pond within a day or so after adding fertilizer, probably by the odors of fermentation, and deposit enormous numbers of eggs. These add considerably to the production of the pond. Mosquitoes likewise are attracted at about the same time and their characteristic floating egg masses become conspicuous all over the surface.

These three associated organisms may be considered beneficial insofar as they increase considerably the production of fish food. The mosquitoes, however, are obnoxious as adults and since they transform to the adult stage long before the Daphnia culture reaches a peak, it is probably better to exterminate them with non-toxic oil spray 4 to 6 days after the eggs appear. Other groups of animals which almost invariably appear are the back-swimmers, larvae of aquatic beetles, nymphs of dragonflies and damselflies, and hydra. All are predatory on Daphnia and midges. It is well known that the oil spray kills all insects that must come to the surface for air, such as the larvae of mosquitoes, beetles and adult backswimmers. The dragonfly and damselfly nymphs and hydras are eliminated when the pond is drained and disinfected.

TABLE I.

Amount of Fertilizer per 100 Cubic Feet of Water and Its Apportionment
(Experimental Ponds at Ithaca, N. Y.)

Fertilizer	Soy Bean Meal	Cotton Seed Meal	Dry Buttermilk	Sheep Manure and Soy Bean Meal
Initial Dose	1 pt.	1 qt.	½ pt.	4 qts. Sh. M. 1 qt. B. M.
2nd Dose	5th day— 1 pt.	7th day— 1.5 pt.	7th day— ½ pt.	14th day— ½ pt. B. M.
3rd Dose	10th day— 1 pt.	14th day— 1.5 pt.	14th day— ½ pt.	
4th Dose	15th day— ½ pt.			

Many different fertilizers have been tried, including manure from horses and cattle, dried sheep manure, acid phosphate, soy bean meal, cotton seed meal, dry buttermilk, and alfalfa meal. The alfalfa meal produced only fair cultures and required such a large quantity of material that experiments were early discontinued. The dried sheep manure used in combination with either acid phosphate or soy bean meal produced average cultures consistently. The wet animal manures were from ordinary barnyard piles containing much straw and slightly rotted. The resulting cultures were about average but not always dependable. The fertilizers which gave cultures averaging the highest were dry buttermilk, soy bean meal, and cotton seed meal. Very little difference between them was noted.

Peak cultures seem to require from 30 to 50% more cotton seed meal than soy bean meal and the culture period is somewhat longer than with the former. On the other hand, cotton seed meal, like animal manures, stains the water a deep brown, resulting in deeply colored red Daphnia. The deep color seems also to prevent undue growth of blanket algae. The soy bean meal produces light gray Daphnia and an abundance of free-moving micro-algae which color the water green. It also encourages the growth of blanket algae.

The quantity of Daphnia necessary to start a successful culture, within certain limits, is not so important as the physiological condition of the mother organisms. They should be active summer egg producers. Almost always a few will be found with winter eggs. If the proportion is large, specimens from such a culture should be discarded. In the experiments reported here, from 25 to 100 cc. of mother organisms were generally used. We believe that 50 cc. is sufficient for 100 cu. ft. of water. They are measured by pouring water containing Daphnia into a tall graduate held in the sunlight. The individuals very soon settle to the bottom and the quantity may be determined with ease.

The water supply of the seven concrete propagating ponds used is controlled by dams in such a way that a constant level is automatically maintained in each pond without overflow. The water is therefore stagnant at all times. Each pond has an independent drain which leads directly into a bass-rearing pond. Hence all food organisms produced may be drained off directly into the rearing pond by removing a standpipe. During the last four years it has been customary to operate them in rotation, thus producing several crops in each during the summer season.

M. E. D.

DAPHNIA CULTURE

Libbie H. Hyman, *New York City*

TO CULTIVATE Daphnia, bring lettuce leaves, preferably of a green, leafy type of lettuce such as Boston lettuce, to a boil. Do not continue boiling. Place the boiled lettuce leaves in containers having 6 to 8 inches of water in the proportions of 1 good-sized lettuce leaf to each 6 square inches of bottom. After 2 or 3 days add Daphnia. These may be obtained often from pet shops or dealers in biological supplies and also in almost any somewhat stagnant pond by means of a plankton net. After the lettuce leaves have disintegrated additional lettuce leaves should be added from time to time and also small pieces of raw liver or the entrails or corpses of small animals such as tadpoles, mice, rats, *etc.* In adding such material it is essential that only a moderate quantity be used. The water must not become foul or cloudy as this will kill the

Daphnias. In general, the Daphnia culture should be kept supplied with fresh food, either lettuce leaves or raw flesh (preferably both) up to the limit possible without making the water cloudy. This limit must be learned by experience and depends upon the size of the container. Whenever it is seen that the Daphnias are not flourishing as rapidly as before, new food should be added.

Daphnias may not be grown indefinitely in the same culture water. From time to time it is necessary to strain out the Daphnias and place them in freshly made cultures. When it is evident that the Daphnias are no longer multiplying well despite addition of fresh food, they should be transferred to an entirely new culture.

REFERENCES

For the culture of Scapholeberis see below.
For the culture of Simocephalus see p. 207.
For the culture of Moina see p. 207.
For the culture of *Moina affinis* see p. 213.

Family CHYDORIDAE

CHYDORIDAE

CHARLES H. BLAKE, *Massachusetts Institute of Technology*

IN RAISING *Pleuroxus hamulatus* I found that a few cc. of water in a Syracuse watch glass sufficed for an individual. The young were removed to separate glasses a few hours after birth, each being provided with freshwater which had been stored in contact with air and with Elodea. An aquarium provided a mixed culture of Stichococcus and Ankistrodesmus. [For culture see p. 227.] Enough of this was placed in the watch glass to form a thin, green coating on the bottom. After a few days most of it had been passed through the animal's gut and had become agglomerated and no longer suitable for food. The specimen was then transferred to a fresh glass made up as before. Crowding caused the production of two of the hitherto unknown males but all specimens were short-lived when crowded. Ephippia are formed in the absence of males or by crowding and, as in Scapholeberis, an individual may revert to the production of parthenogenetic eggs. Unfertilized ephippial eggs degenerate. Mass-cultures were not attempted with this species, but from observations in nature and on *Alona guttata* in the aquarium, it is apparent that a relatively great volume of water must be allowed per individual and an abundance of unicellular green algae as a source of food. The actual food material is unknown to me since Ankistrodesmus is apparently unharmed by its passage through the gut. Abundant oxygen is necessary.

Order COPEPODA

CULTURE METHODS FOR PELAGIC MARINE COPEPODS

GEORGE L. CLARKE, *Woods Hole Oceanographic Institution* and *Harvard University*

PELAGIC marine copepods are extremely delicate and sensitive to slight changes in their environment and no completely satisfactory technique for culturing them has yet been worked out. The methods described below are the result of preliminary experiments which have been undertaken at Woods Hole using the following species: *Centropages typicus* and *C. hamatus, Labidocera aestiva, Acartia tonsa,* and *Calanus finmarchicus.*

Collecting. The copepods were collected by making short hauls with a plankton net from the laboratory power boat. Each haul was just sufficiently long (½-4 min.) to obtain the desired number of specimens (50-200), and no more, in order to avoid overcrowding. The mesh of the net was selected according to the size of the copepods desired, the coarsest possible net being used in each case so that the amount of other plankton material taken at the same time might be reduced to a minimum. The animals were protected from harmful crowding and abrasion by closing the tail of the net with a 2-liter glass jar. At the end of the haul the glass jar was removed from the net and in the case of Centropages, Acartia, and Labidocera, which were obtained in Woods Hole Harbor and Vineyard Sound not more than 15 minutes' run from the laboratory, the copepods were left undisturbed in the jar (but protected from the sun) until the laboratory was reached. But in the case of Calanus, which could be obtained only in Vineyard Sound off No Man's Land (near the bottom)—requiring a 3-hour trip back to the laboratory—the catch was diluted and kept at a low temperature by placing the containers in the boat's ice box. Immediately upon arrival at the laboratory the copepods were transferred by means of a large-mouthed pipette to the containers to be used for culturing.

Containers. The suitability of a variety of containers, including large battery jars, beakers, Erlenmeyer flasks, and small crystallizing dishes was tested. The size and shape of the container was not found to have any significant effect on survival as long as the animals were not unduly crowded. When the culture water was not changed, an allowance of 20 cc. of water per copepod appeared to be adequate provided that the animals did not tend to cluster in one part of the culture dish. For the purpose of keeping track of the condition of individuals small containers were found most suitable. Erlenmeyer flasks of 250-500 cc. capacity, which were plugged with cotton stoppers or covered with inverted petri dishes, were used, and small crystallizing dishes (50 x 35 mm.), a number of which could be set in a large crystallizing dish and covered with a glass plate, were found especially convenient and were suitable for two copepods each.

Water. The water used in the containers was ordinarily taken from the laboratory salt water tap. No improvement was found to result from using water brought in directly from the harbor or from Vineyard Sound. In a few cases the copepods appeared to fare perfectly well for a week or two without any change of water. In other cases the copepods were transferred after a certain number of days by means of a pipette to fresh containers, but this procedure was very laborious and often resulted in the loss or injury of some of the animals. A better method was to pour away all but a little of the original culture medium, leaving the copepods in the bottom corner of the dish and then to replenish with fresh seawater. It has not yet been determined how frequently it is necessary to change the culture water under various conditions. Very good survival was obtained in two sets of experiments, described in detail by Clarke and Gellis (1935), in which the culture medium was run continuously through flasks in which the copepods were confined.

Stirring and Aeration. If the copepods were at all crowded they died off rapidly unless stirring in some form was provided. When beakers, or other wide-mouthed vessels, are employed, stirring may be accomplished conveniently by using glass plungers activated by the Plymouth siphon device [Harvey, 1928, p. 57] or by an electric motor (Hagmeier, 1930). Such stirring provides at the same time a certain amount of aeration, which is probably sufficient in most cases. More effective aeration may be obtained by bubbling compressed air from a tap filter pump slowly through the water by means of glass tubes reaching to the bottom of the containers. The stream of bubbles brings about a slow circulation of the water which makes mechanical stirring unnecessary. This method is especially convenient for narrow-mouthed containers such as Erlenmeyer flasks. When small culture dishes were used with only a few copepods in each, stirring and aeration were found unnecessary.

Temperature. Temperature was controlled by placing the Erlenmeyer flasks and the crystallizing dishes in a constant temperature tank where they rested half submerged on a wire rack. Two of these tanks were available and were maintained at different temperatures (kept constant to 0.1° C.) by means of two Kelvinator cooling units operated by Hiergesell thermo-regulators and relays. A third and lower temperature (5-6° C.) was obtained by placing the containers in a large refrigerator. It was found that for all the species investigated the copepods died off rapidly if the temperature was allowed to rise above 20° C. Below 20° C. in the case of Calanus survival was improved progressively at lower temperatures down to 5-6° C., but the molting of shells became less frequent. Further information on effect of different temperatures on other species is wanting, nor is it known to what degree constancy of temperature must be maintained.

Illumination. The effect of light on the well-being of copepods has not been adequately investigated. Since the constant temperature tanks which were used in these experiments were open at the top only, the culture dishes placed in them received indirect illumination reflected from the ceiling. Direct sunlight is certainly harmful and there is no doubt that the illumination should be weak. The copepods placed in the refrigerator in complete darkness survived well for several weeks, and it is possible that light is not necessary for these animals at any time.

Food. The question of what forms the chief food of copepods is a controversial one and is being intensively investigated at various laboratories and from various angles. The matter has been reviewed by Clarke (1934) and the specific experiments carried out at Woods Hole have been described in detail by Clarke and Gellis (1935). Since a satisfactory food for culturing has not yet been found, a brief statement of methods only will be attempted here. The amount of food and frequency of feeding required in different cases is highly variable for in early experiments with Centropages it was found that death supervened within a few days if food material was not added, whereas in the case of Calanus a few specimens lived for 14 days in continuously flowing water from which all particulate matter had been removed by a membrane filter.

The survival of Centropages, Acartia, and Labidocera was improved by adding to the culture dishes planktonic material obtained by centrifuging seawater, or in larger quantities, by making short hauls with a diatom net. "Persistent" cultures of diatoms and green flagellates grown in the laboratory* were also used. Experience showed that organisms which grow encrusted on the bottom and walls of the vessel were not suitable for food, probably because copepods, being filter feeders, can take in material in suspension only. However, the addition of none of these foods prolonged the life of the majority of the animals for more than about two weeks. When the flagellates were added to the water, green material could be seen in the intestines of the copepods and many excretory casts were found in the bottom of the container, but molted shells were observed only rarely.

In the case of Calanus more elaborate experiments have been carried out since this article was originally prepared. Reference had best be made to the published reports (Fuller and Clarke, 1936, and Fuller, 1937). Briefly, these experiments show that Calanus will live for several weeks and molt readily when provided with fine planktonic material. Bacteria are not, however, an important article of diet. Precisely which

---

*For method see Clarke and Gellis (1935).

elements of the plankton are the chief source of food in nature is still to be determined. When this question has been settled, it will probably be possible to grow the required food organisms in the laboratory and to keep Calanus and other copepods in culture indefinitely. (See addenda on p. 571.)

BIBLIOGRAPHY

BOND, R. M. 1933. A contribution to the study of the natural food-cycle in aquatic environments with particular consideration of microörganisms and dissolved organic matter. *Bull. Bingham Oceanog. Coll.* 4(Art. 4):1.

CANNON, H. G. 1928. On the feeding mechanism of the copepods, *C. finmarchicus* and *Diaptomus gracilis. Brit. J. Exper. Biol.* 6:131.

CLARKE, G. L. 1934. The rôle of copepods in the economy of the sea. *Proc. Fifth Pacific Sci. Congress,* Canada, 1933. 3,A5.5:2017.

—— and GELLIS, S. S. 1935. The nutrition of copepods in relation to the food-cycle of the sea. *Biol. Bull.* 68:231.

CRAWSHAY, L. R. 1915. Notes on experiments in the keeping of plankton animals under artificial conditions. *J. Mar. Biol. Assoc.* N. S. 10:555.

DAKIN, W. J. 1908. Notes on the alimentary canal and food of the copepods. *Intern. Rev. Hydrobiol. u. Hydrogr.* 1:772.

ESTERLEY, C. O. 1916. The feeding habits and food of pelagic copepods and the question of nutrition by organic substances in solution in the water. *Univ. Calif. Publ. Zool.* 16:171.

FULLER, J. L. 1937. Feeding rate of *Calanus finmarchicus* in relation to environmental conditions. *Biol. Bull.* 72. (In press)

FULLER, J. L., and CLARKE, G. L. 1936. Further experiments on the feeding of *Calanus finmarchicus. Biol. Bull.* 70:308-320.

HAGMEIER, A. 1930. Die Züchtung verschiedener wirbelloser Meerestiere. 1930. *In* Abderhalden: *Handb. biol. Arbeit.,* Abt. 9, Teil 5, Heft 4, Lief. 326, pp. 465-598.

HARVEY, H. W. 1928. Biological Chemistry and Physics of Sea Water. Cambridge University Press, Cambridge, England.

LEBOUR, M. V. 1922. The food of plankton organisms. I. *J. Mar. Biol. Assoc.* 12:644.

MARSHALL, SHEINA. 1924. The food of *Calanus finmarchicus* during 1923. *Ibid.* 13:473.

MURPHY, HELEN E. 1923. Life cycle of *Oithona nana,* reared experimentally. *Univ. Calif. Publ. Zool.* 22:449.

YONGE, C. M. 1928. Feeding mechanisms in invertebrates. *Biol. Reviews,* 3:21.

—— 1931. Digestive processes in marine invertebrates and fishes. *J. du Conseil* 6:175.

Families CALANIDAE and HARPACTICIDAE

NOTES ON THE CULTIVATION OF TIGRIOPUS FULVUS AND CALANUS FINMARCHICUS

R. M. BOND, *Santa Barbara School, Carpinteria, California*

TIGRIOPUS FULVUS

THIS harpacticid copepod is very large for the group. It has been reported from the Mediterranean, the coast of California, and elsewhere in warm climates. In suitable localities it is found, often in incredible numbers, in spray-pools above high tide mark. It may be conveniently collected with a tea strainer or any sort of net. It is rarer and sometimes even difficult to find after a severe storm has washed out the pools which it inhabits, but in a few weeks is as numerous as ever. The animal may be raised in Syracuse dishes or in any larger containers. The natural medium is seawater, which may be diluted as much as half, or concentrated to as much as 8% total salinity. The animal can withstand very rapid changes within these limits. I have usually used natural strength seawater.

The food of these copepods probably consists of bacteria, but this has not been determined. They multiply rapidly if there is plenty of decaying vegetable matter in the medium, such as bits of seaweed, or even a piece of cheesecloth. The richest culture I ever obtained had a heavy growth of *Platymonas subcordaeformis* in it. The alga may have served as food, or simply to aerate the medium.

If the food supply is at all abundant, it is necessary to use rather shallow containers or to employ compressed air for oxygenation. In either case, care must be taken to see that evaporation does not increase the salinity of the medium beyond the tolerance of the copepod. The optimum temperature seems to be about 25-30° C.

CALANUS FINMARCHICUS, AND OTHER PELAGIC COPEPODS

These copepods are not easily kept alive in the laboratory, and it is very difficult to raise adults from eggs. The greatest mortality seems to be in passing from the last copepodid stage to the adult. A number of different methods, however, have met with at least partial success. Miss Lebour* and others recommend the Plymouth plunger jar. [See p. 21.] For old stages I have had equal success with 500 cc. Erlenmeyer flasks containing about 300 cc. of seawater in which 4 to 6 copepods were kept.

Probably the natural food consists mainly of small diatoms and other unicellular algae, Protozoa, and bacteria. Enough food is contained in seawater filtered through coarse filter paper if the water is kept flowing. Otherwise Nitzschia [For culture see p. 33.], Dunaliella [For culture see p. 134.], or, still better, *Platymonas subcordaeformis* [For culture see p. 135] may be added (1-5% of algal culture).

Calanus is found in waters with temperatures from about 4° to above 20° C., but has a rather sharp upper limit of tolerance, which appears to be different in races from different regions. Specimens taken off Pacific Grove, California, lived several weeks at 17.5° C. Those from near Woods Hole died quickly above 15° C. It should generally be safe to keep the animals between 12° and 15° C.

Sci. Progr., London, 27:494, 1933.

Medium and containers should be changed once a week or oftener to prevent the animals becoming entangled in bacteria. Calanus and several of the other pelagic copepods may be kept for some days or even weeks in a healthy condition in an icebox at 5°-6° C. if not too crowded, and if kept in containers wide enough to allow an ample air supply.

REFERENCES

Family Diaptomidae
For the culture of Diaptomus see p. 143.

Family CYCLOPIDAE

CULTURE METHODS FOR CYCLOPOID COPEPODS AND THEIR FORAGE ORGANISMS

R. E. COKER, *University of North Carolina*

Cyclops viridis, C. serrulatus, and *C. vernalis* have been reared very successfully when fed on a mixed bacteria and protozoan culture with occasional supplemental feeding from an algal culture; these cultures are prepared by one of the methods described below.

PROTOZOAN CULTURES

Horse Manure. Fill several quart jars each ⅓ full of fresh horse manure and nearly to the top with filtered tap water. After several days add a few pipettes of pond water or some mixed protozoan culture to the original jars; later jars are best inoculated from the best of the older cultures. Putrid conditions existing during the first few days seem effectively to sterilize the culture against copepods that might have been introduced with the tap or pond water. Rich cultures of Protozoa should develop within about a week; selection may then be made of the best as measured by richness in Protozoa and bacteria and freedom from cloudiness due to undesirable bacteria. A good jar may continue to furnish a satisfactory food medium for 1 or 2 months, but fresh cultures should be started at intervals of 2 or 3 weeks.

Sheep Manure. Fill a jar ¼ full of dried sheep manure (obtainable from seed or fertilizer stores) and nearly to the top with water. Treat like the horse manure cultures, although inoculation may not be necessary.

Strong hay infusion. This is prepared by steeping hay, preferably timothy, in hot water for an hour or more (standard laboratory method). Place the strained liquid in open dishes and, after a few days, inoculate as above.

ALGAL CULTURES

Ankistrodesmus, or other unicellular alga. Culture methods may be found in botanical texts, but we have had best results with rich cultures of Ankistrodesmus that have developed naturally in aquaria in the laboratory in which small fish have been kept and fed with fish roe or in cladoceran cultures kept in bright sunlight and fed with small quantities of sheep manure infusion. The green water from the aquarium is passed through filter paper and kept in covered jars for observation during several weeks to guard against the presence of wild copepods. Occasional fertilization of these clean aquaria with sheep manure or with liquid fertilizers in small quantity may be desirable.

Mougeotia. A small dense tuft of the filamentous alga, Mougeotia, is held over a watch glass of water while successive close choppings are made with a scissors. This food medium then consists of short fragments of algal filaments, extruded protoplasm and water; after stirring, a few drops may be used in place of the unicellular algae. Results have been excellent in growth and fertility of the Crustacea.

CYCLOPS

The amount of medium to be used and the frequency of feeding depend upon temperature and conditions of the experiment. In our practice a female with sacs is placed in a small vial with about 3 cc. of filtered pond or aquarium water and 1 cc. of mixed food (Protozoa with a little algae). As the manure cultures become older, dilution with pond water may be unnecessary. The culture water is changed or supplemented about every two days at 23° C. or about every two weeks at 6° C. The condition of the culture water may be appraised, and the need for supplemental feeding determined by looking through the vial toward a light; the liquid should neither appear cloudy nor have the excessive clearness indicative of food deficiency. Adjust feeding to maintain a reasonable abundance of Protozoa, evident to the eye, and a suggestion of greenness in the liquid or on the bottom of the vessel. Nauplii in quantity may be kept in larger containers with about 4 cc. of medium per nauplius and, if required, one or two supplemental feedings in the course of development.

The methods employed have given maximum rates of growth (complete life cycles for *C. vernalis* in 7 days), high fertility through several generations, and virtually no disease or fungus. Copepods reared in the protozoan cultures without algae have lived well, and in many cases have grown rapidly, but they have displayed greater individual variation in rate of growth and less fertility than those given some plant food.

REFERENCES

For the culture of cyclopids see also p. 230.
For the culture of Cyclops see also p. 143.
Family Harpacticidae
For the culture of *Tigriopus fulvus* see p. 224.
Family Canthocamptidae
For the culture of Canthocamptus see p. 143.
For the culture of Copepoda see also p. 136.

Order OSTRACODA

SUGGESTIONS FOR CULTURING OSTRACODS

ESTHER M. PATCH and LOWELL E. NOLAND, *University of Wisconsin*

OSTRACODS are commonly found in nature at the bottom of pools, lakes, or sluggish streams, where there is dead organic matter which has passed the active fermentation stage of decay and is slowly decomposing in a medium where oxygen is present at least in small amounts.

To rear ostracods in the laboratory it is desirable to duplicate natural conditions as closely as possible, for instance by a hay-wheat infusion made as follows: boil 2 grams of whole wheat grains and 3 grams of timothy hay in enough water to cover them. Pond or lake water will serve best since running water may carry pollutions, city water may contain chemicals used in purification, and distilled water may have undesirable materials or lack desirable ones for optimum animal growth. Boil the hay and wheat slowly for about 10 minutes and replace the water with about a liter of that originally used, filtered or boiled so that no Entomostraca will be present. Set aside for a few days until the bacterial decomposition has passed from the acid to the alkaline stage, when the ostracods may safely be placed in the medium. More of the boiled wheat and hay and more of the boiled or filtered water may be added from time to time as required.

Cultures of these small Crustacea thrive well in a wide dish, covered to retard evaporation but not so tightly as to exclude air. There are species differences among ostracods in the requirements for light and temperature as well as for food, but most of the common species do well at ordinary room temperature and in sunlight which favors the growth of algae. The above culture medium has been successful in rearing ostracods to feed to very small salamander larvae. Thin slices of potato (suggested by R. W. Sharpe in "Fresh Water Biology," edited by Ward and Whipple) have also been used, as well as decayed lettuce.

Ostracods may usually be gathered with a weighted net from the mud or vegetation at the bottom of ponds and lakes; at our laboratory they have been obtained during the winter from mud drawn up through an opening in the ice. If the active forms are not available, they may be cultured from egg masses which are often present on submerged stones or plants and may even be found in viable form in the dried mud of seasonal pools.

REFERENCE

For the culture of ostracods see also p. 136.

CYPRIDAE

CHARLES H. BLAKE, *Massachusetts Institute of Technology*

THE usual ostracod of aquaria in the northeast is *Cypridopsis vidua*. This species may be taken from nearly any neutral or faintly acid pond, even if temporary, but is not likely to be found where the margins are marshy.

Cypridopsis will persist for many months in fair numbers in any balanced freshwater aquarium. The eggs are laid on almost any solid object and all instars are easily found. If mud is present on the bottom, no other special food appears to be needed.

Other ostracods may occur for short periods but I have not succeeded in keeping them more than a few weeks. They all require abundant oxygen. There appear to be no records of the reproduction of any marine form in captivity nor do young specimens survive more than one or two molts.

REFERENCE

For the culture of Cypris see p. 143.

Subclass *Malacostraca*, Order ISOPODA

A SUGGESTED IMITATION OF A WOODLAND POOL

CHARLES H. BLAKE, *Massachusetts Institute of Technology*

CERTAIN animals live only in the presence of much waterlogged wood and fallen leaves, and in situations in which there are almost no algae. Early in March I brought in a small amount of mud containing a high proportion of waterlogged bits of twigs, leaves, *etc.*, and a little sand. The freshwater isopod, *Asellus communis*, was rather common in the situation where the material was obtained and some specimens were included in the gathering.

An aquarium, about 6″ x 18″ in floor area, was set up with about ¼″ depth of the mud together with such plants and animals as were present in the original bottom sample and 1″ depth of stored aquarium water. The aquarium was covered with a loose-fitting glass plate as a protection against dust. It was placed in a cool laboratory near a north window and shaded from other windows. By late May almost no algae have appeared and there has been no putrefaction. The death of various insect larvae and of some individuals of the amphipod, *Dikerogammarus fasciatus,* has caused no evident upset in the equilibrium. Instead of the animals being balanced against plants they are balanced against the atmosphere. The aquarium contains a considerable number of ⅓ to ½ grown Aselli, offspring of the original individuals, and a variety of Entomostraca, including a few cyclopids which have maintained themselves without noticeable increase in numbers.

MAINTENANCE OF LAND ISOPODS

JOHN L. FULLER, *Massachusetts Institute of Technology*

MOST woodlice are easily maintained in the laboratory on moist soil rich in humus. A wooden box 18″ x 18″ x 6″ with a tightly fitting glass or wood cover will accommodate about a thousand animals. Land isopods should not be overcrowded, or molting individuals will be killed by their companions. In general, species should not be mixed, for the weaker species will be eliminated. If pieces of rotten wood and small stones are placed on the soil, the woodlice will congregate under them, making it easy to collect animals when desired. Water is added as necessary.

A temperature of from 20° to 25° C. is favorable for most species. Animals collected in the fall and kept between these temperatures will bear their first brood of young in February. Mating takes place readily when the two sexes are together; the fertilized females may be picked out since each carries its eggs in a ventral thoracic pouch. From 12 to 200 young are released in about three weeks, the rate of development and number of young differing for different species.

These animals appear to find sufficient nutriment in the organic matter of the soil, but will also eat slices of raw potato avidly. The nutritive requirements of the young are similar to those of adults.

Greatest success has been obtained with *Oniscus asellus, Porcellio scaber, Trachelipus rathkei,* and *Armadillidium vulgare,* though other species do nearly as well. *Porcellio pictus* is less hardy, and apparently requires lime. Trichoniscus may be kept on wet moss in glass jars with a little water in the bottom. Particular care should be taken to keep Porcellio and Trichoniscus in a cool place.

There appears to be no reason why healthy cultures may not be maintained indefinitely with a minimum of care. Lack of moisture is the chief danger to be avoided.

Family LIGYDIDAE

NOTE ON KEEPING LIGIA OCEANICA IN THE LABORATORY

JOHN TAIT, *McGill University*

KEEP animals in the darkness in a closed biscuit tin (of the English kind) the walls of which are lined with cardboard. Moisten the walls with freshwater or diluted seawater (1 part seawater to 3 parts of freshwater). Give them a good foothold; do not keep them on glass. Clean the tin every four or five days by washing it out with seawater.

Various kinds of animal and vegetable food were tried; the best results were obtained with blades of Laminaria.

BIBLIOGRAPHY

TAIT, J. Experiments on immersion of Ligia. *Quart. J. Exper. Physiol.* 3: 1.

———— 1917. Experiments and observations on Crustaceae. Pt. 1. Immersion experiments on Ligia. *Proc. Royal Soc. Edin.* 38:50.

———— 1925. The Sea-Slater, *Ligia oceanica;* a study in adaptation to habitat. *The Scottish Naturalist.* 151:13-18; 152:49-55.

Order DECAPODA, Family PANDALIDAE

HATCHING AND REARING PANDALID LARVAE

ALFREDA BERKELEY NEEDLER, *Biological Board of Canada*

THE five Pacific coast species under consideration are *Pandalus danae, P. borealis, P. hypsinotus, P. platyceros,* and *Pandalopsis dispar.* All of these species lay their eggs in the autumn, carry them over winter, and hatch them in the spring. The hatching begins about the end of February and continues until the end of May, being at its height about the beginning of April.

Towards the end of February, therefore, five tanks were set up in the basement of the Biological Station. The tanks were made with wooden ends and bottoms and plate glass sides, and were about 2 feet long, 15 inches wide, and 18 inches deep. The wood and joints were covered with black asphalt paint such as is commonly used in hatcheries. The outlets led into beakers covered with muslin so that the larvae when hatched could not escape. The water came from a large concrete tank above the station and about 10 years old, which was daily pumped full of seawater from near the end of the station wharf. In previous experiments it had been found that this water often contained a fine brown débris which clogged the shrimps' gills and killed them. Partly to prevent this and partly to aerate the water each tank was fitted with a large funnel covered with muslin and with a tube leading to the bottom of the tank. Into each funnel a small but steady stream of water splashed from a tap about a foot above. When the larvae began to hatch a series of nursery tanks made of battery jars were fitted up in a similar manner and a few large beakers were also used.

It was found necessary to have the eggs carried until hatching by the females, as larvae were never successfully hatched from eggs that had become separated. Ovigerous females were taken with a small beam trawl on various grounds sometimes 50 miles away or more. During transportation to the station they were carried in a large galvanized tub with changes of water at least every hour. They were placed in the big tanks and kept there until their eggs had hatched. During their captivity they were fed mainly on chopped crab's liver and marine worms. Most of them kept healthy although some of those from deep water acted as if they were blind and bruised themselves badly against the sides of the tanks.

In many cases the larvae appeared to be healthy for a week or ten days and then died before molting. A few *Pandalus danae* larvae reached the second stage but none of the others ever succeeded in passing the first molt (although Spirontocaris and Crago larvae were easily reared in beakers through several stages).

The salinities in the tanks compared favorably with the natural ones. Moreover no sudden ill effects were noted on the days that the salinity dropped and experiments conducted in the laboratory had indicated that the adult shrimps at least could stand a fairly wide range of salinity.

The pH of the water in the tanks remained close to that in the sea near the station.

As the adult shrimps all came from comparatively deep water (20 to 60 fathoms) they were subjected in the tanks to much lower pressures, and perhaps in some cases to stronger light than normal although the latter was kept subdued. The adults, however, appeared healthy during hatching. The larvae occur naturally from a depth of about 4 fathoms to the bottom, the younger stages keeping nearer the surface. It does not appear probable, therefore, that light or pressure were adverse factors in the rearing of the larvae.

The larvae were given various foods—eggs of marine worms, plankton, and finely minced crab liver. Apparently they ate the food, as traces could be found in their alimentary tracts. Examination of larvae obtained in plankton hauls indicated that they had been feeding on the smaller plankton organisms. It is quite possible that unsuitable food was one of the chief adverse factors.

Family CRANGONIDAE

A METHOD FOR REARING SMALL CRANGONIDAE

HUGH H. DARBY, *College of Physicians and Surgeons*

THE rearing of these organisms seems to have given trouble to several investigators. By the following technique it has been possible to keep them alive for at least three months. Small embryological dishes, about 12 cm. in diameter, were used, one for each animal. If two are placed together in the same dish, they tear each other to pieces. No running water was used, but the seawater was changed once every 2 or 3 days. Some of the small Synalpheus were kept in similar dishes without any change of water for 10 days without ill effects. A change of water just after molting is harmful. Much better results were obtained when the organisms were kept for at least 24 hours in the same water in which they had molted. During this time they devoured their own cast skin, and needed no other food. Ordinarily the muscles of small fishes or of other Crustacea were supplied for food. If kept in the ice box for two or three days before use, the food was devoured more readily than when given fresh. Very small pieces were given, so that there was no remnant left to become a source of bacterial infection in the culture dishes. Small marine algae kept in the dishes furnished both aeration and food. Larvae need much more aeration than adults for survival. Temperatures between 22° and 30° C. were entirely satisfactory for organisms found in the Dry Tortugas islands.

BIBLIOGRAPHY

DARBY, HUGH H. 1934. The mechanism of asymmetry in the Alpheidae. *Carnegie Inst. of Wash.* Publ. No. 435.

Family HOMARIDAE

HATCHING AND REARING LARVAE OF THE AMERICAN LOBSTER, HOMARUS AMERICANUS

PAUL S. GALTSOFF, *U. S. Bureau of Fisheries*

THE range of the American lobster extends from Labrador to North Carolina. Every spring lobsters migrate from deep water inshore where they remain until the onset of cold weather. At Woods Hole, Massachusetts, they usually appear in large numbers in May and begin their outward migration in October. Many of them remain in relatively shallow water throughout the winter.

The copulation of lobsters occurs primarily in the spring. During this time the sperm is deposited in an external seminal receptacle situated between the bases of the third pair of walking legs of the female where it retains its vitality for several months. The eggs are fertilized after ejection from the oviducts and are attached to the hairs of the swimmerets by a cement-like substance secreted by special glands of the female. Observations of Herrick show that regardless of its sexual condition the female lobster may be approached by the male more than once. About 80% of the spawning females lay their eggs in July and August, the remainder extrude their eggs in the fall and winter. The peak of the spawning season at Woods Hole occurs during the latter part of July and the first half of August. In Maine it is two weeks later.

The eggs are carried by the females from 10 to 11 months before they are hatched. The newly laid eggs measure from 1.5 to 1.7 mm.; they are of dark olive green color and are easily distinguished from the light-colored old eggs in which the green yolk has been absorbed by the embryo. In the freshly laid eggs the yolk, invested by a transparent capsule, is of uniform granular texture. In 20 to 25 hours after oviposition large yolk segments are distinguishable by the unaided eye. In about 10 days the embryo reaches the egg-nauplius stage and in 26 to 28 days the eye pigment may be seen at the surface. Hatching eggs may be obtained at Woods Hole from the middle of May until the first half of August. According to Herrick the number of eggs laid by the female at each reproductive period increases in geometrical proportion while the length of the female increases in arithmetical proportion. Thus, females 8, 10, 12 and 14 inches long would lay 5,000, 10,000, 20,000, and 40,000 eggs respectively. The relation holds good up to the 14-inch size.

Owing to the unequal rate of development the hatching period of a single brood may last about one week.

The following method is used in obtaining eggs for hatching: An egg-bearing female (with light-colored eggs) is stretched on its back over the table. By cautiously moving the dull side of a knife pressed against the abdomen the eggs are detached from the swimmerets and are immediately placed in a hatching jar (Fig. 47 A). A strong stream of water delivered through a glass tubing, almost reaching the bottom, keeps the eggs stirred, while the newly hatched larvae are carried by the vertical current of water into the tank (T). A screen (S) surrounding the overflow prevents their escape.

A newly hatched larva is a transparent, actively swimming organism, about 8 mm. in length. Its pelagic life continues for about two weeks during which time it grows and molts three times. After the 4th molt the larva bears a striking resemblance to the adult lobster but it has the larval rostrum and its front abdominal somites are still without the appendages. At this stage its color may be bright red, green, or reddish brown. The manner of swimming also has changed; the larva rapidly moves forward by means of the swimmerets and darts backward by sudden jerks of the abdomen. It measures between 11 and 14 mm. All the traces of larval swimming organs disappear after the 6th molt. The ensuing molts follow at rather short intervals. It has been estimated that during the first year the lobster molts from 14 to 17 times and attains a length of from 2 to 3 inches.

The first three stages comprise the most critical period of the larval life of the lobster. The natural food of the larvae probably consists of pelagic copepods and other crustaceans. In the hatching tanks they display strong cannibalistic tendencies, usually attacking their victims from above and nipping into the abdomen at its junction with the carapace. The self-destructiveness of the larvae constitutes the greatest difficulty in rearing them under artificial conditions. The best method of overcoming this consists in preventing the aggregation of the larvae on the bottom and by keeping them afloat. This is accomplished by a continuous stirring of the water by means of a propeller (P) operated by an electric motor (not shown in Fig. 47).

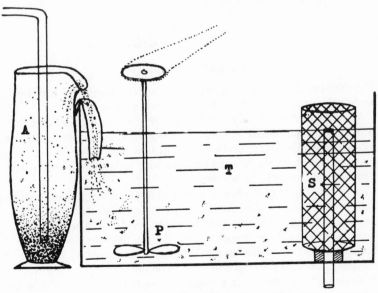

FIG. 47.—Method of hatching and rearing lobsters. A, hatching jar; P, propeller; S, screen; T, tank.

Experiments carried out by the author at Woods Hole prove that boiled and dried fish is the best food for the larvae. A whole fish is cut in several pieces and boiled in freshwater for about 30 minutes, then placed in a porcelain dish and dried in an oven for about 12 hours at 55-60° C. For feeding, a piece of the dried fish is ground in a glass mortar and a small amount of it distributed throughout the tank.

Several kinds of fishes were tried. The best results were obtained with mackerel. Besides fish meat, dried and ground hard boiled eggs have been successfully used at the Rhode Island State Lobster Hatchery.

Care must be exercised to remove the unused meat and prevent the decomposition of the debris and of dead larvae.

By using fish food and exercising reasonable precautions, the author had no difficulty in rearing the lobsters to the 4th and 5th stages, which were reached in 15-17 days.

Young lobsters may be fed on various animal food, as for instance, pieces of clam, oyster, crab meat, *etc*. They should be kept in a tank containing small rocks and a little sand.

BIBLIOGRAPHY

HERRICK, F. H. 1896. The American lobster, a study of its habits and development. *Bull. U. S. Bur. Fish.* 15:1.

MEAD, A. D. 1908. A method of lobster culture. *Ibid.* 28:221.

Family ASTACIDAE

A CRAYFISH TRAP*

IN PONDS and streams where crayfish are abundant they may readily be taken by means of a trap constructed as follows:

A rectangular box of any convenient size, 16 x 24 inches for instance, is built of ¼-inch mesh galvanized screen wire. Into one end of this box a removable funnel of like material is fitted. This funnel should project about 8 inches into the box and have a flattened opening about 4 inches wide and 1½ inches deep.

In setting the trap it should be placed in shallow water on a sloping bank and partially embedded in the mud or sand so that the bottom of the funnel is even with the bottom of the pond. The rest of the trap extends out toward the deeper water. A dead fish wired securely to the bottom of the trap makes an excellent bait. Attracted by this bait, the crayfish crawl into the trap and seem to be unable to find their way out. A single night-set with such a trap will reward the trapper with at least a water bucket full of crayfish for laboratory use, or for the more immediate purpose of providing the camp with an exceedingly delectable breakfast.

M. E. D.

* Reprinted, with slight changes, from *Science* 55:677, 1922, by E. C. O'Roke, *University of Michigan*.

REFERENCE
For the feeding of crayfish see note on p. 49.

CULTURE METHODS FOR BRACHYURA AND ANOMURA

JOSEPHINE F. L. HART, *Pacific Biological Station*

THE methods of successfully maintaining and rearing crabs and hermit crabs in the laboratory are not entirely dependent on the close simulation of natural conditions, but on careful feeding and preservation of hygiene during the progress of the experiment.

Immediately on collection of the specimens, a mature male and female should be placed together in a container. The larger crabs are best preserved in live boxes or aquaria with circulating seawater, but the small ones may be placed in shallow dishes, approximately 3 liters in capacity, in which cases the water should be changed daily.

It has been observed that many species of crabs, scavengers, carnivorous and herbivorous feeders, will live under such conditions, when fed on finely minced, fresh, clam muscle. It is probable that there are more suitable foods (Orton, 1927), but in the instances that have come under direct observation this diet has been found satisfactory.

If sand or other natural bottom material is placed in the jars, detritus, rotting food, and feces may not be effectively removed, and the accumulated decomposition products tend to cause pollution and the subsequent growth of detrimental bacteria and Protozoa. If the specimens are kept in a live box or a barren aquarium with running water, these factors are negligible. If the individual dishes or plunger jars (Brown, 1898; Lebour, 1927) are used, they should be cleaned daily about three hours after feeding. During the cleaning process, the animals should not be handled, in order to avoid the possibility of physical damage to them.

Copulation has been observed to take place under these conditions in *Scleroplax granulata* and *Lophopanopeus bellus*, followed by the deposition of the eggs. The females were then isolated in separate containers and the development of the eggs observed.

The larvae, upon hatching, swim to the surface of the water and should be removed with a pipette and placed in large beakers of freshly obtained seawater, which may be aerated by stirring with a glass rod. The larvae should be examined daily, fresh water and food given, and all the dead material and sloughed skins removed. This is most easily accomplished by transferring the active larvae to a fresh container, already supplied with food material.

The chief difficulty encountered in rearing decapod larvae is the maintenance of a constant supply of suitable living food. Many of the forms eaten in the natural state, when placed in laboratory conditions, soon die and their decomposition products in the water kill the larvae.

Lebour (1927 and 1928) was successful in rearing three species of crabs in plunger jars on a diet of the larvae of Ostrea, Teredo, Echinus, and Pomatoceros. The megalopae and young crabs were fed on small pieces of the mantle of *Mytilis edulis*. The larvae of the native oyster, *Ostrea lurida,* have been found to be a satisfactory food, as they are held for some time in the mantle cavity of the adult and therefore may be obtained in quantity, yet are free-swimming when placed in the water. The veliger larvae of Nudibranchs and the trochophore larvae of the Japanese oyster were also used, but did not prove as satisfactory as those of the native oyster. When the larvae are no longer free-swimming, living food material may be replaced by minced clam muscle, on which the megalopa and young crabs will continue to thrive. It is advisable to provide shells for the glaucothoë and young stages of the Pagurids, and for this purpose the broken off tips of the spirals of Littorina were found suitable.

The length of time spent in each stage seems to depend considerably on the relative abundance of food, the temperature and salinity of the water, and on other such external conditions. The first zoeal stage, in suitable natural conditions, probably lasts for 2 or 3 days, and the time spent in each stage increases as the larva grows. Under laboratory conditions, 4 to 5 weeks is usually required for the development from the egg to the young crab stage. The 6th young crab stage of *Hemigrapsus nudus* appeared 2 months later.

These methods have been applied successfully to the rearing of both Brachyura (Hart, 1934) and Anomura. Some slight variations in technique may be found advisable and these will become evident with the development of the experimental work.

BIBLIOGRAPHY

BROWN, E. T. 1898. On keeping medusae alive in an aquarium. *J. Mar. Biol. Assoc.* 5:176.

HART, J. F. L. 1935. The larval development of British Columbia Brachyura. I. Xanthidae, Pinnotheridae (in part) and Grapsidae. *Canad. J. Res.* 12:411.

LEBOUR, M. V. 1926-27. Studies of the Plymouth Brachyura. I. The rearing of crabs in captivity, with a description of the larval stages of *Inachus dorsettensis, Macropodia longirostris* and *Maia squinado. J. Mar. Biol. Assoc.* n.s. 14:795.

—— 1928. The larval stages of the Plymouth Brachyura. *Proc. Zool. Soc. London,* pp. 473-560.

ORTON, J. H. 1926-27. On the mode of feeding of the hermit crab, *Eupahurus Bernhardus,* and some other Decapoda. *Ibid.* 14:909.

Family CANCRIDAE

NOTES ON REARING THE PACIFIC EDIBLE CRAB, CANCER MAGISTER

DONALD C. G. MACKAY, *Pacific Biological Station*

THE Pacific edible crab, *Cancer magister*, described by Dana in 1852, is a large crustacean which sometimes reaches a carapace width of 22 cm. In Alaska, British Columbia, Washington, Oregon, and California the species is present in large numbers.

LIFE HISTORY

Evidence from several independent sources leads to the conclusion that females become mature at a carapace width of approximately 10 cm. The size at which sexual maturity is attained in males has not been ascertained definitely but it is known that some are mature at a width of 13.5 cm. Maturity is ordinarily attained by females in the 4th or 5th year though, in some instances, it is believed to occur as early as the 3rd year or as late as the 6th year. The normal duration of life in British Columbia is probably about 8 years and the maximum is probably not more than 10 years.

The mating season is from April until September. Mating takes place on the tide flats and invariably occurs between a soft-shelled female and a hard-shelled male. The male embraces the female, sternum to sternum, and the two lie buried in the sand, mud, or seaweed in a nearly vertical position.

The average diameter of fully developed external eggs is about 0.47 mm. During development the ovarian eggs undergo color changes from white to coral red; these changes are closely correlated with the sizes of the eggs. The number of eggs produced by *Cancer magister* is large, the actual number depending upon the body size. In two specimens examined the numbers were 750,000 and 1,500,000 for crabs 5.33 and 6.00 cm. in carapace width respectively. It is estimated that one female in a lifetime might produce 4,000,000 eggs.

The ovigerous period in British Columbia is from October until June. Hatching probably occurs from December until June and there is reason to believe that the season is somewhat earlier in California.

The eggs hatch as protozoeae and pass through several zoeal instars and one megalops instar, after which they closely resemble the adult in form.

The natural sizes of the megalops and first five post-larval instars have been determined and are respectively as follows: 0.28, 0.52, 0.74, 0.97, 1.34, and 1.82 mm. Contrasted with the natural increases just mentioned the experimental crabs are likely to become retarded in growth. That is to say that when they molt they are likely to increase less in size than would be the case in nature. This effect appears to be cumulative, crabs molting more than once falling even further behind in size. Large crabs kept in compartment live-wells, though comparatively more cramped than the small crabs kept in the laboratory, show less retardation of growth upon molting.

SEASONS OF AVAILABILITY

Megalops are to be found during July and August and crabs in the first three post-larval instars during August and September. By the following spring these same crabs, then 1 year old, have reached the 6th and 7th instars.

Mating crabs are occasionally found on the tideflats among seaweed. Molting crabs may sometimes be discovered beneath the inverted shells of bivalve molluscs or otherwise hidden at extreme low tide. Crabs on the verge of molting appear to frequent shallow water and are to be found in large numbers buried in the sand in certain localities during the spring of the year. Except for the fact that the species characteristically inhabits sandy or slightly muddy regions and avoids rocky shores, we can give no rules for finding such areas. Crabs ordinarily found are from 3 to 15 cm. in carapace width. For larger material the investigator must either depend upon fishermen or else employ traps of his own.

METHOD OF COLLECTING

Crabs in the megalops and early post-larval stages may be collected by hand in small numbers on the shore at low tide. The megalops, which are positively phototropic, are frequently found adhering to barnacles and other small objects; occasionally they are found swimming at the surface, sometimes in large numbers. In the latter event they are extremely difficult to capture.

The early post-larval crabs may also be collected by hand in small numbers at low tide. They are, however, ordinarily found buried in the sand or otherwise hidden from view. When the sand is disturbed they may sometimes be observed digging themselves rapidly in again. Crabs at this stage of development may often be taken in large numbers from the gear of fishermen operating on the ordinary commercial fishing grounds which, in Boundary Bay, B. C., are about 10 to 12 fathoms in depth.

HANDLING THE MATERIAL

Young crabs appear to be somewhat hardier than mature crabs and may be handled without extreme care. In all cases, however, it is important to avoid crowding a large number of individuals within a small quantity of water. The chances of survival, where crowding cannot be avoided, would seem to be best where water is not used. When covered with damp seaweed crabs will live for many hours and often for days.

REQUIREMENTS FOR KEEPING ALIVE

Small larval and post-larval crabs were successfully kept by the writer for considerable periods of time, sometimes for several months, in miscellaneous glass vessels of all available kinds. These containers were mostly of the type in which foods are put up and were the only vessels readily available in the small seaside community where the work was carried on. Before being used, all the containers were carefully washed in boiling water. In general large shallow vessels seemed to be the most successful.

Into each container was placed one small crab, some clean sand, one or two pebbles, and a piece of seaweed. Small sticklebacks were found useful for keeping the water in circulation in the individual containers and were sometimes used for this purpose. It was, however, necessary to replace the small fish from time to time since, though they were considerably larger than the crabs, they were frequently caught and partially devoured.

Running water was unfortunately not available but satisfactory results were obtained by changing the water twice daily.

The larger crabs were kept in compartment live-wells anchored to a float. The live-wells were designed to facilitate the natural circulation of water due to the tidal currents. Compartments of various sizes were provided for large and small crabs. Live-wells of 3 feet x 4 feet x 9 inches were found to be as large as could conveniently be handled and two of these dimensions were put in use for two seasons.

FOOD

The young crabs were fed mainly on small pieces of absolutely fresh sticklebacks, a decided preference for fresh rather than stale fish having been shown in feeding experiments. Sticklebacks were readily obtainable with the use of a small dip net and proved very acceptable to the crabs. Small pieces of oyster were occasionally given but proved to be less satisfactory than the fish.

Fresh fish heads and entrails were used as food for larger crabs.

REFERENCES

Family Xanthidae
  For the culture of *Lophopanopeus bellus* see p. 237.
Family Grapsidae
  For the culture of *Hemigrapsus nudus* see p. 238.

Class *Arachnoidea*

FEEDING NOTES FOR CERTAIN ARTHROPODS

Lucy W. Clausen, *American Museum of Natural History*

THE following is a list of arthropods which have been kept for comparatively long periods of time in the cages containing live exhibits in the Hall of Insect Life of the American Museum of Natural History, together with the food organisms which have proven satisfactory for each.

ARACHNIDA

Scorpions (several species) have been fed on mealworms and Oriental roaches.

Tarantulas will eat roaches and mealworms.

Pholcids (false Daddy-long-legs) eat Drosophila when small and larger flies, such as Musca, when larger.

The wolf spider, *Lycosa carolinensis*, has fed upon flies and mealworms.

The garden spider, *Aranea sericata*, has been fed flies and grasshoppers.

The crab spider, *Olios sp.*, is fed mealworms.

ORTHOPTERA

Roaches (American, Oriental, and tropical) are fed sliced potato, lettuce, bananas, bread, and a piece of bacon occasionally. They seem to relish spinach when it is not given to them too often.

Crickets are fed on apple, lettuce, and bread.

Meadow grasshoppers are fed on apple and grass.

Mantids (Chinese Mantis) eat Drosophila when small. When adult they eat houseflies and mealworms. The latter should be dangled before them on a thread to attract their attention.

COLEOPTERA

Tiger beetles (*Cicindela sexgutata, C. dorsalis, etc.*) have been fed on mealworms cut in sections, and on apple.

Caterpillar hunters (*Calosoma calidum and C. scrutator*) have been fed on mealworms and apples with banana occasionally.

The ground beetle, *Harpalus caliginosus*, has been fed mealworms and apple.

Dytiscus eats small mealworms which are dropped into the aquarium.

Mealworms (Tenebrionidae) are grown in bran with a slice of potato added every other day.

The red rust flour beetle (*Tribolium ferrugineum*) grows well in whole wheat flour. Enough moisture is supplied to the culture by keeping a moist wad of cotton attached to the lid of the container.

Dermestids, such as *D. lardarius,* are fed on felt, bones which have a bit of dried substance adhering, and ordinary dog biscuit (which they seem to like).

In all cases moisture is extremely necessary, but care must be taken so that mold does not set in.

Order ARANEAE, Family THERAPHOSIDAE

LABORATORY CARE OF TARANTULAS

W. J. BAERG, *University of Arkansas*

TARANTULAS hatch late in summer, August or September. During the fall they apparently require no food. In the following spring a large family confined in a battery jar will begin to dwindle. In May and June cannibalism becomes so severe that if several specimens are to be saved for rearing to the adult stage they must be isolated. These young individuals may be kept in any sort of small jar that will confine them and admit some air. Small sized battery jars (4″ x 6″) do very well. A thin layer of soil (about ½ inch) is desirable; a deeper layer may crush the delicate spiders when they burrow.

Young tarantulas will feed on any small insects they can handle. Termites are very satisfactory and will serve till the tarantulas are about 3 years old.

Older tarantulas are conveniently kept in large battery jars which should be half filled with soil to satisfy their desire for digging. They may be fed grasshoppers, crickets, cockroaches, or a variety of caterpillars, as well as various moths, butterflies, cicadas, *etc.* Tent caterpillars and catalpa worms serve well for early spring and summer, grasshoppers for late summer and fall.

Tarantulas of the common local species *Eurypelma californica* will feed once a week or a little oftener; the Mexican species *Dugesiella crinita* will accept food more often and in larger quantities. Mature, or nearly mature tarantulas will live without food for about 2 years.

Water should be supplied at frequent intervals. A glass dish, such as a small petri dish, serves well. In seasons of severe drought tarantulas may succumb to thirst in 2 months' time.

During the winter the tarantulas may doubtless be kept in an ordinary laboratory, but to come nearer to natural conditions a basement, not heated, is better. A light frost will not kill them, but it is well to avoid temperatures below 40° F. This is for the local species *E. californica.* Species native farther south should be kept at higher temperatures.

When approaching a molt tarantulas cease feeding. No apprehension need be felt over this lack of appetite even if it lasts for 2-3 weeks.

If females heavy with eggs are brought into the laboratory they will in time produce cocoons. These, if kept in a sufficiently warm room exposed to sunlight, may produce young (600-1200). A more convenient method of rearing young is to bring in cocoons from which the spiderlings are about ready to emerge. The time required from oviposition to emergence of young is about 6 weeks.

KEEPING AVICULARIA AVICULARIA IN THE LABORATORY

Mary L. Didlake, *University of Kentucky*

GLASS stender dishes have furnished satisfactory, though rather cramped, quarters for tropical spiders found in bunches of bananas and brought to me. One large Bird Spider (*Avicularia avicularia*) I have kept now for seven years. It has molted eleven times and measures 2¾ inches from the front of the cephalothorax to the tip of the abdomen. I use a pair of long forceps for moving the spiders to clean quarters. They drink readily from a smaller, 2-inch stender dish, catch living food put in for them (caterpillars, grasshoppers, roaches) and will, when very hungry, feed on a piece of raw liver or beef, sucking it white. A fledgling English sparrow was consumed once, and on two occasions a small mouse.

Specimens have usually been females and no attempt was made to rear successive generations. The jars were kept at room temperature. In very cold weather, and over week-ends when the room was likely to be chilly, they were set on top of an incubator which furnished a slight degree of warmth.

References

Family Pholcidae
For feeding see p. 242.
Family Lycosidae
For feeding of *Lycosa carolinensis* see p. 242.

Family THERIDIIDAE

CULTURE OF LATHRODECTUS MACTANS, THE BLACK WIDOW SPIDER

Elizabeth Burger, *The College of William and Mary*

Caution: Extreme care should be taken in handling "black widow" spiders since their poison is highly toxic and may prove fatal.

Containers. Since these spiders are cannibalistic, they must be kept in individual containers. Glass tumblers, covered with cheesecloth secured by a rubber band, with one inch of sand at the bottom, are satisfactory. Water and food are introduced through a thistle-tube inserted through a hole in the cover. (This hole in the cloth is kept below the margin of the tumbler when not in use.) A small layer of non-absorbent cotton protects the spider from drowning when the sand is moistened.

Food. Adult spiders should be fed upon grasshoppers and other Orthoptera, one insect every three or four days. When these are not available, cultured blue-bottle flies (*Calliphora erythrocephala*) are sufficient. [See p. 415.]

Since the newly hatched spiders apparently are to a large extent exclusively cannibalistic, it has been considered necessary to permit them to feed upon each other for the first three or four days. To conserve stocks the spiders should be separated after this period and fed fruit flies (*Drosophila spp.*). [See p. 305.]

Temperature. For storage: 40° to 50° F. For breeding, oviposition, and hatching of young spiders: room temperature.

Light. Spiders should not be exposed to direct sunlight.

Moisture. A somewhat damp habitat is natural. Satisfactory conditions of moisture are secured as described above.

Breeding. Females captured in the fall will lay fertile eggs. Virgin females raised through the winter may be mated with males, which may be distinguished from immature females by their bulbous palpi.

Egg cases should be separated from adult spiders before hatching. The eggs hatch within three or four weeks.

REFERENCES

Family Argiopidae
For feeding of *Aranea sericata* see p. 242.
Family Thomisidae
For feeding of Olios see p. 242.

Order ACARINA

CULTURE OF NON-PREDACIOUS, NON-PARASITIC MITES (ORIBATOIDEA AND TYROGLYPHOIDEA)

ARTHUR PAUL JACOT, *Asheville, North Carolina*

A CELL FORMED of a microslide, a glass ring, and a large cover has proved most satisfactory. The rings may be 20 x 5 mm. with a # 2 cover glass 22 mm. in diameter. The center of the slide should be etched (with hydrofluoric acid blocked in with paraffin) to give it a rough surface to enable certain species to walk with ease. The ring may be fastened with Canada balsam. The top of the rim must be coated with a very thin film of vaseline, paraffin, or some other substance which will make an air-tight seal with the cover, or the included moisture may escape. It is essential to keep the cells moist. In some cases a piece of blotting paper on the cell-floor will be satisfactory. The animals may be fed on bits of moss, lichens, cheese mold, or on soft, moist, dead wood. The cells must be inspected daily to regulate the moisture content and the growth of molds.

REFERENCES

Family Tyroglyphidae
For culture, including that of *Tyroglyphus linteri*, see p. 266.

Family IXODIDAE

TICK REARING METHODS WITH SPECIAL REFERENCE TO THE ROCKY MOUNTAIN WOOD TICK, DERMACENTOR ANDERSONI STILES*

GLEN M. KOHLS, *United States Public Health Service*

TICKS belong to the order Acarina, superfamily Ixodoidea, which is composed of the families Ixodidae and Argasidae.

Tick rearing is an involved process because of complicated life cycles, the blood feeding habit which necessitates the use of host animals, and the different environmental requirements of different species during aestivation and hibernation and other periods when not on host animals. Rearing methods applicable to specific problems have been developed by different groups of investigators, but lack of space makes it necessary to limit this article to those methods and equipment now in use at the Rocky Mountain Laboratory for the rearing of the Rocky Mountain wood tick, *Dermacentor andersoni*. These methods have been developed by several investigators over a considerable period of years in connection with study of tick-borne diseases of the United States, and especially in relation to that of Rocky Mountain spotted fever and the manufacture of spotted fever vaccine. This vaccine is prepared from the tissues of infected adult *D. andersoni* and necessitates the rearing of this species in large numbers. The methods described are applicable in general to other species of ixodid ticks.

D. andersoni is a three host tick, the adults of which are active in nature from the latter part of March to about July 1st. They are usually found on livestock and the larger game animals, and attach readily to man. When host contact is made the ticks attach and feed to repletion in 8 to 14 days, copulation occurring while the females are still attached. The latter increase enormously in size due to the blood meal, leave the host and, after 2 to 4 weeks, deposit 4,000 to 7,000 eggs in a

*Contribution from the Rocky Mountain Laboratory, United States Public Health Service, Hamilton, Montana.

suitable place. The larvae, hexapod and sexually indistinguishable, infest rodents during June, July and August, require 4 to 7 days for engorgement, then drop and molt to nymphs before the onset of cold weather. After hibernating the octopod nymphs, also sexually indistinguishable, infest rodents in April, May and June. On completing engorgement, which requires 3 to 10 days, the nymphs leave the host and molt to the adult stage during the summer. These adults normally do not feed until the following spring. Thus the life cycle requires a minimum of 2 years for completion. However, under unfavorable conditions it may be extended to 3, and rarely to 4 years, because of the resistance of the adult ticks to starvation.

REARING ROOM

The mass rearing of *D. andersoni* is conducted in a large room (50′ x 25′) specially designed to prevent the escape of ticks and to eliminate, in so far as possible, places in the room in which ticks may remain undetected. There is but one entrance. The floor is concrete, with drains. The apertures surrounding all pipes passing through the floor are tick proofed as shown in longitudinal section in Figure 48. The walls are finished with cement plaster to permit washing down and windows are specially designed and tightly screened with 18 mesh wire cloth. The sash weight boxes are tick tight and crevices between the window frames and walls are packed with oakum. The floor and walls are flushed daily with near-boiling water under pressure to kill or remove ticks which may be free in the room. The temperature is maintained automatically at 21° C. or slightly above.

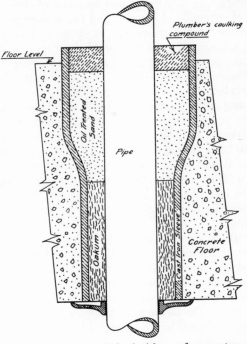

FIG. 48.—Showing method of tick proofing apertures around pipes passing through floor in tick rearing room.

Adjacent to the rearing room there is a workers' street clothes locker room, a shower room, a "deticking" room containing an electrically heated cabinet and a 3 panel full length mirror, and a work clothes locker room. Coming on duty the workers leave their street clothing in lockers in the first room and don one piece white coveralls in the fourth. On leaving at the close of work, the coveralls are placed in the heated cabinet in which the temperature is maintained between 50° C. and 65° C. for an hour or longer to kill any ticks that may be on the garments. The workers then examine their bodies for ticks before the mirror and take a shower bath before dressing for the street.

REARING PROCEDURE

Although *D. andersoni* can be reared through many successive generations under laboratory conditions, stock thus carried on seems gradually to lose its virility. It has been found best, therefore, to start each rearing year's stock from new adult ticks collected from nature. The successive steps involved in rearing this stock through a generation are as follows: (1) collection of adult ticks from nature, (2) engorging of females, (3) oviposition and hatching of eggs, (4) engorging of larvae, (5) engorging of nymphs, and (6) storage of the various stages. Most of the essential equipment is shown in text figures. In order to have 1,000,000 adults of the reared generation, it is necessary to collect or engorge approximately 5,000 females, requiring about 170 rabbits. These females will deposit 20,000,000 eggs yielding approximately this number of larvae. About 700 rabbits are required to feed these larvae, using about 30,000 larvae per host. Approximately 4,000,000 engorged larvae are obtained. These will yield about the same number of nymphs. Nymphal feeding requires about 2,800 rabbits using about 1,200 ticks per host. The approximately 1,000,000 engorged nymphs produced yield an almost equivalent number of adult ticks. Thus only about $\frac{1}{20}$ of the larvae are brought to maturity, the principal losses being incurred in the feeding of the larvae and nymphs. This results in part from the fact that all the ticks of a given lot are not ready to feed at the same time.

D. andersoni is not markedly host specific and all stages feed readily on domestic rabbits. In the routine feeding of *D. andersoni* for mass rearing only rabbits are used. In order that there may be as little moisture and waste food material as possible in the rearing cage bags to be later described, a scanty diet consisting solely of carrots is employed. The larvae and nymphs will feed on almost any small mammal and adults can be fed on any of the larger domestic animals and even on guinea pigs.

Collection of Adult Ticks. To obtain a rearing stock of *D. andersoni* either unfed males and females or fully engorged females can be collected in nature in the early spring. The engorged females, ready to drop for egg deposition, can be secured in numbers from livestock.

The unfed adults may be obtained by means of "flagging." A piece of white canton flannel about 36″ square is tied to a light six foot pole to form a "flag" (Fig. 49). The flag is dragged over grass and low shrubs and ticks coming in contact with the cloth cling to it and are readily seen. As the ticks are collected on the flag they are placed in cork stoppered 4 dram homeopathic vials from which they are later transferred in lots of about 150 each to cardboard pill boxes for temporary storage. By this means an experienced collector working in a fairly heavily infested area can collect 800 to 1,200 ticks a day.

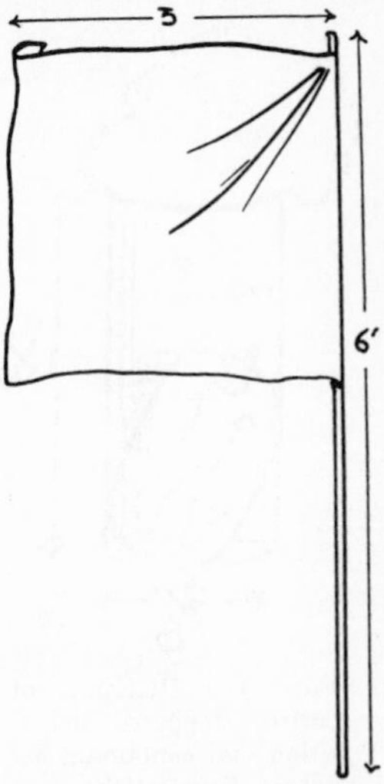

Engorging of Females. For engorging females, a capsule secured to the host by means of an adhesive plaster girdle is used. Figure 50 shows in detail the construction of a girdle with one feeding capsule. Two capsules may be used in the same girdle if it is desired to feed a larger number of ticks per animal.

FIG. 49.—Diagram of "flag" used in collecting adult ticks.

A circular hole slightly less than 2″ in diameter is made toward one end of a band of adhesive tape B, 3″ or 4″ in width and long enough to encircle the animal and allow some overlapping. The capsule is stamped from 20 mesh brass screening so that there is formed a circular depression about ⅜″ in depth and 2″ in diameter surrounded by a ½″ rim, the finished capsule having somewhat the shape of a low crowned hat. The crowned portion of the capsule A is then fitted into the hole in B so that the adhesive surface of the tape is in contact with the upper surface of the rim of the capsule. A slightly smaller hole is made in a shorter band C and the non-adhesive surface of the band is applied to the adhesive surface of B so that the holes in the two bands are con-

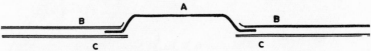

FIG. 50.—Section diagram of tick feeding girdle. A, brass screen capsule; B, long adhesive band for girdle (fine line is adhesive surface); C, adhesive tape, prevents actual contact of rim of capsule with animal.

centric. About 40 ticks are placed in the depression of the capsule and the girdle applied to the animal so that the ticks may feed on a clipped area of the animal's belly. Two strips of ½" adhesive tape, encircling the animal twice, reinforce the margins of the girdle. If two capsules are to be used the capsules are spaced so that their rims are about ¾" apart and their centers in line with the long dimension of B. A total of 80

ticks, half males and half females, may then be placed on the rabbit. A large number of females may cause the death of the host through exsanguination. Female engorgement is completed in 8 to 10 days. The rabbits are then sacrificed, the girdles removed and the engorged females collected. The males are destroyed. From 15 to 20 engorged females per animal are obtained from a single capsule girdle and 30-35 from the double.

Oviposition and Hatching. For oviposition the engorged female ticks are placed individually in glass shell vials ⅝" in diameter and 1¼" in length, the open end being securely but not tightly stoppered with a plug of cotton (Fig. 51). The vials are then laid horizontally in rows on a screen tray as illustrated in Figure 52. The trays are placed almost in contact with moist sand in thermal

Fig. 51.—Diagram of cotton stoppered oviposition vial containing engorged female tick.

cabinets operated at about 22° C. Under these conditions oviposition begins in approximately 6 days and is completed about 21 days later. The female dies on completion of egg laying.

Hatching is completed and the larval ticks are ready to be fed in from 5 to 6 weeks after the engorged females were placed in the cabinets. Readiness to feed is indicated by the presence of a considerable amount of white excretory material deposited by the larvae on the walls of the glass vials.

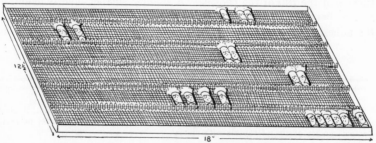

Fig. 52.—Diagram of tray for holding oviposition vials.

Engorging of Larvae. The host rabbit is placed in 68 count white muslin bag 14″ by 18″ in size. The larvae from 4 oviposition vials are quickly placed in the ears and about the head of each animal and the bag securely tied. The bagged animals are then placed in cages supported on frames and racks as illustrated in Figure 53. The cage frames

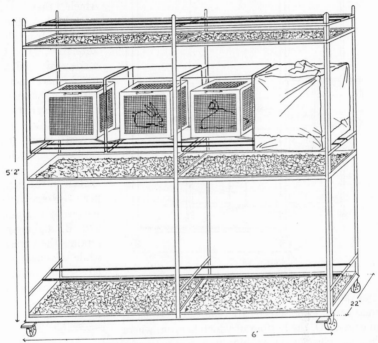

Fig. 53.—Diagram of cage rack and cages used in rearing of large numbers of larvae and nymphs. Capacity of rack is 12 cages.

are made of ¼″ wrought iron rods welded in place, painted with aluminum, and are 15″ x 17″ by 18″ high. Twenty-four hours later the animals are released and the bags and the unattached ticks clinging to them burned. A 10 ounce canvas bottomed bag with an 80 count muslin top is then placed over the supporting frame containing the cage and tied. The canvas bottom has a few small perforations in it to permit drainage into sawdust filled trays below. The frame within which the cage is supported serves to keep the bag from actual contact with the cage thus preventing holes from being gnawed in the cage bag by the tick host. When the feeding is done at room temperature the major portion of the larvae complete engorgement and drop in 5 days. Temperatures above or below shorten or lengthen the feeding period.

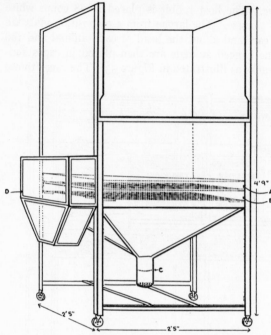

FIG. 54.—Diagram of "tick picker" used in recovering fed immature ticks from the animal cage bags.

A "tick picker" (Fig. 54) is used in recovering fed immature ticks from the bags in which they are contained after dropping from the animals. It is made of galvanized sheet metal with dimensions as illustrated. The bags are removed from the cages, turned inside out and shaken in the hopper. Removable screen A, 6 mesh, and B, 14 mesh, retain the trash while the engorged larvae fall through and are caught in removable cup C, the bottom of which is made of brass gauze. The screens are removed and placed on edge in D, the bottom of which is open, where they are cleaned by washing with water from a hose. The volume of larvae collected is measured in cubic centimeters, 1 cc. equaling approximately 700 ticks. An average of about 5,600 ticks per rabbit is obtained in routine feedings. The engorged larvae in quantities of 10 cc. each are placed in glass cylinders $1\frac{3}{4}''$ in diameter and $4''$ in length, their escape being prevented by pieces of muslin securely taped or tied over the ends (Fig. 55). After being held from 4 to 5 weeks in thermal cabinets at $22°$ C. and relative humidity about 50%, the larvae will have molted to nymphs and the latter be ready to feed.

Engorging of Nymphs. The procedure fol-

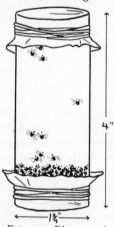

FIG. 55.—Diagram of pyrex cylinder in which fed larvae are held for molting.

lowed in feeding nymphs is similar to that for feeding larvae. One of the 1¾" x 4" cylinders is opened and, with the help of an assistant, the contents are equally distributed among 6 animals in infesting bags. Considerable experience and dexterity is required in completing the process without the escape of ticks. The rabbits are then treated as in larval feeding. Engorgement is accomplished in about 8 days and the tick picker is also used in collecting the fed ticks. The contents of the cage bags are shaken in the hopper and a stream of water from a hose is directed onto the canvas bottom of the bag to wash the remaining ticks and detritus into the picker. The soluble wastes are washed through while the ticks and non-soluble waste of the same size are retained on screen B. The coarse material is retained by screen A. Cup C is not used while the bags are being cleaned. After all the bags are cleaned, water is directed into the picker and the material in it thoroughly washed. Screen A is removed and its retained material discarded. Screen B is set on edge and the material on it washed down into the cup which is now in place. The cup is removed and the contents are slowly centrifuged in a screen container to remove the excess water. This is accomplished in a converted cream separator. Drying is then completed by placing the material in a current of warm air supplied by an electric hair dryer. Final cleaning is accomplished by sorting the remaining debris from the ticks, after which the latter are counted by measuring their volume in cubic centimeters, 35 ticks being the equivalent of 1 cc. An average of about 400 ticks per animal is ordinarily obtained. The nymphs are placed in cardboard pill boxes, 2" in diameter and ¾" in depth, about 200 per box, and the lot number, date and other necessary data stamped on the covers.

Molting of nymphs occurs within a rather wide range of temperature and humidity. Ordinarily nymphs are held at 22° C. and relative humidity of 40-80%. Under these conditions molting takes place in about 21 days. Transformation to the adult stage is accelerated by a low relative humidity, while a high humidity tends to retard the process.

STORAGE OF TICKS

In the course of routine or experimental rearing, situations occasionally arise when it becomes necessary to delay development or postpone the feeding of ticks. The conditions required for minimum mortality during storage are dependent on the stage of tick being dealt with, the principal factors being its ability to withstand desiccation and starvation. Adult ticks are better able to survive long periods of fasting than the immature stages, the nymphs being more resistant than larvae. None of the stages are markedly resistant to desiccation.

Adults. Unfed adults of *D. andersoni* collected in nature or recently molted from nymphs may be stored a year or more without excessive mortality by placing them in pyrex cylinders or "longevity tubes." These tubes are 8" in length by 1¾" in diameter. One end is plugged with well packed earth or with Plaster of Paris for a distance of 2", and a few

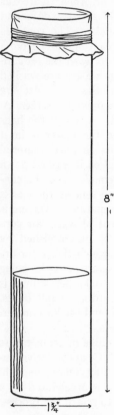

coarse wood shavings or dried leaves are added so that the ticks are not forced into direct contact with the plug (Fig. 56). From 300 to 400 ticks are placed in the tube and the latter is closed by a piece of muslin tied over the open end. The tubes are placed upright inside 4" galvanized metal cylinders set in the ground to their full length. The plugged end of the pyrex cylinder must be in close contact with moist soil. Moisture is supplied to the surrounding soil as necessary. The ticks are thus free to seek favorable humidity conditions. The "tick yard" in which the tubes are placed must be constructed or located so that the direct sun rays will not fall on the tubes. During the winter the tubes may either be left in the ground or stored indoors at 6° C. The ticks will survive outdoor conditions unless subjected to unusually abrupt transitions of temperature, particularly from cold to heat.

For periods of at least 6 months adult ticks may be stored in pill boxes at 6° C. with the relative humidity maintained at about 80%.

Engorged female ticks may be stored to delay oviposition for periods up to 4 months in cardboard pill boxes at temperature and humidity conditions as stated above.

Immature Stages. Unfed larvae may be stored for periods up to 2 months under the conditions just stated.

Fig. 56.—Diagram of pyrex "longevity tube," used for storing unfed adult or nymphal ticks for long periods.

Unfed nymphs may be kept successfully for periods up to 6 months in longevity tubes in the tick yard in the manner described for adult ticks. However, equally satisfactory results will ordinarily be obtained by storing the tubes upright on a tray of moist sand in a thermal cabinet operated at 6° C.

Fed larvae and fed nymphs are susceptible to desiccation at the lower ranges of humidity and to molds at the higher ranges. Therefore, it is more desirable to store immature ticks as unfed nymphs.

REARING SMALL LOTS OF TICKS

In some respects the rearing procedure and equipment described above, while adequate for the rearing of *D. andersoni* in large quantities, are not well adapted for the requirements of a small laboratory where a lesser number of ticks is required.

Small numbers of ticks may be confined in cotton stoppered or muslin capped vials to permit ready observation. In the absence of thermal

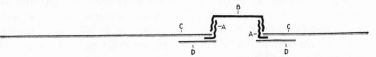

FIG. 57.—Section of tick feeding girdle for experimental purposes. A, threaded and flanged ring; B, cover; C, long adhesive band for girdle; D, short adhesive band covering toothed flange.

cabinets ticks may be kept at room temperature in glass vials or cardboard pill boxes almost in contact with moist sand. In cases where controlled humidity conditions are required the pill boxes or vials may be kept in ordinary desiccating jars containing solutions of salts that will provide the desired relative humidity.

The tick feeding girdle shown in Figure 50, while simple and useful for routine tick feeding, is not adapted for experimental feeding of small groups of ticks where close observation and easy manipulation of the feeding ticks are desired. Once the adhesive tape is in place its partial removal in order to remove or replace ticks causes skin irritation and any active and unattached ticks may escape. Therefore, a tin capsule made from the threaded end ring and cover used in cardboard mailing tubes is substituted for the

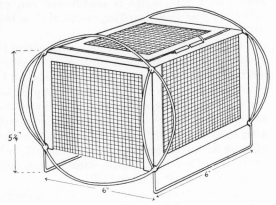

FIG. 58.—Diagram of a cage designed for rearing ticks on small animals.

brass gauze capsule used in mass feeding. A section diagram is shown in Figure 57. For complete details the reader is referred to Public Health Reports 1933, pp. 1081-82.

A diagram of a small cage suitable for rearing ticks on guinea pigs, white rats, mice, chipmunks and other small rodents, is shown in Figure 58. The wire frame, for keeping the sack in which the cage is enclosed from being gnawed by the caged animal, is soldered to the cage. The cage is placed in a cloth bag, the animal introduced into the cage and the ticks to be fed are placed on the animal. The bag is closely tied and the unit placed over a tray of sawdust. No further attention, except for feeding the animal, is necessary until the ticks have fed and dropped. The fed ticks are recovered from the bag with forceps, and after having been immersed in water to remove the animal urine with which they are likely to have been in contact in the bag, are dried and put away in the usual manner for molting.

Family HYDRACHNIDAE

PARASITIC WATER MITES

JOHN H. WELSH, *Harvard University*

MOST parasites may be maintained in the laboratory when it is possible to maintain their hosts, and the modifications which many of them exhibit never cease to interest students. Forms which show structural adaptations are numerous but forms which show clear-cut modifications in behavior are few. It would appear to be of interest to know that a form which is readily obtained and maintained in the laboratory does show a striking modification in behavior due to its parasitic existence.

Unionicola ypsilophora is a common parasitic water mite which is found in several species of Anodonta. It lives on the gills and all of the developmental stages may be found in or on the gills of a form such as *Anodonta cataracta*. A supply of these mussels may be kept for months in the laboratory in running water and the mites may therefore be available at any time, even though collecting conditions are unfavorable. The mites, after removal from the mussels, may also be maintained in finger bowls of water for several weeks and even months if the temperature is around 40-50° F. They require little attention although they may be fed an occasional small bit of mussel gill.

After these mites have been removed from their host they show a well-marked positive phototropism. This at first seems anomalous as it is difficult to understand why they are not attracted from the mussel, by way of the siphons, when a bright beam of light penetrates the mantle cavity as frequently happens at mid-day. The reason they do not leave the host is seen when the following experiment is performed. If water from the mantle cavity of the host or a filtered water extract of the gills is added to water containing the mites they immediately show a negative response to light and maintain this state for a length of time depending somewhat on the concentration of host substance.

It may be further shown that this reversal in phototropism is due to specific host material for if water from the mantle cavity or extract of gills of mussels on which this species of mite is not parasitic is used there is no effect on the phototropism of the mites and they remain positive to light.

The parasitic Unionicola may be identified by reference to papers by Wolcott (1899, 1905) and Marshall (1933).

REFERENCE

For the culture of Hydracarina see p. 136.

BIBLIOGRAPHY

MARSHALL, RUTH. 1933. Preliminary list of the Hydracarina of Wisconsin, Part III. *Trans. Wis. Acad. Sci. Arts and Letters.* 28:37.

WELSH, J. H. 1930. Reversal of phototropism in a parasitic water mite. *Biol. Bull.* 59:165.

———— 1931. Specific influence of the host on the light responses of parasitic water mites. *Ibid.* 61:497.

———— 1932. A laboratory experiment in animal behavior. *Science* 75:591.

WOLCOTT, R. H. 1899. On the North American species of the genus Atax (Fabr.) Bruz. *Trans. Amer. Micr. Soc.* 20:193.

———— 1905. A review of the genera of the water mites. *Ibid.* 26:161.

Family TETRANYCHIDAE

BREEDING OF NEOTETRANYCHUS BUXI, A MITE ON BOXWOOD

DONALD T. RIES, *Ithaca, New York*

THESE mites may be found on the underside of the leaves of Box-wood bushes in some localities.

Small cuttings of boxwood about an inch in length were placed in small pots of earth. The pots of cuttings were then placed in large flats of peat moss in order to facilitate handling and also to keep them from drying out. Since the mites seemed unable to negotiate the distance between the pots over the moss there was no need of covering the individual plants. By this means mites were reared through nine generations.

Each female was allowed to deposit one or two eggs on a plant and every 24 hours was removed to another plant by means of a fine camel's hair brush. In no case were more than two nymphs allowed to live on any one plant.

Newly hatched nymphs are active, moving about from one surface of the leaf to the other. From 1 to 3 days after hatching they become quiescent and cast their skins. The second instar nymphs feed actively on the upper and lower surfaces of the leaves. The entire life cycle is completed in 18 to 21 days, averaging 18½ during the summer months when temperatures are fairly high and humidity low. Females have lived as long as 6 weeks during the summer, while others have laid their full complement of eggs and died within 2 weeks after emerging.

Copulation takes place soon after the female emerges from the third instar skin. In several instances the male was observed standing over a quiescent third instar mite even before she had begun exit from the skin. Later work showed that fertilization may take place during this time. Oviposition usually takes place ½ to ¾ of an hour after fertilization. One egg is deposited at a time and from 1 to 5 may be laid during 24 hours.

Another method for rearing mites on plants having large leaves was to cut small doughnuts of felt. Each of these was fastened to a leaf with waterproof glue and covered with glass or cellophane which was held in place by a paper clip. Fiber circles, such as those used in making microscope slides, were also used with excellent results. A mite working on Rhododendron was reared through two seasons under these conditions.

Class *Myriapoda*, Order DIPLOPODA

EURYURUS ERYTHROPYGUS*

THIS millipede is abundant in the heartwood of much decayed logs, in moist and more decayed sapwood, and on the soil under decaying wood if rather moist conditions prevail.

Specimens were collected and placed in glass receptacles approximately 5½ inches in diameter and about 3 inches deep. These were half-filled with small, broken pieces of moist and much decayed sapwood from a rotten log, together with a little humus. This material was examined carefully for contaminating forms, such as other millipedes, centipedes, mites, earthworms, eggs, insects, *etc*. A layer of vaseline was spread around the rims of the receptacles and glass covers placed over them, thus insuring very little if any evaporation. However, a few drops of water were added occasionally. Moisture and other conditions were kept as natural as possible. Some of the receptacles were opened for observations every day and fresh air entered at these times, but the animals seemed to thrive in receptacles which were not opened so often.

* Abstracted from an article in the *Ohio J. Sci.* 27:25, 1927, by HUGH H. MILEY, *Ohio State University*.

From adults collected in the fall a number reared in the laboratory survived during the following summer and most of the fall. Adult males and females, when observed copulating, and in some cases males and females not pairing, were isolated in separate receptacles. In most cases the females laid eggs in cavities made by themselves a short distance below the surface of the soil. These were permitted to hatch in the same receptacle with the adults. As soon as the larvae started emerging from the eggs, a number of them were placed in petri dishes in order to observe their habits more accurately.

M. E. D.

Order SYMPHYLA

REARING OF SCUTIGERELLA IMMACULATA*

THIS garden centipede will live on a wide range of vegetable matter and probably on decaying vegetable matter within the soil.

Eggs are laid during the early part of the summer in the subsoil runways of the creatures, usually in clusters of 4 to 20. At room temperatures the eggs hatch in about 14 days. When the larvae first hatch they have 6 pairs of legs. One pair is added at the first molt, which occurs in 1 to 4 days, and a pair is added at each successive molt, occurring 7 to 14 days apart, until each individual has 12 pairs.

Rearing of these creatures is done in petri dishes on a thin layer of soil and in stender dishes into which is poured a "muck-plate" made by mixing 10 parts plaster of Paris and 3 parts of finely ground muck. This mixture makes it easy to find the white eggs and to observe the whitish creatures as they move about. Lettuce leaves are placed on the surface of the plates for food and as a hiding place. Rearing records show that individuals may live 11 or 12 months.

M. E. D.

Class *Insecta*, Order THYSANURA

REARING OF THYSANURA
G. J. SPENCER, *University of British Columbia*

Campodeidae. These are difficult to rear because they are extremely sensitive to changes in moisture. A large volume of greenhouse potting soil or compost in a big tin box with a tight-fitting lid, will keep a colony going for a few weeks.

Machilidae. These are also unsatisfactory to rear. The coastal species

*Abstracted from an article in *J. Econ. Ent.* 21:357, 1928, by GEORGE A. FILINGER, *Ohio Agricultural Experiment Station.*

in this province may be kept alive for some time in a mass of damp leaves from the forest floor; I have not succeeded in getting them to breed in captivity. *Machilis maritima* covers much territory on the rocky seashore; it dies quickly in confinement. Of the four (unnamed) species in the dry interior of British Columbia, only one may be kept in cages. It frequents deep moss from under timber in gullies. A square foot of this moss in a large tin will keep a small colony alive for several weeks.

Lepismidae. Thermobia domestica is the easiest of all to rear. Any long box or laboratory drawer will do if it has a close-fitting lid and has one end against a hot radiator, to ensure a temperature, at one end, of 90° to 100° F., and a gradient dropping to 80° F. at the other. Eggs are laid at about 80° to 85° F.

I have kept one colony going for ten years in a large, 27-drawer incubator. The shell of the incubator is double-walled with celotex (corn stalk board), with a 4-inch air space between walls perforated at intervals with 1-inch holes. The back has a baffle-plate of thin asbestos board heated with a battery of six large carbon lamps, two of which dip into a large pan of water. The ends of all drawers touch the asbestos board at the back, whence they get the necessary heat. The drawers are roughly 27 x 10 x 7 inches, open on top with a 2-inch wide strip of celluloid cemented on the edge all round and overhanging inwards.

Lepismids cannot walk on smooth surfaces, and so cannot escape from the open drawers. On the floor of each drawer is a dissecting pan or other shallow tin tray 1-inch deep, full of sand which is kept always damp. At 2-inch intervals on the floor are flat 2-inch squares of cotton-batting blackened with India ink and dried.

Eggs are deposited in the cotton wool at various distances from the heated rear end, and the nymphs find adequate shelter under it until the third instar when they venture further afield. Food consists of whole wheat meal or plain flour; at intervals of 2 weeks I put in a teaspoonful of very lean beef or veal, thoroughly dried on a radiator and pulverized. This meat powder is a great attractant. All food must be dry.

Watch out for overcrowding, or disease will wipe out the whole colony. Five hundred individuals can live in a drawer of the dimensions above; two or three hundred is better. There is one brood per year. Breeding occurs at irregular intervals.

Lepisma saccharina colonies have been kept in the incubator for eight years. They require less heat than *T. domestica* and more moisture. In addition to the tin tray of damp earth or sand, I use a heap of small squares of shingle separated from each other alternately, by a match. This gives narrow crevices in which the colony spends most of its time, especially the young nymphs. On top of the cedar shingles is a small saucer of raw earthenware which is filled with water every week, thus keeping all the shingles damp. Food, as for *T. domestica.* I have also used printers' starch at intervals. There is one brood per year.

Ctenolepisma quadriseriata was brought from Ontario and kept alive in Vancouver for only 1½ years. One brood was produced and then the whole colony died with the exception of a lone male which lived 2 years. This species can stand freezing, requires a much lower temperature than the others, and thrives best on slabs of alder bark. It will eat farinaceous foods but feeds in nature, I think, on algae on roots and on trees.

The incubator and all rearing tins are kept in a small laboratory from which the heat goes off every night at 7:30, coming on again at 7:30 in the morning. In addition, the plug of the incubator is connected at 8 A.M. every day and pulled out at 6 P.M. By this means a change of temperature is ensured, averaging week by week for seven winter months, a difference of 30° F. between night and day. In summer the incubator is set so as to ensure a maximum mid-day temperature of 100° F.

Family LEPISMATIDAE

METHODS OF REARING LEPISMATIDS

J. ALFRED ADAMS, *Iowa State College*

THE FIREBRAT, *Thermobia Domestica*

THIS is the largest commonly available member of the Apterygota. Its possibilities as a laboratory animal have not been generally appreciated.

Firebrats may be reared in great numbers in air-conditioned cabinets such as those described by Brindley and Richardson (1931). The conditions around the culture dishes are: 37° C., 75% relative humidity, gently moving air, and light of twilight intensity or darkness.

The culture dishes (Fig. 59) are of glass, 20 cm. in diameter, with vertical sides, 8 cm. in height. They contain 20 or more paper strips 4 cm. in width and 30 cm. in length folded transversely, the folds occurring about every 2 cm. and alternating in direction so

FIG. 59.—Sketch of apparatus for general use in rearing the firebrat. The tubes are usually omitted.

that the folded strip resembles the collapsible side of a bellows. These strips are stood on edge in the dish. Cotton batting receives the eggs.

Firebrats thrive when they have continuous access to separate heaps of rolled oats, dried ground lean beef, cane sugar, dried brewer's yeast, and common salt. Rolled oats may be used as the sole food. If the tightly closed rearing cabinet has, under its fan, a large surface of brine containing an excess of common salt, the humidity will be held near the desired percentage and watering will be unnecessary. At humidities lower than 70% a slender test tube of water, tightly plugged with cotton batting, may be inverted on a piece of cardboard in the dish so that the insects may be able to rest and moisten themselves on the damp surface.

Such a cage accommodates one to two hundred adult firebrats. A few hours' attention a month suffice for their care.

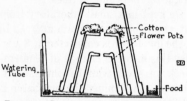

FIG. 60.—Cross section of rearing apparatus for the firebrat for use in ovipositional studies.

Where a careful check on food, population, or oviposition is desired another type of apparatus is recommended. It consists (Fig. 60) of a culture dish, similar to the above, into which are inverted three clay flower-pots graded in size so that the largest covers the medium-sized one, which in turn covers the smallest. In order that the insects may run under them the edges are supported on a thin wedge of wood. Cotton batting to receive the eggs is placed between the middle and outer pot.

To segregate new generations the cotton, bearing eggs, may be transferred to new rearing quarters. Watering is not advised. The tiny nymphs soon leave the cotton for the paper. At this temperature they become sexually mature in about 3 months and gravimetrically mature in about 6 months.

Firebrats must not be grasped directly; they may be passed singly without injury from one glass dish to another. Two species of gregarines, described by the author, are likely to appear in the cultures. To get gregarine-free cultures it is necessary to obtain freshly laid eggs, spore-free, and transfer them to sterilized, lidded, culture dishes. A ring of vaseline around the outside prevents the entry of book-lice.

THE SILVERFISH, *Lepisma Saccharina*

The author has not reared silverfish extensively. Sweetman (1934) states that 28° C. and 90% R. H. are satisfactory conditions for this species.

It has been found convenient to keep silverfish in apparatus similar to that used for the firebrat but at a constant temperature near 28° C., a relative humidity near or above 75%, and with provision for the insects to have access to a small moist wick. The culture dish should be deeper than that for the firebrat or nearly closed and kept in semi-darkness. The papers should be more closely packed.

REFERENCES

For the culture of *Thermobia domestica* see also p. 260.
For the culture of *Lepisma saccharina* see also p. 260.
For the culture of *Ctenolepisma quadriseriata* see p. 261.

BIBLIOGRAPHY

ADAMS, J. A. 1933. *J. N. Y. Ent. Soc.* 41:557.
BRINDLEY, T. A., and RICHARDSON, C. H. 1931. *Iowa State College J. of Sci.* 5:211.
SPENCER, G. J. 1930. *Canad. Ent.* 62:1.
SWEETMAN, H. L. 1934. *Bull. Brooklyn Ent. Soc.* 29:156.

Order COLLEMBOLA

REARING OF COLLEMBOLA

G. J. SPENCER, *University of British Columbia*

MANY species may be kept alive and breeding for long periods, in tightly lidded tobacco cans supplied with the humus or leaf mold on which they were collected. Rotting potato is a good medium for some species. I have kept a colony flourishing on this material for over two years. Another good container is a tin covered with a piece of glass, covered in turn with a piece of dark cardboard. This permits examination of the colony without removing the glass.

Two points are of importance in rearing Collembola: Keep the material on which they are feeding damp; secondly, do not uncover them often or let wind currents disturb them and dry out their culture medium. Flat stones placed in the tins will serve for cover.

REMARKS ON COLLEMBOLA*

COLLEMBOLA are all extremely sensitive to any lack of humidity in their surroundings. The only way to keep them alive in captivity for any length of time is to put in the vial some source of moisture such as wet, rotten wood or damp filter paper.

The white or yellow spherical eggs are laid singly or in masses under bark, among dead leaves, and in many other damp situations. Oviposition apparently takes place only in the dark. Several species lay eggs freely in captivity. Incubation at room temperature takes from 10 to 35 days, according to the species. In captivity, *Achorutes socialis* and some other species lay only in the spring, while *A. humi* and *Neanura muscorum* oviposit late in the fall. The eggs of the last named species require 35 days to hatch at an average temperature of 60° F. This is a

* Abstracted from two articles in the *Canad. Ent.* 51:73, 1919, and 56:99, 1924, by CHARLES MACNAMARA, Arnprior, Ontario.

remarkably long period compared with the 10 or 12 days required by the eggs of *Achorutes socialis* under the same conditions; and in the insect's natural environment incubation would doubtless have been even longer.

Springtails feed largely on the vegetable molds and minute algae which flourish in such situations. Fungi are a favorite food of many species and both spores and pieces of mycelium are often found in their stomachs. Liquid food also attracts these chewers, and in the spring several species, particularly of the genus Achorutes, may be seen in large numbers feeding on the sweet sap exuding from freshly cut maple stumps.

Species that live on the surface of pools and streams, such as *Isotoma palustris* and *Sminthurus aquaticus,* often pick up diatoms and desmids, and in the spring feed largely on the pollen which the conifers lavish upon the wind.

Our pollen-eating species go direct to the flowers of various plants. In Switzerland, Handschin says, *Sminthurus hortensis* is always found in the blossoms of *Ranunculus glacialis,* and in this country the same species is common on dandelion blossoms. In America *Achorutes armatus* sometimes makes a nuisance of itself in beds of cultivated mushrooms, and a few other species have some bad marks against them. *Sminthurus hortensis* feeds upon beans, beets, cabbage, cantaloupes, carrots, clover, corn, cucumber, kale, lettuce, mangolds, onions, peas, potatoes, radishes, rye, spinach, squash, tobacco, tomatoes, turnips, violets, watermelons, wheat, wild cucumber. Its depredations make it the most widely known of the springtails.

The species definitely known to be carnivorous are few, but further study of Collembolan life histories will probably reveal others. An undoubted flesh-feeder is *Anurida maritima,* an inhabitant of the seashore. Folsom says the insect's principal food is the soft tissues of the mollusk, *Littorina littorea,* as well as dead fish cast up on the shore. Imms slightly extends the diet to include an occasional desmid or other green alga. Motter's courageous study of the fauna of the grave brought to light another carnivorous springtail in *Isotoma sepulcralis,* which was abundant with a large percentage of the 150 corpses examined.

Anurida maritima and *Isotoma sepulcralis* feed on dead fish. Two other carnivorous species, *Friesea sublimis* and *Isotoma macnamarai,* are raptorial and devour living prey. The food habits of *I. macnamarai* were mostly observed in vials where the specimens were kept with small pieces of damp, rotten wood to provide the moisture so necessary to all these thin-skinned insects. Cannibalism in captivity was noted in these two last named species and the two species were found to eat each other.

Arthropleona would not eat at all in captivity. M. E. D.

A METHOD FOR REARING MUSHROOM INSECTS AND MITES*

WHILE conducting studies on the biology and control of insects and mites affecting cultivated mushrooms, it was found necessary to rear large numbers of these pests. Various rearing methods were tried, including the use of soil in salve boxes, manure in vials, *etc.*, but none was found more satisfactory than the following:

The insects and mites, in as pure culture as possible, were introduced in small numbers into fresh 1-quart bottles of commercial mushroom spawn, and allowed to breed and develop. This spawn is made of chopped straw and manure thoroughly mixed, sterilized in an autoclave, and later inoculated with mushroom mycelium, grown from spores. With incubation at room temperature, the mycelium penetrates to the bottom of the bottles and completely fills the interstices of the medium. This spawn is thus a pure culture and is uncontaminated with molds. Tight cotton plugs are used in the bottle mouths.

The mushroom mycelium furnishes an excellent food for these mushroom pests, and they gradually eat it out, leaving the original straw-manure medium. Feeding begins at the top of the spawn, and as it progresses, the portion destroyed is sharply differentiated from the uneaten part. Eggs are laid and the stages develop next to the glass, where they are easily observed with a binocular microscope. In studying the development of any particular eggs or groups of other stages, a circle is drawn around them on the glass with a wax pencil. They are thus readily referred to.

It is very important that the flies and springtails to be reared should be free from mites, the hypopi of which are often carried on their bodies. Otherwise the mites may breed so rapidly as to destroy the mycelium and perhaps starve the insects. Contamination with molds should also be prevented as much as possible.

These bottles of insect colonies should be kept in a somewhat humid atmosphere. After the cultures have been developing awhile the insect excreta, as well as bacteria entering with the insects, will usually make the medium moist enough so that further additions of moisture are unnecessary. Most of the rearing experiments were carried on at temperatures between 50° and 65° F. as these represent the usual temperature limits of the bearing mushroom houses.

The following insects have been successfully reared in spawn bottles of this kind:

Collembola. These tiny insects are sometimes rather difficult to rear

---

*Reprinted, with slight changes, from an article in *Ent. News* 40:222, 1929, by C. A. THOMAS, *Pennsylvania State College.*

under experimental conditions, because of their susceptibility to dessication, but in these spawn bottles they thrive remarkably well, and large numbers of several species have been reared.

Achorutes armatus thrives in the spawn bottles, but is quite susceptible to drying. *Proisotoma* (*Isotoma*) *minuta,* collected in the soil, usually breeds rapidly in spawn bottles. *Lepidocyrtus cyaneus* breeds very readily in spawn bottles. It can withstand somewhat dryer conditions than can some of the other springtails. *L. albus* breeds readily in spawn bottles. *Sminthurus caecus* breeds slowly in spawn bottles.

Diptera. Many generations of *Sciara coprophila* and *Neosciara pauciseta,* of the family Sciaridae, have been reared in these bottles. Three generations of a parasite of these flies, a species of the hymenopteran Calliceras (Ceraphron) near *C. ampla* Ashmead, were also reared. Small orange-colored flies of the family Cecidomyidae, the larvae of which were collected in mushroom caps and mushroom beds, have been reared successfully.

Acarina. (Mites). There is usually no trouble in rearing tyroglyphids and numerous other mites in the spawn bottles. In fact it is often difficult to obtain pure cultures of other mushroom insects because of infestation by these pests. The chief species feeding on mushrooms and mycelium are tyroglyphids, chiefly *Tyroglyphus linteri,* another Tyroglyphus species, and sometimes a species of Histiostome which feeds on the decaying tissues of injured or diseased mushrooms. All of the above mites have been reared through many generations in the spawn bottles, and all stages, including the very interesting hypopi of the tyroglyphids, have been found in the spawn. Abundance of moisture is no deterrent to the development of these mites as they may often be found partly submerged in the moist surface of the spawn medium.

It is probable that other fungus insects could be reared in these bottles provided the moisture and other factors were regulated to suit the species. In order to make smaller cultures the spawn may be removed to smaller bottles or vials. However, it is necessary to avoid contamination with molds and mites during this process.

M. E. D.

Order EPHEMEROPTERA

REARING MAYFLIES FROM EGG TO ADULT
HELEN E. MURPHY, *Phoenix, New York*

SINCE no way has yet been found of inducing mayflies to mate in captivity, it is necessary to capture a female carrying her eggs. Late in the afternoon of a quiet, sunny day in late spring or in summer, it is usually possible to locate numbers of males and females dancing up and down in their mating flight near the bank of a pond, lake, or stream. One by one the females leave the throng and fly over the water, here and there dropping with their eggs to the surface. With a net capture one of these females before she reaches the water. Holding her gently by the wings wash the eggs into a culture dish and transfer them to the laboratory.*

Mayflies of the genus Baetis do not carry their eggs in a protruding mass, but crawl into the water and lay them in a flat layer on a submerged stone. These may be removed with a scalpel as soon as laid and carried to the laboratory in water.

With the aid of a lens and a scalpel, separate individual eggs and transfer them to culture dishes by means of a medicinal pipette. Covered culture dishes 75 mm. x 20 mm. prove very satisfactory. Fill each dish ⅔ full with tap water seasoned for 24 hours in an open container at room temperature. With a pipette change half of the water every three days. Avoid sudden temperature changes.

Diatoms and desmids freshly scraped from stones from a stream furnish excellent food. One drop of thick culture every three days is sufficient for a very young nymph. Twice that amount is required later. Diet may be varied by the addition of a small fragment of Spirogyra.

When longitudinal venation is clearly evident in the wing pads prepare for emergence. Cut a piece of No. 12 or No. 16 wire cloth 12 cm. x 30 cm. Remove the glass cover and roll the wire to fit tightly inside the glass rim. Pinch the top together and fold twice, making a closed seam. This cage allows the specimen to crawl from the water and to hang in the air waiting for the final molt.

In *Baetis vagans* there are 27 instars and 6 months are required for the development of the summer brood.

BIBLIOGRAPHY

MURPHY, HELEN E. 1922. Notes on the biology of some of our North American mayflies. *Lloyd Library Bull.* No. 22.

SMITH, O. R. 1935. Eggs and egg-laying habits of North American mayflies. *In* Needham, Traver, and Hsü: The Biology of Mayflies, p. 67.

* Editor's Note: Artificial fertilization of certain mayflies (Hexagenia, Ephemera, *etc.*) is easily effected by mixing freshly liberated eggs and sperms in a watch glass of lake water. A gravid female taken in her ovipositing flight will shed all her eggs with the greatest readiness on such stimulation as snipping off her head or subjecting her to tobacco fumes. Eggs of a subimago are sometimes mature and ready for fertilization. J. G. N.

Order ODONATA

CULTURE METHODS FOR THE DAMSELFLY, ISCHNURA VERTICALIS

EVELYN GEORGE GRIEVE, *Cornell University*

REARING work was begun with the full-grown nymphs which were collected early in the spring from a small, grassy fish pond. From the first generation, which were the stock adults, eggs were obtained for life history studies. As soon as the nymphs hatched they were isolated and reared in separate containers for the entire life span.

FIG. 61.—Breeding cage for *Ischnura verticalis*.

Cages. The type of cage (Fig. 61) used for breeding stock was a fairly large aquarium covered with a screen cage, fitting the aquarium closely at the sides, and allowing room above for the adults to fly, mate, and capture their prey. Aquatic plants, principally *Eleocharis palustris,* were kept growing in one corner of the aquarium; up these the nymphs could crawl to transform. When the females were ready to oviposit, one or two of the flexible stems of *E. palustris* were bent down into the water where they were held by the surface film. The females preferred to oviposit in these floating stems, and each day eggs could be removed and dated for the study of embryonic development.

In order to keep records of all individuals, and also because the species is cannibalistic, separate containers were used for all reared specimens. The most satisfactory type for the young nymphs was a small boat (Fig. 62), floating with others in a large pan of water. The frame of the boat is of balsa wood, which is very light and buoyant, and the "hold" of the vessel is made of silk. Although the illustration of the boat is about natural size, the silk was of finer mesh than that shown, namely about

144 threads to the inch, which is fine enough to retain the smallest nymph and its food organisms, and yet permits circulation of water. The silk was fastened to the frame with paraffin, and the frame was covered with a film of paraffin to reduce "water-logging." The little "sail" was a paper tag, attached by a special pin, and was used to record dates of molting and other data.

The advantage of such containers, over Syracuse watch glasses for instance, is that the nymph has all the benefits of a large vessel of water, which does not stagnate so quickly, and is less subject to temperature fluctuations.

When the nymphs were nearly full grown (*i.e.*, in the last two or three instars) and were inclined to crawl out of the boats, they were transferred to glass tumblers, provided with a strip of wire screen to

Fig. 62.—"Boat" for rearing nymphs of *Ischnura verticalis*. (About natural size.)

serve as a perch. Previous to transformation, the glasses were covered with cheesecloth fastened down with an elastic band, thus making convenient emergence chambers in which to observe molting.

The young imagos were then transferred to individual aquarium-cages, similar to, but smaller than, the stock cages (Fig. 61), one pair to a cage, so that data might be kept on mating, oviposition, color changes, *etc*.

Feeding. Both nymphs and adults are strictly carnivorous, and for any large scale rearing it is necessary to maintain colonies of food organisms. The adults have a preference for dipterous insect prey. One method of supply was to stock the breeding tank with quantities of full grown blood worms and mosquito larvae and pupae, and to allow the damselflies to feed on the emerging midges and mosquitos. Later in the season when this supply failed it was necessary to collect midges in the woods with a net, morning and evening, and liberate them in the cages.

For the very young nymphs, Paramecium cultures were tried and abandoned. Very minute chironomid larvae were fed to the next group of damselfly nymphs that hatched, with good results, and their use was continued for all nymphs up to the 5th or 6th instar. The method was to collect chironomid egg masses each morning from out-door troughs or ponds, and to keep them in small pans of water until they hatched; then to transfer the infant blood worms with a pipette to the boats with the nymphs. The nymphs seemed to thrive on them. But the blood worms have a nasty habit of making little dwelling tubes out of anything they can fasten down, and occasionally they would weave in the cast skin of a nymph, thereby destroying the evidence of the length of instars. From the 6th or 7th to the 9th or 10th instars, the nymphs were fed Ceriodaphnia, and *Daphnia pulex;* and after the 9th or 10th, *Daphnia magna.* The latter were also used to feed the full grown nymphs which developed the breeding stock. Cultures of these Daphnia had to be maintained in the laboratory throughout the season. [For culture see pp. 207 to 220.]

Diseases. This species is susceptible to a disease which may occur under laboratory conditions (as well as in nature), if pond water is used. The invading organism is a green protozoan which lives in the lumen of the rectum, and is fatal to a large percentage of infected nymphs. A heavy infection is detectable, even with the naked eye, for the rectum appears green and may be seen in any but heavily pigmented nymphs. Methods of preventing infection were not worked out, but it might be effective to boil the water in which the insects are to live.

The species is also subject, under natural conditions at least, to two species of trematode parasites, which may or may not be fatal; to a Gregarine infection; and to external infestation by an aquatic mite.*

REFERENCE

For the rearing *Sympetrum vicinum* see p. 272.

METHODS OF REARING ODONATA

P. P. CALVERT, *University of Pennsylvania*

THE following methods were successful in rearing larvae of *Nannothemis bella* and *Anax junius* from egg to adult. †

Eggs of *N. bella* were obtained in the field in July, 1925, by dipping the abdomen of a female, caught in the act of oviposition, in a vial of water. As the eggs hatched the resulting 1st instar larvae were removed to various small dishes. After they made their first larval (nymphal) ‡ molt they were isolated, each one being placed in a glass salt cellar having a capacity of about 5 cc., covered with a sheet of glass, and numbered. In each dish a small quantity of an aquatic plant (Elodea in

---

*Editor's Note: Others have reared Odonata from egg to adult both in Europe and America, but the preceding account appears to be the only one of maintenance of any species through successive generations. W. H. Krull (*Ann. Ent. Soc. Amer.* 22:651, 1929) reared *Sympetrum obtrusum,* finding 9 (in one case 10) nymphal instars. He fed the very young nymphs on Paramecium and Tubifex. (For culture see pp. 119 and 142.)
The larger nymphs will eat almost any small living animals that come in their way. It is easy to rear them in pillow cages of the sort shown in figure 42, and if the size of wire mesh be just small enough to retain them and large enough to admit their prey, they will feed themselves in any natural pond, protected by the cage from predatory enemies.
J. G. N.

† Abridged by the author from a paper in *Proc. Amer. Philos. Soc.* 68:227-274, 1929.

‡ Editor's Note: Equivalent terms; nymph is used in preference elsewhere in this book to denote this type of larva. J. G. N.

earlier months, Lemna later) was kept growing. Through the nearly three years during which the rearing of *N. bella* was carried on, the dishes containing the larvae were kept on the inner sill of a window facing north. The temperature of the room, as indicated by a self-recording maximum and minimum thermometer, ranged from 89° to 50° F. (31.6° to 10° C.).

In December, 1925, each of the four living larvae, then somewhat over 2 mm. long, was transferred from the salt cellar to a glass "caster cup" having a capacity of 15 cc., with the water and other contents in which it had been living previously. In June, 1926, each was again transferred from the caster cup to a finger bowl. Each caster cup and finger bowl was kept constantly covered with a piece of glass.

In June, 1927, when the first of the *N. bella* larvae gave indication, by the whitening of its eyes, that transformation was approaching, its finger bowl was placed uncovered in a cylindrical glass battery jar. In the finger bowl was put a stick of wood so placed that it extended below the surface of the water; its upper end rested against a strip of wire netting attached to a framed window screen in front of a closed window facing south. Thus was provided a place for transformation.

One larva, from the same lot of eggs, lived for another year, until June 1928, before it transformed.

When the larvae were about one week old drops of a culture of Paramecium were placed in the vessels in which they were living. [For culture see pp. 112-128.] Soon after, other Infusoria, small copepods, ostracods, rotifers, larvae of Anopheles, and other organisms smaller than *N. bella* were added. For nearly a year from Sept. 19, 1925, the food supply was chiefly small Crustacea, some of which bred in the dishes containing *N. bella*. In August, 1926, chironomid and ephemerid larvae, in September and October 1926, corixid and culicid larvae were given in addition. In late February, 1927, mayfly larvae were more frequently furnished; although these were taken from a swiftly flowing stream they lived in the absolutely still water of the dish for at least eight days and possibly longer. Similar observations were made in connection with other mayfly larvae, those of the genus Heptagenia being much more able to survive in still water than those of Baetis, for example.

Special attention was paid each day that the *N. bella* larvae were examined to noting whether any possible living food material had survived from the previous week and in only three cases was an entire lack of such found. The slow rate of development of the larvae may not, therefore, be ascribed to absolute starvation, although it is of course possible that the optimum food was not in the dishes. The hairs on the body of the larvae are fairly dense, and to them vegetable débris usually adhered to such an extent as to hide the body surface. This mass which the slowly moving *N. bella* carried constantly served as a part of the food supply of the small Crustacea or of the still smaller animals (Infusoria, rotifers) on which the Crustacea fed.

Almost identical methods were employed in rearing a larva of *Anax junius** up to the time when it reached a length of 28 mm. It, the water in which it had been living, Lemna and other plants, were then transferred from the finger bowl to a battery jar, 145 mm. in diameter and 160 mm. high, and covered with a sheet of glass as before. A stick of wood was leaned against the side of the jar to give the larva an object on which to climb. It was there that its final exuviae was found.

For the earlier stages small Crustacea were the chief food; when 5 mm. long, Culex and Anopheles larvae, small corixids, Daphnia, and mayfly larvae were used. During the final months the last named, especially those of the genus Heptagenia, were almost the only food given. *A. junius* seemed to pay no attention to Asellus.

Nevin † reared *Sympetrum vicinum* from egg to adult in stender dishes. During the first instar specimens from a protozoan culture were placed in the dishes. This culture proved to be mainly of *Paramecium aurelia* which were so small that the larvae did not seem to notice them and continued to die, probably from starvation. When *Paramecium caudatum* were fed the larvae ate them greedily. Another mixed culture used at this time contained many Stylonychiae and a few Vorticellae, although the larvae were never seen to eat the latter except with Daphnia to which Vorticellae were attached. Several ostracods of the family Cyprididae were eaten before the first molt. Later larger ostracods and copepods, including Cyclops and Diaptomus, were eaten. The copepods proved more proficient in capturing Paramecia than the dragonfly larvae and had to be removed until the larvae were larger. They also destroyed the exuviae of *S. vicinum* or parts of them if the latter were left too long after the individuals had molted. During the last few instars Daphnia, Hyalella, and small mayfly and stonefly larvae were fed. Daphnias were not eaten from choice, but formed an important part of the food, especially when mayfly larvae were not at hand. All larvae were fed and cared for three times a week.

Miss Laura Lamb,‡ in rearing *Pantala flavescens*, removed the larvae soon after hatching from the dish in which the eggs were laid and placed them in small stender dishes which were kept in a shaded part of the

---

*Editor's Note: Freshly laid eggs of *Anax junius* may easily be obtained by setting a stem of cat-tail (Typha) in a place to attract ovipositing females. It should be set aslant in the surface of the open water several yards out from the pond margin. It will then have preference over stems at the margin (where, presumably, enemies may lurk). If a fresh stem be used each day, the eggs may be dated. J. G. N.

† *Trans. Amer. Ent. Soc.* 55:79, 80, 1929.

‡ *Trans. Amer. Ent. Soc.* 50:289, 1924.

laboratory. During the first instar no food was given; during the second and third stages Paramecium and small mosquito larvae formed the food. The remaining stages fed upon mosquito larvae and small crustaceans until the tenth instar, when pieces of earthworms and mayfly larvae were supplied. In the eleventh instar small fish were eaten. The individuals were kept in separate dishes after the third instar on account of cannibalism.

Order PLECOPTERA

REARING THE STONEFLY, NEMOURA VALLICULARIA*

THIS herbivorous stonefly is an inhabitant of clear-flowing cold spring brooks in the eastern United States. Adults appear on the wing in the latitude of Ithaca, N. Y., about the middle of March and disappear about the middle of April. They live among the vegetation of the brookside where they run about actively and make short flights when the sun shines warmly about noon. They eat sparingly of the young leaves of wild Touch-me-not (Impatiens). They are able to survive without food for several days.

About a week after transformation they reach sexual maturity and mate about midday. After mating, the females live for about a week, hiding in shaded places, and depositing gelatinous clumps of whitish eggs, numbering about 150 to 200 each.

To obtain eggs for rearing, adults of both sexes were confined in a small box with porous bottom, so placed that it rested on the surface of the brook. This insured high humidity. Leaves of wild Touch-me-not were added for food, and blocks of decayed wood were placed inside, supported on slender twigs. The eggs were deposited on the under side of these blocks.

Newly hatched nymphs were isolated in numbered shell vials, closed at the mouth with silk bolting cloth. These vials, assembled in an enameled tray, were immersed in the bed of the brook. They were examined each day for cast skins. For food the nymphs were supplied with bits of decaying elm leaves. The vials were cleaned and the food was renewed once a week.

Twenty-two instars were recorded during the nine months of development from hatching on the 2nd of July until emergence on the 29th of the following March.

J. G. N.

*Abstracted from an article in *Lloyd Library Bull.* 23, 1923 (Ent. Ser. No. 3) by CHEN-FU FRANCIS WU, of *Yen Ching University*, Peiping, China.

REARING FALL AND WINTER PLECOPTERA*

BECAUSE of their habit of congregating in places exposed to the warming influences of the sun's rays, most of the fall and winter stonefly adults are easy to capture. During the warmer days of late fall and early winter they are likely to be found crawling about on exposed tree trunks, fence posts, or rocks located close to a stream inhabited by the nymphs, particularly if these objects are covered with an algal growth.

In spite of the general belief that most adults of stoneflies do not feed, all of the fall and winter stoneflies of the Oakwood, Illinois, region have been found to feed. On many occasions the adults of *Taeniopteryx nivalis, Allocapnia recta, A. vivipara, A. mystica,* and *A. granulata* were observed feeding upon blue-green algae (*Protococcus vulgaris*) growing on tree trunks, fence posts, and stones near the habitat of the nymphs. A single specimen of *T. parvula* was also seen feeding on algae on a tree trunk.

Eggs have been obtained by the simple expedient of catching females with egg masses and submerging them in water. The egg mass soon falls from the female and the individual eggs separate and settle to the bottom of the dish.

Simple methods have sufficed for rearing fall and winter stoneflies. Fullgrown nymphs are collected and kept alive in small tins containing moist leaves until the emergence of the adults. In order to observe closely feeding, mating, and egg-laying habits, the adults may be kept alive and healthy in small hermitically sealed aquarium jars containing a layer of moist sand, a supply of bark bearing a good growth of green algae, and old leaves and stems on which the adults may run around or in which they may hide or rest. The eggs will hatch in glass tubes covered at both ends with fine bolting and submerged in unpolluted streams. No doubt, if supplied with the proper quality and quantity of food, the nymphs will develop under the same conditions.**

The nymphs of Taeniopteryx and Allocapnia, both young and nearly grown, are herbivorous. No doubt a few protozoans are occasionally

---

*Abstracted from an article in *Ill. Nat. Hist. Bull.* 18: 345, 1929, by THEODORE H. FRISON, *Illinois Natural History Survey.*

** Editor's Note: Lucy Wright Smith, of Cornell University, reported in *Ann. Ent. Soc. Amer.* 6:203, 1913, the use of essentially these same methods for *Perla immarginata.* Adults were kept in small wire cages and mating and egg laying occurred readily in captivity. These nymphs are carnivorous, however. Black fly larvae and mayfly nymphs proved satisfactory as food.

By these same methods adults of Pteronarcys have been obtained and kept in captivity where mating takes place readily. Eggs obtained from these or from wild adults have been taken in June and have hatched in running water the following February. Due undoubtedly to a lack of the proper food, however, these newly hatched nymphs were not reared. Older nymphs eat well decayed leaves. M.E.D.

taken into the alimentary tract along with the diatoms, but yellow fresh-water diatoms and decaying vegetation constitute their main food. Old leaves which have fallen into the water apparently supply the bulk of decaying vegetable matter used by the nymphs for food.

M. E. D.

Order ISOPTERA

LABORATORY COLONIES OF TERMITES*

ESTHER C. HENDEE, *Limestone College, Gaffney, South Carolina*

DAMP-WOOD TERMITES

THE damp-wood termites, *Zootermopsis angusticollis* and *Z. nevaden-sis,* because of their comparatively large size and the ease with which they may be maintained in laboratory colonies, are satisfactory termites for experimental work. These species are confined to western North America. Although they are sometimes found in sound wood, they more frequently inhabit rotten wood. Rotten logs which lie near a stream are favorable places in which to look for damp-wood termites. Since the termites seal up the entrance to their burrows, it is usually necessary to chop into the log in order to detect their presence.

The termites are brought to the laboratory in large pieces of the wood in which they have been found. If more than a few hours are to elapse before they reach the laboratory, the wood is wrapped in damp paper to prevent drying.

Upon reaching the laboratory the termites are removed from the wood by splitting it cautiously so as to expose the termite galleries and then gently knocking the ends of the pieces. The termites thus dislodged are allowed to fall into a large container or, as an extra precaution against injury, onto a sheet of cloth. At best, a few termites will be injured. It is therefore advisable to wait two or three days before using the termites for any experimental purpose. During that time weak or injured indi-viduals may be detected and removed from the group.

If it is desired to transport termites which have already been removed from the wood in which they were found in the field, the following method of packing is used. Numerous holes are bored in some blocks of wood by means of an auger. The termites are placed in these holes. The blocks are then wrapped in many layers of damp paper and finally en-closed in heavy dry paper or a box.

Termites from different natural colonies are, if possible, kept separate

* Further information concerning the biology of termites and a bibliography are given in "Termites and Termite Control" which is edited by Kofoid, Light, Horner, Randall, Herms, and Bowe (1934).

in the laboratory. More nearly similar genetic constitution within the group, a condition often desirable in experimental work, is thereby assured. Furthermore, the excessive cannibalism which is likely to follow the mixing of colonies is avoided. If colonies must be mixed, as is sometimes necessary in order to get the numbers of termites desired for a given experiment, about a week is allowed for cannibalism to subside before the mixed group is used in any experiment.

Individual termites are most safely handled by lifting them on a camel's hair brush or a tapering piece of stiff paper. Large numbers of termites may be transferred from one container to another by pouring them through a trough or funnel made of cellophane.

Petri dishes or shallow stender dishes are suitable containers for colonies of 100 or fewer termites. For larger colonies refrigerator dishes or moist chamber dishes have been found satisfactory. The lids of the containers, while not air tight, should fit closely enough and be heavy enough to prevent the escape of the termites. Anyone who has observed the crowded condition in termite galleries in nature will realize that there is little danger of getting too many termites into one container so long as there is opportunity for each termite to get at the food provided. In fact, large colonies thrive much better than small cononies.

The dishes containing the termites are kept in a dark room or cabinet. Large, open dishes of water placed nearby aid in maintaining a desirable humidity. Damp-wood termites live and reproduce at ordinary room temperatures (20° to 23° C.). They will survive throughout a considerably greater temperature range, provided the change is gradual. They should be protected from sudden changes in temperature.

Rotten, fungus-containing wood constitutes a satisfactory diet for damp-wood termites (Hendee, 1934). The pieces of wood should be sufficiently heavy and so placed that they may not be moved by the weight of the termites.

Cook and Scott (1933) describe an artificial diet for termites which consists of sucrose, casein, "Crisco", salts, cod liver oil, and rice polishings, all incorporated in an agar gel. Filter paper, while it fails to comprise a complete diet for termites (Cook and Scott, 1933; Hendee, 1934), affords a convenient source of the carbohydrate portion of the diet.

The food should be kept slightly damp. If the containers are left undisturbed, the termites will partially seal the lids from the inside with fecal matter. In this way they partially control the humidity within the container and prevent evaporation of water from their food. If the containers are opened frequently, however, a few drops of water should be added to the food every two or three days.

Fungi have been shown to supply an essential part of the natural diet of termites (Hendee, 1934). At the same time they constitute a potential hazard to the termite colony. A large colony will keep the fungi eaten down, but a small colony is often unable to do so and the termites themselves are attacked by the fungi. Precautions which may be taken to prevent this are: (1) choice of wood for food which does not contain excessive amounts of fungus mycelium, (2) frequent changes of the food when an artificial diet is used, (3) avoidance of excessive moisture in the food and of temperatures much above 20° C., (4) constant watch for excessive fungous growth, and (5) prompt removal of diseased termites.

Colonies of damp-wood termites, as found in nature, are composed of nymphs and adults. The adults are of two distinct castes, soldiers and reproductives. There are two types of reproductives: primary reproductives and supplementary reproductives. In some colonies a pair of primary reproductives, founders of the colony, may still be present. They may be distinguished by their brown bodies. In colonies from which the primary pair has disappeared, and in groups of nymphs which have become separated from the parent colony, some of the nymphs develop into supplementary reproductives. The latter are caramel colored.

Either type of reproductive, if included in a laboratory colony, will provide for the increase of the colony. Reproduction is carried on much more rapidly, however, by the supplementary reproductives. In a laboratory colony set up with nymphs alone, supplementary reproductives will develop and become functional within 4 to 7 weeks after the establishing of the colony.

Primary reproductives, before they swarm, have wings. When these alate forms develop in a laboratory colony, they are either removed from the colony or allowed to swarm. If it is desired to start colonies with primary pairs, the alates, as soon as they become fully pigmented, are allowed to swarm in the laboratory. The covers are removed from the containers, and the alates, which are positively phototropic, fly toward a window or other source of light. After a few minutes they drop to the floor and shed their wings. They are then picked up and males mated with females for the founding of primary colonies. Males may be distinguished from females by the smaller size of the posterior three or four sternites. The growth of primary colonies, however, is very slow. So for most purposes it is preferable to use nymphs alone or nymphs and supplementary reproductives for establishing laboratory colonies.

So far as I know, no one has succeeded in rearing termites from eggs without the presence of adult termites or older nymphs to care for the eggs and to groom and feed the young nymphs. I have found nymphs of the 4th instar satisfactory for experiments such as those on nutritional requirements. At that stage in development they are able to care for themselves; their growth rate is rapid; and they are far enough from the adult stage to allow time for experiments of several months' duration. Individuals of different instars may be distinguished by their relative head widths and the number of antennal segments (Heath, 1927).

DRY-WOOD TERMITES

The dry-wood termites which belong to the subgenus Kalotermes are found in Mexico and in the southern part of the United States. They live typically in the dry, sound wood of buildings and other wooden structures.

In choosing sound wood for feeding laboratory colonies of these termites the pieces are looked over carefully and all pieces which show evidence of a high content of resin or volatile oils are rejected.

Examination of the wood upon which *Kalotermes minor* feeds in nature has shown it to contain fungus mycelium, even when it shows no macroscopic evidence of decay (Hendee, 1933). Therefore, if wood other than that in which the termites have previously been living is supplied to laboratory colonies, it is first infected with fungi so that it will be similar to the natural diet of the termites. This is done by dampening the wood, scattering crushed termite pellets over it, and allowing five or six days to elapse before it is fed to the termites. By that time fungus spores which were contained in the pellets will have given rise to a growth of fungus mycelium in the wood.

While Kalotermes does not require as much moisture as Zootermopsis, the wood upon which it is fed should not be allowed to dry out completely. Light (1934) reports that many species of Kalotermes require a minimum of 10% moisture in their food.

Dry-wood termites will survive at ordinary room temperatures. For normal growth and reproduction, however, they require a minimum of 25° C. For swarming, Harvey (1934) reports a temperature ranging from 80° to 100° F. (27° to 38° C.) to be the optimum for *Kalotermes minor*.

Kalotermes minor is recommended by Kofoid and Bowe (1934) as the best species for use in testing wood and other materials for termite resistivity. They give a detailed account of the method of making the tests.

SUBTERRANEAN TERMITES

Subterranean termites of the genus Reticulitermes are found in nearly all parts of the United States. They demand a constant supply of moisture and are found in wood so situated that they may maintain runways into the soil.

Dr. A. L. Pickens (unpublished communication) has devised what is probably the most successful method of keeping laboratory colonies of Reticulitermes. A thin piece of wood, preferably decayed, is carved with grooves along the grain and occasional connecting grooves across the grain. The grooves are made wide enough to allow termites to pass each other. The piece of wood is dampened slightly and placed with grooved side down on the bottom of a lidded glass vessel. A mixture of damp soil and sand is then packed in above it. By means of a wire a tunnel is sunk to connect with the end of one of the grooves in the wood. The termites are introduced through this tunnel and soon establish themselves in the wood below. A few drops of water are added as needed to keep the soil damp. The colonies are kept at ordinary room temperature.

BIBLIOGRAPHY

COOK, S. F., and SCOTT, K.G. 1933. The nutritional requirements of *Zootermopsis* (*Termopsis*) *angusticollis*. *J. Cell. Comp. Physiol.*, 4:95.

HARVEY, P. A. 1934. The distribution and biology of the common dry-wood termite *Kalotermes minor*. II. Life history of *Kalotermes minor in* Kofoid, Light, Horner, Randall, Herms, and Bowe, *Termites and termite control* (2nd edit. [2]; Univ. Calif. Press), pp. 217-233, figs. 72-75.

HEATH, H. 1927. Caste formation in the termite genus Termopsis. *J. Morph.* and *Physiol.*, 43:387.

HENDEE, E. C. 1933. The association of the termites, *Kalotermes minor, Reticulitermes hesperus,* and *Zootermopsis angusticollis* with fungi. *Univ. Calif. Publ. Zool.*, 39:111.

———— 1934. The rôle of fungi in the diet of termites. *Science* 80:316.

KOFOID, C. A., and BOWE, E. E. 1934. A standard biological method of testing the termite resistivity of cellulose-containing materials *in* Kofoid, Light, Horner, Randall, Herms, and Bowe, *Termites and termite control* (2nd edit. [2]; Univ. Calif. Press), pp. 517-553, figs. 131A-131C.

LIGHT, S. F. 1934. Habitat and habit types of termites and their economic significance *in* Kofoid, Light, Horner, Randall, Herms, and Bowe, *Termites and termite control* (2nd edit., Univ. Calif. Press), pp. 136-149, figs. 33-38.

SNYDER, THOMAS E. 1935. Our enemy, the termite. 8°, pp. xiv + 196. Comstock Publishing Co. Ithaca, N. Y.

Order CORRODENTIA

TROCTES DIVINATORIA*

THE book-louse, a more or less cosmopolitan, parthenogenetic insect, is excellent as a source of material for life history studies by classes in entomology. Each student is given a mature specimen from which to obtain eggs, and the following equipment must be available:

*Abstracted from an article in *Ann. Ent. Soc. Amer.* 23:192, 1930, by O. W. ROSEWALL, *Louisiana State University.*

A large supply of drop-culture slides (those of matte finish with bottom of cell smooth but not polished are the best).

Trays to hold slides which are of a size easy to handle.

Cover slips, size 22 mm.

Vaseline

Corn meal (yellow meal seems to be the most satisfactory as food).

The book-louse is placed in the cell of a drop-culture slide with a few grains of corn meal. Too much corn meal will make it impossible for a beginner to find the eggs. The cell is then covered with a 22 mm. coverslip held in position by a trace of vaseline. As the eggs appear they are placed in separate slides and properly labeled. The eggs usually adhere to the point of a needle when touched, so it is an easy matter to transfer them. The work is best handled indoors in a room of fairly constant temperature.

M. E. D.

Order MALLOPHAGA

LIPEURUS HETEROGRAPHUS*

IN 1930 the writer undertook the study of Mallophaga under controlled laboratory conditions. A standard incubator which had a volume of 29,970 cc. was used. Ventholes allowed for proper ventilation. Glass dishes exposing a total water surface of about 100 sq. cms. were placed on the bottom of the incubator to supply the air with moisture.

Feathers were obtained from the neck region of a white fowl, and were cut into two parts. The fluffier basal portion was fastened in the center of a Syracuse watch glass by means of paste applied to the quill. The barbs of the feathers were trimmed so that they did not come in contact with the edges of the watch glass.

A male and a female *Lipeurus heterographus* of unknown age were placed on the feather in each watch glass. The watch glass was numbered and put in the incubator. The satisfactory temperature was found to be 33°-34° C. When an egg was laid, the male and female were placed on a fresh feather in a new dish.

Breeding was carried on during the summer of 1930. Specimens kept in the incubator until December bred actively during the entire period. The life cycle, from egg to adult, may take 32-36 days. There are three nymphal instars.

It was found by experiments that lice reared in the incubator would mate and produce fertile eggs. The males and females of *Lipeurus heterographus* copulate readily in captivity. For study purposes it was

*Abstracted from an article in *J. Paras.* 5:304, 1934, by F. H. WILSON, *Tulane University.*

more satisfactory to keep the males and females in separate dishes. After isolation, when placed together on feathers they would copulate in a very short time and their activities could be observed.

In the life history studies the lice were given only the fluffier parts of the feather as food. They fed readily, particularly if they were removed from the feather for a time and then replaced. Experiments with feathers from the Little Green Heron (*Butorides virescens virescens*) showed that *Lipeurus heterographus* of the hen will feed on these feathers.

Experiments on feeding with pulverized dried blood from a fowl show that this species relies on feathers for its essential food supply but supplements this with blood when it is obtainable. The maximum time for which 1st instar nymphs and adults could be kept alive on dried blood alone was three days. This is, however, not true of all biting lice since the writer failed to rear *Menopon gallinae* and *M. stramineum*, or even to induce them to lay eggs, under the same conditions under which *Lipeurus heterographus* thrived. Quite different food habits are indicated for *Menopon stramineum* (Wilson, 1933).

BIBLIOGRAPHY

WILSON, F. H. 1933. A louse feeding on the blood of its host. *Science* 77:490.

M. E. D.

Order EMBIIDINA

OLIGOTOMA TEXANA*

DURING the spring and early summer a number of Embiids belonging to the species *Oligotoma texana* were captured alive and kept in captivity in a vial for three months. They were killed at the end of that time only because it was impossible to care for them longer. No difficulty was experienced in keeping them alive; in fact they seemed quite hardy.

The individuals were kept alive in a loosely corked vial on a piece of rotting wood which they immediately covered with their webs. After a few days a cake crumb was dropped into the vial, and within thirty seconds embiid heads appeared at the openings in the webs, followed by their slender brown bodies as they made their way toward the food. By the next morning the crumb was completely hidden in a maze of silken tunnels which led from the rotting wood to it. Thereafter they were fed a diet of bread crumbs, and they always elongated their tunnels to include the food.

M. E. D.

*Abstracted from an article in *Ann. Ent. Soc. Amer.* 25:648, 1932, by HARLOW B. MILLS, *Montana State College.*

Order DERMAPTERA

DERMAPTERA

B. B. FULTON, *North Carolina State College*

EARWIGS may be reared in any jar or cage provided with moist sand, but a large petri dish makes a very convenient cage. One side of the dish is filled to the top with moist sand and the other side left vacant for placing food materials. If the dish is shallow enough the nest will be made against the glass if kept darkened. If the dish is too deep, it may be partly filled with plaster or other material that the earwig can not dig into. Earwigs feed on a great variety of food but most species prefer food of animal origin. They require very little ventilation and little care. I have had a petri dish with some *Anisolabis annulipes* living in it for about a year. Sometimes I have forgotten to feed or water them for several weeks at a time but have always found a few still alive.

Order ORTHOPTERA, Family GRYLLOBLATTIDAE

GRYLLOBLATTA

NORMA FORD, *University of Toronto*

IN KEEPING Grylloblatta in the laboratory an attempt has been made to provide natural conditions. Found in their native habitat in the Rocky Mountains, they live in cold, damp places, where the temperature ranges from 0°-5° C., and the rotten logs or mosses are almost dripping with moisture.

In the laboratory each insect is kept in a separate jar because of cannibalistic tendencies. The pieces of moss or decayed wood in the jar are always kept wet. In fact, a quarter to a half inch of water may be left in the bottom of the container. The jars are kept packed in ice in a large, insulated tub. Covering the tub and jars is a fairly loose packing of cotton batting. This allows for a certain variation in temperature.

The insects are usually fed on mealworms, cut in small pieces, although pupae of ants, dipterous larvae, or adult flies give variety to the diet. The insects are fed about once a month and care is taken to remove from the jar any food which is left and has become moldy.

Under these conditions the grylloblattas have lived for three and four years, slowly reaching maturity and depositing eggs.

Family BLATTIDAE

CARE AND REARING OF BLATTELLA GERMANICA

C. M. McCay and R. M. Melampy, *Cornell University*

Blatella germanica is a useful insect for physiological studies because of its quick rate of growth, rapid reproduction, and omnivorous feeding habits. An ordinary fish aquarium or museum jar covered tightly with cheesecloth may be used as a cage for a stock colony. Water may be supplied by an ordinary baby chick waterer. Absorbent cotton should be placed in the pan of the fountain as it prevents drowning of the insects. A stock diet of ground whole wheat 50%, dried skim milk 45%, and dried bakers' yeast 5% is adequate for growth and reproduction.

For experimental work with individual insects or small groups, ordinary half-pint milk bottles may be used as cages (Fig. 63). The milk cap is perforated with numerous pin-holes to allow air to enter the container. The water is supplied by a vial containing damp cotton which is mounted on the cap by a cork. The diet to be studied is placed in a small paper cup or similar container.

F I G.   63.— Rearing bottle for *Blatella germanica*.

COCKROACHES*

Cockroaches may be kept in wide-mouthed gallon glass jars, each containing a layer of sawdust on the bottom and a small pan of water. Over the top of each jar is stretched a piece of cheesecloth, held in place by a rubber band. A thin line of vaseline is placed around the inside shoulder of the jar, and the cockroaches do not attempt to pass this line.** The jars are kept in a rather dark place where the temperature averages 70° F.

* Reprinted, with slight changes, from *Turtox News* 7:No. 11, 1929, by John M. Kelley, *General Biological Supply House.*

** Editor's Note: J. Franklin Yeager, of *Iowa State College,* has described to us the cage he uses for keeping large numbers of Periplaneta. It consists of a wooden framework on legs, with a bottom of pressed board, sides of glass below for observation and copper wire above for ventilation, and a top of pressed board with a hinged door for easy access. The legs supporting the cage are set in cups of water to keep out ants.

A covered hole in the bottom with a metal shaft leading downward serves for removal of numbers of the roaches. They are swept down this shaft into a beaker edged at the top with vaseline. A rim of vaseline is also kept around the top of the glass portion of the sides of the cage.

"Ootheca dropped by the females may be removed to other containers for hatching purposes. When the cage is kept clean of ootheca, molted exoskeletons, and dead individuals, it is suitable for retaining large numbers of roaches over considerable periods of time. The cage may also be used with certain other species of insects." J. G. N.

The food of these insects is very variable, but they exhibit marked preferences. We have found that a mixture of bread, cornstarch, and water, with added bits of lettuce or other green material, serves as a fine food. Sour milk and library paste are also relished. A great amount of water is required by the cockroaches.

M. E. D.

Family MANTIDAE

TWO SPECIES OF PRAYING MANTIS*

TWO species, the common *Stagmomantis carolina* and a big Chinese species, *Paratenodera sinensis*, have been reared in the laboratory and carried through several successive generations in as many successive years.

Eggs taken from twigs out-of-doors, or laid in the laboratory, were placed outside all winter. When they began to hatch, in May or June, individuals were isolated in homeopathic vials, tightly stoppered. These vials were handled in wooden racks holding about a dozen. In each vial a strip of filter paper furnished a support to which the baby mantis could cling. About the third molt the insects became rather too big for the vials and were transferred to 4-ounce wide-mouthed bottles with cork stoppers and a strip of cardboard to stand upon, individuals still being kept separate. Before the last molt they were given still larger accommodations, either quart specimen jars or 6-inch stender dishes.

As is well known, the praying mantids are preying insects and are classed as beneficial because they eat plant lice, caterpillars, and various other enemies of vegetation. They are, furthermore, very cannibalistic. When hungry they ate readily almost every insect species that came their way, the only invariable requirement being that the food be served "alive and kicking." Tiny leafhoppers, Drosophila, Meromyza, minute "looping" caterpillars, *etc.*, collected in a sweep net and distributed to each vial, furnished most acceptable food.** Bigger leafhoppers, larger flies and caterpillars, and young grasshoppers became suitable food as the mantids increased in size. After the third molt, they could capture houseflies, and never seemed to tire of the diet. Quantities of these were

* Abstracted from an article in *Ent. News* 37:169, 1926, by MARY L. DIDLAKE, *University of Kentucky.*

** Editor's Note: R. A. Roberts, of Iowa State College, reports in *Canad. Ent.* 60:209, 1928, the breeding of *Stagmomantis carolina* in glass lantern globes with gummed labels stuck on the inner surface to provide footholds. In each cage a twig with several leaves was held upright in a glass vial filled with water and plugged with cotton. Sufficient moisture was important for the young mantids and it was found necessary to sprinkle these leaves daily. For the first few weeks the mantids were fed entirely on aphids by sticking aphid-infested twigs in the vials of water. M. E. D.

caught in wire traps placed outside a laboratory window, baited with banana.

Full-grown adults, if hungry, ate almost any living thing: spiders, hairy caterpillars (Datana, Apatela), furry moths, bad-smelling stink bugs, hard-bodied wasps (Vespa), huge cockroaches, and grasshoppers as large as themselves. Some individuals which survived late in the season when other insects grew scarce, relished fat chestnut worms, meal worms, *etc*.

M. E. D.

REFERENCE

For the feeding of mantids see also p. 242.

Family TETTIGONIIDAE

CEUTHOPHILUS*

THE eggs of the majority of the species of these camel crickets are deposited in the ground at a depth determined by the length of the ovipositor. However, eggs have been found in rotten wood. Many of the more strictly hypogeic species probably oviposit in their burrows. Eggs of *C. latibuli* laid at night in cages in the laboratory hatched in between two and four weeks. On the other hand it is highly probable that many species normally overwinter in the egg stage, wholly or in part.

Post-embryonic development varies in rate, depending on the amount and nature of the food supply and presumably on temperature and moisture conditions. Specimens of *C. virgatipes* reared with abundance of food but under otherwise normal conditions reached maturity long before adults were taken in the open and are far larger and differently proportioned than any feral specimens seen.

Observations on caged individuals of several species of Ceuthophilus show that the members of this genus are immobilized by strong light, are inactive by day but extremely energetic by night, are unaffected by sound stimuli, but highly sensitive to air movements and other mechanical stimuli, and to odors.

All Rhaphidophorinae appear to be practically omnivorous. Blatchley** states that caged Ceuthophilus fed upon meat as well as upon pieces of fruit and vegetables, appearing to prefer the latter. My own observations accord with these; caged individuals of *C. virgatirpes*, *C. latibuli*, *C. peninsularis*, and *C. pallidipes* ate with avidity cheese, butter, jam, sweet fruits, fresh and dried meat, sugar, dead insects, and other items of

* Abstracted from *Univ. of Fla. Biol. Ser.* 2, No. 1, 1936, by T. H. HUBBELL, *University of Florida.*
** Blatchley, W. S. The Locustidae of Indiana. *Proc. Ind. Acad. Sci. for* 1892, p. 141.

food. They were especially fond of peanut butter, neglecting other favorite foods when it was available. A few individuals of *C. latibuli* were reared to maturity on a diet consisting solely of peanut butter and sugar. Grass and other green vegetation were rejected, as were bread, flour, and other starchy substances unless no other food was supplied, when they were eaten sparingly. In colonies of Ceuthophilus there is heavy mortality when ecdysis occurs for the soft, helpless teneral insects are eaten by their cannibalistic mates. Only a small proportion of the individuals in a crowded cage survive to reach maturity.

The need for shelter and protection from low humidity are dominating factors in the lives of these insects. Caged individuals of *C. latibuli* continually undermined dishes of food and water placed on the sand. Though many spent the day clustered together in the shadowy upper corners of the cage, others hid themselves more or less completely in burrows.

M. E. D.

REFERENCE

For the feeding of meadow grasshoppers see p. 242.

Family GRYLLIDAE

ON REARING GRYLLIDAE

B. B. FULTON, *North Carolina State College*

GROUND crickets, Nemobius and Gryllus, may easily be reared in large battery jars of one gallon or more capacity. Single pairs do fairly well in jars as small as one quart. There should be about one inch of sand in the bottom, kept slightly moist. If the jars are at least 8 inches tall it is not necessary to cover them. Mold develops more rapidly on the food materials if the jars are covered. A watch glass or small dish of water may be kept in the jar with larger crickets but the very young crickets may drown in it. This is not necessary if the sand is kept moistened. The jars should be kept out of direct sunlight in the summer. The crickets may be fed on a great variety of food materials.* Those things that do not mold too quickly are satisfactory. I have used lettuce, grass, and fruits, but the least troublesome food is one that I make from rolled oats. The rolled oats are ground in a mortar with a little sugar and skim milk powder and enough water to make a stiff paste. This is spread thinly on heavy wrapping paper with a spatula

*Editor's Note: Norman Criddle reported in *Canad. Ent.* 57:79, 1925, that *Gryllus assimilis pennsylvanicus* and *G. a. luctuosus* consume animal matter with relish and that he has reared 1st instar nymphs on tabanid flies alone. Moistened bran was also used. M. E. D.

and allowed to dry. This food will keep indefinitely. About 1 square inch every three days, or oftener in damp weather, will feed several crickets. I have kept cultures going on this food for over a year. I have not experimented to find out whether the sugar and milk are necessary. The crickets will eat dry rolled oats readily.

Burrowing crickets such as Anurogryllus and mole crickets may be reared in jars supplied with several inches of sand. If observations are to be made on the underground habits a special type of cage is necessary. For this I have confined the sand between two vertical pieces of glass, separated by not more than the width of a normal burrow. The food and water may be introduced by having the top of the frame removable. Burrowing crickets that forage above ground need a small attached cage at the top. They may also be kept in a cylindrical jar containing a shorter and narrower jar or tin. The space between the two should be only the width of a burrow and filled with sand. This type, or the glass plate cage, should have an outer removable cover to keep the burrows dark except when under observation.

Tree crickets and bush crickets need a screen or cloth-sided, partly glassed, cage supplied with potted plants or cut plants in water. The plants should be sprinkled with water every day. A known host plant should be used if possible. Most adult crickets may be kept alive a long time by placing a few drops of sugar water or pieces of sweet fruits on the foliage. For life history work it is necessary to have the proper kind of plant material for oviposition, for many species are inclined to be exacting in their requirements. If these are not known it is best to supply at the same time a variety of kinds and sizes of plant stems.

REFERENCE

For the feeding of crickets see also p. 242.

Family ACRIDIDAE

CULTURE METHODS FOR GRASSHOPPERS

E. ELEANOR CAROTHERS, *State University of Iowa*

WITH foresight and a little equipment, these insects may be used as a convenient source of live material which a laboratory may have on hand in any desired stage at all times. The rearing of hardy species, like many other things, is simple if one knows how, but faulty methods may result in the loss of a stock in the midst of an experiment. Aside from studies growing out of economic problems and the recognized value of short-horned grasshoppers as cytological material, they are well adapted for physiological, embryological, and genetical studies.

I. *Equipment*. One of the chief essentials is a sunny, warm room with good ventilation. Exposure to direct sunlight without the intervention of glass is desirable and may be achieved usually during the spring and summer. Constant temperature rooms or an incubator where one can obtain temperatures of from 25° to 30° C. at will and an electric refrigerator for the storage of hibernating eggs are necessary for a continuous supply of the various stages.

Two types of cage are desirable. A large size for stock or mass-cultures and a smaller size for special experiments. The following description applies to cages which have proven satisfactory. They may be made in any ordinary workshop. The frame and bottom of each are made of ½-inch cypress, since this wood does not warp, split, or rot easily. The ends, top, and back of each type are of copper gauze with 18 meshes per inch. All parts of the cages must be tight enough to prevent the escape of the newly hatched insects and the sifting out of sand or soil. The bottom in both cages is built up with the cypress to form a box about 2½ inches deep.

The larger cage is 25 inches long, 15 inches wide, and 18 inches high. A sliding tray for the floor which may be pulled out without otherwise opening the cage, while not essential, greatly facilitates cleaning the cage. The front is a glass plate fitted into grooves above and below so that it slides in from one end. It may be cut vertically at the center for greater ease in handling. Such a cage will accommodate several hundred newly hatched grasshoppers and twenty-five to fifty adults, depending upon their size and hardiness. Crystallizing dishes 2 or 3 inches deep or even cigar boxes packed firmly with damp sand are placed in these cages during the egg-laying period. If eggs of known age are desired the sand may be removed and gently sifted daily.

The smaller cage is 7 inches long, 6 inches wide, and 8 inches high. The front is a glass plate fitted vertically into grooves. It is cut about 3 inches from the bottom so that the top part may be slipped up to open the cage, thus the bottom of the cage will hold sand to the depth of 3 inches. Twelve to twenty-five young individuals may be kept in such a cage. The amount of care necessary varies greatly with the hardiness of the species. For the immature insects a thin layer of clean, dry sand is kept on the floor and changed as often as cleanliness demands. Mold must be avoided. When it is time for eggs to be deposited, 3 inches of sand is placed in the bottom and the cage dipped in water every week or ten days. The egg pods may be obtained by passing the sand through a sieve. After ten days to two weeks of development the eggs of most species reach the diapause and may be stored in moist sand in a refrigerator. After a few weeks they may be removed to an incubator or a laboratory room in batches as desired and will resume development.

II. *Choice of a Species.* The following points should be considered in selecting a species for laboratory culture if the problem does not necessitate the use of a particular species: (1) hardiness, (2) availability, (3) availability of natural food plants, (4) number of generations per year and size of broods. Let us briefly consider these points.

1) Hardiness and 2) availability. Usually indigenous species are preferable since change of climate and altitude are thus eliminated. The shift from freedom to captivity is severe under the best conditions. Correlated with the above advantages are natural conditions for their food plants. I have no doubt that hardy species may be found in every locality. In general, tryxalines are the most delicate, oedipodines intermediate, and acridines the most vigorous, but as a group the latter are the most restricted as to their food plants. However, many species of Melanoplus in addition to being extremely hardy are almost omnivorous so far as plants are concerned. *M. differentialis* in particular on account of its wide distribution and large size is very favorable for general laboratory purposes. *M. bivitatta* in its range would be equally satisfactory. *Romalea microptera,* a large, almost flightless acridine from the south thrives in captivity and may be purchased from collectors. Owing to its size the provision of food and space becomes a problem if it is necessary to keep large numbers on hand. *Dactylotum pictum* is another acridine which does well in captivity, perhaps because of its wingless condition.

Most oedipodines are strong flyers and perhaps for that reason do not thrive in captivity. Notable exceptions exist, however. *Encoptolophus subgracilis* taken from Tuscon, Ariz., to Philadelphia, proved to be the most satisfactory grasshopper I have ever raised so far as ease of culture is concerned. It is hardy and produces a generation in six weeks. *Chortophaga australior,* also a southern form, is nearly as favorable. More northern species of these genera normally hibernate over the winter, *E. sordidus* in the egg and *C. viridifasciata* in the nymph stage. Both will complete their development without a pronounced pause if kept at 22°-25° C. *Trimerotropis maritima* and *T. vinculata* are satisfactory but will produce normally only one generation per year.

The tryxaline, *Chloealtis conspersa,* is a notable exception to the rule. It is very hardy and conveniently lays its eggs in old, somewhat rotten wood, preferably fallen branches of trees. The eggs are laid in August and September and normally hatch in the spring.

All of the species mentioned are known to be sufficiently hardy to make good laboratory stock. But no one should be deterred from trying out other species, especially if they are indigenous so that the stock may be replenished from nature.

3) Availability of natural food plants. As has been stated, many

acridines are limited to certain weeds as food plants. These plants in turn are restricted to given soil and climatic conditions. Alkalinity or acidity of the soil is often a limiting factor for the plants. In case it is desirable to use a restricted species away from its normal habitat, not only seed or young specimens of its food plant should be take but also soil should be shipped or at least samples taken for analysis so that the necessary constituents may be added to the soil in the new locality.

4) Number of generations per year and size of broods. Some species, like *Hesperotettix viridis,* lay only 5 to 8 eggs per pod and one female does not make more than 6 pods, so that, if there is normally only one generation per year, a given female will not produce more than 40 offspring. Most oedipodines lay from 15 to 24 eggs in a pod and produce 3 to 4 pods, so that one female may have as many as 75 offspring. Furthermore, some southern species, already mentioned, may produce 6 to 8 generations per year in the laboratory, although they probably do not produce so many in nature.

Melanoplus differentialis, M. bivitatta, and *Romalea microptera* females on the other hand lay as many as 150 eggs in the first pod and a given individual may make 3 pods each with progressively fewer eggs. Such females will produce from 200 to 300 offspring. Fortunately they are restricted normally to one generation per year.

III. *Life Cycle.* Three well defined stages occur: 1)—Embryonic, extending from the first cleavage of the egg until hatching. Some eggs, as noted by Nabours for tettigids and Slifer and King or *M. differentialis,* develop parthenogenetically. Most northern species hibernate over winter in the eggs. 2)—Nymphal, from hatching to the last molt, marked by 5 instars during which progressive development of pre-existing structures takes place. Certain species hibernate for the winter in the 2nd and 3rd instars. 3)—Adult, extending from the last ecdysis until death. Usually an individual does not live more than 3 months after becoming an adult.

IV. *General Care.* In order that experimental results may be valid the stock must be healthy. The following suggestions may help to attain that end.

1) Cleanliness. Debris should be removed and clean dry sand should be scattered on the floor of the cages at least once each week. Except during egg-laying the cages should be kept dry. Warmth and sunlight are essential.

2) Handling. Shell vials are convenient for capturing the young insects when it is necessary to study or move them about. Older ones may be caught gently by the thorax or wings with the fingers. Never catch them by the jumping legs since these are readily detachable. The blood clot which then forms, as well as the inability of the crippled insect

to properly suspend itself, causes trouble at ecdysis. The loss of a leg is not so serious for an adult as for a nymph.

3) Food. An abundance of suitable food should be present in the cages at all times, either growing in soil or kept fresh in water. If water is used, care is necessary to prevent the insects from drowning. Tryxalines and oedipodines feed mostly on grasses. Various species of Poa and Andropogon are suitable. Wheat and millet are satisfactory and readily grown in small flower pots in the laboratory. Oats are totally unsuitable, as are some grasses. Dandelion, plantain, and clover are good for giving variety. Lettuce and apple will tide many species over a period of food scarcity. For some species lettuce will serve as the chief food. These foods are adequate for the previously mentioned acridines also. But many of this group are highly specialized in regard to their food plants. *Hypochlora alba* is restricted largely to *Artemesia frigida*, *Hesperotettix speciosus* to sunflowers, *H. viridis* to Grindelis and certain species of Solidago, *H. pratensis* to a different Solidago. In fact, the experienced collector in this group looks for the food plant of the species sought rather than the animals themselves when starting to collect in a new region.

4) Diseases and Parasites. The chief dangers to laboratory cultures are diarrhoea caused by an Amoeba (recently described by R. L. King) which may wipe out cultures during cold damp periods, and molds which thrive in damp places in the absence of sunlight. Hyphae of the fungi grow throughout the body cavity. Gregarines also cause trouble, especially when cages with damp sand and much debris are kept at a constant high temperature as in an incubator. Nematodes, too, sometimes become troublesome, especially if the cultures are fed on grass brought in from a cool, damp place and put into the cages without a thorough washing. And, finally, a small parasitic wasp may attack the eggs. It thrives chiefly on dead eggs and I am not sure that it ever attacks those in a healthy condition. It is more apt to be present when soil is used in place of clean sand for the eggs.

None of the above troubles is a serious menace to cultures which are given proper care. In case the insects start to die transfer them daily to cages which have been washed and sterilized in very hot water, discard all individuals which are obviously sick, and correct faulty cultural conditions.

THE GROUSE LOCUSTS*

ROBERT K. NABOURS, *Kansas State College*

THE grouse locusts, so-called probably because of a fanciful resemblance of some of them to the grouse (Tetraoninae), are among the smaller Orthoptera. They show conspicuous dimorphism as to length of wings and pronotum, with occasional intermediates. There are extraordinary variations in the conspicuous color patterns on the pronota, the legs, and other parts of the body. The stripes along the median pronota vary in color and width, and there are many kinds of spots, specks, mottlings, and all-over colors. One species, as *Paratettix texanus*, may exhibit nearly all the colors and patterns. Food, light, and other features of the environment do not appear to condition the colors and patterns in any special way. (Hancock, 1902; Nabours, 1925 and 1929.)

The subfamily Tetriginae is widely distributed over the tropics and temperate zones. Hancock (1902) estimated that there were more than 100 species in North America alone. They mainly inhabit moist areas, along the margins of ponds and streams, and in forests, though they may live, temporarily at least, in quite dry places. Some, as *P. texanus* and *A. eurycephalus* in southern Texas and Mexico, are found more abundantly along the flat, algae-covered margins of ponds and streams, in the absence of larger vegetation and much exposed to the sun. Others, as *Tettigidea lateralis*, are found farther back in the grasses, or higher vegetation, where there is more shade.

The northern grouse locusts (roughly from the line of the Ohio, lower Missouri and Kansas rivers in the U. S. A.) probably produce one, or an average of about one and one-half generations a year. The cold weather coming on in October, or November, finds both adults and nymphs, and they all go into hibernation for the winter. They stop in tufts of grass, under stones, pieces of wood, *etc.*, but receive little real protection from the weather. They have been observed to endure and survive a temperature lower than 0° F. However, there is usually a high mortality, due probably as much to desiccation as to cold. There is no regularity about their going into, or emerging from, hibernation. They do not become inactive till the cold weather actually arrives, and they become active during any very warm periods. During aberrantly early warm weather they emerge from hibernation, to be driven back later in the spring if there is more cold weather.

When warm weather arrives in the spring the adults mate and soon

---

*Pending a much needed, comprehensive revision of this subfamily by taxonomists, I have undertaken to follow Hancock's classification of the few species used in the studies of inheritance. However, I now propose to follow A. N. Caudell's (Smith. Inst.) suggestion, in a letter, 1932, of subfamily Tetriginae; family *Acrididae*.

lay eggs during a period of several weeks, in March, April and May, depending on the latitude and season. The nymphs which have hibernated become adults, mate, and lay eggs some weeks later.

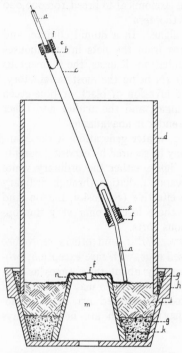

The southern species give about four generations a year in the greenhouse. They probably do not have a definite hibernating period in their natural habitàts.

Paratettix texanus, Apotettix eurycephalus, Tettigidea lateralis, Telmatettix aztecus, and *Acrydium arenosum* have been bred in the greenhouse at the Kansas Agricultural Experiment Station. The first two mentioned have been bred extensively. *A. eurycephalus,* due to factors which have not been ascertained, breeds better than any of the others used. All, except *A. arenosum* and some of the *T. lateralis,* were from stocks secured in southern Louisiana and Texas, and the region of Tampico, Mexico.

They are bred best in a greenhouse laboratory, with the temperature ranging around 80° F. A variety of cages may be used, but 8″ x 12″ glass cylinders, with lids of 16-20 mesh wire, set in steam sterilized loam in bulb pots, serve very well. Sterilized sand is placed in the lower part of the pot, and around the cylinder. A smaller empty pot is placed upside down over the hole in the bottom of the bulb pot. It is supposed to aid in aerating the soil, and the food is

FIG. 64.—Cage for rearing grouse locusts and apparatus for transferring progeny. (*Transfer apparatus developed by Edgar Millenbruch.*) The glass cylinder is 8″ in diameter and 12″ high. a, suction connected with water air pump or sweeper; b, cheesecloth; c, glass chamber into which progeny are sucked; d, the glass cage (covered with 16- to 20-mesh wire screen lid); e, tape; f, corks; g, sand; h, bulb pot; i, loam; k, inverted pot; m, air chamber; n, algae.

placed on its extension above the soil (Fig. 64). A pair of adults is placed in a cage. The eggs are laid in the soil, or in masses of algae. A few hours or a day or so after hatching the offspring are picked up by a suction tube and transferred in batches of 20-25 to newly made-up cages. At the 3rd-4th instar records may be made of the color patterns, which do not materially change at any time, and the males and females separated.

The extraordinary and diagram-like color patterns, the good size of their chromosomes and, perhaps, a few other features justify the extreme effort necessary in breeding the grouse locusts for genetics studies. I believe that it would be easier and more economical to breed 100,000,000 Drosophila than 1,000,000 of these Orthoptera.

As already stated they eat mainly algae. In a humid climate, and where they are available, the scrapings from the pots in greenhouses serve very well. In the climate of Manhattan, Kansas, the filamentous algae only are available, *Hydrodictyon sp.* being the most satisfactory. Much difficulty is exerienced from the invasion of black or blue-green algae, fungi, and masses of decayed algae, and the acidity and other chemical conditions of the soil which render it unavailable.

It has been ascertained that an extra, winter generation of the Manhattan, Kansas. *Acrydium arenosum* may be secured by exposing parents and then the offspring to continuous lights, either the ordinary white light from Mazda bulbs or mercury vapor radiation through ordinary glass, the latter being somewhat more effective (Sabrosky, Larson, and Nabours, 1933). It is believed that these insects offer very fine opportunity for irradiation work of various sorts.

The females of *P. texanus, A. eurycephalus,* and others reproduce also parthenogenetically, the unfertilized eggs, with rare exception, producing females. The females are generally about three times as prolific when mated as when unmated. A mated female may have part of her ova fertilized, and also produce from unfertilized ova, by parthenogenesis, an additional number of offspring which are nearly always females.

BIBLIOGRAPHY

HANCOCK, J. L. 1902. The Tettigidae of North America

NABOURS, R. K. 1925. The grouse locust *Apotettix eurycephalus. Kan. Tech. Bull.* 17.

—— 1929. The genetics of the Tettigidae. *Bibliographia Genetica* 5:27.

NABOURS, .R. K., and Robertson, W.R.B. 1933. An X-ray induced translocation in *Apotettix eurycephalus,* Hancock (Grouse Locusts). *Proc. Nat. Acad. Sci.* 19:234.

ROBERTSON, W. R. B. 1935. Demonstration of effects of X-rays on male germ cells in *Apotettix eurycephalus; Amer. Nat.* 69:

SABROSKY, LARSON, and NABOURS. 1933. Experiments with light upon reproduction, growth, and diapause in grouse locusts (Acrididae, Tetriginae) ; *Trans. Kan. Acad. Sci.* Vol. 36.

Order THYSANOPTERA

REARING THRIPS TABACI*

THE thrips were reared on successive plantings of onions in a green-house. The thrips were transferred from the plants to vials by sucking them into a glass tube which was about 4 inches long and about ½ inch diameter. [See Fig. 41.] A cork was placed in one end of this tube, through which a 2-inch length of glass tubing ⅛ inch in diameter was inserted. A 12-inch piece of rubber tubing was inserted in the other end of the large glass tube. A piece of silk placed over the end of the rubber tube prevented the passage of thrips into it when they were being sucked into the glass tube and also furnished a tight fit between the rubber and the glass, thus preventing the escape of the thrips. The rubber made the apparatus flexible so that it was easy to reach the thrips on any part of the plant. When the desired number was secured, the cork was removed and the thrips shaken into vials, from which they might later be transferred to the feeding cages.

The cage finally evolved for controlled feeding experiments was a Syracuse watch glass and its cover. The inside of the bottom of the glass was covered with white blotting paper, the edges of which were sealed to the glass by means of hot paraffin to prevent the thrips being caught between the paper and the glass. When the cage was inverted the blotting paper absorbed the excess moisture, preventing con-densation within the cage and the possible drowning of the thrips. It also aided in maintaining a high humidity which seemed de-sirable. Three discs of blotting paper the size of the coverslip, placed one on top of the other, were used as feeders. The feeder was placed on the cover of the watch glass, covered with a coverslip to keep the thrips from sticking to the feeder, and then saturated with the substance to be fed. The saturated feeder adhered fairly well to the cover of the cage. After the thrips were shaken into the cage, the cover was sealed to the watch glass by means of hot paraffin. This prevented the escape of the thrips and aided in maintaining the humidity. The cage was then placed cover downwards in the oven where a constant tempera-ture of 21° C. was maintained. Even though the cage was placed in an oven, the relative humidity remained high throughout the experiment for condensation occurred between the blotting paper and the bottom of the cage which it lined. The feeders were also damp when the cages were opened at the end of the experiment. There seemed to be sufficient

*Abstracted from "The utilization of carbohydrates and proteins by onion thrips, *Thrips tabaci* Lindeman," a thesis submitted to the faculty of Cornell University, Sep-tember 1932, by BURL ALVA SLOCUM, *University of Nanking.*

air within the cage to meet the needs of the insects for some of them lived as long as 25 days thus enclosed.*

Order ANOPLURA

REARING HOG LICE ON MAN

LAURA FLORENCE, *N. Y. Homeopathic Medical College and Flower Hospital*

THE hog louse, *Haematopinus suis*, is the largest of the lice affecting domestic animals. It is suitable for experimental work, because it is easily obtained and feeds readily on man. Its size and its habit of taking hold of any slender object placed in front of it lessen the difficulty of keeping it in confinement.

On infested hogs, lice are readily found in the folds of the skin on the neck and jowl, within and at the base of the ears, on the under side of the legs, on the flanks, and in smaller numbers on the back, where they crawl under the scales in order to come in contact with the new skin. From these regions they may be collected with small forceps or with the fingers and placed in any easily handled receptacle to be taken to the laboratory. Without undue delay they should be transferred to small vials, approximately 5 cm. x 1 cm., containing some hog bristles and threads of gauze. Four to six lice should be placed in each vial. The mouth of the vial should be closed by tying over it two layers of gauze with a very thin layer of absorbent cotton between. These vials must be worn continuously under the clothing, so that the lice may be kept as near body temperature as possible.

The captive lice are fed on the forearm, and should not be handled unnecessarily. In the vial they will be found attached to the threads and bristles. These should be withdrawn from the vial and placed on the arm. The lice will then move to the skin and may feed at once or move about more or less rapidly. The peculiar structure of the feet enables them to grasp the hairs on the arm. After the insertion of the stylets the insect holds itself in a more or less straight line and at an angle of 40°

*Editor's Note: C. O. EDDY and W. H. CLARKE (*J. Econ. Ent.* 23:704, 1930) report life history studies carried on with the onion thrips by the use of 1-gram homeopathic vials, ¾ by 6 inch test tubes, absorbent cotton, insect-free seedling cotton leaves, and water. The females were confined separately in the homeopathic vials and a section of a fresh seedling cotton leaf placed with each of them every 24 hours. The used sections of leaves were removed from the vials, wrapped individually in moist absorbent cotton, and each placed in a sterile test tube. The open ends of both vials and test tubes were closed with absorbent cotton plugs. The leaves in the test tubes were removed daily and observed under a low power binocular microscope for emerged larvae. When a larva was found, it was removed from the leaf with a small brush and transferred to a fresh leaf in a small homeopathic vial where development was observed. Fresh leaves were supplied to all larvae when needed. Vials and test tubes containing the thrips were inserted slightly in the soil of soil tables in an out-door insectary. M.E.D.

to 45° with the arm. As the feeding progresses the body is gradually lowered, until it rests on the arm. Blood is seen passing into the alimentary canal in which a continuous peristalsis is evident. Feeding is continued until all feces and a drop of fresh blood have been ejected from the canal. The average length of a meal is from 8 to 12 minutes, but it may last from 20 to 30 minutes. At its close the mouthparts are withdrawn, apparently by a short jerk of the head. The lice should then be carefully removed from the arm with a small forceps and returned to their vial. They should be held by the legs and not by the body in order to avoid rupturing the distended alimentary canal. Newly hatched lice will feed readily and must be given at least four opportunities to feed in 24 hours until they reach maturity. Mature lice should be given two, and if possible three, opportunities to feed in 24 hours, since those exhausted by too long fasting will not feed on man.

The unfed louse is of a grayish color and much wrinkled, while the fed louse has a highly refractive, smooth tegument, showing very clearly the areas of sclerotization.

At every feeding the threads and bristles from each vial should be examined carefully for eggs. These, if present, are found attached to a thread or bristle which should be removed to a second vial. If worn continuously at body temperature and if fertile, the eggs will hatch in 13 to 15 days. In the course of their development hog lice undergo three molts. Rearing in captivity has proved the cycle from egg to egg to occupy from 29 to 33 days. The life history, as we have observed it, may be summarized as follows:

```
Time from laying to hatching of eggs........13 to 15 days
First molt occurred after.................. 5 to  6 days
Second molt occurred after...............     4 days
Third molt occurred after................. 4 to  5 days
Sexual maturity occurred after.............       3 days
Time of development from first stage larva to
    mature adult .........................16 to 18 days
Temperature ....................................35° C.,
                (continually next to body in vials)
Number of feedings in 24 hours............ 1 to  4
Duration of cycle from egg to egg...........29 to 33 days
```

This method of keeping lice in captivity has proved satisfactory in investigations carried over a period of years, and large numbers of lice have been fed on the forearm without any harmful results. Egg-laying and molting have been observed and lice have been reared from the egg to maturity. All our attempts to rear a second generation of captive lice have failed. Eggs laid by reared females, kept in separate vials with males, have all quickly changed color and become shriveled, although the insects were seen in position for copulation a number of times.

In the course of this study hog lice have been found to be the normal host of a symbiont, living in enlarged epithelial cells of the mid-intestine and passing from generation to generation through the egg. In artificially reared lice these symbionts tend to disappear, and the possibility of an intimate relationship between the symbiont and the blood ingested by the insect host may be the explanation of the impossibility of rearing hog lice elsewhere than on their natural host.

BIBLIOGRAPHY

FLORENCE, LAURA, 1921. The hog louse, *Haematopinus suis* Linné: its biology, anatomy, and histology. *Cornell Univ. Agric. Exper. Sta. Mem.* 51.

——— 1924. An intracellular symbiont of the hog louse. *Amer. J. Trop. Med.* 4:397.

Order HEMIPTERA, Family SCUTELLERIDAE

NOTES ON REARING A SCUTELLERID

H. M. HARRIS, *Iowa State College*

THE geographical distribution of *Acantholoma denticulata* is limited by the range of its host plants, *Ceanothus pubescens* and the related *C. ovatus*. The species hibernates in the adult stage and usually may be taken at any season by sifting leaf mold from around the host plants. However, the bugs congregate in the corymbs at the time of seed-pod formation and may be collected in numbers most easily at this time by quietly approaching the plant and cupping the hands beneath the flower-heads. Adults mate and oviposit readily in captivity. Eggs normally are placed in the vegetable mold, but when deprived of this (as is desirable in rearing studies) the females will oviposit on leaves or other surfaces. Almost any type of cage with provision for ventilation will suffice for the adults when fresh seed-heads of the host plant are available for food. For the eggs and nymphs, however, small stender dishes serve best. It is essential to preserve proper moisture relations in the cage if success in rearing is to be achieved. A disc of absorbent paper (white is preferable) tightly fitted in the bottom of the dish and slightly moistened once or twice a day is all that is necessary. The paper must be renewed and the dishes cleaned regularly to hinder the growth of molds. Food for the young consists of seeds of Ceanothus. In nature the seeds must remain in the duff layer of soil for varying periods of time before the very durable outer coats are softened sufficiently to allow penetration by the feeding stylets of the young bugs. For use in feeding caged individuals it is sufficient to soak the seeds in water to soften them or to crush them mechanically. The insects readily feed on these soaked or crushed seeds.

It is worth pointing out that related bugs, particularly the Cydnidae and the Corimelaenidae, in many cases have habits similar to those of *Acanthaloma denticulata* and no doubt might be reared successfully by collection and use of the proper seeds as food. Likewise, in the Lygaeidae (Andre, 1935), cultures of almost any of the so-called milkweed bugs (Lygaeus and Oncopeltus) may be kept going easily and almost indefinitely simply by providing the caged insects with dried seeds or ripened seedpods of milkweeds for food, water for drink, and cotton in which they will readily oviposit.

BIBLIOGRAPHY

HARRIS, H. M., and ANDRE, FLOYD. 1934. Notes on the Biology of *Acantholoma denticulata* Stal (Hemiptera, Scutelleridae). *Ann. Ent. Soc. Amer.*, 27:5.

ANDRE, FLOYD. 1935. Notes on the Biology of *Oncopeltus fasciatus* (Dallas). *Iowa State College J. of Sci.* 9:73.

Family PENTATOMIDAE

A METHOD OF REARING FOUR SPECIES OF PLANT BUGS

F. G. MUNDINGER, *New York State Agricultural Experiment Station*

THE species concerned here are *Acrosternum hilare, Euschistus euschistoides, E. variolarius,* and *E. tristigmus.* These species are common in central New York State from early spring until late fall and may be captured by sweeping grass or beating the bushes with a strong insect net. Some of the natural food plants are *Viburnum acerifolium, Cornus racemosa, Vaccinium stamineum,* and a species of Smilax, probably *S. herbacea.* Cucumber serves as an excellent supplementary food but only the firmer portions of this or any other fruit should be used where small nymphs are concerned. Screen-topped, glass jars, quart-size or smaller, partially filled with sterile, moist sand packed down to support a small twig of the food plant, make good breeding and rearing jars. Daily inspection of these should be made in warm weather and wilted food material replaced by fresh. The same technique may. be followed for the four species.

I have not reared successive generations of these species. In this region these plant bugs appear to be single-brooded. I have caged reared specimens for some time but failed to secure any eggs. Each year I have begun my experiments with material captured in the field.

PERILLUS BIOCULATUS*

T HE adults of Perillus come forth from hibernation as soon as the ground thaws out in the spring. By the time potato plants show above ground and the first potato beetles appear, Perillus may be found in the potato fields. Their first meal in the spring is sap from the potato plant, but after that their food is almost exclusively the body fluids of potato beetles, eggs, and larvae.

For rearing Perillus the ordinary type of jelly glass was found to be a very convenient cage. One pair of bugs in a glass will take very kindly to this arrangement, and, when fed daily, will produce eggs quite as freely as in the field. After the bugs have been confined in the jars for two or three weeks they become very tame, rarely trying to fly when handled. The female bug will lay her eggs on the potato leaves when these are provided, but in the absence of these will lay eggs readily on the sides of the jar or on cheesecloth when it is supplied. As fast as the eggs are laid they may be removed to new jars for rearing. After the nymphs attain the 3rd instar it is best not to keep more than 6 or 8 in one jar. Unless plenty of food is available at all times the bugs may develop cannibalism. However, when the bugs are not overcrowded this difficulty rarely occurs. It was found necessary to clean the breeding jars frequently, especially when rearing nymphs on larvae of the potato beetle.

The writer reared Perillus from egg to adult on nothing but mature beetles, but the beetles were always rendered helpless for the benefit of the nymphs in the 2nd and 3rd instars. The bugs should be fed once or twice a day, although they will get along if neglected for a day. More labor is necessary in rearing Perillus on adult beetles alone than when grubs are available, yet it has been done in order to rear a fall generation of bugs after the potato beetle grubs have disappeared. By this method of rearing Perillus might no doubt be kept active and breeding during the winter months if proper greenhouse facilities were available.

M. E. D.

Family COREIDAE

CORIZUS HYALINUS AND C. SIDAE**

T HE writer has reared *Corizus hyalinus* through the whole course of its life history on a wild lettuce, *Lactuca scariola,* and has observed numerous adults, nymphs, and eggs on this plant in the field. Eggs of

*Abstracted from an article in the *19th Rept. State Ent. of Minn.* p. 50, 1922, by HARRY H. KNIGHT, *Iowa State College.*

** Abstracted from an article in *Ann. Ent. Soc. Amer.* 21:189, 1928, by PHILIP A. READIO, *Cornell University.*

this species have also been found on a seed pod of velvet leaf, *Abutilon theophrasti,* and the young have been reared through to the 5th instar on this plant. Two successive generations have been reared in the summer. The insect has been reared from adult to adult in 17 days. The adult life is comparatively long, one adult female having been kept in confinement for 50 days.

The writer has had difficulty in getting *Corizus sidae* to thrive on Sida, though it has been seen to feed on this plant when confined. It has been found as nymph and adult on the seed pods of velvet leaf, *Abutilon theophrasti.* Furthermore, the eggs have been laid on this plant in the laboratory and the nymphs reared through two instars before the cold weather put an end to the food supply. *C. sidae* has not been reared through its complete life cycle. Eggs were obtained from confined adults kept in a warm room during late October and early November. These eggs hatched in from 10 to 11 days, but probably would have hatched in a shorter time out-of-doors in the summer.

These rearings were conducted at Lawrence, Kansas, during late August and early September when the temperature was high, reaching the high eighties and nineties during the middle of the day. The insects were reared in an outdoor insectary, confined in glass stender dishes, and fed daily with pieces of the food plant.*

M. E. D.

Family LYGAEIDAE

LYGAEIDAE

F. M. WADLEY, *U. S. Bureau of Entomology and Plant Quarantine*

THE chinch bug, *Blissus leucopterus,* has given considerable difficulty in rearing. Cages must be tight because of the insect's habit of crowding itself into any possible crack. Humidity seems important with younger stages; very dry conditions are unfavorable, and free water causes bugs to stick to the cage. The species thrives at ordinary summer temperatures, but not under cool conditions. The chinch bug may be reared on bits of fresh food-plant put in daily, growing plants not being absolutely necessary. Seedlings of corn, wheat, and sorghum have been used with success; corn has a greater tendency than the others to cause free water in the cages. Bits of crab-grass stalks have also been used, but are less desirable.

*Editor's Note: J. C. Hambleton, *U. S. Bureau of Entomology and Plant Quarantine,* reported in *Ann. Ent. Soc. Amer.* 2:272, 1909, that several broods of *Corizus lateralis* were reared to maturity on blossoms and young seed of *Polygonum persicaria* and on *P. pennsylvanicum.* Eggs were deposited on the latter. The adult forms fed freely on these plants in captivity. M. E. D.

To obtain eggs, adults were confined in flat-bottomed vials about 4 inches long and 1 inch in diameter, stoppered with cotton. A little ground litter such as occurs in the field, consisting of bits of soil and plant material, was put in, and pieces of fresh food-plant were supplied daily. This method gave fair results.

Nymphs when confined with food in ordinary vials did not thrive; few matured, and growth periods seemed to be much lengthened as compared with those in the field. After trying several devices, one was hit upon which gave more nearly normal development. The 1" x 4" vials mentioned were prepared with plaster casts about ½" thick in the bottom. The eggs were placed in these vials in a little ground litter. The vials were kept upright and stoppered with cotton. The nymphs on hatching were kept in these vials during the first two instars, several in a vial, with fresh food supplied daily. With practice the 1st and 2nd instars could be readily distinguished; and by daily inspection those in the 2nd instar were removed to other vials soon after molting. After the 2nd instar, nymphs did not do so well in these vials, and were reared through later instars in little, individual, chimney cages on growing sorghum seedlings. These were made of 1" x 4" vials open at both ends. The vial was placed around the seedling, pushed well into the soil, and the soil inside carefully smoothed and tamped with a pencil. The top was closed with cotton. Several such cages may be placed on one flower-pot. Sorghum seedlings are favorable in cages because of their slow growth.

The writer assisted Mr. F. B. Milliken in rearing the false chinchbug, *Nysius ericae.** This work also presented some difficulties. The species feeds on a number of plants; small crucifers such as shepherd's-purse and pepper-grass are important early in the season, and a spurge, Euphorbia, of procumbent habit, is used in late summer. Adults were confined for egg-laying in small vials on potted food-plants. The vials were stoppered with cotton, which pinched a branch of the plant projecting into the vial. Eggs were deposited in the cotton. Mr. Milliken had best success rearing nymphs individually in small muslin bags tied on the food plants. The bag was made of two pieces of muslin, perhaps 2" wide and 3" long, stitched together with fine stitches around 3 sides. By careful examination molts could readily be found in these bags.

REFERENCE

For the rearing of Lygaeus and Oncopeltus see p. 299.

**J. Agric. Res.* 13:571-578, 1918.

REARING METHODS FOR CHINCH BUGS, BLISSUS HIRTUS

KENNETH E. MAXWELL, *Cornell University*

FOR a study of the length of nymphal instars, it was desirable to isolate individual nymphs and observe their moltings. A satisfactory cage for this work was a ⅝″ x 2¾″ round-bottom flint shell vial, of the same shape as biological laboratory test tubes. The tubes were stoppered with cotton plugs and supplied with the stems of grass plants for food. The food used was creeping bent grass, a variety in which the bugs breed very readily and which is commonly used for lawns and putting greens in the Northern United States.

It was found necessary to replenish the food supply nearly every day because of the drying out of the grass. The grass furnished both food supply and moisture. Grass stems were cut at the base and immediately immersed in water, where they were kept until ready for use. Frequent moistening of the cotton plugs aided in maintaining a high humidity. Attempts to conserve the moisture content of the grass by the use of cork stoppers were not successful, due to the fact that evaporation from the food material saturated the air, and moisture condensed on the glass. The insects, particularly the younger stages, frequently stuck to the wet surface, and suffered a high mortality.

The nymphs undergo five molts, with considerable variation in the time required for each instar under different conditions. The shortest time required from egg to adult, under field laboratory conditions, was 44 days, in contrast to the longest, which was 81 days. As many as 9 chinch bugs have been successfully reared through all stages in a single tube, and a larger number may be used, depending on the food supply.

Oviposition. For fecundity studies of individual females, single pairs were confined in the same type of cage as that used for life history studies. Copulation occurred frequently during the oviposition period, and some females oviposited daily for several consecutive days. There is considerable variation in the fecundity of individual females, and oviposition fluctuated with the temperature and with the quantity of food material and moisture present. Oviposition decreased with low temperatures, and almost ceased when the prevailing temperature remained below 70° F. It was desirable to maintain a high humidity, keeping the air as nearly saturated as possible without obtaining condensation on the sides of the cages. No difficulty was experienced with fungus killing the insects in the laboratory studies.

When a female was ready to oviposit, she inserted her ovipositor beneath the leaf sheath, and deposited the eggs, sometimes singly, but usually in groups. When the leaf sheath was pulled back, the eggs were found to lie side by side, frequently stuck together in a compact row. In such cases they could be removed in a group.

Incubation. When first laid the eggs are opaque, pearly white or with an amber tint. They soon darken, take on a pink coloration, and become deep red prior to hatching. The incubation chambers consisted of glass tubes similar to those used for rearing, into the bottom of which had been poured a small quantity of plaster of Paris, and closed with cork or moist cotton stoppers. In these observation of hatching was as possible without removal of the stoppers.

The length of the egg stage was largely dependent on prevailing temperatures, and the eggs hatched under a surprising range of moisture conditions. Eggs placed in dry containers with cotton plugs became shriveled in a few hours, and remained pale yellow for a number of days. A large percentage eventually hatched, requiring, however, a somewhat longer time to do so than those which were kept moist. Eggs which were kept for long periods in closed containers with moisture present, likewise remained viable until hatching. The emerging nymphs, however, floundered in the water film present, and soon perished.

BIBLIOGRAPHY

JANES, MELVIN J. 1935. Oviposition studies on the chinch bug, *Blissus leucopterus* Say. *Ann. Ent. Soc. Amer.* 28:109.

LUGINBILL, PHILIP. 1922. Bionomics of the chinch bug. *U. S. D. A. Bull.* 1016.

SHELFORD, V. E. 1932. An experimental and observational study of the chinch bug in relation to climate and weather. *Ill. Nat. Hist. Surv. Bull.* 19:487.

Family REDUVIIDAE

REDUVIUS PERSONATUS*

ADULTS of *Reduvius personatus,* collected at a light trap and paired, were confined in small cartons and were fed daily on houseflies which had been caught in a net and disabled before being introduced into the cages. Eggs were removed daily and placed in a salve box, $5/8$ of an inch high by $1\frac{1}{2}$ inches in diameter. It was found desirable to line the box with a tightly fitting wad of heavy, unglazed paper, which served to give the bugs a foothold and also to absorb excess moisture from food and excrement. Later, in work involving humidity, $3/4$ inch holes were punched in the lids, and these openings covered with coarse silk bolting cloth, so that the atmosphere could come into equilibrium readily with that of the rearing cabinet.

The nymphs also were fed houseflies since there was a large supply

*Abstracted from an article in *Ann. Ent. Soc. Amer.* 24:19, 1931, by PHILIP A. READIO, *Cornell University.*

available. However, later a change was made to the larvae of *Tribolium confusum*, the confused flour beetle. This insect proved to be a very satisfactory food supply for Reduvius, since it could be reared in any numbers desired, and in a short time, on common flour. The greatest objection to its use was that occasionally a larva would crawl upon and kill or cripple a molting Reduvius.

M. E. D.

Family MESOVELIIDAE

HOW TO REAR MESOVELIA

C. H. HOFFMANN, *U. S. Bureau of Entomology and Plant Quarantine*

ADULTS were collected and divided according to species, after which they were isolated in finger bowls containing lake water and several pieces of decayed cat-tail leaf available for oviposition. The water was changed daily. Fruit flies or houseflies served as food. When a large number of eggs were laid in the stem provided, it was then removed to a petri dish and given a number that corresponded with that on a card. Permanent data were, of course, kept on cards. An eye dropper was used to change the water in the egg containers, and a dropper or two full of water was sufficient for the daily change.

The little nymphs that hatched out were isolated in small stender dishes 1 inch deep and 2 inches in diameter and in some other stenders slightly larger. In the case of individual rearings, each stender was supplied with a single dropper full of water, a small piece of white card, and two adult fruit flies for food. The card served as a support for the small nymphs, and, being white, did not interfere in the search for molted skins. The bugs flourished with a daily change of water and a fresh supply of food every other day, the remains of the previous feeding being removed at this time.

It is often difficult to find the newly hatched bugs, because they cling to the surface of the cat-tail stem. In changing the water of the egg cages daily, therefore, the fresh water was squirted directly on the surface of the stem and the young washed off into the clear water. These were then easily transferred to stenders by tilting the petri dish and placing the tip of a pair of curved forceps under the nymph, thus lifting it out together with a drop of water. Mass rearing in finger bowls was tried and found to be satisfactory. All rearings were carried on in a room which maintained a temperature of approximately 24° C.

Houseflies served as good food but scarcity during the winter necessitated the finding of a food supply plentiful enough to care for many rearings. It was found that adult fruit flies filled the need, and of course they were easy to rear in quantities. The technique used might well be related, however, for it affords a simple way of capturing the adults to be used as food for winter rearings.

A lamp chimney covered at one end with a piece of cheesecloth, fastened by means of a rubber band, was placed over a pint jar in which a banana and the fruit flies were placed. In a short time, the chimney was swarming with the adults. To capture a hundred or more specimens, a 4-inch vial was slipped through a piece of cardboard, in which a sufficiently large hole had been cut, and placed over the top of the chimney as soon as the cheesecloth was removed. If an electric light was placed above the vial, the desired number of flies was readily secured. When this number was obtained, the vial was quickly corked and a dark cover put over the chimney until the flies were scattered again. The chimney was then re-covered with cheesecloth.

The adults in the vial could be killed by placing it over a hot radiator for a few minutes, or by applying the flame of a match to the bottom of the vial. In the latter case, the fruit flies could be forced to the bottom of the vial by sudden taps against something that would not break it. Heat kills the flies quickly and does not injure them for feeding purposes.

Successive generations of two species of Mesovelia have been raised in the laboratory. The reared adults readily paired and deposited fertile eggs.

Family NABIDAE

A METHOD OF REARING TWO SPECIES OF NABIDAE

F. G. MUNDINGER, *N. Y. State Agricultural Experiment Station*

THE species here concerned are *Nabis roseipennis* and *N. rufusculus*. These insects are fairly common throughout New York State during the summer and may be captured by sweeping grass with an insect net. Screen-topped lantern globes placed over potted grass stalks or small raspberry plants make suitable breeding cages. Aphids are excellent food for the nabids. A petri dish containing a small green leaf and a drop or two of water serves well as a rearing cage for one or two nymphs. These cages should be cleaned daily, fresh leaves and drops of water supplied, and a few live aphids dropped in for the nymphs to feed upon. Since the Nabidae are predacious it is not advisable to place more than one or two in the same cage.

I have not reared successive generations of these species. In this region the nabids appear to be single-brooded.

BIBLIOGRAPHY

MUNDINGER, F. G. 1922. *N. Y. State College of Forestry Tech. Publ.* 16:149.

Family CIMICIDAE

BREEDING AND REARING CIMEX LECTULARIUS

R. M. JONES, *Liquid Carbonic Corporation, Chicago, Illinois*

THE experiments were conducted under constant conditions of temperature and relative humidity. Incubating ovens were used to obtain the desired temperatures and relative humidities were kept constant by using saturated solutions of certain inorganic salts [see footnote on p. 307]. The eggs were obtained from bedbugs kept in small stender dishes in a glass battery jar under a constant condition of 27° C. and 75% relative humidity. These bugs were fed every six days by being placed in wide-mouthed glass tubes and held against the forearm.* The females deposited their eggs on small circular pieces of paper toweling placed in the dishes for that purpose. At least once a day, or oftener when an experiment required an accurate record of the time the eggs were laid, the papers were taken out and the eggs removed with a camel's hair brush. They were then put in other jars under the same conditions and used for experimental work as soon as they were hatched.

The following method was employed in rearing the bugs. Short pieces of 8 mm. by 40 mm. glass tubing were ground to a roughened surface on one end by applying to an emery wheel. On this end was then glued a small circular piece of 60 mesh bolting cloth, the other end being closed with the cap of a No. ooo gelatin capsule in which holes were punched to allow free circulation of air. One egg was placed in each tube and this furnished the permanent home for the bedbugs. The cages containing the eggs were kept under the conditions outlined above. After hatching, the nymphs were permitted to feed by holding the tubes against the wrist, no difficulty being experienced by the nymph in inserting the rostrum between the meshes of the bolting cloth. By using this method it was not necessary to remove the bugs from the cages until after they had reached the adult stage. The jars were aerated each day by fanning in fresh air with a piece of cardboard.

In determining the length of time required for incubation the eggs were placed in 10 mm. by 50 mm. shell vials. These were then placed in 20 mm. by 80 mm. vials containing a saturated solution of the salt

*Editor's Note: Ezekiel Rivnay, in *Ann. Ent. Soc. Amer.* 23:758, 1930, gives a list of recorded hosts for bedbugs and on which they presumably may be fed for experimental purposes. This list includes: bat, cat, calf, dog, guinea pig, hare, mouse, rat, monkey, rabbit, duck, goose, hen, pigeon, sparrow, starling, and swallow. M. E. D.

giving the desired relative humidity and tightly corked. The vials were also aerated once a day.

To determine the length of life of the 1st instar nymphs without food the nymphs were placed in No. ooo gelatin capsules in which many holes had previously been punched to allow a free circulation of air. The capsules were put in a small screen cage which was suspended in a pint Mason fruit jar containing a saturated solution of the salt giving the desired relative humidity. Aeration of the jars was performed daily as in the previous experiments.

BIBLIOGRAPHY

JONES, R. M. 1930. *Ann. Ent. Soc. Amer.* 23:105.

Family HYDROMETRIDAE

HYDROMETRA*

"Hydrometras are easily kept in captivity and breed in aquaria, thriving on a diet of flies and other small, soft-bodied insects. They are, therefore, ideal for observation."

Family GERRIDAE

THREE SPECIES OF GERRIDAE**

GERRIDS are not easy to rear for the reason that they do not lend themselves readily to life in captivity. If good-sized containers are used and placed well back on the laboratory table, the specimens are less likely to injure themselves by dashing against the sides. If placed near the edge of the rearing table the striders will be disturbed each time someone passes. At feeding and observation time the bugs make frantic efforts to escape and in so doing continually butt against the sides of the breeding jar. Observations may not be made if the rearings are carried on in a large container, unless one has access to a movable-arm binocular.

A recently captured female *Trepobates pictus* laid a small mass of eggs on the underside of a small willow twig that was placed in the aquarium jar. Individuals reared in captivity and depositing eggs every day will usually fail to deposit eggs the first day after they are placed in a new breeding jar.

---

* From an article in *Ent. Amer.* 7:87, 1926, by J. R. DE LA TORRE BUENO, Tucson, Arizona.

** Abstracted from an article in *Ann. Ent. Soc. Amer.* 17:419, 1924, by WILLIAM E. HOFFMANN, *Lingnan University.*

Gerris buenoi laid eggs in the laboratory on sticks, stems, bark, and other floating material that was supplied. With aquaria large enough to accommodate growing plants more satisfactory studies could be made.

Limnoporus rufoscutellatus, like the other members of the family Gerridae, is predacious, feeding upon insects to be found on the surface of the water. The adults prefer to cling to vegetation or other support most of the time. The nymphs seem to be more independent of supports, as they were reared in jelly glasses with no supporting surface afforded.

The rearing methods were essentially the same for the three species. Jelly glasses were used for the most part as containers, while the food consisted of flies, leafhoppers, and other soft-bodied insects. The jelly glasses were half filled with water. Sand was not used in the containers. Care had to be taken not to disturb the nymphs. When disturbed they would make frantic efforts to escape and would often become waterlogged. When the body pile becomes thoroughly wet, the bugs will drown unless removed to an aquarium containing only wet sand. After the body is again clean and dry and the bug has recovered from the weakening effects of its struggles, it may be returned to the aquarium containing water. *Gerris remigis* and *G. marginatus* were kept under the same conditions with about the same degree of success.*

M. E. D.

Family VELIIDAE

WINTER FOOD FOR WATERBUGS IN AQUARIA**

FLIES may be collected within buildings in limited numbers all winter. Bruchus and Tribolium adults may be secured in quantities from places where there are heavy infestations, kept in a large container with their respective foods, and used as needed. *Tenebrio molitor* larvae and Drosophila are satisfactory.

However, the most successful food in the experience of the writer has been cockroach nymphs. They are easy to secure, easy to handle, and

*Editor's Note: C. F. Curtis Riley, of the *University of Manitoba*, reported in *Ent. News* 33:86, 1922, on the rearing of *Gerris remigis* and *G. marginatus*. Both will feed on a variety of insect food, such as the pupae and adults of Culex, small and large species of Tipulid flies, Syrphid flies, *Musca domestica*, Chironomus, Tabanus, and Drosophila. *G. remigis* is a more vigorous and daring feeder than is *G. marginatus* and has been observed to feed on *Notonecta undulata*, Chrysopa, *Calopteryx maculata*, *Hetaerina americana*, and Arctocorixa. Both species have at times been noticed feeding on the soft parts of banana fruit and on the inner soft parts of the skin in the absence of other food. During confinement both species will suck the juices of freshly killed snails, Physa and Planorbis, and also small pieces of fresh beef. M. E. D.

** Abstracted from an article in *Bull. Brooklyn Ent. Soc.* 19:149, 1924, by WILLIAM E. HOFFMANN, *Lingnan University*.

they produce healthy bugs. Five species of Microvelia and two species of Velia have been successfully reared on a straight diet of cockroaches. Several specimens of Curicta have been carried from the 3rd instar to the adult on this diet while adult Nepa, Curicta, Ranatra, Velia, and Microvelia have been kept through the winter.

Immediately upon hatching the nymphs are large enough to make a meal for Microvelia or Velia, while those a week or two old serve nicely for the larger waterbugs. If one has access to a place infested with cockroaches it is a simple matter to catch nymphs. A space on the floor is cleared, a few bits of food placed there and covered with a piece of cardboard or beaverboard. After the lights have been turned off a few minutes they may be turned on, the cardboard lifted, and dozens of the nymphs killed or crippled with a fly swatter. The clean floor makes them readily visible and they are easily picked up with a forceps. Often they will come in numbers while the lights are on and even during the day. The scattering of food particles or even sprinkling of water on the floor will attract them. They may also be trapped by placing a heavy paper funnel in a deep bottle, but specimens caught in this manner are unsatisfactory for they get wet and for that reason sink through the surface film of the water. Microvelia and Velia will catch living organisms beneath the surface film, but they do not care for flies, cockroaches, or other similar food that does not rest upon the surface. Because of this it is preferable to kill the nymphs just before feeding time. If placed on their backs they are not likely to sink and in this position the parts easiest to pierce are uppermost.

To insure a continuous supply of food, adult cockroaches bearing egg-cases may be trapped and the cases removed to containers with damp blotting paper or other damp material on the bottom. Corked bottles or glass containers with rather tight-fitting lids will serve the purpose. Upon hatching the nymphs may be reared by giving them a piece of apple every few days.

J. G. N.

VELIA WATSONI*

FIFTH-STAGE nymphs and adults of *Velia watsoni*, taken among the roots of smartweed and other weeds and grasses on the moist banks of pools in the bed of a small stream, were placed in tin boxes with damp vegetation. Little trouble was experienced in keeping the bugs in captivity and in rearing them.

Mating in captivity has taken place during every month of the year, but has been more frequent during the warmer part of the season.

*Abstracted from an article in *Canad. Ent.* 57:107, 1925, by WILLIAM E. HOFFMANN, *Lingnan University*.

In the aquarium they deposit eggs on the side of the glass container and on rocks, as well as on floating objects. Eggs have been deposited in the laboratory during every month but December, with the peak of production occurring during August and September.

This species is predacious and cannibalistic. The adults will kill the nymphs and the nymphs will kill each other. Consequently it is necessary to remove the adults to new containers as fast as the eggs are ready to hatch. *Velia brachialis* was found to differ in this respect, for a number of nymphs, or even a number of both nymphs and adults, have been kept in the same aquarium with little danger of cannibalism developing.

Velias, like Microvelias, feed upon the very small animals swimming beneath the surface film as well as upon food particles on the surface. The Velias are very leisurely in their feeding activities. They feed on living, crippled, or dead insects placed on the surface of the water. The adults do well on any insect food, while the nymphs thrive better on cockroach nymphs than upon any other food. Many nymphs were reared from hatching to maturity on a straight diet of cockroaches. The adults have been fed on flies, nymphs and adults of cicadellids, cercopids and mirids, grasshopper nymphs, adult Tribolium, Bruchus, Dermestes, and larval forms such as Tenebrio, Mediterranean flour moth, and various caterpillars.

M. E. D.

Family SALDIDAE

SALDULA MAJOR AND S. PALLIPES*

NYMPHS of *Saldula major*, captured in June, transformed into adults and mated by June 18. Newly laid eggs were found at the base of a blade of grass on June 21. These hatched on July 3. The nymphs liked to stay hidden most of the time, but would come out readily to feed.

Nymphs of *Saldula pallipes* (?), captured on June 1, became adults and laid eggs before June 23. These were thrust in the stems and blades of grass growing in the jars in which the saldids were confined.

In all the rearings dead flies were used as food as well as other soft-bodied insects, chiefly mirids and cicadellids, which were usually easy to obtain in large numbers either by sweeping or at light at night.

M. E. D.

*Abstracted from an article in *Kan. Univ. Sci. Bull.* 14:301, 1922, by GRACE OLIVE WILEY.

Family NOTONECTIDAE

REARING NOTONECTIDAE*

Buenoa margaritaeca, B. scimitra, B. elegans, Plea striola, and *Notonecta undulata,* all common species in Kansas, have been reared from egg to adult. Successive generations have been raised in the case of several of these species.

Since about 1895 various attempts have been made to rear the notonectids, but usually they have been only partially successful. The difficulties have been in establishing conditions in the aquarium duplicating those of the ponds or natural habitat of these insects. At least three important factors have been at fault: the oxygen content of the water, the condition of the surface film, and the food supply.

In attempting to rear the early stages of Buenoa it was found that few nymphs ever reached the 2nd instar in the stender dishes used. It even took the eggs longer to hatch there than out in the ponds. Frequently changing the water in the stender dishes did little good. When it was not so changed, a scum formed over the surface after one or two days. The bugs died more quickly. The daily removal of this scum helped the situation but did not remedy it. It occurred that the trouble probably was due to oxygen deficiency and the greater difficulty in breaking the surface film when it was covered with scum. Air forced through the water with a large pipette almost immediately revived the dying bugs, but the relief was only temporary. Then a device first described in 1910 ** for continuously aerating an aquarium was used. It was a success, and must be credited for the life histories of the genus Buenoa.

Another difficulty was the food supply. Ostracods and such minute organisms as the Buenoae and Pleae usually fed upon were inconvenient to collect. Other workers had reported mosquito wrigglers as good food for notonectids. So during most of the season mosquito eggs were collected each morning from one or two tubs of rainwater and kept in a smaller vessel until next day when they hatched and served well as food for all species. A barrel of rainwater near the insectary supplied larger mosquito larvae for the more mature nymphs and adults of Notonecta and Buenoa. But even tiny Plea will not hesitate at times to attack almost full grown mosquito wrigglers.

Other factors than those just mentioned should be considered. The laboratory in which the rearing work was done was in a basement which affected the temperatures and lighting, and it was artificially heated during the latter part of the season. All aquarium jars except a few kept

*Abstracted from an article in *Ann. Ent. Soc. Amer.* 19:93, 1926, by CLARENCE O. BARE, *Sanford, Florida.*
** SCHAEFFER, A. A. 1910. *Science* 31:955.

as controls were constantly aerated, and each was supplied with sprigs of Ceratophyllum. All aquaria were filled with pond water. Careful regulation of the air was necessary to prevent too vigorous bubbling. With strict attention to details Notonecta and Plea were easily reared, but several attempts were necessary to get the full life story for the Buenoae. The mortality due to molting was considerable, as must also be true in the ponds; and nematodes seemed to cause the death of many.

M. E. D.

Family NAUCORIDAE

PELOCORIS CAROLINENSIS*

A LARGE number of rearings were started in April when eggs were laid, attached to a sprig of Nitella. The incubation period varied from 32 to 45 days with the majority requiring 39 to 40 days. By the time the eggs were ready to hatch the plant sprigs to which they were attached were dead and in some cases in a state of disintegration.

Since *Pelocoris carolinensis* is fiercely predacious it was necessary to isolate each newly hatched nymph. Each specimen was placed in a tall stender dish or jelly glass half full of water and supplied with a sprig of Nitella. Mosquito wrigglers, Chironomus larvae, corixids, and Entomostraca were given as food and the water was replaced by fresh pond water at frequent intervals. There was something grievously wrong with the rearing technique for only nine specimens were reared to the adult stage out of 134 isolations. Several females mated and laid eggs.

M. E. D.

Family NEPIDAE

CURICTA DRAKEI**

SEVERAL pairs of adult *Curicta drakei* were collected and the pairs placed in separate glasses. Small glass containers were used with gauze tied over the tops. Sand and a few pieces of water plants were placed in the bottoms and made rather wet.

Like Nepa, Curicta is a mud-loving bug. When the adults were given mud, rotten wood, decayed vegetation, and live water plants, the mud was always chosen for the deposition of the eggs. Both nymphs and adults are fond of getting out of the water and lying close to the ground, where they are hardly discernible.

---

* Abstracted from an article in *Bull. Brooklyn Ent. Soc.* 22:77, 1927, by H. B. HUNGERFORD, *University of Kansas.*

** Abstracted from an article in *Kan. Univ. Sci. Bull.* 14:507, 1922, and one in *Ent. News* 35:324, 1924, by GRACE OLIVE WILEY.

Only occasionally are these bugs cannibalistic. This may happen when no other food is available. Sometimes when hard pressed for food both young and adults have been observed to feed upon the eggs that were found in the water. They like small notonectids, corixids, small carabids, freshwater shrimps, and such. They refused small minnows, however. It is not uncommon to see three feeding quietly on one shrimp or two feeding on one small beetle. In the rearing work all sorts of insects were used as food, such as grasshoppers; stink-bugs; various species of beetles including blister beetles, flies, mealworms, and small snout beetles; membracids; and mosquito larvae, of which they are very fond. It was a problem to procure food for these insects during the winter, as they were kept in a warm room and were more or less active. Many times when the bugs were hungry and no insect food was available they were fed on small bits of raw beef.

Adults readily mated and laid eggs in captivity. Curicta adults were kept over the winter and the following summer a number of these insects laid eggs from which young were again reared.

M. E. D.

REFERENCES

For the feeding of Nepa, Ranatra, and Curicta see p. 310.

Family GELASTOCORIDAE

GELASTOCORIS OCULATUS*

TALL stenders, or staining jars, of glass, about the size of jelly glasses, were used as containers. In each of these was placed an inch of sand or soil that had been sterilized by heat. The paired adults were confined in low stenders of various sizes, and the sand searched every day for eggs. The young were isolated in the tall stenders as soon as they hatched, for they are cannibalistically inclined. The sand was moistened each day, and the jars were covered with ground glass covers.

The insects were fed houseflies, oscinid flies, cicadellids, and many other small insects taken in sweeping the grass. Each day the dead carcasses were cleaned out of the rearing jars and freshly killed insects inserted. Nymphs and adults of Gelastocoris pounce upon their prey, which appears to consist of almost any sort of insect they can capture, from a grouse locust to a lacebug.

Mortality in captivity was very high and indicates that some essential factor of their natural habitat was lacking. Mortality was greatest in

---

* Abstracted from an article in *Kan. Univ. Sci. Bull.* 14:145, 1922, by H. B. HUNGERFORD, *University of Kansas.*

the 1st stage and the nymphs usually succumbed on the date when molting might be expected to occur.

M. E. D.

Order HOMOPTERA, Family CERCOPIDAE

REARING CERCOPIDAE

KATHLEEN C. DOERING, *University of Kansas*

SPITTLE insects, like all sucking insects which are plant feeders, are difficult to rear. It is very necessary that they have healthy, succulent plant tissue upon which to feed in order to get sufficient nourishment for their proper development. In addition, spittle bugs need vast quantities of plant juice in order to form their spittle masses. Normally, in the field, spittle nymphs perhaps do not move around to any great extent. In the laboratory, however, they are apt to be exceedingly restless, especially the tiny first instars. The restlessness of the nymphs is usually caused by disturbance of them in their spittle mass, or by lack of juice in the plant.

In bringing spittle insects into the laboratory great care must be taken not to lose them enroute. The most satisfactory method for the author was to cut the entire plant stalk without disturbing the insects in the spittle mass and then to wrap the stem tightly in a newspaper. At the laboratory they should be transferred to growing young plants by means of a camel's hair paint brush. They ramble aimlessly over the plant for some time but eventually settle down when they find a favorable feeding spot. They should be watched carefully during this wandering period for very frequently they fall off the plant onto the dirt beneath where they sometimes are not able to regain their feet. Spittle bugs dry up quickly when not living in their spittle mass. When once settled upon the plant, and if the plant is growing, they give little trouble.

Certain precautions should be noted in regard to the care of the host plants. In the first place if more than one host plant is found for the insect the plant chosen for rearing should be the one that lends itself best to transplanting and for which it is easiest to get small, seedling, or tender plants. For *Lepyronia quadrangularis* which has some sixty-two host plants, small plants of the common ragweed, *Ambrosia artemisifolia*, proved most satisfactory. Secondly it was found that cuttings of plants placed in water are unsatisfactory apparently because there is not enough plant juice present to supply the amount of fluid needed to make the spittle masses. Small, tender plants should be planted in flower pots. The nymphs are then confined on the plants under lamp chimneys. Over the top of the lamp chimney is placed a covering of cheesecloth. For the tiny 1st instars it was even necessary to double the cloth to keep the nymphs from straying away from the plant. It is necessary to use lamp chimneys for the first instar or two because they are so small at this time and so restless that they become lost easily in any larger space. For later stages wire cages would be better because the plants would do better in less cramped quarters and no difficulty is likely to be experienced in keeping the larger nymphs under observation.

ARTIFICIAL FEEDING OF LEAFHOPPERS*

A METHOD has been devised whereby a reasonably large number of leafhoppers may be caged and fed simultaneously upon a nutrient solution. It consists (Fig. 65) of a shallow "saucer" to which had been

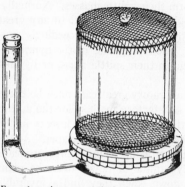

FIG. 65.—Apparatus devised for simultaneously feeding large numbers of homopterous insects on a nutrient solution.

sealed a vertical L tube. This vessel is capped with a mesentery membrane of the type recommended by Carter.** The solution is added to the feeding apparatus until the liquid is in contact with the entire surface of the membrane by means of the side arm, which is corked to prevent contamination. This feeding vessel may be washed and sterilized in alcohol without removing the membrane or impairing its efficiency.

For use with this feeding dish, a cage made of a 3-inch cylinder of 1⅝-inch glass tubing, capped at both ends with a fine open-mesh cloth such as georgette or scrim, is employed. The upper end of the cloth capping has a small opening for admission of the test insects, which is at other times closed by a cotton plug. The cage containing the test insects is placed upright upon the membrane surface over the solution.

"With this arrangement, feeding will begin almost at once and freely continue as long as the insect lives. No evidence of unwillingness or inability of the leafhopper to locate the solution or to feed upon it was found. Furthermore with this arrangement it was possible to transfer feeding insects from one solution to another without handling them,

---

* Abstracted from an article in *Science* 79:346, 1934, by R. A. FULTON and J. C. CHAMBERLIN, *U. S. Bureau of Entomology and Plant Quarantine.*

** Animal mesentery sold under the name of "fish skin" at a drug store. *J. Agric. Res.* 34:449, 1927, and *Phytopathology* 18:246, 1928.

merely by lifting the cage from one saucer to another. From 25 to 50 test beet leafhoppers may be confined in this cage without apparent overcrowding."

J. G. N.

Family CICADELLIDAE

THE BEET LEAFHOPPER, EUTETTIX TENELLUS*

THE adults were confined in a cylindrical cage (12 by 8 inches) with top and sides covered with lawn, except for a glass plate (10 by 5 inches) through which observations were made. The bottom of each cage was covered with denim fastened with a loop of copper wire. The leaves of a sugar beet with the base of the petioles wrapped in cotton projected through two central intersecting incisions in the denim. The denim rested against 2 inches of dry sand covering the surface of the soil in a 10-inch pot. The hoppers might be transferred rapidly to another potted sugar beet by blowing a breath of air through the sides and by jarring the cage, causing the insects to change their resting place from the foliage to the cloth; the cage was then lifted so that the leaves pulled through the incisions, leaving the bugs in captivity. This removal of the cage from the potted beet was performed in a dark chamber provided with a glass plate, outside of which was a 50-watt electric lamp covered with a shade, so that any specimens which perchance remained on the plant, resting between the petioles, were attracted to the light after the cage was removed. The glass of each cage faced to the north in the field. Each pot was placed in a saucer and the saucers were watered daily during hot weather. To prevent ants from entering the cage, the sides of the saucer were smeared with tanglefoot.

M. E. D.

Family CHERMIDAE

CULTURE METHODS FOR THE POTATO PSYLLID

GEORGE F. KNOWLTON, *Utah Agricultural Experiment Station*

THE potato psyllid, *Paratrioza cockerelli,* yields readily to domestication in the laboratory, when suitable cultural methods are used.

Collecting Methods. A colony of potato psyllids may be readily established by collecting large nymphs upon potato or matrimony vine leaves, and then transferring them to vigorous young potato plants in the labora-

---

*Abstracted from an article in *Univ. of Calif. Pub. in Ent.* 5:37, 1930, by HENRY H. P. SEVERIN, *University of California.* See original publication for illustrations of equipment.

tory. Another method of establishing a colony is to collect the adult psyllids by "sweeping" infested plants with an insect net equipped with a heavy gauze or sheeting bag. For removal to the laboratory the adult psyllids may be placed in a temporary gauze cage, together with portions of a succulent plant, or inside of celluloid cages placed over young potato plants. In the laboratory, the adults may be transferred from the field cages to the rearing cages by means of a common aspirator. [See p. 46.] Care should be used to prevent aphids from entering the rearing cages with the psyllids or upon host plants. Plants upon which potato psyllid eggs have been laid may be potted and moved to the laboratory, if desired. A high nymphal mortality usually occurs when the leaves are picked off and become dry before the eggs hatch or when the egg stipes are shaved from the leaves and the eggs placed upon moist blotting paper inside of petri dishes.

Cages. Several types of cages have been found to be suitable for the rearing and handling of potato psyllids:

1. Large gauze cages, built to the width of laboratory windows, and about 20 inches deep, were found to be excellent for rearing potato psyllids. West windows were best in the winter and shaded east basement windows during the hot summer weather.
2. Medium to large gauze cages with a wooden bottom and frame work. Cages 12 to 18 inches wide, 16 to 24 inches long, and 16 to 20 inches deep were well adapted to rearing the psyllids. The front end consisted of a celluloid observation sheet which covered approximately the upper ⅓ to ½ of the frame; to this was cemented (with acetone) a gauze flap extending approximately 2 inches beyond the margins of the end. This gauze flap serves as a door, being fastened snugly with thumb tacks, except when potted plants are to enter or leave the cage. Small slits, which may be kept plugged with cotton, admit the 6 to 8 mm. aspirator, for capturing adult psyllids, and the glass tube, used with a funnel to water the host plants.
3. Other suitable breeding cages consisted of round or square gauze cages, with a glass or celluloid panel and with a round opening in the bottom to fit upon a flower pot containing a host plant.
4. Celluloid cages of various sizes to fit 6- to 8-inch pots. Cages fitted with a top and two side ventilators of gauze usually were satisfactory, but moisture would occasionally collect, resulting in the drowning of adult psyllids.
5. Small clip cages, made of 4-dram homeopathic vials, with the closed end cut off, flanged, and covered with gauze, made satisfactory cages for one to several psyllids. These cages were held in place by means of a piano wire spring, a flat metal disc covering the top. To prevent the death of contained portions of the leaf, it was necessary to move such cages daily.
6. A similar cylindrical cage, made of fine screen wire or celluloid and set into a small, thin, padded board, with a matching, padded board to fit on the opposite side of the leaf, avoided this difficulty. Such cages were held together, without excessive pressure, by means of rubber bands around the ends of the small boards. (Cages 5 and 6 are similar to those used on beet leafhopper investigations.)
7. Individual nymphs may be reared, when under constant observation, by placing

but one to a leaf and only two or three upon a small plant. If disturbed the nymphs may move around.

Nymphal mortality was somewhat higher in the small than in the larger cages. A high mortality often occurred at the first and second molts, where conditions were for any reason unfavorable.

Optimum conditions for egg-laying and nymphal development seem to occur between 70° and 75° F., with slight temperature fluctuations. The eggs, which are at the extreme end of a short stipe, are laid principally upon the younger, apical potato leaves. Females have a rather long oviposition period, and nymphs and adults of all stages may be had by adding a new potted potato plant to the breeding cage about once or twice each week. Where caged in pairs, it may be necessary to replace males that die in order to maintain the fertility of the eggs. Adults reared in cages appear to live longer in captivity, and to be less excitable than do wild adults collected out of doors. The mortality of freshly captured wild adults is sometimes heavy, especially if they are placed in small cages during hot weather.

When the nymphs become excessively abundant, it may be necessary to kill or to remove part of the insects to save the plants. As many as 2,000 to 3,000 nymphs, in addition to adults, have occasionally been found upon medium sized potato plants under both field and laboratory conditions.

Greenhouse rearings are usually successful during the fall, winter, and spring months, but the psyllids have difficulty surviving during the summer if temperatures become excessively high. Nymphs and adults have been observed to survive when the potato plants upon which they were feeding were destroyed by frost.

In order to have vigorous potato plants at all seasons of the year for rearing potato psyllids, it sometimes becomes necessary, in order to induce growth, to use chemicals to break the rest period upon potato tubers to be used for seed. [See footnote on p. 328.] Tomato plants, and some other solanaceous hosts, may be used to raise psyllids in smaller numbers.

Biological Control. Potato psyllid colonies may be lost by allowing heavy aphid infestations to develop upon and destroy the host plants. Adult and larval ladybird beetles, predacious Hemiptera such as damsel bugs and big-eyed bugs, lacewing fly larvae, syrphid larvae, spiders, and other predators may attack laboratory colonies of psyllids, unless the cages are kept free from them. No insect parasites have been noted in the area under observation, but when kept under humid conditions a few adults have been found which appear to have been destroyed by fungus.

Family APHIDIDAE

A USEFUL CAGE FOR REARING SMALL INSECTS ON GROWING PLANTS*

IN THE rearing of aphids and their parasites and scale insects for the past two years, the writer has found a specially designed cage of sheet celluloid very satisfactory. Any cage for rearing these insects must allow for a free circulation of air, permit the entrance of light, and not cause a concentration of heat or moisture. Still another feature bears considerable importance when dealing with small insects, and that is the absence of any cracks or niches in which the insect may hide or escape.

The simplest and most suitable form of cage is the cylindrical type made by bending together the edges of a rectangular piece of celluloid and sealing them with 95% alcohol. Ventilation holes of any size and position on the sheet, may be cut in before bending. After the edges are sealed together and the cylinder is formed, the ventilation openings and one end opening are covered with fine cheesecloth or voile shellacked on the celluloid around the edges of the openings. The cage is now ready to be placed over the plant, usually a small one in a pot. In order to hold the cage securely in position and provide a smooth white surface on the bottom of the enclosure about the plant, melted paraffin is poured on the soil around the plant, and the open end of the cage set down into it after the edges have first been given a thin coat of vaseline to prevent the adherence of the paraffin. Thus treated the cage may be lifted free when the paraffin cools, leaving a smooth tight groove into which the edges just fit and prevent the escape of any insect when the cage is in place. Entry for the introduction or removal of material is easily made by tearing back a corner of the cloth ventilator, or lifting up the cage from its paraffin base.

Sheet celluloid is a very satisfactory material with which to construct small cages for a portion of a plant like a small twig, or a part of the surface of a leaf or fruit on which it is desirable to confine small sedentary insects such as scales and aphids. In these small cages, ventilation may be secured by punching small holes in the celluloid with a fine needle. Shellac was found useful in joining together the sharp edges of the cage and sticking it to the plant surface. This material soon drys, with a hard surface so that it will not entangle the insects, and yet remains soft enough to prevent cracking and breaking apart.

Cages constructed from sheet celluloid are as transparent as glass, and do not "sweat" like the glass cages. They may be made any size

*Abstracted from an article in *Ohio J. of Sci.* 23:201, 1923, by E. A. HARTLEY, N. Y. State College of Forestry.

and shape desired. They may be ventilated by cutting any number and size of openings in the side. They are very neat and smooth within, making it easy to observe specimens at all times.

J. G. N.

THE NASTURTIUM APHID, APHIS RUMICIS

H. H. SHEPARD, *University of Minnesota*

APHIS *rumicis* is used more as a test insect for determining the relative effectiveness of contact insecticides than for any other purpose. It is the common black aphid, or plant louse, infesting nasturtium (*Tropaeolum majus*) and many other plants, and is known as the bean, dock, or nasturtium aphid. Although this aphid is reported from many woody and herbaceous plants, some of these do not seem to furnish suitable food, for after a few generations the aphid leaves them for more favorable locations. In laboratory work in this country it has been reared upon nasturtium plants, whereas in the work of Davidson and of Tattersfield in England, the broad bean (*Vicia faba*) was employed as its food. There is some confusion regarding the number of species of aphids included under the name *A. rumicis* (Franssen, 1927, and others). Horsfall has pointed out that there are two distinct types of life cycle; one with woody shrubs as primary food plants on which the eggs are laid and the first generations develop in the spring, the secondary food plants being herbaceous; the other with primary food plants such as *Chenopodium album* and Rumex, and these and other herbaceous plants as secondary food plants.

There are several reasons why *A. rumicis* is to be preferred for the purpose mentioned. The individuals are black and show up well on a light background, resulting in less eye strain after counting large numbers of them than if a green species were employed. *A. rumicis* is short legged and less likely to be injured in handling than the other species which are long legged and more awkward. It moves more slowly when disturbed by irritating chemicals, and hence is easier to keep within artificial barriers.

This species is easily reared in the greenhouse, reproduction being continuous throughout the year if favorable conditions are maintained. Colonies may be started easily on young nasturtium plants by transferring to them a few aphids. The most important consideration is the growth and condition of the nasturtium plants. The seeds of the dwarf nasturtium, soaked in tepid water for an hour or so, should be planted in rich black loam. For convenience in handling it is customary to plant several seeds in a 3- or 4-inch flower pot and set the pots closely on the surface of the soil in the greenhouse bench. However, after the plants become of medium size the roots extend into the soil of the bench and are broken if the pots are moved, the plants wilting as a result. In order that the soil be kept fairly moist without becoming soggy; watering should be more frequent in sunny or warm weather and less so in cool, damp weather. When young and well watered, the plants have a very succulent growth upon which aphids do well. On the other hand very young plants of but two or three leaves may be injured by too heavy an infestation. It is well to plant about twice a week so the aphid population may continually expand to plants of suitable size. It is also well to eliminate the older, heavily infested plants gradually so the population will not become too great and overrun the young plants excessively. The older plants are less succulent and less attractive to migrating aphids; colonies developing upon them produce increased numbers of winged migratory females. Furthermore, the older colonies are likely to become so parasitized by hymenopterous parasites that the entire aphid culture is in danger of being affected.

Other factors than moisture may influence the physiological activity of the plant, thereby affecting the nature of the cell sap upon which the aphids feed. In the heat of summer the greenhouse should be kept as cool as possible and the plants shaded with cheesecloth or white-wash on the glass overhead. In midwinter in the north it is difficult to keep aphids in health because of the reduction of available daylight.

In his tests of the toxicity of contact insecticides, Richardson used undisturbed colonies of *Aphis rumicis* by cutting the leaves and plants bearing them and inserting the stems through two-hole rubber stoppers in small bottles of water. These bottles were then set on white paper and surrounded by tanglefoot bands. Tattersfield used only adult wingless parthenogenetic females, descended from a single female. The successive generations were reared upon broad bean plants in pots. In order to separate the desired individuals the plants were cut and allowed to wilt slightly to make the aphids remove their stylets from the leaf tissue and wander about. Then the insects were easily and safely handled with a camel's hair brush. If the mouthparts were to remain inserted in the leaf they might be injured when the aphids were brushed off.

BIBLIOGRAPHY

DAVIDSON, J. 1926. The sexual and parthenogenetic generations in the life-cycle of *Aphis rumicis*, L. *Verh. III Internat. Ent. Kongr.* Zürich, 1925, 2:452.

FRANSSEN, C. J. H. 1927. *Aphis fabae*, Scop., en aanverwante soorten in Nederland. 90 pp. Wageningen. (Abst. in *Rev. Appl. Ent.* 15:464, 1927).

HORSFALL, J. L. 1925. The life history and bionomics of *Aphis rumicis*. *Univ. Iowa Studies Nat. Hist.*, 11, No. 2, 57 pp.

RICHARDSON, C. H., and SMITH, C. R. 1923. Studies on contact insecticides. *U. S. Dept. Agric., Dept. Bull.* 1160.

TATTERSFIELD, F., and MORRIS, H. M. 1924. An apparatus for testing the toxic values of contact insecticides under controlled conditions. *Bull. Ent. Res.* 14:223.

APHIS MAIDI-RADICIS*

THE complete life history of this corn-root aphis from the egg stage in spring to the eggs in autumn has been obtained. The vivaria used for the rearing and observation of the aphis consisted of 8- or 10-dram vials, each containing a ball of moist cotton in the bottom and plugged at the top with a piece of cotton. In this cage a sprouting corn plant was placed, a reserve supply of these food plants being constantly kept for use. The first young and the last young of each generation were placed on corn roots in separate vials. These vials were kept in closed boxes to exclude light, thus giving conditions probably most favorable to the optimum development of the aphis. As soon as the plant began to wilt it was replaced by a fresh one, the aphids being transferred by means of a camel's hair brush.

During the life cycle of this aphid there appear five different forms, namely: winged viviparous females, wingless viviparous females, oviparous females, males, and eggs. Eggs were collected originally in the nests of the common brown ant (*Lasius niger* L. *var. americanus* Emery) in April. Taking the first young of the first young all through the series, 22 generations were obtained.

M. E. D.

REFERENCE
For the rearing of *Aphis maidis* see p. 397.

REARING METHODS FOR APHIDIDAE

F. M. WADLEY, *U. S. Bureau of Entomology and Plant Quarantine*

CONSIDERABLE work has been done in rearing the green bug (*Toxoptera graminum*) and the apple-grain aphid (*Rhopalosiphum prunifoliae*); some rearing has been done with *Macrosiphum granarium*, the pea aphid, the melon aphid, the corn-leaf aphid, and several other aphid species. Aphids have been reared almost entirely on growing plants, though they will live for a time on cuttings in water. It seems inadvisable to try rearing them on detached bits of food plant, as feeding appears to be almost continuous. Many aphids seem to thrive under a wide range of humidity and light conditions if on a favorable and thriving food plant. They also develop under a fairly wide temperature range, but it is difficult to carry some species through a hot summer. In warm weather a shady, moist, well ventilated place should be sought for cages for such species. Some species are quite susceptible to fungous disease, and precautions must be taken against its entry.

Cages must permit food plants to thrive, but otherwise have not

* From an article in *U. S. D. A. Tech. Ser.* No. 12:Pt. 8, 1909, by J. J. DAVIS, *Purdue University.*

presented a difficult problem. Most aphids develop well in confinement, and do not often try to leave a favorable plant. The old device of a cloth topped lantern globe on a flower pot containing the food plant answers the purpose fairly well. Several modifications have been used. Glass lamp chimneys with the top closed with cloth or stoppered with cotton have been successful; light weight mica chimneys have been unsatisfactory outdoors because they blow off easily. If plants in the flower pot are small, observations may be made easily, and special precautions may be taken to make the cage tight and to keep the soil smooth and bare. If it is desired to find molts and dead insects without fail, paper may be placed on the soil, or melted paraffin may be poured over the soil to form a temporary floor.

Plants should be of a favorable species; aphids will not thrive on all the plants they are known to infest. They should also be in a thrifty growing condition; new and vigorous seedlings are especially favorable. Transferring has been done with a small camel's hair brush; in transferring, the worker should be sure the aphid has a good foothold on the plant before leaving it. Some aphids, especially small nymphs, will fail to get back on the plant if they fall on the soil.

REFERENCES

For the culture of *Toxoptera graminum* see p. 397.
For the culture of *Macrosiphum cornelli* see p. 499.

CULTURE OF APHIDS

A. FRANKLIN SHULL, *University of Michigan*

THE breeder of aphids needs to remember that many species will feed only on certain plants. They wander from any others on which they may be placed and starve rather than accept them. No artificial method of feeding them has yet proved feasible. There are, however, a number of cosmopolitan species which feed on many different plants.

If a phenomenon is to be studied which is exemplified in only one or a few species, the investigator's first question is whether he can supply the food plant for the duration of the study. Aphids feeding only on a deciduous tree or shrub are not usually suitable for such studies. If the problem is one of general physiology or of a wide spread anatomical feature, the cosmopolitan species are available. One who is not well acquainted with the group would do well to consult a taxonomist, to learn the accepted food plants, before essaying a breeding problem with any given species. Once the suitable plant or plants are known, the possibility of providing them for the length of time required will be easily ascertained.

Some of the common vegetables and garden flowers may be grown from seed at any time of year. Among these are beans, peas, cabbage, radishes, tomatoes, nasturtiums, calendulas, and asters. Wheat and oats are also useful. Each of these is accepted by some of the cosmopolitan species, and some of them are the favored food of certain species. The most convenient plants for experiments are those which grow rather slowly. If a group of aphids is to be left on one plant during its entire reproductive period of several weeks, the food plant should not become unmanageable in that time. Calendulas and cabbage are among the best of the plants named, in this regard, but are not always the most favorable to aphid growth. If more rapidly growing plants are used, the aphids may need to be transferred to fresh plants at intervals.

Seeds should be planted, not in the pots with which the experiments are to be conducted, but in seed plats. The young seedlings should be transplanted to very small pots, and, when they are satisfactorily established in these and begin to grow actively, should be removed, soil and all, without disturbing their roots, to the larger pots to be used in the experiments.

The common potato is suitable for cosmopolitan species, and is likewise the host of species peculiar to it. The plants may be furnished in quantity the year round, but one must look ahead. New potatoes require 6 or 8 weeks of rest before· they will sprout. Through the winter, any potatoes harvested in the fall may be counted on to sprout fairly promptly. Old potatoes planted later than May, however, especially indoors, are likely to produce a proportion of unhealthy plants. Hence it is better to begin to obtain new potatoes (shipped in at first from warmer regions) at least as early as March, and periodically thereafter through the summer and fall, so that a supply capable of sprouting is always on hand. There are ways of hastening the sprouting of potatoes, [See footnote on p. 328.] but none of them is superior to the method of allowing time for rest, which requires only foresight. The soil used for any plants should be renewed occasionally, and pots should be cleaned.

Aphids which in nature ordinarily alternate between two host plants may often, perhaps usually, be induced to live indefinitely on one of them. The most extensive experiments yet done with aphids concerned a species that alternates irregularly between rose and potato. It would be difficult to use the rose in experiments, but potato plants were found to suffice.

In general, aphids should be placed on a plant while it is still very small, and be allowed to accumulate while the plant grows. Since most aphids wander on slight provocation, they must be confined. Lantern globes closed at the top with voile or cheese cloth are suitable. The pots for the plants should be large enough to let the lantern globe rest on the soil, thus making an aphid-tight seal of the enclosure. Water for the plant may be introduced at the bottom from saucers, or more conveniently and with little harm through the voile covers of the lantern globes. If the aphids are to be kept for long periods of time at constant temperatures, light must be supplied for the plants. This may be done by having one wall of the temperature chamber made of glass and placing an electric lamp outside. If the offspring of certain parents are to be separated into successive groups in the order of their birth, it is better to transfer the parents from one plant to another, leaving the offspring on the plant where they were born.

The insects are best handled with a moist camel's hair brush. For examination alive under a microscope, the aphids may safely be etherized. They may also, without serious injury, be immersed for a short time in water on a hollow-ground slide to bring out details of structure.

Family COCCIDAE

METHOD FOR REARING MEALYBUGS, PSEUDOCOCCUS SP.*

STANLEY E. FLANDERS, *University of California*

EARLY investigations by Professor Harry S. Smith in connection with the study of the life history of certain parasites of the Baker mealybug indicated that the potato sprout was the most suitable host plant for the latter. While numerous other host plants have been tried, none has yet been found which has the year-round availability of seed potatoes, the adaptability to simple laboratory methods, and the ability to stand the continued abuse of laboratory practices.

While the propagation of the potato sprouts is a comparatively simple problem, success is dependent upon close attention to several details, the neglect of any one of which may result in failure.

The first and a very important point to be considered is the selection of seed tubers. In this respect many varieties which possess a reputation for heavy top growth have been tried. The variety known as British Queen produces an excellent long, succulent, sturdy sprout but seems to retard the development of certain mealybugs with which it is infested. California Burbank also produces an excellent sprout, but not all mealybugs will feed on it satisfactorily. Red Rivers and Bliss Triumphs produce an abnormally rapid growth of numerous, large, succulent sprouts, but have exhibited at times a tendency to break down very rapidly under heavy infestation and high temperatures. Idaho Rurals produce very usable sprouts but have too few eyes.

The Idaho Russet to date has met best all of the requirements of laboratory use. It is readily available on the open market from October 1

*Extracted from paper by HARRY S. SMITH and H. M. ARMITAGE. *Univ. Calif. Agri. Exper. Sta. Bull.* 509, 1931.

to July 1. It comes from an area free from tuber moth. This fact is very important, because this potato pest develops rapidly under insectary conditions, often destroying valuable host material before it may be put to its proper use. The Idaho Russet variety produces an abundance of long, slender, succulent sprouts which are susceptible to easy infestation, and it withstands to a marked degree heavy infestation and other necessary insectary abuses.

Well matured, small to medium sized tubers, averaging 4 to 8 ounces in weight, possessing an abundance of well formed eyes, are selected for planting. Freedom from cuts and bruises is desirable, since the conditions under which the tubers are placed in the insectary makes them very susceptible to destructive rots and molds which gain entrance through such injuries. Lots of tubers which show any appreciable percentage of Fusarium wilt should be rejected, and as far as possible those affected with scab and particularly Rhizoctonia should be avoided.

Though small seed pieces, split tubers, and seed end pieces have all been tried repeatedly in the interest of economy, careful experimentation has demonstrated that whole tubers produce better and more hardy sprouts under insectary conditions. Sprouts developed from whole tubers seem less dependent on the medium in which they are being grown and consequently are less seriously affected by the fluctuating moisture content of the trays, which may occur under the most careful handling.

The whole tubers are planted in a prepared soil medium composed of 4 parts of light sandy loam to 1 part of screened dairy manure. The top is then covered with ½ inch of coarse sand, which serves as a mulch, minimizing the danger of drying out and baking under the heated room conditions. Fifteen to eighteen tubers, depending on size, weighing approximately 6 pounds, are required to plant one tray.

When planted the trays are placed in the production rooms, usually on well constructed racks. These racks should be in the form of evenly spaced shelves not less than 12 inches apart. The weight of each filled tray is approximately 38 pounds, and vertical supports must be placed between the shelves for every 3 trays, allowance being made for sufficient side clearance between trays so that they may easily be installed or removed. The first tier of trays is never placed directly on the floor but is supported on 1-inch floor strips.

By stacking the trays checker-board fashion, racks may be dispensed with, but permanent cleat supports on the walls at both ends of the room are needed. A specially constructed tray is used for this purpose. It has a depth of 6 inches on the ends while the sides are the standard 4 inches in depth. By stacking the trays on the wider ends a 2-inch opening is provided laterally between trays, permitting cross ventilation throughout the entire stack and continued lateral growth of the sprouts from one tray to another. The trays are usually staggered 12 high, leaving 2 feet between the top trays and the 8-foot ceiling.

Each method of handling has its advantages and either may be used with satisfaction. Where racks are used the trays are more easily placed in position; poor trays may be easily removed and new ones added; and less labor is required to keep the sprouts out of the aisles and within the confines of the racks. Where the stacking method is used all of the host plant or host insect material in the entire lot of trays is directly accessible to the mealybugs.

The average period required for developing the potato sprouts to the point where they are ready for infesting with the mealybug is 60 days. However, this period is considerably lengthened during the winter months when the "new crop" seed tubers are more or less immature, and reduced almost to 30 days in midsummer when fully matured seed from cold storage is used.

The sprouts are allowed to develop in subdued light in order to promote longitudinal growth and to limit the formation of chlorophyl, which tends to inhibit the settling down of the mealybugs during the period of infestation. A temperature averaging 65° F. and a humidity of approximately 70% is maintained during the growing period. The moisture requirements of the growing sprouts necessitate that the trays be watered at 10-day intervals. Top trays and others directly exposed to ventilators dry out rapidly, and must be watered every 5 days.

Materials, such as sphagnum moss, wood shavings, sawdust, and coarse sand have been used as growing media but with less satisfactory results than with prepared soil mixtures.

Whole tubers in open trays with no growing medium may be used. Twice the number of tubers are then required, but a proportionate increase in production is secured, without any increase in equipment or room space. Other advantages of this method of operation are the material decrease in the amount of labor involved in the initial planting and in the subsequent care of the room. The necessity for frequent waterings with their attendant troubles from overwatering or drying out is eliminated. In addition, the tuber itself serves as a host of the more mature mealybugs. This method, so far as now understood, is limited, however, to late-season use when completely mature seed tubers are available; otherwise the prolonged period of sprout development makes it unpracticable. The development of more effective methods of accelerating sprout growth in new tubers would give this method of host plant culture preference over any other.*

*Editor's Note: The Cobbler, Green Mountain, and Russett Rural varieties of potatoes have been sprouted successfully when taken from the field in mid-season and stored at 40°F. for a month. The use of ethylene as an aid in speeding up maturity has also been successful.—G. F. MacLeod, *Cornell University*.

There are several attendant troubles in the growing of the host plant material, the more important of which are "tip burn" or "tip dieback"; damping-off due to Rhizoctonia; aphis, and potato tuber moth. "Tip burn," which affects the sprouts soon after they are out of the ground, produces numerous weak laterals, which in turn are themselves often affected. Its cause has not been determined. It is, however, believed to be entirely physiological and due to a combination of conditions in the rooms, particularly relating to ventilation and humidity.

Damping-off is induced by overwatering and slow evaporation, in spite of the fact that each tray is drained through a ¼-inch crack through the entire length of its bottom and that care is taken to avoid saturating the soil. Some insectary operators report successful control of damping-off by spraying with Semesan, but in general it may be prevented by avoiding the humid conditions which favor it. Rhizoctonia usually gains access because of non-elimination of infected seed when planting. It girdles the sprouts at the surface of the soil and, if it docs not kill them immediately, it so weakens them that they soon succumb to the attack of the mealybug.

The common mealybug (*Pseudococcus citri*) is best adapted to laboratory production. This fact is due to its restricted migratory habits, its inclination to remain on its host even under over-infested conditions, its short life cycle under laboratory temperatures, and a possible high degree of infestation with least injury to the potato sprouts.

An ample supply of mealybugs should be made available for evenly infesting the host plant material as it matures.

Infestation of the sprouts is accomplished through the use of temporary host material such as the stems and leaves of sunflower and mallow. This material is distributed over trays of hatching mealybugs and left there until completely infested. It is then collected and placed on new trays of sprouts to which the bugs migrate as the temporary host dries. The proper degree of infestation is determined by experience.

When mealybug material is collected in the field and used to infest the sprouts it should be placed in cloth bags or perforated paper sacks to permit the egress of the young mealybugs and retain any parasites that may be present.

METHODS USED IN REARING THE MEALYBUG, PSEUDOCOCCUS COMSTOCKI

W. S. HOUGH, *Virginia Experiment Station*

TWO methods were used in rearing *Pseudococcus comstocki* on catalpa: the vial method, and by using potted seedlings 6 to 18 inches in height. In the vial method I used straight edged vials 1-inch in diameter and 4 or 5 inches long. Either a newly hatched mealybug or an egg was placed on a catalpa leaf which was then inserted in a vial and tightly corked. At intervals of two or three days each individual was transferred by means of a camel's hair brush to a fresh leaf and the old leaf removed from the vial. When the females reached maturity an adult male which was still in its cocoon was placed in each vial. The eggs were removed daily from each vial during the period of oviposition.

The potted catalpa seedlings were used to a limited extent in the second method. A narrow paper band was placed on the trunk of each seedling and each band was kept covered with a fresh coating of tanglefoot to prevent migration on or off the tree. Above the tanglefoot band on the main trunk or on one of the laterals a band of burlap was loosely tied in order to afford a convenient place in which the males could cocoon. Sometimes the females also preferred to crawl beneath the burlap band just before beginning oviposition. When one individual shifted its position between molts so that it could no longer be distinguished from another specimen, both specimens were considered lost from the records for that stage of their development. No difficulty was encountered in rearing the mealybugs on the potted seedlings, but the fact that the individuals shift about from place to place makes observations very difficult to obtain if a consecutive record from molt to molt is desired for each specimen. Usually two to ten mealybugs were kept on each seedling and as far as possible not more than one individual was allowed to remain for any length of time on a leaf. The occurrence of a molt was indicated by the cast skin beside the insect. For a continuous record of the same individual from egg to adult it was necessary to employ the vial method of rearing rather than rearing a few individuals on each potted seedling.

It was learned that burlap bands placed on limbs of *Catalpa bungei* as well as on potted seedlings of catalpa offered favorable feeding places for mealybugs in all stages of development. A gall-like growth usually developed beneath each band after the insects had been feeding for a short time.

REFERENCE

For a convenient caging method for the Coccidae see p. 320.

Order NEUROPTERA

METHODS OF COLLECTING AND REARING NEUROPTERA

ROGER C. SMITH, *Kansas State College*

CHRYSOPIDAE (Lace-wings, aphis-lions)

ADULT chrysopids may be most successfully collected at lights in the early evening and by sweeping vegetation or beating bushes and trees during the days (Smith, 1922, 1934). Gravid females have distended abdomens and the more common species deposit their stalked eggs very readily in captivity. It is desirable to line the bottle or vial with leaves or paper so that the eggs will be deposited on them. The leaves or paper may then be removed and cut in pieces with an egg to a piece for placing in small individual vials. This is desirable because the larvae are cannibalistic.

Adult chrysopids require food. Place leaves with a few aphids on them or a pledget of cotton made wet with water or dilute sugar solution in the bottle. The vials or bottles must not be so moist as to allow droplets of water to form because the wings will be caught in the water and the adults will die. Adults may be kept for a week or more in a bottle, and eggs may be deposited over most of the period. The food should be changed daily. The rarer the species of chrysopid the greater the reluctance to oviposit and live satisfactorily in confinement. Hibernating prepupae and adults may be brought into the laboratory after they have experienced a cold stimulus. They will then develop or lay eggs during the winter months.

Eggs of this family may be collected in the normal habitat of the species. Eggs of the tree-inhabiting species may be taken on leaves, where they occur generally on the under side, and on the trunks and limbs of the tree. Those lace-wings inhabiting low vegetation lay their eggs on the under-side of leaves (generally), or on the stems.

Larvae may be taken by sweeping and beating. Use a regular beating or sweeping net and examine the contents carefully. Practice is required to see them readily in a mass of net contents. Larvae often occur in or near aphid colonies, in aphid-curled leaves, and under or on the bark of trees infested with aphids, psyllids, some scale insects, and mealybugs.

Cocoons may be collected by pulling off pieces of bark on oak and maple trees, especially during the winter or spring. Cocoons should be placed in large bottles in which there are some twigs or vegetation so the pupae may climb up, shed their pupal molts and spread their wings. Otherwise many reared adults will have crumpled wings.

While chrysopid adults and larvae feed on all kinds of aphids, the smaller green aphids are more satisfactory for feeding than the larger ones. The cabbage aphid (on cabbage and turnip) is one of the easiest of all aphids to maintain as a constant supply for continuous rearing in summer and winter. During the season aphids on Spiraea, apple, dock, shepherd's purse, and the corn-leaf aphid (also on young sugar cane) are wholly satisfactory.

HEMEROBIIDAE AND BEROTHIDAE
(Brown lace-wings)

Collecting and rearing methods described for chrysopids apply almost equally well for hemerobiids (Smith, 1923). Members of these families are more difficult to collect and all stages are generally less plentiful than are chrysopids.

Adults are best collected by sweeping low vegetation and beating the limbs of pines and oaks with a strong insect net. Larvae may be collected in the same way particularly from pines and oaks. Eggs and pupae are very difficult to collect and are discovered usually only when making close observations on aphid-infested branches. Some brown lace-wings are known to overwinter as adults, and so may be collected during the fall and spring.

CONIOPTERYGIDAE

Adults and, less commonly, larvae of the "mealy-winged Neuroptera" have been taken by beating the foliage of pine, apple, and oak trees with a beating net. These insects are difficult to see in a net because of their small size. The net contents must be sorted over carefully. It is well to familiarize oneself with the appearance of these insects by looking at specimens in collections repeatedly or studying pictures before doing much collecting. They occur from midsummer to fall but the writer has never found them plentiful. The females may be confined in small glass vials plugged with cotton. Place in the vial a portion of a leaf with some small aphids, young scale insects, or young mealybugs on it for food. A little moisture is taken by adults also. Eggs may be laid on the leaf or cotton plug. This same food is accepted by the larvae which should be kept in individual vials because of their cannibalistic habits.

MYRMELEONIDAE

The writer has been unable to obtain eggs by confining mid-western ant-lion adults in various kinds of cages. The larvae of the pit-forming species may be collected readily by scooping up the sand pits, with a coarse tea strainer or other strainer, or with a large spoon, being careful to dip below the larvae. Then sift or pour off the sand until the larva is found. When thus disturbed the larvae are difficult to see because they feign death or remain immobile for a time and their color blends perfectly with the sand.

Since many of the ant-lions are known to overwinter as larvae, they may be collected in the late summer or fall and allowed to form pits in pans of sand. When half grown or larger they will survive several weeks to four or five months without food. The pans of sand may be kept in a greenhouse and the larvae fed on sow bugs which abound under pots or in other places in greenhouses. Any kind of insect is accepted unless too large or active to be subdued by the larvae.

The overwintering ant-lions complete their development in the spring and spin their cocoons during May, June, and July (Smith, 1934). Large, nearly grown larvae may be collected in the spring and raised with little effort. The writer has used a self-feeding device with fair results. A small receptacle filled with a sugar solution or diluted molasses is set on the sand in the pan. Some of the solution is poured around the pan and on the sides of the pan to attract ants. Eventually they come and, in attempting to reach the syrup receptacle among the pits, many of the ants drop into the pits. Usually it is necessary to supplement this method with other feeding, however.

The non-pit-forming species may be collected under stones, sticks, and sometimes under loose soil or dust (Wheeler, 1930). Since there is little or no external evidence of their presence, their discovery is largely accidental. The writer has been unsuccessful in rearing mid-western non-pit-forming ant-lions.

Cocoons of ant-lions should be placed in some sort of cage provided with vegetation upon which the emerging adults may cling to shed the pupal molts and spread their wings. Unless this is done a large percentage of reared adults will be imperfect.

MANTISPIDAE

Eggs have been obtained on several occasions by the hundreds and even thousands by confining gravid mantispid females in bottles and jars. The eggs were laid on the cloth tops or, less commonly, on vegetation and sides of the bottles. The young larvae have refused to eat any insects offered or to enter spider egg sacs. The writer has never reared these insects to adults. The mantispid adults eat small insects readily in confinement and live for a week or two.

Pupae and cocoons have been taken in the nests of a spider (*Philaeus militaris*) during October (Smith, 1934). No doubt they might be taken during the early spring in spider egg sacs and nests on shrubs, weeds, and under stones up to early May in the mid-west. The adults are ordinarily first taken in May.

ASCALAPHIDAE

The writer has been unable to rear from egg to adult this uncommon group of Neuroptera. Eggs are sometimes deposited by adults in almost any kind of container (Smith, 1931). They are unstalked and adhere to the substratum. They hatch readily enough, but the young larvae have so far refused to feed.

Larvae of this group have been collected by sweeping grass and other vegetation. They live on the leaves largely exposed and sometimes almost in colonies. If one is swept up, the search for others should be continued. The writer has attempted to rear them through by placing them on aphid-infested plants but without success.

Larvae of other species are found sometimes in digging in loose soil or in examining dust layers. Since they do not form pits there is no readily perceived evidence of their presence, and their discovery has been largely accidental.

SIALIDAE

Adults of Corydalis have been reared by bringing in nearly grown larvae and placing in an aquarium in which one end is water and the other soil. The larvae migrate to the moist soil when fully grown, form a pupal cell, and emerge usually in May or June in the mid-west.

Egg masses of Corydalis are readily recognized as white blotches on trees, foliage, rocks, and bridges over water. They hatch normally in the laboratory but the writer has never attempted to rear them. They have a three year life cycle and are aquatic carnivores which would require an elaborate equipment for normal living conditions.

BIBLIOGRAPHY*

ANTHONY, MAUD H. 1902. Metamorphosis of Sisyra. *Amer. Nat.* 36:615.

BRISTOWE, W. S. 1932. Mantispa, a spider parasite. *Ent. Mo. Mag.* 18:222.

BRAUR, F. 1851. Verwandluggsgeschichte des *Osmylus maculatus. Weigm. Archiv.* 17:255.

KILLINGTON, F. J. 1934. On the life histories of some British Neuroptera. *Trans. Soc. Brit. Ent.* 1:119.

——— 1932. The life history of *Hemerobius atrifrons* McLach. *The Entomologist* 65:201.

——— 1932. The life history of *Hemerobius simulans* Walk. *Ent. Mo. Mag.* 18:176.

——— 1932. Notes on the life history of *Hemerobius pini. Trans. Ent. Soc. South Eng.* 8:41.

HAGEN, H. A. 1852. Die Entwicklung und der inners Bau von Osmylus. *Linn. Entomol.* 368-418.

HUNGERFORD, H. B. 1931. Concerning the egg of *Polystoechotes punctatus* Fabr. *Bull. Brooklyn Ent. Soc.* 26:22.

MOZNETTE, GEO. E. 1915. Notes on the brown lace-wing. *J. Econ. Ent.* 8:350.

*Writings on Neuroptera in which some reference is made to rearings.

SMITH, ROGER C. 1917. The Chrysopas or Golden Eyes. *Nat. Study Rev.* 6:261.

———— 1920. The process of hatching in *Corydalis cornuta* Linn. *Ann. Ent. Soc. Amer.* 13:70.

———— 1922. Hatching in three species of Neuroptera. *Ibid.* 15:169.

———— 1922. The Biology of the Chrysopidae. Cornell Univ. Agric. Exper. Sta. Mem. 58:1291.

———— 1923. The life histories and stages of some hemerobiids and allied species. *Ibid.* 16:129.

———— 1926. The life history of *Eremochrysa punctinervis* (Nerr.). *Bull. Brooklyn Ent. Soc.* 21:48.

———— 1926. The trash-carrying habit of certain lace-wing larvae. *Sci. Mo.* 23:265.

———— 1931. The Neuroptera of Haiti, West Indies. *Ann. Ent. Soc. Amer.* 45:798.

———— 1934. Notes on the Neuroptera and Mecoptera of Kansas with keys for the identification of species. *J. Kans. Ent. Soc.* 7:120.

TOWNSEND, LEE H. 1935. Key to the larvae of certain families and genera of Nearctic Neuroptera. *Proc. Ent. Soc. Wash.* 37:25.

WELCH, PAUL S. 1914. The early stages of the life history of *Polystoechotes punctatus* Fabr. *Bull. Brooklyn Ent. Soc.* 9:1.

WHEELER, W. M. Demons of the Dust, A Study in Insect Behavior. N. Y. 1930.

WITHYCOMBE, C. L. 1922. Notes on the biology of some British Neuroptera. *Trans. Ent. Soc. London*, p. 303.

———— 1924. Note on the economic value of the Neuroptera with special reference to the Coniopterygidae. *Ann. Appl. Biol.* 11:112.

Order MECOPTERA

BITTACUS

LAUREL R. SETTY, *Park College, Parkville, Missouri*

Method of Collecting. An insect net is not a satisfactory instrument to use in collecting adult hanging-flies (Bittacus) which are to be used for experimental purposes. These long-legged, soft-bodied insects ordinarily fly among weeds and grasses. Many individuals are injured by sweeping the foliage or on being removed from the net.

The instrument which I have frequently employed is a very large lamp chimney, the top end of which is closed with a piece of cheesecloth held in place by a rubber band. By holding the lamp chimney at the elongated, closed end, the large basal opening may be quickly thrust over the insect as it hangs quietly from some support. Then, after making a successful grab in this fashion, one may hold the palm of his hand over the opening and carry the fly to a prison box.

A convenient box to take into the field for holding the flies that are collected is one made of wood, about 18″ x 16″ x 12″, and provided with several fresh twigs of some woody or semi-woody plant to serve as supports for the insects. The box should have a closable opening about the size of the base of the lamp chimney. When the opening of the chimney is placed against that of the box, the hanging-fly will drop into the container.

Not more than twenty or thirty specimens should be placed at one time in a prison box of this size, for there is danger that the flies will entangle their long legs with those of the other flies.

Individual Cages. The ordinary Mason glass fruit jar was found to be a very satisfactory cage for an individual or a single pair of hanging-flies. The jar must be furnished with a twig of buck-brush, or of some other woody plant, to serve as a support from which the insect may suspend itself. The opening may be closed with a small piece of cheese-cloth fastened in place by a rubber band. All jars should be kept in a shady part of the laboratory and preferably upon the floor or upon low stools, in order to make conditions as nearly natural as possible.

Such cages I have found advantageous for the following reasons: (1) they are convenient to handle; (2) the hanging-flies seem satisfied in this sort of a cage; (3) the insects may easily be transferred from one jar to another; (4) the eggs may be collected readily by inverting the jar; and (5) small flies and other insects placed in the jar for food cannot escape.

Care of the Immature Stages. The most convenient containers for keeping the hanging-fly eggs are small or medium sized clay flower pot saucers lined with moist, white cellu-cotton over each of which the flower pot itself is inverted. By adding a small amount of water each day to the cellu-cotton, the eggs may be kept moist.

After hatching, each larva should be transferred to a similar container, that differs only in having a little pile of about a tablespoonful of rich garden soil upon the cellu-cotton. Moisture and tiny pieces of beef steak must be provided daily on the cellu-cotton near the soil.

When the larvae enter the soil to pupate, less moisture should be provided, but by no means should the soil be allowed to dry out.

Order TRICHOPTERA

ON REARING TRIAENODES*

CADDISWORMS of this genus are common in beds of the water-weed Elodea. They swim freely about, carrying their slender, spirally-wound cases with them. They eat plant tissues, especially Elodea, and are easily maintained in aquaria, even in tap water, and at all seasons. When grown they attach their cases lengthwise to the stems or to other solid support for pupation. The pupal stage lasts 7 to 12 days. When ready for final transformation the pupa leaves its

---

* Abstracted from a thesis by Wynne E. Caird in the Cornell University Library.

case and swims to the surface of the water. It often meets with difficulty in breaking through the surface film, and may, after a brief struggle, fall exhausted to the bottom.

The slender, straw-yellow adults may be placed on emergence in an aquarium cage having a celluloid window for observation in one side of the wirecloth top, and a sleeve for ingress and egress at the other (see figure 61 on page 268). They cling immobile to the sides and the top of the cage during the day, and run about the walls in the early evening, rarely flying.

J. G. N.

Order LEPIDOPTERA

A METHOD OF COLLECTING LIVING MOTHS
AT SUGAR BAIT*

IN COLLECTING adults of the army worm and other moths for oviposition studies, a simple method of capture at baits was found useful. [See also p. 364.] An electric flashlight, having a flat lens, was used with a flat-bottomed vial ¾ inch in diameter, straight-sided and about 5 inches deep. When the bottom of the vial is placed against the lens of the flashlight both may be firmly grasped in the right hand. The encircling fingers prevent the spread of light rays to the sides while full illumination is given in a narrow beam through the bottom of the vial. When this is placed over or close to a moth feeding at bait, the tendency of the moth is to dash towards the light. Entering the vial, it goes at once to the bottom and does not try to escape. The vial may be closed with a cork or the moth may be examined before the vial is closed and, if not wanted, it may be allowed to escape by moving the vial from the light. A number of vials may be carried in a coat pocket and a number of individual moths collected in a short time. In the closed vial the moths remain quiet for a number of hours and may be removed to breeding cages.

The same method was found useful in collecting the large and shy Catocala moths. A wide-mouthed bottle was used in this case, the flashlight directed through the bottle, and chloroform or cyanide placed in holes in the cork. [See also p. 364.]

REFERENCE

Family Eucleidae
  For rearing see p. 365.

*Reprinted, with slight changes, from *Canad. Ent.* 60:103, 1928, by R. P. GORHAM, *Dominion Ent. Lab.,* Fredericton, N. B.

Family TINEIDAE

A METHOD FOR BREEDING CLOTHES MOTHS
ON FISH MEAL

GRACE H. GRISWOLD, *Cornell University*

WHERE large numbers of clothes moths are used for testing various methods of control, it is often difficult to keep on hand a supply sufficiently large to meet all needs. With fish meal as the sole food supply, an efficient method for rearing them has been devised at the Cornell Insectary.

The meal which has been found so satisfactory is "white fish meal" and is manufactured by the Dehydrating Process Company, Boston, Massachusetts.

Cylindrical cardboard cartons, such as are used for packing butter and cheese, make good rearing cages. The gallon-sized carton is about 7 inches high and 6¾ inches in diameter. The cartons are inexpensive, and, since they may be stacked upon shelves, they occupy very little space.

In the center of a large square of cloth (about 22 by 22 inches) is pasted a circular piece of heavy cardboard, slightly smaller than the bottom of the carton. The cloth is placed in the container so that the cardboard rests on the bottom. A layer of fish meal, about half an inch thick, is spread evenly over the circle of cardboard. The cloth is then folded back against the sides of the carton and the cover is put on. Adults are admitted to the container through a small opening cut in the cover. This opening is closed on the outside with a piece of cheesecloth secured by a little paste. To infest a new container it is only necessary to catch a few adults in small vials and drop them into the opening in the cover of the carton. The females have easy access to the fish meal and will lay quantities of eggs. At temperatures similar to those of an ordinary living room, adults will begin to emerge within about two months after a container has been infested.

When one wishes a supply of larvae, the carton may be opened and the square of cloth carefully lifted out. In this way the entire contents of the carton may be removed without disturbing the layer of fish meal, which rests on the circle of cardboard in the center of the cloth. Larvae will be found crawling all over the cloth and may be removed with the aid of a camel's hair brush. If the cloth is black, the white bodies of the larvae stand out clearly.

Since adults shun the light, they will be found hiding in the folds of the cloth where they are easy to catch. Some, of course, will escape when the carton is opened. To obviate this, one may have a second piece of dark cloth ready and throw it over the carton as soon as the cover is removed. Adults will hide in the folds of this second cloth as well as in those of the cloth already in the carton. If the folds of the two cloths are turned back slowly and carefully, a number of adults may be caught in a few minutes.

It has been found that larvae are more easily removed from small containers than from large ones. The half-pint size, commonly used at stores for cottage cheese and ice cream, is just about right for this purpose. Several pieces of flannel, on which eggs have been laid, are placed in one of these small containers, each piece of flannel being sprinkled lightly with fish meal. The larvae get enough to eat but cannot bury themselves in a thick layer of meal such as is put in the large containers. By using a number of these small containers, one can keep on hand a supply of larvae of any age desired.

Adults are difficult to catch in the small containers, since they have no place in which to hide and can so easily escape. For rearing adults it is advisable to use the gallon size and black cloth. Hence at Ithaca both the large and small containers are in constant use.

In the summer of 1933 some of our containers became infested with predacious mites. Although the point was never proved, mites were probably carried from old containers to new ones on the bodies of adult moths. It therefore appeared advisable to start new colonies with eggs instead of with adults.

To get a supply of eggs, moths are placed in a glass jar or vial with pieces of flannel. Each day fresh flannel is put in and the pieces on which eggs have been laid are removed. If the flannel is cut into squares, about 3 x 3 inches, the pieces are easy to examine under a binocular microscope, and any mites present may be removed. The gallon cardboard containers are prepared as explained above. After examination under a binocular, the pieces of flannel, on which the eggs have been laid, are placed on the layer of fish meal in the bottom of the container. Each piece of flannel is sprinkled lightly with some of the fish meal before another piece is added. Since this method of starting new colonies was adopted, no further trouble with mites has been experienced.

By this method literally hundreds of clothes moths may be reared in a very small space. At the Cornell Insectary, one or two large cartons and several small ones are infested each month, in order to insure an adequate supply of insects for all needs that may arise. Just how long an infestation will keep itself going, has not yet been determined. If a little fresh fish meal is occasionally added to each container, it seems probable that the various colonies will maintain themselves for a considerable period of time.

Although the method was developed for breeding the webbing clothes moth (*Tineola biselliella*), the case-making species (*Tinea pellionella*) may be reared satisfactorily in a similar manner.

Family GELECHIIDAE

THE GOLDENROD GALL-MAKER, GNORIMOSCHEMA GALLAESOLIDAGINIS*

THE writer has never encountered any difficulty in securing eggs from adults of *G. gallaesolidaginis* in the fall. Moths have been caged time after time with living goldenrod stems in glass cylinders with cheesecloth top, and in large outdoor cages 5 x 5 x 4 feet in size built over clumps of goldenrod. In this way thousands of eggs have been secured.

Female moths begin to deposit eggs within 4 or 5 days after emergence when they have been previously confined with males. The eggs are placed on both surfaces of a leaf, but usually on the under side and preferably on one that is dried, and on the stems among the hairs.

Moths have been observed to partake of nourishment in the form of sweetened water when placed in indoor cages. It may be this factor which causes females to deposit a greater average number of eggs in indoor cages than under the semi-natural conditions of outdoor cages.

The first determination of the time of hatching of the eggs followed the failure in three successive winters of attempts to keep them through the winter under semi-natural conditions. During the fourth winter of experiment, eggs deposited regularly on dried leaves and stems of goldenrod in the fall were carried through by placing these leaves and parts of stems in small shell vials stoppered loosely at both ends with cotton; the vials were in turn placed in larger vials similarly stoppered. This method solved the problem of continued excessive moisture previously encountered. The eggs hatched normally, the larvae producing galls which were found on the new goldenrod shoots at the same time that the galls of a similar size were present in the field.

M. E. D.

MASS PRODUCTION OF SITOTROGA CEREALELLA

STANLEY E. FLANDERS, *University of California*

AMONG the Lepidoptera, those that feed on stored products are most readily reared. The grain moth, *Sitotroga cerealella*, is the most adaptable for continuous reproduction in large numbers. This is largely due to certain habits and tropisms that permit efficient mechanical manipulation of the species. Also Sitotroga appears to have a much

*From an article in *J. N. Y. Ent. Soc.* 30:81, 1935, by R. W. LEIBY, *North Carolina State Department of Agriculture.*

greater immunity to disease epidemics than any other species of grain moth.

Sitotroga feeds on a number of different grains, among which are wheat, corn, and oats. The dry kernels are used in bulk for rearing purposes. The hygroscopic moisture within the kernels should not be below 8%. During the feeding and pupal stages, the insect occupies the interior of the individual kernels so that the interspaces between the kernels are not clogged with excreta or webbing. The newly emerged adult moths, therefore, always have free egress from the mass of grain. Upon emergence from the kernels the moths worm their way upward and outward until they reach a space of sufficient size to permit their wings to expand and mating to take place.

By day the moths tend to climb upward and come to rest in positions of positive thigmotropism and negative phototropism. By night they become active and oviposit in crevices about 0.23 mm. in width. The newly hatched larvae are negatively phototropic and positively geotropic, so that they readily permeate a mass of grain. If the moths are collected daily, few, if any, deposit their full quota of eggs or die within the production unit.

The type of unit used depends to some extent on the rearing medium and the size of the grain used. Small kernels yield smaller moths than do large kernels, and the smaller moths deposit fewer eggs. Moths reared in corn deposit over three times as many eggs per moth as those reared in wheat. On the other hand, given equal weights of grain, the rapidity with which the grain is utilized varies inversely with the size of the kernels; so that a much greater number of moths is obtained in a shorter period of time with wheat than with corn. This is due to the fact that a kernel of grain, irrespective of its size, is usually inhabited by only one larva at a time.

Laboratories producing for seasonal field requirements find that soft varieties of wheat form the most satisfactory rearing media. In experimental work where a uniformly non-seasonal supply of moths is needed, without the necessity of frequently replenishing the food, soft varieties of corn are used.

The "tilted bin" type of production unit adapted particularly for holding corn, has been developed by the University of California. A "vertical bin" type of unit for holding wheat was developed by the U. S. Bureau of Entomology.

Of these two types of production units, the "tilted bin" type (Fig. 66) is the simplest in construction but is not as readily refilled as the "vertical bin" type; therefore it is only well adapted for use with a slow productive medium such as corn. Essentially it consists of a series of similar shallow trays (36″ x 26″ x 3″) placed one on the other and topped with a cover. It rests on a base frame so constructed that the trays are tilted to an angle of 22.5° to the horizontal. The slope thus formed is slightly less than the "angle of flow" of corn when piled in a loose heap. It is sufficient, however, to direct the egress of the moths from the trays, and to provide good ventilation.

The floor and two sides of each tray should be made of material of sufficient strength so that when the tray is filled the bottom will not sag, and when stacked each tray will support the entire weight of the trays above.

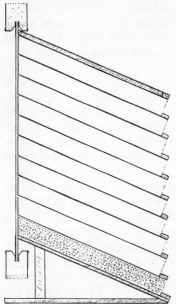

The upper end of each tray should be at least $\frac{3}{16}$ inch below the top edge of the other three sides, in order to provide exit for the moths. The lower end should be formed of 30-mesh copper screening for ventilation. Across the top of the tray and flush with the rear end is firmly fastened a wooden "stop," 2 inches wide, in order to hold each tray and the top cover in position. The upper ends of the trays should be formed so that when the trays are stacked in place they form a flat, vertical wall.

In setting up a unit, each tray is filled with corn before adding the next tray. Care should be taken to make the top surface of the corn even with the top edge of the upper end and parallel with the bottom of the tray above, thus leaving a space of $\frac{3}{16}$ inch in height over the entire surface of the corn.

FIG. 66.—Diagrammatic cross section through the center of the "tilted bin" type of production unit.

When the unit is filled and the cover in place, a strongly woven cloth is loosely draped over the vertical front of the stack and fastened on top and at the sides with felt-lined batten placed flush with the front surface. The lower edge is fastened to a flange of the collecting tube extending along the entire front below the bottom tray.

The tube is made of sheet iron, $1\frac{1}{4}$ inches in diameter, with flanges $2\frac{1}{2}$ inches in width, which diverge outward from a slot $\frac{3}{16}$ inch wide extending along the top side of the tube for the width of the trays. The tube is held in position by the inner flange, which is inserted between the base and the bottom tray. It is placed so that the inner side of the slot is flush with the upper end of the bottom tray. Attached to the outer flange by small bolts and winged nuts is a rigid wooden bar. The cloth is fastened against this by the pressure of the bar against the flange. The cloth then forms an enclosure with the front of the stack within which the moths collect.

The collecting tube extends several inches beyond each side of the stack. One end is plugged with a cork and the other connects with a tube extending through the cover of the moth trap. This trap consists of a Royal electric hairdryer fastened permanently to the cover of a gallon mayonnaise jar. The air intake opening of the dryer is connected by a short right-angle tube to an aperture in the cover containing a 30-mesh copper screen to retain the moths in the jar. When the jar is screwed onto the cap it completes an air suction circuit between the hairdryer fan and the moth enclosure.

The moths are collected in a few seconds by starting the fan and shaking the cloth to dislodge the moths accumulated on it and on the front of the stack. This is possible because the moths when suddenly disturbed habitually drop down and slide through the slot at the bottom. The air suction carries them into the jar without injury. Moths that remain in the tube are pushed through with a bottle brush inserted through the opposite end.

In setting up a production unit it is necessary to use a pure culture of Sitotroga. Contamination by other grain insects or by enemies of Sitotroga, such as the mite *Pediculoides ventricosus* and the chalcid *Habrocytus cerealellae,* must be avoided in order to insure continuous and economical production. This may be accomplished by using clean rooms and by sterilizing equipment and grain with carbon bisulfide in a vacuum fumigator. The grain should not be inoculated with Sitotroga until the fumigant has dissipated and the proper hygroscopic moisture has been reached through holding the grain at 70% relative humidity for several days. Then it should be well infested with a pure culture of eggs. This may be done while the grain is in the sacks. If the units are to be operated continuously they should be refilled with infested grain that has produced one or more generations of moths. At a temperature of 80° to 85° F., the period from egg to adult is from 25 to 30 days.

The "vertical bin" unit (illus. in Peterson, 1934) consists of a series of narrow trays of 12-mesh wire (24″ x 12″ x ½″) open at the top and suspended in a row in a metal box about 30 inches square having sides of 60-mesh copper screen. Six-inch holes in the top provide openings for the moths to enter the traps placed above each hole. These traps consist of coffee tins with inverted funnels soldered to the rims of the screw tops. The percentage of moths collected through such "geotropic" traps used with this type of unit is probably less than in the suction trap used with the "tilted bin" type.

The geotropic method of collecting the moths may also be used with the "tilted bin" unit (Fig. 66). Instead of hanging loosely, the cloth across the front of the stacked trays should be stretched taut and fastened securely about ¼ inch away from the trays. The enclosure thus formed should open at the top and at the bottom into sheet iron funnels. The base of each funnel should be ¼ inch wide and as long as the width of the stack, and the small end of each funnel should fit into the opening of the moth trays.

The temperature and humidity in the rooms housing the production units should be regulated so that the air surrounding the kernels in the mass of grain will range in temperature between 75° and 85° F., and in humidity between 60% and 70%. Such humidities provide optimum hygroscopic moisture for the development of the insect larvae, and the temperatures mentioned result in the most rapid succession of generations.

The activity of the larvae themselves is a source of heat that raises the temperature of the grain mass higher than the surrounding air (heat of infestation). If the grain is not permitted to heat as a result of excessive moisture (heat of respiration) the status of the infestation may be roughly gauged by taking the temperature of the mass. The temperature of the room housing the production units should be comparatively low.

REFERENCE

For the culture of the Angoumois grain moth see also p. 497.

BIBLIOGRAPHY*

BAILEY, C. H. 1921. Respiration of shelled corn. *Univ. Minn. Agric. Exper. Sta. Tech. Bull.* 3.

FLANDERS, S. E. 1927. Biological control of the codling moth. *J. Econ. Ent.* 20:644.

—— 1929. The mass production of *Trichogramma minutum* Riley and observations on the natural and artificial parasitism of the codling moth eggs. *Trans. Fourth Inter. Congress Ent.* 2:110.

—— 1934. Sitotroga production. *J. Econ. Ent.* 27:1197.

PETERSON, ALVAH. 1934. A Manual of Entomological Equipment and Methods. Part I, plate 137, fig. 1-4.

SCHREAD, J. C., and GARMAN, P. 1933. Studies on parasites of the Oriental fruit moth. *Conn. Agric. Exper. Sta. Bull.* 353:691.

SIMMONS, P., and ELLINGTON, J. W. 1932. A biography of the Angoumois grain moth. *Ann. Ent. Soc. Amer.* 25:265.

Post script: Since the completion of this Compendium there has appeared Circular No. 376, U. S. Department of Agriculture: New Equipment for Obtaining Host Material for the Mass Production of *Trichogramma minutum*, an Egg Parasite of Various Insect Pests, by Herbert Spencer, Luther Brown, and Arthur M. Phillips, all of the *U. S. Bureau of Entomology and Plant Quarantine.*

SITOTROGA EGG PRODUCTION

STANLEY E. FLANDERS, *University of California*

IT is estimated that the moths produced from one pound of corn will deposit about 40,000 eggs, while those produced from an equal weight of wheat will yield about 80,000 eggs under mass production conditions.

The moths will oviposit in almost any narrow crevice, such as found between strips of paper fastened together by clips or between the bodies of the moths themselves in crowded containers. Almost any type of container may be used, provided it is small enough to cause the moths to crowd together. The cover should consist of a 20-mesh screen if moths are from corn, or a 30-mesh screen if from wheat. They deposit most of their eggs within 72 hours after emerging from the grain if held at a temperature of 80° F. and relative humidity of 70%. At the end of this period the moths should be vigorously stirred and shaken to dislodge any eggs adhering to them. The eggs are then sifted out through the screened cover and winnowed to free them from moth scales and debris. The finest of the scale dust may be eliminated by keeping the moth container inverted over a trough in a constant current of air.

By this method loose eggs are obtained. They are then evenly spread in a single layer over cards of uniform size thinly coated with shellac. This affords a fairly accurate means of measuring production. The chorion of the egg is relatively tough so that they may be handled in mass as readily as grains of rice. At 80° F. the moth larvae hatch in about 5 days.

BIBLIOGRAPHY

FLANDERS, S. E. 1928. Developments in Trichogramma production. *J. Econ. Ent.* 21:512.

———— 1930. Mass production of egg parasites of the genus Trichogramma. *Hilgardia* 4:465.

Family TORTRICIDAE

NOTES ON BREEDING THE ORIENTAL FRUIT MOTH, GRAPHOLITHA MOLESTA

W. T. BRIGHAM, *Connecticut Agricultural Experiment Station*

THE present need of large numbers of larvae of the Oriental fruit moth for mass production of parasites has led to the adoption of the following procedure in breeding at the Connecticut Agricultural Experiment Station.

The original moths were obtained from infested twigs collected from orchards during the first and second broods. Infested terminal twigs are easily observed due to their wilting. Clip these twigs to a length of 3 to 4 inches, stripping off the leaves to prevent overheating when put in bags for convenient carrying. Upon completion of collections and arrival at the laboratory, the twigs are spread on pans of 1½-inch green apples so that larvae emerging from the drying twigs may have sufficient food for normal development. Pans used are galvanized refrigerator pans, 15 inches in diameter, placed in an incubator regulated for 80° F. and 50% relative humidity. Twigs are removed after three days and corrugated paper strips, ½ inch in width, are fastened around the pan tops by means of metal strips doubled to form a V, one end being longer and bent over the pan lip to hold it in place. Unbleached muslin covers are tied over the pans to prevent mature larvae from crawling away, as not all find openings in the strips. As soon as the larvae begin spinning, the corrugated strips are removed every other day or, at times, daily, and new strips substituted. Strips containing the spun larvae are treated in two ways. Those for immediate emergence are placed in refrigerator pans, covered with muslin and kept in the emergence cage. The others are clipped into jelly jars and held at a temperature below 45° F.

An emergence cage may be constructed by making a framework of two by fours with a door hung at one side. Shelves are built along the side to hold the refrigerator pans and a bench for working. The frame is enclosed with black cambric except for one end (covered with white cheesecloth), which faces the room windows. A temperature of 75° to 80° F. and a humidity of about 50% is maintained by means of air conditioning apparatus. After about 6 days from date of spinning moth emergence starts and the pans are left open, allowing the moths to fly directly to the white screen. Covering the pans is an emergency measure, as parasites attacking the moths in the prepupal stage may become numerous.

The moths, being phototropic, are easily collected from the white screen by means of a suction apparatus. An ordinary hand hair dryer with the heating unit removed is used for creating a suction sufficient to draw the moths from the screen into the prepared containers. The containers used are ordinary pint Fonda cartons with a 1-inch hole cut in the bottom and stopped up by a cork covered with cheesecloth. The top is partly cut away, leaving just the outer ring and a narrow section to help stiffen the cover on its being replaced. A section of cheesecloth placed over the carton and the cover forced back in place makes a tight container with plenty of ventilation. The cheesecloth may be dampened to aid in preserving the confined moths. A ring of cardboard slightly larger than the pint containers mentioned is fastened to the side of the hair dryer where the air is sucked in. Elastic bands with clips attached hold the Fonda carton in place on the dryer, and a cork bored with a ½-inch hole in which is inserted a 2-inch length of glass tubing is substituted for the cloth-covered cork. By using a rheostat to regulate the speed of suction, moth collection is quickly and easily carried out. As many as 400 moths may be caught in one carton if transfer to the oviposition cages is made immediately.

The oviposition cage found most effective is a 15″ by 16″ by 28″ frame covered with cheesecloth. The cloth should be on the inside of the frame, as the moths will deposit eggs on the smooth frame surface. Temperatures should be maintained at 80°-85° F. This cage is placed on damp sand directly below a window of a celotex incubator in the greenhouse. A strip of turkish toweling with one end immersed in a pan of water, the other end lying on the top of the cage, furnishes moisture for the moths. Egg laying begins in 2 days, reaching a peak at 6 days. Peach seedlings grown from pits, or seedlings obtained from orchardists and grown in the greenhouse in 5-inch pots are used for egg deposition. The pots are introduced and removed daily. The leaves are stripped from the plants and estimates of egg depositions kept. In exposing the pots the leaves should rest against the top or sides of the cage, as a much larger egg production results when the moths crawl about from the cloth of the cage to the leaves for oviposition. A temperature of 80° to 85° F. and humidity of 50 to 60% should be maintained at dusk when maximum egg deposition takes place.

The leaves on which the eggs have been deposited are placed in jelly jars or may be refrigerated at 50° F. for 2 weeks without reducing below 80% the number of eggs hatching. Usually the jars are placed directly in an incubator, temperature 80° F., relative humidity 50%. After 3 days the eggs appear to be black-spotted because of development of the embryos. At this time they are removed from the jelly jars and spread out upon green apples in refrigerator pans. Approximately 4,000 eggs are used for each pan of about 70 apples. To facilitate entrance to the apples, punctures are made in the apples or they may be sliced, as described later. It has been found that a larger number of larvae tunnel into the fruit after the tough outer skin has been broken and a depression, into which larvae may crawl, made available. A 6-inch knife with a thin flexible blade is used in cutting the apples into slices of ¼-inch thickness. The apples are not cut all the way through, so that the slices stay in place. The green apples used are 1½ to 2 inches in diameter, gathered when orchardists are thinning, and placed in cold storage for use at any season of the year.

As the larvae develop it is necessary to divide the apples into two pans and add a fresh supply of green apples to make sure sufficient food is available for normal growth. Corrugated strips are fastened around the edge of the pans and held by clips as described earlier. These strips are removed and handled like the original stock.

Another method of augmenting the stock of moths in the fall is by the use of infested quinces placed in butter tubs prepared for their reception. Three or four ¾-inch holes are bored in the bottom of the tubs and covered with a fine mesh wire screen. This aids in ventilating and delays fruit rot. Two inches below the tub rim two rows of corrugated paper strips are tacked completely encircling the sides. The tubs are half-filled with infested quinces, and muslin covers tied over the top. The fruit moth larvae, upon completing development, leave the fruit and spin in the corrugated paper. The strips must be removed when filled with larvae and new strips tacked in place. These tubs are left in the insectary and the spun larvae allowed to remain in covered refrigerator pans where hibernation takes place as a normal procedure, due to low temperatures. Hibernation may be broken by the end of December, the spun larvae being placed in a refrigerator at 55° F. for about 3 weeks and then brought out into the emergence cage. A gradual change in temperature is found better than a sudden change.

There are numerous pitfalls along the path of fruit moth breeding. Ants and spiders in the greenhouse oviposition cages and spiders in the dark emergence cage may cause trouble. Parasites may develop unless pans are kept covered, *Dibrachys boucheanus* being especially troublesome at Connecticut for two years. There is need in the fall to control temperatures since at that time larval hibernating tendencies increase and temperatures fluctuating below 60° F. may cause hibernation of developing larvae. Once hibernation has started, we have been unsuccessful in breaking it until after approximately two months have elapsed. Oviposition-cage temperatures at dusk are very important if a fair ratio of increase in numbers is to be maintained.

Fruit rot is another difficulty causing serious losses of larvae. Apples from different sources rot differently; that is, some will produce a wet slimy mass which apparently drowns the larvae before they can escape to other fruit or reach maturity. Other apples rot with less moisture, becoming pithy or corky, allowing the larvae to escape when the fruit becomes unsuitable for food. Green Baldwins are plentiful in Connecticut, keep well in storage, and are used by us almost exclusively. Other varieties, however, may be employed.

In refrigeration of spun larvae or eggs, it is necessary to guard against the loss of moisture which may prevent transformation of the larvae and hatching of the eggs.

Maintenance of seedlings for use in the oviposition cages requires a certain amount of thought. By use of fertilizers and cleaning off any eggs laid upon the stems of the seedlings, these plants may be used at least twice. In summer small branches are clipped from peach trees and placed in vials of water. These remain fresh long enough for exposure to the moths. Forsythia and privet are also used, the moths laying on the leaves of such shrubs nearly as well as those of peaches. Lilac, pear leaves, and probably others, may be used successfully.

Careful adherence to the above methods of breeding has led to successful year around production of the Oriental fruit moth in Connecticut. The numbers which may be reared are apparently only restricted by the amount of space, time, material, and labor available.

Our average ratio of increase is 17 to 1, although in some cases 30 to 1 may be obtained. The sex ratio is about 50% each, males and females. Maximum production was reached during the month of August 1934, when 376,000 fruit moth eggs were obtained.

REFERENCE

For the culture of *Harmologa fumiferana* see p. 488.

Family PYRALIDAE

BREEDING METHODS FOR GALLERIA MELLONELLA

T. L. SMITH, *College of the Ozarks, Clarksville, Arkansas*

The Wax Moth, *Galleria mellonella*, is found wherever bees are cultured. The adults never eat; the larvae feed only on honeyless bee combs, preferably the old brood combs. To the apiarist, it is a very potent pest and quickly destroys his weaker colonies. Throughout the larval stage during which there are eight instars with their terminating ecdyses, food is consumed in great quantities. The larvae also spin silken threads from the time they hatch to the time of pupation. During the last few days of their larval life each larva spins about itself a compact silken cocoon. The duration of the larval stage is about 35 days, the pupal stage 12 to 14 days, and the adult stage about 10 days at ordinary room temperature. Mating ordinarily occurs the first day after eclosion. The females lay from 200 to 1,000 eggs or more.

The adults show a distinct sexual dimorphism. The male is generally lighter in color than the female and the posterior edges of the fore wings are notched at their ends while the ends of the wings of the female are almost straight. The antennae of the male are 10% to 20% shorter than those of the female. In the male the labial palps are hooked inward while those of the female protrude forward and slightly upward giving a pointed or beak-like appearance to the front end of the head. The female has a distinctly long ovipositor which is almost prehensile in its use for seeking out places for oviposition. The eggs are whitish in color and generally spherical or slightly ovoid and are deposited in any available niche or corner in the comb. About 9 to 10 days are required for the eggs to hatch. The newly hatched larvae are very small—about 1 mm. in length and perhaps $\frac{1}{10}$ mm. in diameter. The young larvae begin to eat and to spin their webs immediately after hatching. They have a tendency to congregate into a rather compact colony, and in this colony they often have the power of raising their temperature some 10° to 15° C. above that of the environment.

For culturing purposes, the regular milk bottle used for Drosophila has been found very adaptable. Instead of using the cotton plugs (which will not retain the larvae), the regular waxed cardboard milk bottle tops with attached lifters have been found preferable. These fit the top of the bottle very tightly and serve to prevent the young larvae, which crawl up the sides of the bottles, from crawling out and leaving the culture. Since mating may occur within a few hours after eclosion, it is necessary to isolate the female pupae before eclosion if virgin females are desired for mating purposes. This may be done very readily by careful observation of the pupa cases. The wing and antennal distinctions of the adults may be detected, by close observation, in the portions of the pupa case which cover these respective parts of the adult. By this means it is possible to segregate males and females before eclosion. It is not safe at any time to regard a female as virgin if it is found that a male is also present in the culture bottle. However, a newly hatched moth always has a tuft of loose, fluffy hair-like scales on its head and if these are present, it is a fairly safe indication of the moth's virginity.

The young larvae upon hatching start eating the portion of the comb known as the "midrib," which is the sheet of wax at the base of the cells. They bury themselves in the wax and throw out piles of masticated wax at the surface. This is a sure indication of their presence in the combs. Since offspring of a given female are fairly numerous, it becomes necessary, as the larvae grow older, to segregate portions of the colony into subculture bottles; for instance, if a colony has 300 larvae present, after they are about 2 weeks old, it is better to divide them into cultures of about 40 or 50 larvae each. Also at this stage, it becomes necessary to arrange an aerating device for the culture bottles. For this purpose a special ventilator cap has been devised. It consists of two regular milk bottle caps with a $1\frac{5}{8}$ or $1\frac{3}{4}$ inch hole cut through the center of each. Then a piece of 40-mesh copper wire screening cut to about the same size as the cap itself is inserted between the two perforated caps and these layers are stitched together with some wire stapling device.* This special aerating cap permits free circulation of air through the bottles. The metal screen between the caps is necessary since the larvae

*The Hotchkiss or Bostitch letter stapler is very satisfactory for this purpose.

otherwise would cut their way through the caps and escape. These aerating caps may be used repeatedly.

Special care must be taken to prevent the food from becoming infected with wild or stray larvae. The comb, when it is received from the apiarist, is sterilized by placing in an oven at 60° to 70° C. and leaving for about 2 hours. The sterilizing process is primarily to kill any wild larvae which might be present; otherwise, sterilizing would not be necessary since fungus and other disturbing organisms do not attack dry bee comb. After sterilization the combs are packed into metal cans with close-fitting metal covers. The ordinary pretzel or lard can is very satisfactory and easily handled. For the current supply of the comb a smaller can is preferable. It may be refilled as needed from the supply in the large can. The large storage cans should be kept in a separate room or at least some distance away from the culture bottles containing the larvae and the moths. This is necessary since the young larvae, if they escape from the culture bottles, may go a considerable distance and may chance to get into the stored supply. If several stray larvae get into the stored supply and are not apprehended, the next generation will likely be sufficient to destroy the whole lot of combs.

The larvae flourish in a temperature around 30° to 35° C. The regular Drosophila incubator, or any other incubator which has a temperature-regulating device, is satisfactory for incubating purposes. If an incubator is not available a very serviceable one may be made of ordinary fibrous building board. A convenient size is 4 feet wide, 3½ feet high, and 14 inches deep. Material 2 x 2 inches is adequate for the framework and, if it is lined both inside and outside, leaves a 2-inch dead air space in the wall. The shelves should be about 2 inches narrower than the space inside and perhaps 2 inches shorter, permitting a free circulation of air all through the incubator. It is helpful so to arrange the shelves that the free space on one shelf is on the opposite side of the incubator from the free space on the next shelf above. Also, if a small fan is placed in the incubator it keeps the air disturbed and aids in the aeration of the cultures. The DeKhotinsky thermo-regulator has proved a very efficient and dependable mechanism for regulating the temperature. This regulator, attached to a 40-watt electric light bulb for each shelf in the incubator, is a very adequate heating device and is easily installed.

The handling and inspecting of Galleria is comparatively simple and easy, but different from that of Drosophila. Galleria may not be shaken from the culture bottles into an etherizing chamber as in the case of Drosophila. The food in the culture bottles is loose and dry, and also the moths adhere firmly to the walls or to pieces of the comb. Furthermore, it is not necessary to anesthetize them in handling and examining them. Normally these moths move about at night but sit motionless throughout the day. Thus, their natural characteristics lend them excellently to handling unanesthetized. The apparatus for handling consists of the "moth dipper," a quantity of ¾ x ¾-inch shell vials and of the cardboard milk bottle caps. The dipper may easily be made by gluing one of the ¾ x ¾-inch vials to a wooden tongue depressor, or any strip of wood whittled down to about ⅛ x ¾ x 6 inches. It is used to "dip" the moth from a piece of comb, or from the walls of the culture bottle. This is done by gently placing the dipper over the moth and moving it slightly. This generally will cause the moth to shift in one movement to the side or bottom of the dipper and remain there, and it may thus be moved to any part of the room or to the binocular for examination. If the dipping causes the moth to become irritated, one may slide the dipper up the side of the culture bottle to its top, then slip the thumb of the same hand over the mouth of the dipper, thus confining the moth. It has proved to be a saving of time to transfer the irritated moths to the ¾ x ¾ vials and invert each of these on a milk bottle cap. In a few minutes the moths ordinarily will come to rest on the milk bottle cap. Once the moth becomes quiet the vial may be removed and the moth taken to the binocular or handled in any way desired.

LABORATORY BREEDING OF THE EUROPEAN CORN BORER, PYRAUSTA NUBILALIS*

CONSIDERABLE time has been devoted to the development of a technique for rearing larvae of the European corn borer, *Pyrausta nubilalis*, in quantity. This work was necessary for the breeding of parasites working on the first instars of the borer, such as *Microgaster tibialis*.

All material is incubated at a temperature of 85° F. with a relative humidity of 60% or higher. This has been found to provide optimum conditions of propagation.

Full grown larvae collected in the field are used to rear moths for egg production, since all the young larvae reared in the laboratory are used in the parasite breeding. The cages that are now used for this purpose have proven to be very satisfactory and are, at the same time, very simple. They consist of lantern globes closed at both ends with fine mesh wire screening to facilitate air circulation, and strips of corrugated cardboard one inch wide which are placed side by side in a single row across the diameter of the globes so that they form a partition.

The full grown borer larvae are put into the globe and crawl into the

*Reprinted, with slight changes, from *Canad. Ent.* 61:51, 1929, by L. J. BRIAND, *Parasite Laboratory*, Belleville, Ontario.

corrugations, which open to the sides, where they remain to pupate. Not more than 200 larvae should be put in each cage. Before being placed in the incubator the globes and their contents are immersed in water for from five to ten seconds. All excess water is drained off and the water absorbed by the cardboard supplies sufficient moisture for pupation.

During the time of incubation it is necessary to look the material over two or three times a week and remove the dead larvae which would

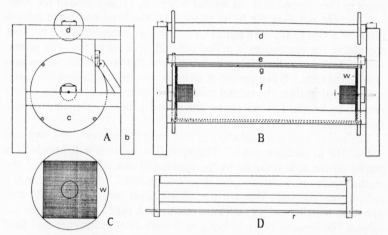

Fig. 67.—Oviposition cage for *Pyrausta nubilalis.* A, end view: b, frame; c, wood disc closing end of cage. B, front view with lower roller removed: d, upper roller; e, second roller; f, cylinder forming the cage; g, wire rods (4); w, wire screening; i, wire screening cylinder for feeding cotton. C, inside end view of cage. D, lower roller (hinged): r, wire rod.

otherwise contaminate the healthy ones. The mortality among larvae varies between 5% and 10%. When overwintered larvae are used the moths begin to emerge in three weeks' time, but if using fresh larvae collected during the late summer and fall a much longer period of incubation is required. Emergence extends over a period of about 2 weeks.

A cage for oviposition (Fig. 67) consists of a cylinder 12 inches long* and 5 inches in diameter suspended in a small frame (A, b) in a horizontal position by means of a central axle on which it revolves. The frame also supports a series of three rollers which hold the waxed paper in place. The cage is so constructed that its sides, which represent the greatest surface, are of waxed paper. The ends of the cage (A, c) are

*This dimension must correspond to the length of the roll of waxed paper used: not all rolls are 12 inches long.

made of two discs of laminated wood ¼ inch thick and 5 inches in diameter held apart by four stiff wires (B, g), and when the waxed paper is placed around the wires it forms an oblong cage, 12 inches long by 3½ inches square. The ends, which expose the smallest surface, are covered with wire screening (C, and B, w) in order to keep the moths from laying eggs on that part of the cage. They are also provided with a wire screen cylinder (B, i) 1 inch long and 1 inch in diameter to hold a feeding cotton which is kept moistened with water. When putting paper on the cage a roll of waxed paper is placed on the top roller (B, d), the paper is then passed over the second roller (B, e), run around the wires and brought out over the lower roller (D), the loose end being held in place by a clip to the wire rod (D, r). It is so arranged that the paper containing the egg masses is pulled out and replaced in the same operation. The lower roller (D), which is hinged and removable, serves as a door to the cage. When opened it gives an opening 2½ inches wide, and when closed against the second roller the distance between them is just enough to let the egg masses on the waxed paper go through without being crushed.

The newly emerged moths are picked from the globes every day and put in the oviposition cages. The operation requires a light which is placed on the side opposite to the opening of the cylinder so that the moths, which are positively phototropic to artificial light, are held in the cylinder by the light through the waxed paper and very few fly out. About 40 females and 30 males are put in each cage. If kept in the incubator the females begin to lay 4 or 5 days after emergence and they live from 10 to 12 days. The dead moths are taken out of the cage every day and replaced by newly emerged ones. Since the moths are more active in the dark it is necessary to cover the cage with a heavy, dark paper.

The eggs are taken out of the oviposition cages every morning and left in the incubator 2 or 3 days until they are ready to hatch; then they are cut from the paper and placed in 4-inch flower pot saucers with food. To make a container one saucer is inverted on another and, in order that they may fit closely, their edges are ground until an even surface is obtained. Before being used the saucers are immersed in water for 24 hours; this method has proven to be satisfactory since a large quantity of water is absorbed by the pottery which supplies sufficient moisture for the hatching of the eggs. Twenty egg masses are put in each container with food and then the containers are placed in the incubator. They are kept in the incubator until the larvae have reached the proper stage for parasitism, which takes about 4 or 5 days. During that period it is necessary to examine them daily and replace food material when it begins to decay.

After the 3rd instar it is necessary to isolate the larvae on account of their cannibalistic habits. They are, therefore, fed in 2-inch glass vials, wire screen stoppers being used in order to provide for ventilation.

A large number of foods have been experimented with including the following: curled dock (*Rumex crispus*), string beans (yellow and green pods), celery, corn, beet, turnip, rhubarb, apple, cabbage, chard, potato, corn flakes, lima bean, and sprouted grains. Of these the first named have proven most satisfactory with others in the order given.

REFERENCE

For the breeding of *Pyrausta nubilalis* see also p. 512.

REARING EPHESTIA KUEHNIELLA LARVAE IN QUANTITY

P. W. Whiting, *University of Pennsylvania*

Equipment Needed. A warm room, 25° $\pm$ C., for starting the caterpillars; a cool room, 20° $-$ C., for slowing development of the caterpillars; a refrigerator for cold storage of full-grown caterpillars; wash boilers or other convenient, covered vessels for raising humidity; pasteboard boxes (wire-stitched, not glued) of convenient size, 8" x 5" x 4" high, giving a fair amount of floor space; glass tumblers or tin cans; a few shell vials, 70 x 20 mm., for collecting the moths.

Directions. Hold the box or cover with moths resting on it in the left hand. Collect the moths in a vial held in the right hand. The vial must be held approximately upright while the vessel containing moths is adjusted so that the moth will drop down into the vial. There is thus little danger that the moth will escape. Twenty-five to fifty moths may be collected in one vial. If the moths fly actively they may be quieted by cooling the box in the refrigerator or on a window sill in cool weather. A pasteboard box with the bottom spread thinly with rolled wheat (Pettijohn's Breakfast Food), 1 cup per 40 square inches, is opened and the cover held in the left hand. The vial of moths, held in the right hand, is emptied into the box by a quick motion so that the cover may be replaced before the moths escape.

Boxes containing moths are placed in covered boilers in which one or two glasses of water are set. The boilers are then left for about 2 weeks in a warm room. Boxes should then be inspected and the webbiness of cereal and the presence of young caterpillars noted. Add more cereal according to the needs of the larvae. The advantage of having a small, measured amount at first (1 cup to 40 square inches) is that thus the number of caterpillars may be better judged. Enough food should be present so that all larvae have plenty, but the whole mass should become matted and the cereal for the most part be consumed.

After the boxes have been in the boilers about five weeks they should be removed so that the water of metabolism may escape and thus mold be avoided. Some boxes may be retained in the warm room for more rapid growth of caterpillars and to obtain a further supply of moths. Larvae pupate in cocoons in the cereal or on the cover of the boxes. Moths will emerge in four or five weeks after the two weeks' inspection.

If the boxes are placed in a cool room after the two weeks' inspection, pupation is delayed but growth continues so that the caterpillars attain much larger size. Boxes may be placed in a refrigerator, 5° or 6° C., and used when desired.

Dangers. Rats or mice, if present, will gnaw into the boxes, eating cereal and caterpillars.

Beetles or mites may infest the cereal and eat the moth eggs. Habrobracon or other parasitic wasps may attack the caterpillars. Protozoan and other diseases may infect the caterpillars. All of these dangers may be avoided by using clean cereal, by using new boxes or by returning the boxes to the warm room only after sterilizing in a hot oven, and by removing from the warm room all cultures showing any signs of infection.

"The White Plague." Chalky, opaque, white caterpillars are full of Coccidian spores, which may be seen as fusiform bodies if the caterpillar is macerated on a slide and placed under a microscope.

"The Black Death." Black spots may appear on the caterpillar or the whole body may become black and disintegrate with a foul odor. The infection may appear in one corner of the box while caterpillars in other parts may be unaffected. Wash and sterilize hands before handling cereal in uninfected boxes after contact with infected ones.

Mold. If cultures become very moldy, caterpillars will not develop well. Avoid by lowering humidity and by disposing of infected cultures. When caterpillars were reared in tin boxes the danger from mold was much greater and the water of metabolism sometimes condensed in crowded cultures to such an extent that caterpillars would drown. Even when there was no mold, caterpillars did not grow as well in tin boxes.

Failure of cultures to set may be due to extreme aridity. It is important to have humidity high when cultures are being started. This is conveniently arranged by means of covered boilers and glasses of water as above directed. In summer and in humid regions it is unnecessary to use boilers.

Family SATURNIIDAE

REARING POLYPHEMUS MOTHS

R. W. Dawson, *University of Minnesota*

THE polyphemus moth is for the most part easily handled under laboratory conditions. It is short-lived, does not feed, and readily and promptly deposits its full quota of eggs in any cage without the stimulus of appropriate food plants. The eggs are relatively hard-shelled and may easily be removed by hand and placed in small boxes for incubation.

Care of Moths. The chief difficulty in caring for the moths lies in getting them to mate in captivity. The method of clipping the wings of a recently emerged female and placing her in the open on a small tree or a bush during the season of flight of the species is attended by the highest per cent of success in securing matings. Caging both sexes together in a large screen enclosure out-of-doors is the next best procedure. If this cannot be arranged smaller cages by an open window should be tried. Only a relatively small number of matings will occur under unmodified laboratory conditions.*

Care of Eggs. Eggs are best collected from the cages daily and kept in small tin boxes. Beginning about the sixth or seventh day fresh pieces of leaves should be placed in the boxes each day to bring the relative humidity up to a favorable level. Frequent changing and cleaning of the boxes is necessary to check molds and bacteria which might otherwise develop in the moist, enclosed chamber. From eight to fourteen days will be required for incubation at ordinary temperatures.

Care of Larvae. The most successful method of starting newly hatched larvae is to keep them in tight containers, glass jars or tin boxes, for the first 24 hours with fresh leaves of the intended food plant. The wandering instinct seems to weaken during this time and the larvae settle down to feed. Glass cylinders, open at the ends, are excellent for confining the larvae during their early stadia, and sometimes longer if they are not crowded or if they are being reared at low temperatures. Ventilation must be provided by covering the top of the containers with open-meshed cloth or screening. Larger larvae are best confined in screen cages. A remarkably satisfactory cage may be made by taking window screening and cutting it into appropriate lengths, bringing the cut edges together and tacking them to a strip of wood. The lower selvage edge of the cylinder so formed will fit close to the floor or table so that no bottom for the cage will be needed. The upper selvage edge will make

---

*Editor's Note: W. T. M. Forbes states that mating takes place normally about 2-3 A.M. and that if a flown male and a fresh female are held together at that time they will usually mate. It has been known to succeed even earlier in the evening. M. E. D.

an even support for a loose lid, best made with a loop of heavy wire covered by some open-meshed cloth. If need be the lid may be weighted to keep a tight contact with the cylinder. Such a cage is easily and quickly prepared at a low cost, gives perfect ventilation, and affords the maximum facility for cleaning and reprovisioning. If several cages are to be used the diameters should be in a graded series so that the cages will telescope one inside the other for storage until again needed.

A few items of the utmost importance in rearing the larvae should be noted. Food should be furnished either by growing plants, or by twigs kept fresh in jars or bottles of water. In the latter case the water surface must be blocked off or the larvae will drown themselves. Most food plants will not support their full quota of leaves on twigs kept in water. If possible choose a species of plant that keeps well when cut. For *T. polyphemus* basswood, hazel, dogwood, and birch are especially good. In any case, always reduce the leaf surface to one-half or one-third the normal. The leaves also keep better if washed or dipped in water. This procedure removes dirt and supplies the larvae with a certain amount of drinking water comparable to that available in nature in the form of dew and rain. That water is important for their best development is evident from the greed with which they drink when the above precaution has been neglected. On one occasion the writer observed the drinking of 25 drops of water in succession by a large *T. polyphemus* larva that had been reared without drinking water.

All twigs, whether their leaves are largely consumed or not, should be discarded on the second day, or at the latest on the third day, and the larvae transferred to fresh foliage. This procedure is a fundamental factor in avoiding diseases among the larvae. The only other factors of parallel importance are proper ventilation of the cages, and the immediate destruction of all abnormal larvae. The transfer of larvae to fresh food may be quickly accomplished by closely trimming the leaves or stems upon which they are clinging with the scissors, and laying them on the new leaves. This procedure is necessary because the larvae will not move from the old twigs to fresh ones promptly of their own accord, and may not be transferred forcibly without injury.

As the larvae come to maturity their droppings become large and moist. Finally a large amount of partially digested food and fluid is evacuated. Immediately after this the larvae seek a place to spin their cocoons. The great majority will begin to spin upon the food plant. As soon as well settled they should be removed from the cage and the leaves and twigs supporting the cocoon pinned to the margin of the lid covering the cage. It is important to keep the emergence end of the cocoon upward until spinning is complete—about 2 or 3 days. Otherwise the structure of the emergence end may be modified so that the moth cannot later escape from the cocoon.

Care of the Cocoons. The cocoons are best kept out-of-doors in woven wire or screen cages if they are to overwinter. Otherwise the pupae are injured or killed by a shortage of moisture, and without exposure to cold do not usually come out of hibernation satisfactorily. Refrigeration is possible in keeping the pupae over winter. On one occasion the writer kept thirteen hundred cocoons in a refrigerator room where the humidity was high and the temperature held constantly at the freezing point. Ninety-eight per cent of emergence occurred the following spring, mostly during a brief period of about two weeks. Refrigeration at about 42° F., however, sometimes proves highly fatal to the pupae, and should be avoided. Apparently this temperature is too high for complete dormancy and too low to sustain development.

REFERENCE

For the rearing of Hemileuca, Automeris, *Tropaea luna,* and Callosamia see p. 365.

BREEDING LYMANTRIID AND SATURNIID MOTHS*

WILLIAM TRAGER, *Rockefeller Institute for Medical Research*

EGGS and pupae of lymantriid and saturniid moths may be readily obtained from professional collectors.

Eggs are placed for hatching in small covered glass dishes (diam. 7 cm., volume 150 cc.). The newly hatched larvae are kept on twigs of food plant placed in the same dishes, the dishes being inverted over pieces of blotting paper to absorb excess moisture and facilitate removal of the excreta. The larvae are transferred to fresh leaves as often as the old leaves dry out. In transferring, they are gently shaken off the old leaves on to the fresh ones and are handled as little as possible, and then only with a soft brush. Larvae which cling tightly to their substrate, and those about to molt, should be put on fresh food together with the leaf to which they are attached. After the first molt the caterpillars are put in larger containers and it is well to put them in wire gauze cages as soon as they are large enough to be unable to escape through the mesh. The larvae may also be kept outdoors on growing plants surrounded by suitable cages. When kept indoors, the trouble of providing a constant supply of fresh food may be somewhat reduced by placing twigs of the food plant in a bottle of water with the opening plugged with cotton to prevent the caterpillars from crawling in and drowning. Leaves supplied in this way must be changed at least every other day. As the larvae get

*Abstracted from "Die Zucht der Lymantriidae und Saturniidae" by K. Pariser in "Methodik der wissenschaftlichen Biologie," T. Péterfi, Verl. Julius Springer, Berlin, 1928, Bd. II, S. 290-300.

larger, mass-cultures should be divided up into smaller ones to reduce the chances of disease epidemics. When the caterpillars are ready to pupate it is especially important that they should not be too crowded.

*Lymantriidae.** The nun moth (*Lymantria monacha*) and the gypsy moth (*L. dispar*) overwinter in the egg stage. Eggs should be kept through the winter in cotton plugged tubes held in a protected place outdoors, as the eggs require a prolonged frost period. In the early spring, the eggs are placed in an icebox and kept there until leaves of the food plant become available. The eggs hatch very soon after being brought to room temperature. Crataegus serves as food for both species of Lymantria, although *L. dispar* will feed on oak, fruit trees, pine, and larch, and *L. monacha* on beech and oak. Polyhedral virus diseases are the chief difficulty to be overcome in the rearing of Lymantria. The spread of these diseases is favored by overcrowding, excess heat and moisture, and poor or insufficient nutriment. Breeding cages, before being used for new cultures, should be washed with hot water or with 10% formalin in 50% alcohol, or some similar disinfectant. The pupae of Lymantria, when several days old and sufficiently hard, are placed in suitable combinations (depending on the purpose of the experiment) in glass jars having blotting paper on the bottom and sides, and strips of cardboard. The pupal stage lasts 2 to 3 weeks. Copulation and egg-laying follow soon after emergence. The eggs are laid on the cardboard strips, enabling subsequent convenient handling.

Saturniidae. The moths of this family overwinter in a cocoon in the pupal stage (with the exception of *Antheraea yamamai* which overwinters in the egg stage). Some species (*Saturnia pavonia, S. spini,* and *S. pyri*) require frost and should be kept outdoors during the winter, while other species (of the Samia group) do not require frost and may be kept in any cool place. [See also P. oo.] For purposes of mating, the cocoons are placed in large breeding cages in the spring. Where special crosses are to be made, and it is necessary to know the sex of the insects before they emerge, the pupa may be removed from its cocoon, or better, the cocoon may be opened just enough to reveal the posterior tip of the pupa. Here in the genital region, the two sexes may be readily distinguished. The moths mate soon after emergence and the female then begins laying eggs. For most of the species the eggs hatch within 10 to 21 days of the date of laying. European species are easily reared on Crataegus; Antheraea on oak, apple, or hawthorn; and Samia on Prunus or apple. Like the Lymantriidae, Saturniidae larvae are susceptible to polyhedral diseases, and the same prophylactic measures should be taken.

---

*Editor's Note: W. T. M. Forbes cautions that Lymantria is a very serious pest and *L dispar* should be handled only in areas already infested. *L. monacha* should not be handled at all in this country. M. E. D.

REFERENCES

Family Lasiocampidae
  For the rearing of Malacosoma see p. 365.
Family Lymantriidae
  For the rearing of Notolophus, and Hemerocampa see p. 365.

Family NOCTUIDAE

THE COLUMBINE AND IRIS BORERS

GRACE H. GRISWOLD, *Cornell University*

DURING a study of the columbine borer (*Papaipema purpurifascia*) and the iris borer (*Macronoctua onusta*) it was found to be almost impossible to tell the sexes apart in living adults, but an examination of cast pupal skins revealed that the genital opening in the female pupa is further cephalad than is that in the male pupa. This fact made it easy to differentiate the sexes in the pupal stage.

The rearing work was carried on in an outdoor cage. Full grown larvae of both species were collected and placed in individual salve boxes with damp sphagnum. When pupation occurred each pupa was examined to determine the sex and then removed to a jelly glass with the sex marked on the cover. Each jelly glass contained, in addition to some damp sphagnum, a piece of wire netting about 3 inches long and ¾ of an inch wide. This netting rested on the bottom of the jelly glass and extended up the side nearly to the top. Almost without exception, every adult that emerged walked up the netting and rested there until its wings were spread. Since the sex of each moth had already been determined it was a simple matter to place pairs of moths in individual cages.

The most satisfactory cage used for the columbine borers was a cylindrical glass cage 12 inches high and 5½ inches in diameter with a piece of cheesecloth tied over the top. Each cage rested on a circle of paper toweling placed in a large shallow saucer. A wide-mouthed bottle held the columbine foliage. About each bottle was wrapped a piece of wire netting to provide a rough surface on which the moths could easily walk. A long strip of absorbent cotton extended to the bottom of the bottle, the upper end being wrapped several times around the petiole of the columbine leaf. The cotton acted as a wick and the part at the top of the bottle was always wet. Thus the moths were constantly supplied with drinking water.

Pairs of iris borer moths were placed in the same type of cylindrical glass breeding cage. To insure an adequate food supply each cage was also provided with a small watch glass of the Plant Industry type, containing a 5% solution of dextrose in water. Fitted into the top of each watch glass was a circle of wire netting to prevent the moths from falling into the liquid. Black cloth was substituted for wire netting as a cover for the bottles containing the foliage and the wick of absorbent cotton. Since the moths of both species are very sluggish during the day no difficulty was experienced in moving them from one cage to another.

Although leaves and other debris were placed in the cages of the columbine borer, eggs were rarely laid anywhere but on the bottom. No debris of any kind need be provided, thus making it easy to find and count the eggs. Eggs of the iris borer are placed in clusters of from 2 to as many as 150, carefully glued down. Although females deposited their eggs on dried leaves, they also pasted them on practically everything in the cage that had a rough or crinkled surface. The females evidently prefer to lay their eggs between two surfaces as clusters were often placed in folds of cloth or between two pieces of paper toweling.

Eggs were collected from the cages in the fall and placed in salve boxes. These small boxes were buried in dead leaves in large cartons and these in turn were kept out of doors all winter. When hatching was desired in the spring the eggs were brought inside and placed on the soil beside iris or columbine plants growing in pots. Larvae were hatched as early as March, although outdoors they did not hatch so soon. These larvae found their way to the plants and developed satisfactorily under these nearly natural conditions.

REFERENCES

For the trapping of Catocala see p. 337.
For the trapping of Noctuidae in general see p. 364.
Family Arctiidae
For the rearing of Utetheisa, Euchaetias, Hyphantria, Halysidota, and Ammalo see p. 365.

Family BOMBYCIDAE

METHODS FOR THE LABORATORY CULTURE OF THE
SILKWORM, BOMBYX MORI

WILLIAM TRAGER, *Rockefeller Institute for Medical Research*

METHODS for the large scale rearing of Bombyx are readily available in books and government publications. I will attempt here merely to describe the technique used by Dr. R. W. Glaser and those in his laboratory in connection with studies on silkworm diseases.

The silkworm eggs (which may be obtained from a dealer) are kept at room temperature in groups of about 50 in small glass dishes. The larvae hatch within 10 to 14 days, and are provided with a mulberry leaf on which they crawl and begin to feed. Only young, tender mulberry leaves should be used for the small caterpillars. In all cases clean, healthy leaves should be selected, and it is usually well to wash the leaves. The mulberry leaf with the young larvae on it is transferred to a shallow tray, about 6 inches square with sides 1½-inches high, made out of previously autoclaved cardboard. No cover is needed. Fresh mulberry leaves are supplied and the trays cleaned at least once a day. The young larvae are not handled but are removed together with the leaves to which they cling. The excreta and dry leaves are shaken out of the tray. The leaves with the larvae are replaced and covered with a few fresh leaves, to which the larvae crawl. Caterpillars which must be handled directly are best taken up with a camel's hair brush. The larval stage of the silkworm consumes from 4 to 6 or 7 weeks, depending on the temperature, and consists of 5 instars. When a group of about 50 larvae enters the 3rd instar it should be transferred to a cardboard tray about 12 inches square with sides 3 inches high. Larvae in the 4th and 5th instars are large and may be handled directly. Larvae entering the 5th instar should be thinned out to not more than 20 to 30 to a large tray.

When one is working with a silkworm disease, the healthy stock larvae should be kept in a separate room in which no diseased material is present. They should be fed in the morning before diseased material has been handled. If it is necessary to go to them again later, one's hands should first be thoroughly washed. Observation of these simple precautions prevents infection of the stock from the diseased experimental worms. The washing of the leaves and autoclaving of the cardboard for the trays reduce the chances of infection from external sources. If an occasional caterpillar does get sick or dies, it should immediately be removed. If a number of larvae in one tray die, this tray with all the larvae in it should be discarded.

For careful studies of disease, the experimental worms should be kept singly in ½ pint bottles, previously capped with paper and sterilized by dry heat. When it is desired to feed known quantities of infective material with a pipette, the worms (preferably in the 5th instar) should be starved for one day.

The stock may be perpetuated by allowing the full grown worms not needed for experiments to spin cocoons. The cocoons are conveniently kept in large cardboard trays. The moths, which emerge about 2 weeks after spinning of the cocoon, mate readily, and each pair should be placed on a large sheet of cardboard under a ½ pint bottle or a small lamp chimney. Eggs laid by the female moths adhere to the cardboard, which may later be cut into squares, each square holding the eggs laid by one moth. The newly laid eggs are yellow but, unless they are sterile, they gradually darken and become gray within 7 to 10 days. When the eggs are gray and fully embryonated they should be stored in an icebox. Eggs of the ordinary univoltine race will not hatch unless they have been kept about 2 months in the cold. They may be kept a year in the cold and will still hatch when brought to room temperature. Eggs of the Japanese multivoltine race hatch within 10 to 14 days after the date of laying and require no cold period. They may, however, be stored in the cold without injury.

FURTHER NOTES ON BREEDING LEPIDOPTERA

W. T. M. Forbes, *Cornell University*

COLLECTING moths at bait [see also p. 337] is very nearly a special method for Noctuidae, although it is successful also for a few members of other families. A diffuse light is better than a torch since there is less likelihood of a sudden bright illumination frightening them. When frightened many moths dash down or sideways instead of to the light.

A useful collecting outfit consists of a wide-mouthed (6 oz.) bottle with a vial of cotton inverted in the cork. Wet the cotton well with ether. If the moths are wanted alive ether should be used and *not* chloroform or cyanide. Catch moths from the bait in the bottle and remove when the legs are still twitching. They may then be examined safely for sex, *etc.*, and either transferred to pill boxes, freed, or cyanided. The bottle should be kept open between periods of use to avoid poisonous decomposition products of the ether.

In sexing the moths, note that the female has an extensile fleshy ovipositor and the male two chitinous valves which may be seen by squeezing the abdomen gently. The male has a frenulum running through a hook near the base of the fore wing while the female has interlocking scales and bristles only.

Most moths which do not feed in the imago may easily be reared for successive generations by the general method described for Lymantriidae and Saturniidae [see p. 359]. Others usually give trouble in mating. Moths seek their mates by smell and a slight drift of wind may help them find each other. Confining them in a very small box may also be successful. Some males need to fly a time before mating and should have a large emergence cage. Avoid a strong light from one side or moths will congregate there.

To avoid handling in transferring caterpillars to fresh food, some silk breeders use a light frame carrying a coarse net. The fresh food is put on this and laid over the tray of caterpillars. When they have climbed up to the fresh food the tray is lifted off and the lower tray discarded with any larvae too sick to move. At molting times extra time must be allowed as they will not then move up to the fresh food. This method is used on a commercial scale in Asia Minor and China.

Eucleidae. Slug caterpillars spend the winter as larvae in the cocoon and need careful protection at that stage. According to Dyar most members of this family mate only on the day of emergence and fairly large lots are necessary if matings are to be obtained.

Lymantriidae. Tussock moths, Notolophus and Hemerocampa, may be reared by the same technique as the Lymantrias [see p. 360]. They also overwinter in the egg stage. Young larvae are extremely active and especially fine screening may be needed for cages during the first few days.

Saturniidae. Hemileuca hibernates in the egg stage. Most pupae need no protection during the winter, even in a dry room. A few with light cocoons (*Tropaea luna*, Automeris) should be protected during the winter [see p. 360]. To determine the sex pupae of this family I prefer to make an opening in the side of the cocoon in order to note the width of the antenna. The opening may be resealed with a small cover glass if it is desired to keep track of the stage of development.

The following are somewhat specialized in their food preferences: Callosamia feeds on members of the family Magnoliaceae and Sassafras; *C. promethea* is less particular and will also eat lilac, *etc.; Samia columbia* feeds by exception on Larix and Tsuga; Hemileuca feeds on oak in the east and willow in the west, while *Hemileuca lucina* prefers Spiraea.

Lasiocampidae. Tent caterpillars (Malacosoma) are particularly easy to breed indoors, even under adverse conditions of temperature and humidity and thus form excellent material for the school classroom. They give no trouble even with mating. For *M. americana* the food should be supplied in water or a growing plant should be provided. When the first food grows stale or is exhausted the twig and tent should be removed from the water but not discarded. New food may be put beside it and discarded when stale unless it is too much involved in the tent. Eggs are laid in early July and need no care during the winter, though they should be exposed to the winter weather.

Arctiidae. Most members of this family are general feeders. Euchaetias and Ammalo are limited to the Asclepiadaceae and Apocynaceae; Halysidota needs tree foods as a rule; Hyphantria makes a tent and should be treated like Malacosoma, with apple forming a satisfactory food; Utetheisa is partial to seed pods of Crotalaria.

BUTTERFLIES

JOHN H. GEROULD, *Dartmouth College*

THE stage of development in butterflies at which experiments in genetics are most conveniently begun is the adult. Any captured female, in species which I have bred, may be safely assumed to be already fertilized, though very likely by more than one male.

Paper bags, carried into the field and inflated, make useful receptacles for gathering live specimens. The wings of large, active species such as the "Monarch" should be clamped together over the back with paper clips.

Live butterflies may be sent even across the continent by parcel post or express in a large mailing tube or tin can lined with wet blotting paper, sewed securely, through punched holes, to the inner side. The strap-hanging butterfly should have a good foothold, and there should be no loose projecting walls upon which to beat its wings. Never more than two or three live specimens may be shipped together, for they stimulate one another and are likely to be smashed to pieces.

Plenty of pure (unsweetened) water should be used in wetting the lining of the mailing tube or other receptacle, which must be kept moist throughout the journey. Five days en route is about the maximum. For a long trip, a tin container should be packed in excelsior to avoid jarring.

On arrival, the female should be set over a growing food plant, preferably potted and in a greenhouse, or insectary, to avoid predatory ants, wasps, mice, birds, *etc*. The atmosphere in the greenhouse should be moist, or at least never very dry.

The cage, a wooden frame lined with soft, black netting, should fit the potted plant closely enough so that the butterfly will hover close to the foliage. She is fed conveniently by a bunch of flowers frequently dipped in clean water sweetened slightly with brown sugar to a consistency resembling that of maple sap. The bouquet should be kept in a tall, widemouthed bottle close to the plant on which she is to lay.*

For cultures of Colias (= Eurymus), circular patches of white clover turf are cut with a rounded spade to fit a bulb pan 10 or 11 inches in diameter and 5 or 6 inches high. This is then covered by a cage 15 inches square and 10 inches high. The frame may be made of pine strips $1\frac{3}{8}''$ x $\frac{3}{8}''$, supported by corner posts $\frac{7}{8}''$ square, with the exposed vertical edge of each smoothed off.

To avoid caterpillar diseases, it is of utmost importance to have the eggs thinly distributed, with not more than one egg to a leaf. If the butterfly is actively flying in the sunlight, there is not likely to be much crowding, but the pot should be rotated 180° when the side toward the sun is sufficiently furnished with eggs. Six or eight pots of clover may be required for the eggs of a single female during the week or fortnight of her laying.

---

*Editor's Note: W. T. M. Forbes says that he has had surest results in obtaining oviposition (with some risk of killing the butterflies by overheating) by covering the butterfly with a glass bell jar with some twigs of the proper food-plant and setting in the sun. Also that in many long-lived butterflies there are no mature eggs when the butterfly emerges, and there must be a long period of feeding and flying; this is true of anglewings for instance. M. E. D.

If the eggs are at all crowded, dispersion of the larvae as widely as possible over the food-plant must be undertaken after the first molt; later, when the foliage becomes sparse or covered with aphids, the larvae must be transferred to a fresh pot of clover.

Even though the caterpillars are sedentary, as in Colias, the pots carrying a culture must be covered with cages, or, better, with a single large cage extending over all the pots of the culture. Such a cage may be made of a wooden frame covered internally with fine black netting (white is too opaque) and accurately fitting the surface of the table. This should be as flat as possible and preferably of cement, so that it may be washed frequently with a hose.

Most caterpillars are subject to diseases corresponding to flacherie and pebrine of the silkworm. If a green, naked caterpillar is off-color or slightly pale, it should immediately be isolated, for "polyhedral disease," resembling flacherie, is highly contagious, and the leaves near the sick caterpillar soon become contaminated. If the disease does not kill the larva, it slows up development, the suspended caterpillar later droops and dies, or the pupa turns black and purulent.

The healthy full grown larvae usually leave the plants and pupate on the walls of the cage, though some will be suspended on the plants. The cage, with all the pupae, may now be removed to any laboratory table, preferably in a cool, dark room where the emerging butterflies will not mate.

On emergence, it is desirable to mark each one with a letter designating the brood and a number indicating the individual. This may be done with a stub pen and India ink diluted with 50% alcohol to make it flow freely. I regularly mark the ventral side of the right hind wing. The date of emergence having been recorded, the butterfly's age is always accurately known. The males and females of any brood are now kept in separate cages in a cool, dark room with adequate humidity. Once or twice a day they should be brought into the sunlight and allowed to feed on moistened flowers.

Mating is easily brought about by placing a few individuals of each sex together in a cage of the dimensions mentioned or others 15″ x 15″ x 15″. The cage is set upon a square wooden tray (16″ x 16″ inside), with sides about 2″ high to prevent the escape of flying butterflies when the edge of the cage is lifted. The cage upon its tray is then put into the sunlight; pairs are taken out and isolated as soon as they form. Mating lasts from a half hour to several hours, usually one or two. The same male may be mated again the next day with a different female. This is important in testing a male's genetic make-up. Females known to be impregnated are thus ready to set over potted food plants, or are kept in reserve for use if others prove sterile. A female requires only a single mating.

Hibernation presents no problem in Pieris, Euchloe, and other butter-flies which winter as chrysalids. It is more difficult in *Colias spp.*, which usually hibernate as half grown caterpillars. Loss of moisture and haemolymph by the chrysalids of these species during the winter usually prevents eclosion in the spring; the wings cannot expand.

The natural method of hibernation, burying the caterpillars deeply in moist, sandy soil, sometimes succeeds, if they are placed in boxes or tins inverted so that moisture will not collect, and packed in a bushel or more of excelsior; but even in a cool, well-shaded excavation they may be killed by molds in early spring before clover in the fields begins to grow. An electric refrigerator, with atmosphere well humidified, is far more likely to give dependable results.

Order Diptera

Superfamily TIPULOIDEA

CRANEFLIES

J. SPEED ROGERS, *University of Florida*

APPROXIMATELY 700 to 800 species of craneflies, distributed among 4 families* and about 120 genera and subgenera are known from North America. Many of the species are rare, restricted in distribution, or little known, but a large number are common and widely distributed. They often form a considerable element of the insect fauna of stream-courses, swamps, marshes, woods, and grasslands where their larvae occur in a wide variety of aquatic, semi-aquatic, wet, or moist situations. Indeed, along the shaded banks of upland rills and seepage areas and on wet, mossy cliffs craneflies are frequently the dominant forms of insect life.

A partial knowledge of the life histories and immature stages of representative species of each of the families and subfamilies and of more than ⅔ of all the genera has been obtained; but the life histories of more than ⅔ of the species are wholly unknown, and few of the others have been carried through a complete life cycle within the breeding cage. The following discussion of rearing and culturing methods is thus limited and conditioned by a very incomplete knowledge of the life histories of a large majority of the species.

For the purpose of rearing adults or maintaining cultures, craneflies may be divided into five broad and overlapping groups:

*Tanyderidae, 1 genus, 3 species; Ptychopteridae, 3 genera, 7 species; Trichoceridae, 3 genera, about 12 species; Tipulidae, 3 subfamilies, some 110 to 115 genera and subgenera and more than 700 species.

I. Immature stages inhabiting rotten wood and fungi: The larvae mycetophagous, xylophagous, or nekrophytophagous.

II. Immature stages inhabiting saturated silt, mud, or sand:
  a. The larvae herbivorous, phytophagous, or geophagous (detritus).
  b. The larvae carnivorous and predacious (cannibalistic under culture conditions).

III. Immature stages inhabiting wet or damp soil: This group includes both grassland and woodland species; the larvae herbivorous (chiefly rootlets and leaves in contact with the soil) or phytophagous.

IV. Immature stages inhabiting wet or damp growths of algae, liverworts, and mosses: A large assemblage of species that overlaps somewhat with Groups I and II, and markedly with Group V; principally from hygropetric or neuston situations; the larvae feeding upon the living plants and the accumulations of detritus and micro-flora.

V. Larvae aquatic, pupae aquatic (Antocha) or semi-aquatic: A considerable number of genera and species with habitats that range from strictly aquatic to those of groups I, II, and IV. Typically lotic and lenitic habitats and both herbivorous and predacious food habits are represented.

SOME GENERAL CONSIDERATIONS

Cultures may be started from either the immature stages or from fertile females taken in the field. In most instances (all unless the larval habitat is known) it is more practicable to begin with the larvae or pupae.* Within each of the groups listed, the various species have more or less specific requirements for culturing that are best learned by observing the conditions of the larval habitat.

Except for some of the species in Group V, wide-mouthed glass jars or small aquaria with loosely fitting glass lids make satisfactory cages. Stacked finger bowls are useful for the smaller species, and for the younger larvae of larger species if their contents can receive enough diffused daylight to permit photosynthesis (Groups II, III, IV), and if they may be stacked within a large aquarium or other glass enclosure where the evaporation rate may be held uniformly low. Maintenance of the requisite moisture is of first importance. The medium in which the larvae live will need to be moist to saturation, and the air in the space above,

---

*The following papers give considerable data on the habitats and methods of collecting the immature stages:

ALEXANDER, C. P. 1920. The craneflies of New York; Part II; Biology and phylogeny. *Cornell Univ. Agric. Exper. Sta. Mem.* 38:691.

—— 1931. Deutsche Limnologische Sunda-Expedition; The craneflies. *Arch. fur Hydrobiologie*, Suppl. Bd. IX, Tropische Binnengewasser 2:135.

ROGERS, J. S. 1933. The summer cranefly fauna of the Cumberland Plateau in Tennessee. *Occas. Papers Mus. Zool. Univ. Mich.* 215:1.

—— 1933. The ecological distribution of the craneflies of northern Florida. *Ecol. Monog.* 3:1.

into which the adults will emerge, should have a relative humidity of from 85% to 100%. Marked or rapid changes in temperature, aside from any deleterious effect upon the craneflies and their food material, cause much difficulty and frequent losses from their effect upon moisture conditions. Condensed moisture on the sides of the jar traps and kills the adults, and, falling on the larval medium, damages its surface and may drown larvae or pupae. This is particularly true when the medium is silt or agar. Exposure of the rearing jar to direct sunlight is especially to be avoided.

Except for larvae from markedly acid or basic habitats (sphagnum bogs and swamps or seepage from limestone cliffs) considerable variations in pH are tolerated. Since it is necessary to keep the jars closed to maintain a high humidity, it is advisable to have a comparatively large air space in proportion to the space filled with the larval medium, and to include a few small green plants (usually mosses, liverworts, or algae) for photosynthesis.

All predacious larvae are strongly cannibalistic in rearing jars, even if well fed, and should be isolated. Stacked finger bowls or jelly glasses, the centers of the tin lids of which have been replaced by fine meshed wire gauze, make good culture dishes. The younger instars of many species of Tipula are also somewhat cannibalistic when crowded and, since the females lay from 200 to 300 eggs, are very likely to be crowded if the full complement is oviposited in one jar. However the survivors appear to thrive upon such a diet and, if the culture is well supplied with food, the number of larvae is only reduced to the proper population for the space provided.

For a number of species in groups I, II, III, and IV, it has been possible to maintain a continuous culture of successive and overlapping generations in one large rearing jar with no more attention than to maintain proper conditions of moisture and food. For a maximum production of individuals, however, it is better to start one or more new cultures from each mated female.

If sufficient space above the larval medium is provided in the rearing jar (500 cc. or more for large species, 4,000 cc. for the larger Tipula), the adults of the majority of species will mate and oviposit. It is usually preferable, however, to remove the newly emerged adults to a large glass jar, kept humid by a carpet of wet filter paper, where mating and often oviposition will take place. If one can obtain recently emerged males and females at the same time there is no necessity to provide food, since mating and oviposition are usually completed within 48 to 72 hours and water is obtained from the wet filter paper. If adults are emerging slowly so that individuals of both sexes are not always available, the adults may be kept alive for one or two weeks by providing food and keeping the jar at a moderately low temperature, 12° to 20° C. A 10% to 15% solution of cane sugar, or honey, or the juices pressed from over-ripe fruit may be fed in small saturated pellets of filter paper or from a drinking fountain made by closing the upper end of a short length of small glass tubing.

Although the females of a number of species will oviposit in or on wet filter paper, others require a layer or clump of the same or similar material that is utilized in nature. The species that will oviposit on filter paper will oviposit more freely in a more natural medium. If mud or silt is required, it is convenient to provide a layer several millimeters deep of fine silt that has been washed through a sieve fine enough to retain the eggs (a mesh with openings about 0.25 mm.). The eggs may then be secured readily by washing the silt again through the sieve. Species that oviposit in algae and mosses, on wet rocks or elsewhere, will usually oviposit freely in tufts or "ropes" of filamentous algae, about the size of a lead pencil, coiled about on the wet filter paper. A considerable number of species that normally oviposit in wet rotten wood, fungi, silt, or algae, oviposit freely in a stratum of rather soft agar, where the eggs are easily seen and from which they are readily removed.

When adults are scarce one male may be mated with two or three females in succession. If males are plentiful this practice is not advisable for, in a number of instances and in several species, a considerable proportion of the eggs of the 2nd and 3rd females were infertile.

GROUP I. IMMATURE STAGES INHABITING ROTTEN WOOD AND FUNGI

Representative genera, subgenera, or species: Rotting hardwoods (feeding mainly on mycelia)—Atarba, Elephantomyia, Epiphragma, Gnophomyia, *Limonia (Rhipidia) fidelis, Orimarga (Diotrepha) mirabilis, Teucholabis complexa, Tipula trivittata.*
Rotting wood and fungi—*Limonia (Limonia) cinctipes, L. (L.) rara.*
Fungi—*Limonia (L.) globithorax, L. (L.) macateei, Ula.*

Rotten wood- and fungus-inhabiting forms are probably the easiest of all craneflies to rear and may, in many instances, be carried through repeated generations within the breeding cage. Since any sample of rotting wood or fungus in which larvae and pupae are found may contain the immature stages of still other species (as well as possible predators), if one wishes to culture but a single species it is necessary to sterilize the habitat material for arthropods without destroying the microfungus or algal flora. This is best done by air drying. Part of the material is dried for several days or weeks, while the possibly mixed culture is kept alive in another portion. The dried material may then be placed on pads of wet filter paper or on a layer of wet sand in the rearing jars where it will become re-saturated with moisture within two or three days;

then the selected larvae or pupae may be added. It is necessary to keep the filter paper or sand wet, but not submerged, during the life of the culture. Since it is probable that the actual food material of nearly all wood- and fungus-inhabiting larvae consists of mycelia and other soft parts of the mixed flora of fungi (and sometimes algae) that grows on the wood or larger fungous body, it would seem logical to re-infect the previously dried material with scrapings from the original, undried wood or fungus, but this procedure usually seems unnecessary.

With some exceptions, the precise species of wood or fungus does not appear to be a specific requirement. *Limonia cinctipes, L. macateei,* and *L. rara* have been carried through 4 to 12 successive generations in a supply of dried and re-wetted *Polyporus tsugae.* A large supply of this fungus was collected and dried in North Carolina and then brought to Florida where it does not occur. In it a stock of *L. cinctipes,* obtained in Florida from a *Polyporus sp.* on a sweet-gum (Liquidambar); also a stock of *L. macateei,* obtained in Florida from *Poria sp.;* another stock of *L. macateei,* obtained in North Carolina from *Polyporus tsugae;* and a stock of *L. rara,* obtained in Florida from mycelium-riddled wood of a Magnolia log, were all successfully maintained as long as the supply of the re-wetted fungus was provided. For *L. cinctipes,* a new supply was required about every two generations; for the other species, about every four generations.

A "Polyporus agar," made by steeping shreds of fresh Polyporus for a week or so in tap water and then boiling, straining, and adding sufficient dry, plain agar to make the infusion set when re-boiled and cooled, forms a medium in which *L. macateei* and *L. rara* will oviposit freely; the eggs will hatch and the larvae feed and grow. The agar is poured into the usual petri dishes and, when set, the cover is temporarily replaced by a lantern globe with screened top, set directly on the agar. Mated females, introduced from the rearing jars containing fungus, not only oviposit but infect the agar with spores so that mycelia soon penetrate the agar in all directions. It is the mycelia that furnish food for the young larvae, and the movements and feeding of the latter may be watched under a binocular microscope until the agar becomes opaque from fungous and bacterial growth. Transfers of the larvae to fresh plates inoculated with smears from decaying fungus may easily be made, but if visibility of the larvae is not required they will thrive in the original plates as long as the agar neither liquifies nor dries out. Accumulations of moisture on the surface of the agar are likely to drown the larvae.

GROUP II. IMMATURE STAGES INHABITING SATURATED SILT, MUD, OR SAND

Representative genera, subgenera, or species: Non-predacious larvae—Erioptera (all subgenera), Gonomyia, Helius, Helobia, Molophilus, Ormosia, Pseudolimnophila, *Tipula annulata, T. jacobus, T. sayi, T. subeluta, T. synchroa, T. tricolor, Trimicra.*

Predacious larvae—Adelphomyia, *Hexatoma (Eriocera) albitarsis,* Lasiomastix, Phylidorea, Pilaria, Polymera, Ulomorpha.

Here, perhaps more than in any other group, silt, mud, or sand from the larval habitat is likely to contain the immature stages of several species of craneflies as well as various predators upon them. If it is only desired to carry late larvae through to the adult stage, the wet silt, mud, or sand may be placed in a layer an inch deep on top of a layer of coarse wet sand in the rearing jars and pasteurized. When cool, any loss of water should be made up and the larvae introduced into the jars. If younger larvae or eggs are to be reared, or a continuous culture is to be maintained, the silt, mud, or sand should be washed through a wire sieve of 12 to 16 meshes per inch into a jar of water. When the material has settled* the water may be decanted and the semi-fluid silt or muddy sand may be placed in a layer an inch deep on about an equal depth of coarse, wet sand in the rearing jars. (A cylindrical glass jar, 150 x 150 mm., ¼ filled with sand and silt, is of ample size for a score or more of Erioptera larvae.) Some small green plants that will thrive in the wet silt or sand should be provided, but not allowed to choke the surface. Small pond-margin grasses (Websteria), Hydrocotyle, and silt-inhabiting liverworts and algae have been used successfully in rearing Erioptera, Molophilus and Pseudolimnophila. It is important to keep very nearly saturated cultures in which fine silt is the medium. Once the surface becomes dry it is likely to acquire a texture that prevents the larvae from reaching the air with their respiratory disks.

Predacious larvae require much the same culture conditions but should be isolated. Several living Erioptera or Pseudolimnophila larvae, somewhat smaller than the predacious larva, or some small aquatic or silt-inhabiting annelid worms should be dropped into the jar once or twice a week.

GROUP III. IMMATURE STAGES INHABITING WET TO DAMP SOILS

Representative genera and species: Cladura, *Dactylolabis cubitalis,* Dicranoptycha, *Nephrotoma eucera, N. ferruginea, N. macrocera, Tipula bicornis, T. borealis, T. dietziana, T. disjuncta, T. dorsomaculata, T. duplex, T. fuliginosa, T. georgiae, T. grata, T. oxytona, T. perlongipes, T. triplex, T. triton.* It is probable that many Nephrotoma and a large majority of the species in the subgenera Oreomyza and Lunatipula of Tipula belong here.

---

*Small larvae or other arthropods that pass through the sieve usually soon rise to the surface of the water where they may easily be seen.

The only species of this group that I have carried through one or more complete life cycles are *Nephrotoma suturalis* and *Tipula oxytona,* but the others have been reared from early or mid-stage larvae to adults and would apparently be no more difficult to maintain in cultures than these two. Glass jars or aquaria, about as tall as their diameter and a gallon or more in capacity, form good rearing jars for about a dozen larvae. Soil from the habitat, crumbled in the hands and sifted through a sieve of about 10 meshes to the inch, should be placed in a layer 1½ to 2 inches deep over an inch layer of coarse, damp sand and lightly tamped. It is advisable to include all leaf fragments and other small bits of decaying vegetation that are found in the sieve. The purpose of the sifting is to remove unaccounted-for larvae and the various predatory arthropods that occur in the soil. A few plants (grasses or small herbs) from the habitat should be planted but kept from growing so tall as to fill the space above the soil. For *Nephrotoma suturalis* centipede grass, small cabbage plants, or young lettuce appeared to serve equally well. The soil should be kept about as damp as or slightly damper than the habitat from which the larvae were taken, but gravitational water should never be present. A small well, formed by a piece of large glass tubing, open at both ends and extending to the bottom of the jar, forms a convenient well from which any surplus (standing) water may be "pumped" with a pipette, and through which required water may be added.

GROUP IV. IMMATURE STAGES INHABITING ALGAE, MOSSES, AND LIVERWORTS

> Representative species: In algae (including diatomaceous sludges), and mosses on wet cliffs, rocks and piling (Fauna Hygropetrica)—*Dactylolabis montana, Elliptera illinoiensis, Limonia humidicola, L. pudicoides, L. stulta, L. canadensis, L. distincta, L. rostrata, L. simulans, Dolichopeza carolus, Tipula caloptera, T. floridensis, T. furca, T. kennicotti, T. iroquois, T. oropezoides.*
>
> In filamentous algae floating in quiet waters (Infraneuston)—*Limonia distans, Megistocera longipennis, Tipula caloptera.*
>
> In submerged algae (and mosses) of rocky or gravelly stream bottoms—*Limonia gladiator, L. iowensis, Limonia sp., Tipula caloptera.*
>
> In mosses and liverworts on damp earth or logs—*Limonia divisa, L. diversa, Dolichopeza dorsalis, D. obscura, D. sayi, D. subalbipes.*

A number of the species listed are aquatic or semi-aquatic, from the standpoint of an ecological classification, but all may be successfully cultured with no more water than is required to keep their food plants from rapid deterioration.

The rearing jars should have a thin layer (5-10 mm.) of sand covered with one or two sheets of filter paper, the sand and filter paper being saturated, or barely submerged in water. If algae are to be the food plants, a small quantity of filamentous strands should be spread one (or at most a few) filament deep over the filter paper. Mosses and liverworts should be strewn in as thin a layer as possible. If the culture dishes are placed in a strong north light the plants will remain green and suitable for food for a maximum time—several days to a week or more for the algae, several weeks to indefinitely for the mosses and liverworts. If more than a very few or very young larvae are present, the plants will be eaten more rapidly than they will spoil. Frequent inspections are advisable and fresh material must be added as needed. Accumulations of detritus are not harmful unless considerable quantities of plant material are undergoing rapid decomposition. Young larvae, in fact, appear to thrive best on a thin, brownish-green detritus that accumulates from the decomposition of a small excess of plant material. The newly hatched larvae of *L. distans, L. rostrata, D. subalbipes, T. caloptera,* and others do best on detritus from algae or mosses, or on algae, but may be fed on mosses after they have reached the 2nd instar. Stock supplies of algae, mosses, and liverworts may be maintained in large jars or aquaria that are kept in strong, diffused light. Almost any species of filamentous or colonial alga that is available appears to be satisfactory for food.

GROUP V. THE LARVAE AQUATIC, PUPAE AQUATIC OR SEMI-AQUATIC

Since it is generally tedious and expensive to simulate aquatic, especially lotic, habitat conditions in breeding cages, Group V includes only the residue of aquatic species that may not be reared or cultured by the methods used for groups II and IV.

Some or all of the known larvae of the various species of Dicranota, Hexatoma, Pedicia, Protoplasa, and Longurio live in the gravel, sand, or sandy silt of rill, creek, or shallow river bottoms and margins but migrate well above the water-line to pupate. The larvae of Dicranota, Hexatoma, and Pedicia are predacious and very active. Half grown or older larvae of *Hexatoma fuliginosa, H. aurata, H. tristis, Pedicia inconstans, P. johnsoni,* and *P. paludicola* have been carried through to the adult stage in rearing jars in which wet sand or sandy gravel was piled an inch or more above the water-line on one side of the jar. Water from a reservoir was allowed to drip slowly onto this emergent bank, while a low water level was maintained in the jar by means of a constant-level siphon. These larvae were all provided with tubificid or lumbriculid worms for food.

Tipula abdominalis larvae, 6-8 mm. long and probably early 2nd instar, have been carried through to the adult stage in a small artificial sand-bottom stream. A stream course with emergent banks was molded in coarse wet sand in a cypress trough, 3 feet by 2 feet by 10 inches deep. The trough was nearly divided longitudinally by a wooden partition so that about 6 feet of stream course, in the form of a "U" was provided.

Tap water was run through the stream in a very slow current and leaf drift from natural streams was allowed to form drifts against pilings made from skewers. This arrangement was most successful in a shaded position out of doors, where it received enough light to permit the growth of diatoms and blue-green algae on the submerged leaves. *Pedicia albivitta* larvae have lived in a somewhat similar arrangement for over 3 months and then pupated and emerged, but this species is predacious and should be provided with annelid worms or small larvae for food.

Bittacomorpha clavipes and *Ptychoptera rufocincta* are easily reared in aquaria provided with water from the habitat and containing enough sphagnum and coarse plant detritus to form feeding and resting places within breathing-tube-reach (5-15 mm.) of the surface. For Ptychoptera some of the sphagnum should project above the surface. Bittacomorpha has been carried through 3 generations in one such aquarium, the females ovipositing while in flight above the surface of the water. Some support, such as loosely hung horizontal lengths of thread across the top of the aquarium, should be provided for the adults.

Mature larvae of many, probably most, aquatic forms may be carried through to the adult stage in loosely packed, wet, but well aerated, mosses. Wet, aerated mosses also form the best medium in which to store temporarily and to transport aquatic immature stages. Larvae and pupae will remain alive and vigorous for several days in such moss but usually die within a few hours if placed in water.

Family CULICIDAE

METHODS OF REARING, MANIPULATING, AND CONSERVING ANOPHELINE IMAGINES IN CAPTIVITY*

MARK F. BOYD, T. L. CAIN, JR., and J. A. MULRENNAN, *Station for Malaria Research, Tallahassee, Florida*

CERTAIN earlier publications (Boyd, 1926, 1930) presented improved methods for large scale rearing of anopheline larvae which depended upon feeding the larvae abundant quantities of Fleishmann's yeast, placed in accessible positions in the rearing vessel. However heavy larval mortality continued and the resulting imagines were smaller than those encountered in nature and unreliable in their biting proclivities. This problem has been solved by rearing the larvae in vegetable infusions kept at a constant temperature.

The technique was originally developed with *Anopheles quadrimaculatus* and has been found equally applicable without modification to the

---

*Arranged from articles in *Amer. J. Hyg.* 16:832, 1932; *Amer. J. Hyg.* 16:839, 1932; and *Amer. J. Trop. Med.* 15:385, 1935.

successful maintenance of a colony of *A. punctipennis*. A limited success has been achieved in the culture of *A. crucians* sufficient to learn that some of the procedures necessary to the rearing of *A. quadrimaculatus* and *A. punctipennis* must be more or less modified for this species.

Colonies have been started by the collection of ova from gravid wild females confined in small cages above dishes of water. These were given a blood meal every three days as long as their ova were required.

In the insectary a large tank raised 2 feet from the floor is maintained as a balanced aquarium filled with water to a depth of 6 inches and stocked with aquatic vegetation and snails. Normally the water is never changed, though more is added as replacement is necessary to maintain the proper level. A small handful of hay is placed in it once a week, as a source of food for the snails. A small amount of lime water is added once a month to provide calcium for them, and about 5 grams of ammonium nitrate in solution is added twice a year as an extra source of nitrogen for the aquatic plants. The aquarium attracts the female mosquitoes as a place for oviposition. Oviposition is most abundant along the edges and where the horizontal vegetation breaks the surface film. The space beneath the tank serves as a dark, humid diurnal shelter for the imagines.*

In routine insectary operations, ova are collected from the aquarium by skimming the water surface (which is an egg trap for ovipositing females) with a cereal bowl. Before skimming, the bowl should be wet to prevent the ova from sticking to the sides. The ova are dipped from the bowl with a bent spoon, and poured into a folded paper in a funnel. After the collection has been made, any larvae present are removed with a pipette, and the ova are washed to the bottom of the filter cone by a gentle stream of water.

The surplus ova are stored in a Frigidaire at the laboratory for 2 weeks, as an insurance against any accident. The moist paper filters bearing the ova are kept in ½ pint fruit jars.

As required but before the end of two weeks the ova are taken from the Frigidaire and returned to the insectary to be incubated. The ova are washed from the filter paper by means of a pipette into the space within a cork ring floating in a small bowl of water. The cork ring prevents them from stranding on the sides of the bowl as evaporation lowers the water level. They are incubated by floating the bowl in the aquarium in the summer, and in the water bath with a temperature of 70° F. in the winter. They should be kept in the bowl until they enter the second stage, and during this period are fed only on yeast.

In the outdoor insectary optimum temperature is provided by rearing

---

* For further details of the construction and operation of the insectary see: MARK F. BOYD, T. L. CAIN, JR., and J. A. MULRENNAN: "The insectary rearing of *Anopheles quadrimaculatus.*" *Amer. J. Trop. Med.* 15:385, 1935.

the larvae in a constant temperature water bath which has capacity for 6 pans. In the winter months this is heated to 70° F. by contained electrical heating units. In the summer it is cooled to 70° F. by the coils of a Frigidaire refrigerating plant.

The infusions are made, and the larvae subsequently kept when the infusion is ripe, in white enameled cream pans, about 12 inches in diameter and 2½ inches deep.

Early successful culture of the larvae on a large scale is attributable to the employment of pans of hay infusion for their rearing, the rich autogenous plankton of which, especially when supplemented by a supply of yeast, affords an abundance of food and results in the production of large vigorous pupae and imagines. While successful, hay infusions have not been satisfactory; their qualities vary widely depending on the hay employed; they are from a biological standpoint very complex; and they may only be employed for larval nutrition after a lengthy process of fermentation. It was observed that pans were satisfactory for larval nutrition after the reaction had become alkaline and if a dense growth of Paramecium and flagellates occurred. Considerable experimentation was carried on in an effort to reproduce these conditions in a simpler manner. After trying extracts from various vegetables and seeds, as well as synthetic media, wheat infusions were found to serve as a satisfactory base for cultures and now hay infusions are abandoned.

Wheat infusions are prepared as follows: One or two ounces of sound wheat grains are placed in a beaker which is partly filled with tap water. The beaker is then placed over a flame and the water boiled for a few minutes. When boiled, about 250 grains are placed in an enamel pan with 2 liters of tap water. The pan is placed where it will receive very diffused light in the laboratory. After 2 or 3 days when a visible bacterial growth is present it is heavily inoculated from a previously prepared plankton culture in wheat infusion. After 4 or 5 days' further incubation at room temperature nebulous masses of flagellates in descending convection currents are clearly visible and the pan is ready for the introduction of larvae. At the time when a series of pans is prepared a separate culture is made to serve for the inoculation of the next series. The original mixed culture of Paramecium and flagellates was secured from a satisfactory ripened pan of hay infusion. Alkalinity is maintained by adding 1 gram of powdered calcium carbonate to each pan and neutralization of acid is probably facilitated by the gentle stirring of the settled $CaCO_3$ from the bottom once a day. After being placed in service a culture will give from 2 to 3 weeks' service before being discarded. Water loss by evaporation should be replaced. If a slimy envelope developes about 4th stage larvae, the affected larvae may be placed in a 1% solution of NaCl for 30-45 minutes and then returned to their pan.

For both *A. quadrimaculatus* and *A. punctipennis* an alkaline reaction is required. For *A. crucians,* the hay infusion pans have been used while in the acid phase, and later employed for the other species. The acid phase may be prolonged by the addition of small amounts of sugar from time to time.

To start a new rearing pan, approximately 250-300 larvae, with the larger stages predominating, are transferred to the infusion by means of a teaspoon or a pipette. It is imperative that the larger larvae preponderate, in order that they may consume any surface pellicle as it forms, thereby preventing undue mortality among the smaller larvae. Our experience indicates that it becomes necessary at times, to vary the number of larvae from the normal limits for a few days in individual pans to maintain a balance between food production and consumption. There is no criterion that may be given, whereby an inexperienced person would be justified in increasing or decreasing the number. This is a matter of experience.

Pans are operated to contribute a quota of pupae daily. If 250-300 larvae are maintained, 20-25 pupae will be furnished daily by each pan. The places vacated by the pupae are filled by adding about 50% more small larvae than the number of pupae removed, which is done to offset the mortality.

The food supplied by the infusion does not appear to be wholly adequate for satisfactory development. Hence in order to obtain imagines of maximum size, it is still found advantageous to supplement the diet with Fleishmann's yeast. The yeast is placed on a glass slide which is floated about ⅛-inch below the surface of the water by means of a cork float. The amount of yeast to be placed upon the slide must be determined by the rapidity with which it is devoured. Experience indicates that best results are obtained when moderate amounts are used and renewed several times each day if necessary. The glass slide and float should be washed daily to remove the old yeast cells adhering.

It is found desirable to employ some type of floatage to secure uniform distribution of the larvae in the pans. This reduces the opportunity for cannibalism and serves to equalize feeding opportunities. Chaff is scattered over the surface or several paraffined sticks or cork strips may be floated on the surface.

As transformation into pupae takes place, they are removed daily with a pipette to an eclosion pan of tap water. Some type of floatage must be used on the water surface of this pan to keep the pupae spaced apart. If this is not done they tend to collect around the edge, where they nervously bump into one another and jeopardize the safety of those emerging. Broken hay, chaff, or ground cork may be used for floatage. The floatage also aids the emerging adults by providing support for the tarsi and thereby reducing the risk of the adults becoming caught in the surface film.

It is advisable to change the water in the eclosion pan daily to prevent pellicle formation, which will kill the pupae. This pan is placed beneath a specially built eclosion cage in the form of a screened cone that fits over the edge of the pan. It is kept in a cool dark place in the summer, and in the water bath in the winter.

Small pupae indicate that the larvae are undernourished. This may arise from either the use of pans with insufficient plankton or from keeping too many larvae in a pan. Undersized pupae should be killed, as the imagines they produce will be useless.

Early attempts at insectary rearing of anophelines indicated that considerable space was required for nuptial maneuvering. Mating of individuals recently derived from wild stock did not occur in small cages, and it was not until the imagines were confined in a cage with dimensions of approximately 8 by 10 by 13 feet, that the fertilization of sufficient females was secured. In addition to adequate space, mating also requires that the breeding stock of the colony be composed of large, vigorous imagines.

A. quadrimaculatus can become well adapted to life in such an artificial environment. Up to the present (June, 1936) the Florida colony has passed through the 48th generation, allowing an average of one generation per month in captivity. This adaptation probably accounts for the successful establishment of a sub-colony in a small cage with screened sides, 30 inches square and 36 inches high. The imagines originally introduced were taken from an eclosion cage before mating, about 56 hours after emergence and had just previously been fed, the males on glucose and the females on blood. In the new environment, the colony has already been maintained for several generations.

The breeding colony requires very little attention other than the establishment of a reliable source for blood meals. This is most satisfactory when furnished from the person of the technician in charge. One of the most important factors in establishing a new colony is to have an attendant who will conscientiously endeavor to persuade all the females to feed as often as possible. The males are fed on raisins continuously kept on several small trays, or they may be fed on dextrose solution, which is a satisfactory food. Dead imagines are picked up daily to keep out fungous and bacterial contamination.

In Florida, density of the colony is maintained at about 5,000 adults in the winter, and decreased to about 3,000 in the summer. This is done because we find that mortality is greater in the winter months, while feeding and egg laying are diminished. A ratio of approximately 2 males to 1 female is maintained.

The sand on the floor of the space under the aquarium (diurnal shelter for imagines) is kept saturated with water the year around to increase the humidity. Periods of excessively dry weather necessitate the flooding of the floor of the insectary with water in the summer. By so doing it has been possible to reduce the imaginal mortality which follows high temperature and low humidity. When the mosquitoes are kept in lantern chimneys or glass cylinders, considerable trouble arises from the condensation of moisture on the surface of the interior of the containers upon their removal to warm air. In order to keep the mosquitoes from contact with any solid surface on which moisture might condense, a type of cage has been developed consisting of a bobbinet cylinder stretched on a brass frame and tied in position. Only a very narrow ring of brass at each end is exposed in the interior of the cage, and this is covered with a narrow strip of filter paper which absorbs any condensing moisture. When cages become soiled, the cylinders are removed, washed, starched, and stretched over glass bottles to dry. Closure of the ends of the cages is effected with squares of bobbinet secured by rubber bands.

For the catching of individual mosquitoes in cages there has been devised a special catching apparatus consisting of a test tube secured over one tine of a spring forceps and a sliding lid placed over the other tine.

When the mosquitoes are being removed from a cage with a catching tube a special cover is placed over the open end of the cage. This is made from a heavy rubber bathing cap consisting of two flat pieces of thin rubber cemented along the crown. In the center of each flat piece a slit is cut. These slits intersect at right angles and form a self-closing orifice. The rubber band securing the bobbinet square over one end of the cage containing mosquitoes is removed, and the bathing cap is laid over the bobbinet with the slits over the center of the cage. The bobbinet square is then drawn out from underneath and the cap is secured in place by the rubber band. If the mosquitoes are to be transferred to an empty cage with the catching tube, the transfer cage is similarly prepared. The cage containing the mosquitoes is taken up in the left hand, with the cap-covered-end toward the operator. The catching tube is held in the right hand; it is closed by pressure on the forceps tines, inserted through the slit orifice in the cap, and opened. The open tube is then gently placed over a mosquito resting on the opposite bobbinet end of the cage. The mosquito will fly into the tube, and the open end may be closed by pressure on the tines and the tube removed. If the mosquito is to be transferred, the closed tube is inserted through the orifice into the second cage and is opened by decreasing the pressure on the tines. The mosquito is induced to fly out by gentle tapping. If it is desired to kill the mosquito, a pledget of cotton saturated with chloroform is placed over the mouth of the tube.

When females are required for experimental purposes they are separated from the males by means of the catching tube after transfer from the eclosion cage to a small bobbinet cage to be transported to the laboratory. The males and surplus females are released in the insectary to join the colony. A pledget of cotton moistened with a 10% dextrose solution is placed over the top or side of the cage. We have found that longevity of the females is greatly increased if they have fed on dextrose some days prior to their application to a malaria patient.

The females are carried to the laboratory and placed in a 20° C. incubator, where they remain 2 or 3 days, or until they have all had a feeding of dextrose. They are then put into a large bobbinet storage cage holding approximately 300 mosquitoes and placed in a Frigidaire, where they remain until required for use.

When females are to be infected, they are starved about 2 days before they are to be given the infecting blood meal. They will take a feed better if they are given their opportunity from 7 to 10 days after eclosion.

It is desirable for various reasons to infect mosquitoes on their first feed. On this occasion they can ingest a larger volume of blood than at any subsequent time. Immediately after feeding, the insects which fed should be separated from those which did not, and the latter are discarded. This separation must be done with great care in order to avoid injury to the distended mosquito.

After mosquitoes have received their initial infecting feeding on an infectious human subject, their subsequent nutritional or conservation feedings are taken from a rabbit. This rabbit is secured to an operating board and the hair is clipped from its side over an area sufficient to permit the application of the cage end directly to the skin. We find it very important to first apply the mosquitoes to the rabbit the day following their infective feeding, and to then employ great patience in order to persuade the maximum number to feed on the animal. Thereafter during the extrinsic incubation period, they are given an opportunity to feed every third day by exposing the caged insects to the rabbit for about fifteen minutes. After sporozoites are present in the salivary glands of the mosquitoes, the cages are transferred to the Frigidaire. They are then only allowed to feed on the rabbit once a week. Pledgets of moist cotton are kept on each cage to maintain humidity at saturation and to give the insects an opportunity to drink. All cages are examined daily for the detection of dead mosquitoes, which are removed for dissection. After they become infective, they are stored in a Frigidaire at a temperature varying from 2° to 17° C. except when they are permitted to feed weekly for purposes of conservation. Mosquitoes are transported to and from the hospital in a picnic refrigerator.

Insects that are incubating an infection are kept in a cool incubator, adjusted to maintain as closely as possible a temperature from 20° to 22° C. Close attention must be paid to the operation of incubators, as mortality progressively increases as the temperature ascends above 22° C. For their control they should be provided with maximum and minimum thermometers which are read and set daily.

Wooden rings are used as cages for the application of individual infectious-mosquitoes' inoculation of patients. The rings have the same diameter as the large cage frames and a small rim around the outer edges so that the bobbinet squares may be retained by a rubber band. One square is dyed black to facilitate observation of the mosquito. The rings may be turned out of any dense wood. Their interior should be sandpapered, painted white and sandpapered again to present a smooth surface. A number of these rings, each with its mosquito, may be placed in a copper petri dish can during transportation in the icebox.

Overcrowding of the mosquitoes in a cage is an important cause of injury. The risk increases with a rise in the temperature of storage. The best results are secured when about 5 cubic inches of space is allowed for each insect. The chilling of mosquitoes during transportation is very important to immobilize them and reduce the danger from contusion arising from collisions especially when they are full of blood.

Success requires close and conscientious daily attention to the mosquitoes and in all handling and manipulation they should be treated with all possible gentleness.

BIBLIOGRAPHY

BOYD, MARK F. 1926. A note on the rearing of anopheline larvae. *Bull. Ent. Res.* 16:308.

———— 1930. The cage rearing of *Anopheles quadrimaculatus*. *Amer. J. Trop. Med.* 9:165.

A MOSQUITO REARING CAGE

F. C. BAKER, *U. S. Bureau of Entomology and Plant Quarantine*

THIS indoor mosquito cage (Figs. 68 and 69) was constructed in the spring of 1933 as a modification of the Boyd anopheline breeding cage. A brief description of this cage is recorded, not because it is an ideal type to be copied in detail, but for three other merits: (1) It was fairly successful, both in the maintenance of a cage colony of *Anopheles quadrimaculatus* and in culturing *Aedes triseriatus* and *Culex pipiens*. (2) The cage and equipment cost only about $25. (3) It may help someone else in designing his own artificial mosquito habitat to fit prevailing circumstances when a greenhouse is available.

The mosquito rearing cage is located in one of the compartments of an insectary greenhouse. It is 4' x 10' and 11' high. Its length extends in an east-west direction. On the south and west, 3' of its height is concrete wall, 4′ is glass sash, and 4′ is beaver board. On the north side the wall comprises the bottom 1.5′ of its height; the center 5.5′ is covered with 16-mesh, iron wire gauze; while the top 4′ is beaver board. The east end is covered by the same kind of mosquito netting for a distance of 7′ from the floor; then beaver board for the top 4′ of the

MOSQUITO REARING CAGE

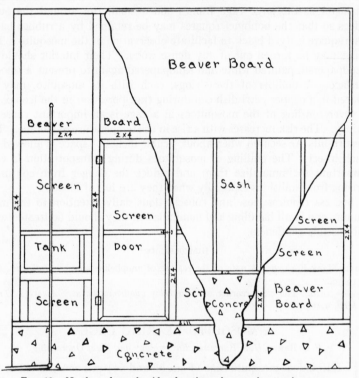

Fig. 68.—North and south side elevation of mosquito rearing cage.

wall. The ceiling is beaver board. There are opaque curtains that are hung just above the glass or screen on all sides. These may be rolled down from the outside, so that light intensity may be fairly accurately controlled. The screen door swings outward. Inside, it is guarded by three, weighted cheesecloth curtains.

Across the west end and about 3 feet from the floor level is a permanent shelf that is 2.5′ wide. Its under surface and nether walls are blackened. The opening to the space under the shelf is partially closed by a concrete foundation wall which extends upward for about half of

the distance from the floor to the free edge of the shelf. The bottom
of this pit is covered by a layer of moist white sand. It was designed as
a dark, humid, quiet resting place for imagos. From the 1.5′ fore-wall
that is below the edge of the shelf, to the east end of the cage is a

MOSQUITO REARING CAGE

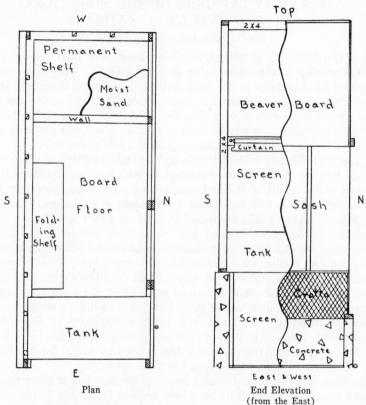

FIG. 69.—Plan and end elevation (from the east) of mosquito rearing cage.

wooden floor. Across the east end is a 44 gallon wooden tank, the
bottom of which is 3′ above the floor. It has a free water surface of
6.4 square feet. Four feet directly above the vat is a water vaporizing
nozzle that is similar to those used on vegetable stands. It is kept
continuously in action. That fraction of the water jet which is not
beaten into a mist is conducted out of the cage and allowed to flow over
the walk of the greenhouse compartment. The element of the mist that
does not evaporate falls into the tank. The overflow from the vat passes

through a small pipe to the west end where it moistens the sand of the grotto. A few potted plants usually are kept on a shelf which is within range of the humidifier. It is felt that vegetation adds something to the naturalness of the artificial habitat in the cage.

LABORATORY BREEDING OF THE MOSQUITOES, CULEX PIPIENS AND C. FATIGANS

CLAY G. HUFF, *University of Chicago*

MOSQUITOES of the genus Culex have been bred chiefly for studies on the transmission of avian malaria. They have substituted for Anopheles and human malaria in many studies where the breeding of Anopheles or the experimental inoculation of human malaria has proved impossible or very difficult. When more research has been devoted to the laboratory breeding of mosquitoes it will very probably be found that they are adaptable to many other kinds of research.

The chief difficulty encountered in trying to adapt either *Culex pipiens* or *C. fatigans* (=*C. quinquefasciatus*) to laboratory conditions is the failure of the adults of the first generation reared in the laboratory to copulate. This is true to a much lesser extent of *C. fatigans* than of *C. pipiens*. When adults are reared from larvae which have been either collected in nature or hatched from wild-caught females, the second generation females will readily engorge on blood and will oviposit, but only in a very small number of cases will their eggs hatch. This indicates that copulation has probably not occurred. It should be stated, however, that this is the case when the adults are kept in small containers (no larger than lantern globes). It seems likely that copulation would occur frequently in large insectaries such as those employed by Boyd for Anopheles. The only method of overcoming this difficulty has been that of breeding entirely from the very few mosquitoes which did copulate in captivity. At times I have been fortunate in securing a raft of fertile eggs from a comparatively small number of females, but at other times many thousands of egg rafts have been secured before any fertile ones would be encountered. In all cases, however, in which a strain of mosquitoes had been secured from females which had mated in captivity, no further difficulty was met in securing copulation of the adults of the succeeding generations.

FOOD REQUIREMENTS OF ADULTS

Adults of these two species will survive for fairly long periods on many different fruits, but the one which has proved most satisfactory in the laboratory is cooked raisins. The large varieties are most satisfactory. A beaker is half filled with raisins and covered with water. They are boiled until almost dry and the water replenished and the boiling continued until the raisins are suspended in their own syrup. These may be kept in a refrigerator in good condition usually until they are all used up. One or two of these large raisins placed on top of the gauze netting of the bréeding cage, if moistened each day, will usually not need to be replaced for 4 to 10 days.

Although it has been shown (Huff, 1929) that females of *C. pipiens* will ovulate and produce viable eggs upon diets other than blood (such as egg yolk, ox gall, and potato, carrot, and apple juices) as well as the various fractions of blood, it is advisable to feed them upon living animals if one wishes to use them or their progeny in blood feeding experiments.

Gravid females require the free surface of water, or completely saturated substances such as cellucotton, for oviposition. For maintaining stock I use lantern globe cages placed over crystallizing dishes into which the globes fit snugly (a dish 90 mm. in diameter and 50 mm. deep is required for most makes of globes). For isolation of progenies the females may be placed, one each, in standard-sized bacteriological test tubes ⅓ filled with water and plugged with cotton. Oviposition occurs much earlier and in a larger number of cases when test tubes rather than larger cages are used. The period elapsing between the blood meal and oviposition may also be appreciably shortened by selection of those progenies derived from the eggs earliest laid.

The feeding and care of the larvae is the most difficult part of the whole technique of caring for these two species. The larvae may be grown satisfactorily in white enameled pans or the square refrigerator dishes which nest one in the other when many different lots must be stored in a small space. Although these mosquitoes normally live in foul water, great care must be exercised to prevent the cultures from becoming too viscous and turbid when grown in the laboratory. This precaution is much more important, too, while the larvae are young. By judging the amount of food carefully it is often possible to rear a brood of larvae to the pupal stage without changing the water. As they grow, the amount of food should be greatly increased. If the pabulum becomes viscous or a surface pellicle forms upon it, the larvae must be transferred to fresh water. This is most conveniently done by pouring the entire contents of the pan upon a piece of fine-meshed bolting silk. The larvae are thus filtered out and may be transferred to the clean water by turning the bolting silk over onto the surface of the water. A variety of substances may be employed as food, such as banana, old protozoan cultures, and dehydrated blood serum, but the one found most satisfactory is dehydrated, skimmed milk. This is available at all times in the same condition and may be administered in carefully graded amounts. It should be added daily from the time of hatching until pupation, in very small amounts at first and then in increasing amounts as the larvae become able to keep the water clear. The amounts needed must be learned by experience.

When the pupae appear they are removed daily by means of a pipette with a large opening. They are placed in containers exactly like the ones previously described for oviposition. Successful emergence from the pupal stage requires that the surface film of the water be quiet, clean, and free from oils. An example of the extreme susceptibility of pupae to oils is afforded by my discovery at one time that eclosion could not occur in a room containing pigeons. The dandruff or scales from the feathers of these birds which settled from the air upon the surface of the water disturbed the surface tension sufficiently to effect this result.

The newly-emerged adults may be kept in lantern globe cages placed over petri dishes into which pads of cellucotton have been fitted and then moistened. While adults of *C. pipiens* and *C. fatigans* will live and grow in a wide range of temperatures, they thrive best at about 80° F. Although they will probably live longer at the lower temperatures used by Boyd for Anopheles, they will live for two months or more at 80° F. This, of course, is an advantage, since a cool incubator is not required for storing them. The females may be fed upon birds or other experimental animals by allowing them to bite directly through the gauze netting of their cages. Separation of the unengorged from the gorged females may be accomplished by catching them singly by means of a small vial from a catching bag made of netting and provided with a sleeve. I have for some time been anesthetizing them with ether in the globe cages and then separating them quickly by picking them up carefully by the wings or legs with small forceps having very flexible points. If the minimum exposure to ether sufficient for immobilizing them is used they very quickly recover from the anesthesia and show no harm as a result of it.

When attention is directed to the essential requirements of these species it will be found that they may be grown with ease. Indeed, the simplicity of the task is the chief argument for employing them in many types of experiment.

BIBLIOGRAPHY

HUFF, C. G. 1927. Studies on the infectivity of Plasmodia of birds for mosquitoes, with special reference to the problem of immunity in the mosquito. *Amer. J. Hyg.* 7:706.

———— 1929. Ovulation requirements of *Culex pipiens* Linn. *Biol. Bull.* 56:347.

———— 1929. The effects of selection upon susceptibility to bird malaria in *Culex pipiens* Linn. *Ann. Trop. Med. and Paras.* 23:427.

———— 1931. The inheritance of natural immunity to *Plasmodium cathemerium* in two species of Culex. *J. Prev. Med.* 5:249.

THE CULTURE OF MOSQUITO LARVAE FREE FROM LIVING MICRO-ORGANISMS

WILLIAM TRAGER, *Rockefeller Institute for Medical Research*

A METHOD has recently been described (Trager, 1935) whereby bacteria-free larvae and adults of the yellow fever mosquito, *Aedes aegypti,* may be readily obtained. The essentials of this method will be briefly summarized here.

STERILIZATION OF THE EGGS

This is accomplished by a slight modification of the method of Mac-Gregor (MacGregor, 1929). "Boats," made out of coverslips by heating their edges in a flame to make them curl down and sterilized by dry heat, are placed in small sterile petri dishes containing a 5% solution of Castile soap. From 5 to 20 eggs (as desired) are put in each boat and left in the soap solution 5 to 7 minutes. With sterile forceps each boat is then lifted out (the eggs coming with it), drained of excess liquid and placed in a sterile petri dish holding 80% alcohol. The eggs are left 15-17 minutes in the alcohol and are then transferred, as before, to a sterile petri dish holding sterile water. Finally, the boat with its contained eggs is lifted with sterile forceps and dropped into a tube of culture medium. This method is nearly 100% successful as long as the eggs used have been laid recently (within 1 to 3 days) on filter paper partly immersed in distilled water.

THE CULTURE MEDIUM

Liver extract. To every 100 cc. of distilled water, 0.5 gm. of Eli Lilly and Company liver extract #343 is added. The somewhat turbid mixture, when filtered through paper, gives a clear amber-colored filtrate. The pH of this solution is adjusted to 7.0 by the addition of N/1 NaOH (about 0.25 to 0.3 cc. per 100 cc. of solution). The medium is then sterilized either by passage through a Berkefeld "N" filter or by autoclaving.

Yeast. A strain of Fleischmann's bakers' yeast may be used. Two- to 4-day growths from the surface of Blake bottles of dextrose agar are suspended in sterile tap water, centrifuged down, re-suspended in sterile distilled water, again centrifuged, and finally suspended in enough sterile distilled water so that 10 to 11 cc. of suspension contain the yeast from one Blake bottle. The yeast suspension is then killed by heating at 80°-85° C. for 30 minutes. Ordinarily, 1 cc. of such a yeast extract is added to each large test tube (22 x 180 mm.) containing 12 to 14 cc. of the liver extract.

An even simpler but equally effective medium may be made by using a 1% suspension of Harris brewers' yeast (dry powder) in the liver extract, the mixture being tubed and autoclaved. If not more than 5 to 10 larvae are present in a tube containing 14 cc. of the liver extract-killed yeast medium, the larval stage of *Aedes aegypti*, at a temperature of 27°-28° C., consumes about 8 days.

BIBLIOGRAPHY

MacGregor, M. E. 1929. The significance of the pH in the development of mosquito larvae. *Paras.* 21:132.

Trager, W. 1935. The culture of mosquito larvae from living micro-organisms. *Amer. J. Hyg.* 22:18.

REFERENCES

For the rearing of mosquito larvae see also pp. 376, 383, and 386.

Family PSYCHODIDAE*

PSYCHODA ALTERNATA AND P. MINUTA**

A STUDY of the breeding habits and life history of *Psychoda alternata* was made with the view of determining whether it might not be used for studies in genetics. The effort was attended with unusual success both in breeding the flies and in the discovery of at least two mutations.

The adults are about 2 mm. in length. They ordinarily breed in decaying vegetation, but dung from either horses or cattle has proved to be an excellent medium. Breeding takes place readily under laboratory conditions, the life cycle being completed in from 12 to 16 days. Adult females are favorably stimulated by the culture medium, so that oviposition takes place quickly. The eggs hatch in a little less than 2 days into active, eyed larvae resembling those of midges. The larvae feed for about 10 days, after which they become quiescent and pupate. Adults emerge 2 days later.

Pedigreed strains were maintained in test tubes and small flasks, while battery jars were employed for large mass-cultures.

M. E. D.

---

* Editor's Note: The reader may find an excellent summary of what is known of the biology of other members of this family in an article entitled Aquatic Diptera Part I. *Nemocera, exclusive of Chironomidae and Ceratopogonidae, Cornell University Agricultural Experiment Station Memoir* 164, pp. 23-24, 1934, by O. A. Johannsen.

** Abstracted from an article in *Science* 60:338, 1924, by C. L. TURNER, *Beloit College.*

Family CERATOPOGONIDAE

METHODS OF COLLECTING AND REARING CERATOPOGONIDAE

LILLIAN THOMSEN, *Bethany College, Lindsborg, Kansas*

LARVAE were collected from various localities and from such materials as blanket algae in ponds; algae in springs, streams, ponds, and lakes; mud taken from the shores of springs, ponds, and lakes; water in tree-holes; and the ooze of ulcers on maple and elm trees.

The material was examined in different ways after being brought in. The larvae in algae could be removed by placing the algae on a screen over a silk bolting cloth bag and playing a strong stream of water on them. This method removed about 75% of the larvae of the swimming type, but such larvae as the Atrichopogon, Stilobezzia, and Dasyhelea had to be removed singly from the algae, the material being examined filament by filament under the binocular microscope. The larvae found in mud were obtained in like manner by sifting the mud. The pebbles were retained by the screen while the mud was washed into a shallow enameled pan and the larvae were then readily seen swimming at the edge or over the bottom of the pan. The larvae living under the bark of trees had to be picked off singly with a needle under a microscope.

After thus collecting and sorting out the various species, each was placed in a separate Syracuse watch glass containing water and material from the natural environment of the larvae. The watch glasses were stacked to prevent evaporation. The herbivorous larvae did not require more food than the algae or bark first supplied them, but the carnivorous larvae required frequent feeding.

The food of the carnivorous forms consisted of newly hatched chironomids, and mosquito and trichopterous larvae. Some of the Bezzia and Probezzia larvae would also attack chironomid larvae two or three times their own diameter. Often a number would help to devour one larva. If no food was available they would become cannibalistic, the victim often being one of their own number in the prepupal stage. The larger larvae such as those of the genera Bezzia and Probezzia would also eat larvae of the smaller Culicoides and Alluaudomyia.

The larvae had to be placed in individual watch glasses, where pupation occurred. The pupae, after remaining in the algae for one or two days, worked their way to the edge of the watch glass by awkward movements of the caudal end of the body. From here they were transferred to cotton-stoppered vials lined with wet blotting paper, where with a wiggling movement they would work their way up the sides. After emergence the flies were transferred to dry vials. Attempts were made to feed the adults and to obtain eggs in captivity but these were unsuccessful.

Family CHIRONOMIDAE

METHODS FOR PROPAGATION OF THE MIDGE, CHIRONOMUS TENTANS*

THE fact that chironomid larvae and pupae constitute one of the staple food items in the ration of nearly all carnivorous young fish has been observed and mentioned by many writers. It has now been observed that chironomid larvae may be reared profitably, in conjunction with Daphnia and other fish food organisms, in small propagating ponds treated with artificial fertilizer and connected with a natural rearing pond for young fish.

The midge, *Chironomus tentans,* is well adapted to such propagation. It has many of the characteristics essential to any organism that is to be propagated in such quantities as to render its use as food for fish both desirable and practical. It has a high reproductive capacity. Each female lays one batch of eggs averaging about 2,300 in number, which hatch in about three days at normal summer temperatures. The larvae attain a size sufficiently large for feeding purposes in 16-20 days. They may be reared on plant products which are inexpensive and everywhere easily obtainable. There are at least four generations a year with an overlapping of the cycles which ensures a fairly constant supply of adults and eggs.

In the vicinity of Ithaca, N. Y., the breeding season ordinarily begins about the last of April and continues throughout the summer and early fall, ending about the first of October. These dates are based on normal weather conditions and seasonal changes, and will vary as they do. The species overwinters in the larval stage. By the time the water has warmed up to 10° C. the larvae commence to pupate and shortly thereafter the adults appear. As the water cools down in the fall transformation becomes less rapid and ceases completely about 8° C.

The rate of mortality during the egg stage is exceedingly low. That during the larval stage is high, and as yet the controlling factor is unknown. The results of several experiments indicate a loss of from about 15% to 30%. The major portion of this loss occurs during the first 8 or 10 days of larval life.

In general, midge larvae eat whatever is offered them, but under permissive circumstances they do exercise a certain amount of selectivity

* Abstracted from *Cornell University Agric. Exper. Sta.*, Memoir 173, 1935, by WILLIAM O. SADLER, *Mississippi College.*

in feeding. I have found evidence of a selection of milk in preference to algae; a fact which agrees with the observations of Branch (1923) in regard to *C. cristatus* [see p. 395]. Except for milk, algae are preferred to other materials. Obviously the larval habitat determines the variety of food, but where algae are present in sufficient quantities they comprise the bulk of the diet.

Three methods of feeding midge larvae have been tried experimentally. In all cases the actual procedure in rearing the larvae has been the same, namely that of treating stagnant concrete ponds or wooden troughs or tanks with different kinds of fertilizers and stocking them with eggs. The fertilizer, besides attracting the adults for the purpose of egg laying, produces a rich culture of microscopic algae. In ponds fertilized with soybean meal, Chlamydomonas and Chlorella were the two principal algal forms; in those fertilized with sheep manure and superphosphate, diatoms and desmids predominated.

Sheep manure and superphosphate, sheep manure and soybean meal, and soybean meal alone have been used as fertilizing agents. Where the soybean meal was used by itself or in combination with sheep manure, it was first poured into a good-sized pan, and enough water added to form a thin soup. The pan was then set out in the open and the mixture allowed to ferment for at least 24 hours before it was poured into the pond. This procedure prevented over-pollution of the water unless an excessive amount of fertilizer was used. After the ponds were fertilized, they were allowed to stand until a culture of larvae was produced.

Controlled spawning. In this method of propagation all operations were performed within a screen wire enclosure. Under such conditions it was possible to control the spawning of the adults and thus insure that the basins in which the larvae were reared were sufficiently stocked with eggs.

The equipment used for testing the practicability of this method consisted of a screen wire cage 8½ x 11 x 12½ ft., enclosing three of a series of six concrete ponds, 5 x 8 ft. with a water volume of 18 cu. ft. Water was supplied to each pond from a raceway controlled by slash boards. Each pond was equipped with a separate intake and drain. By plugging the drains the ponds could be kept stagnant, and at the same time a constant level maintained.

One pond was used to supply adults. It was stocked with grown larvae at the beginning of the season and a few were added about 20 days later. After that the eggs deposited in the pond kept it well stocked. The other two ponds were used for rearing larvae. Since the number of eggs deposited in these ponds was always more than sufficient for stocking them, and as natural enemies were excluded, it would seem that the limiting factor of production was perhaps insufficient or improper food or the chemical composition of the water.

The highest rate of production was obtained under these controlled spawning conditions. This method, however, has the disadvantage of being the most expensive of the three. The breeding cage described cost $91.11, but this amount could be greatly reduced by reducing the height of the cage. After the cage was built it was discovered that it was twice as high as was necessary, since the adults will mate in a very small enclosure.

Natural spawning. This method of propagation differs from the preceding in that the ponds used for rearing the larvae were not screened in and were stocked with eggs by the natural supply of midges attracted to them. Under such conditions it was, of course, impossible to limit the stocking to a single species. "Blood worms" of several species occurred in these cultures; the predominant ones were *Chironomus tentans, C. cayugae,* and *C. cristatus,* enumerated in the order of abundance.

The natural spawning method requires less labor and time, and does not necessitate the expense of a screen cover. On the other hand, the rate of production is considerably lower than that of the other two methods. The results obtained, however, and the fact that the method is very simple in operation and practical in application, seem to justify its use.

Natural spawning supplemented. In this method the natural supply of eggs deposited by wild breeders was supplemented with eggs taken from the breeding cage. The procedure in operating these ponds was to fertilize them as before and then, two days later, to stock them with a supply of midge eggs from the breeding cage. The eggs were collected with a small dip net and transferred to a pan of water in which they were carried to the ponds or troughs to be stocked.

The natural spawning method supplemented by eggs from breeders reared in captivity has also a high rate of production, but here again a breeding cage must be maintained. However, the rearing pond does not need to be screened in, and therefore the expense is not nearly so great as for controlled spawning. The breeding cage used in this investigation supplied an average of 94 egg masses per day over a period of 6 weeks, and this number of eggs is sufficient for supplementing six or eight 8 x 12 ft. ponds. Therefore, a single cage properly operated will support a number of ponds. One can collect 100 egg masses in 30 minutes if the water in the ponds is not deeper than 4-5 inches.

Of the fertilizers which have been tried, soybean meal gave the best production; sheep manure plus soybean meal gave the second best; and the combination of sheep manure and superphosphate gave the poorest. Soybean meal alone is less expensive than the other two combinations.

The correct amount needed for treating a pond may be determined only approximately because of the limited data at hand. Often two ponds equally fertilized and run parallel show a wide variation in production. It appears that the best results were obtained with soybean meal used at the rate of 2½ pts. to 100 cu. ft. of water. The method of administering the fertilizer which has proved the most satisfactory is that of starting the pond with 1 to 1½ pts. of the fermented meal per 100 cu. ft. of water and then fertilizing again at the rate of 1 pt. per 100 cu. ft. of water when the culture begins to clear up—that is, when the green color, due to the presence of microscopic algae, begins to disappear. This happens usually 6 to 10 days after the culture is started, but it varies greatly with different ponds and with weather conditions. If too much fertilizer is used in starting the pond it becomes so polluted that all the midge eggs are killed. Two quarts of soybean meal per 100 cu. ft. of water will produce such conditions in a pond. It is better to under-fertilize than to over-fertilize, because more may be added as it is needed without over-polluting the water and killing the larvae.

The length of time required to produce a culture of larvae varied with the water temperature. Summer temperatures for the ponds experimented with ranged from 20° to 28.5° C. Usually 18 to 20 days were sufficient for the culture to run, but when cool, cloudy weather conditions prevailed for several days the period was extended 3 or 4 days. It is probable that in a warmer climate the period could be reduced to 15 or 16 days.

M. E. D.

BIBLIOGRAPHY

BRANCH, HAZEL E. 1923. The life history of *Chironomus cristatus* Fabr. with descriptions of the species. *J. N. Y. Ent. Soc.* 31:15.

CHIRONOMUS CRISTATUS*

THE larvae grow readily in water charged with milk and no difficulty has been experienced in obtaining heavy cultures and having them thrive and maintain themselves in such a medium both indoors and out.

In the indoor experiments, white enameled pans of various sizes were used. In these water was put to a depth of not less than ¾ of an inch and soil was added to cover the bottom. These pans were then stocked with either egg masses or young midge larvae. Milk in a known proportion to the volume of water in the pan was added to these pans daily; thus the dilution for the best growing conditions was determined. The water was not changed but sufficient fresh water was added each day to

*Abstracted from an article in *J. N. Y. Ent. Soc.* 31:15, 1923, by HAZEL E. BRANCH, *University of Wichita.*

maintain the original volume. By these means the conditions of a semi-stagnant pool were simulated. By screening the pans, several generations of bloodworms were raised in the same pan.*

In the outdoor experiments, a sluice of about 125 ft. x 3 ft. and also a series of three ponds fed by pipes from this sluice were constructed. This sluice and the ponds, having been artificially stocked, received milk waste daily. Other forms naturally found their way into these artificial breeding places but *Chironomus cristatus* easily maintained itself as the dominant form present.

During the 1st instar a thousand larvae will not take care of more than 0.1 cc. or 2 drops of milk waste in 300 cc. of water each day. They will, however, thrive in this medium and keep the water clear and odorless. The length of this instar varies with temperature but around 65° F. it is normal to look for the molt about the eighth day. During the 2nd instar, which lasts about 7 days, the food percentage may be raised to 0.2 cc. per 300 cc. of water for a thousand larvae. The 3rd instar lasts about 11-18 days and during this stage the food percentage may be raised to 0.5 cc. per 300 cc. for a thousand larvae. This is also the best growing medium for a mixed lot of larvae of all ages. The duration of the 4th instar is extremely variable and during this stage the same food percentage is used as for the 3rd instar, though a higher one may be used for several days without detriment.

The pupal stage seldom lasts more than 3 days and the adult life is about 4 or 5 days.

M. E. D.

REFERENCE

For the rearing of midge larvae see also p. 392.

Family CECIDOMYIDAE

A METHOD FOR STUDYING THE HESSIAN FLY AND OTHER INSECTS**

IN THE Hessian fly investigations, the wheat was planted in soil or sand and allowed to grow to a height of two or three inches. The plants were then removed from the soil, the roots thoroughly washed to

---

*Editor's Note: In *Canad. Ent.* 49:418, 1917, Chi Ping, of Cornell University, reported the rearing of *C. riparius* and *C. decorus* larvae on ground leaves of Potamogeton and on leaves and stems of Elodea. He kept imagines in the laboratory in bell jars near a window where they were exposed to sunlight for only several hours during the day. Moisture was maintained to saturation by keeping Elodea and Sphagnum in the jars, by sticking a few pieces of fully saturated blotting paper to the inner surface of the glass, and by wetting the cheesecloth that covered the top. M. E. D.

** Abstracted from an article in *Ann. Ent. Soc. Amer.* 14:227, 1921, by the late JAMES W. McCOLLOCH, *Kansas State Agricultural Experiment Station.*

remove all soil particles, and then placed in wide-mouthed bottles of 200 cc. capacity, containing about 150 cc. of the water culture. One plant was placed in each bottle, the roots being immersed in Pfeffer's plant food solution,* and the stalk kept in position by being held lightly against one side of the neck of the bottle with a cotton stopper.

The plants grew well in this solution. The growth of algae in the liquid was largely overcome by painting the bottles black. Usually the plants lived long enough for experimental purposes without changing the liquid. When the experiments were prolonged the solution was changed as often as necessary.

By using this method, it was possible to follow the life history of the Hessian fly from oviposition to the formation of the puparium. The plants could be handled conveniently and the various stages studied with greater ease and exactness than when the plants were grown in the soil. When necessary, the plants could be removed from the bottle and placed under the binocular for close study. By carefully shaving the epidermis of the leaf sheath, it was possible to keep the larvae under observation at all times. As the larvae increased in size they could readily be seen through the neck of the bottle.

This method proved so successful in the Hessian fly work that it was adopted for the study of a number of other insects infesting cereal crops: chinch bug (*Blissus leucopterus*), green bug (*Toxoptera graminum*) and corn leaf aphis (*Aphis maidis*).

Certain modifications in the method of handling the plants were necessary for these insects. In order to confine them on the stalks of the plants, a small cell was formed in one side of the cotton stopper. The cotton fibers served as effective barriers in holding the insects in the cell and exact data could be obtained on molting and the length of the instars, and, in the case of the aphids, on the number of young produced. This method was also used to study certain phases of activity of several parasites of the Hessian fly puparium. The parasites were confined in the cells and their behavior and methods of oviposition were easily observed. In a similar manner a study was made of the chinch bug egg parasite (*Eumicrosoma beneficia*).

REFERENCE

For the culture of other members of this family see p. 266.

*Pfeffer's solution:

Calcium nitrate	4	grams
Potassium Nitrate	1	gram
Magnesium sulphate	1	gram
Potassium dihydrogen phosphate.	1	gram
Potassium chloride	0.5	gram
Ferric chloride		trace
Distilled water	5	liters

Family MYCETOPHILIDAE

CEROPLATINAE AND MACROCERINAE*

SOME larvae were kept in glass-topped tin boxes (3″ diameter by ¾″ high), the bottom of the box being covered about ¼″ deep with cotton wool saturated with moisture. On this were placed four or five microscopic coverslips, under which the larvae would retreat on being alarmed. The inside of the glass lid was smeared with a thin layer of pure glycerine, which, while fresh, kept the larvae from attaching their threads to the lid. Two larvae were placed in each box.

Other larvae were kept in the same kind of tins, but on their original bark, as controls on the behavior of those on cotton wool.

Again, other larvae were kept, with small strips of bark and decaying leaves, between two sheets of glass spaced ¼″ apart. This last method was an attempt to imitate more closely their natural haunts and yet keep them under observation.

In every case the larvae readily adopted their new surroundings (provided they were kept sufficiently moist), but it was a week before they had spun the usual amount of web, and not until this did they show the sure quickness of movement which is evident when they are accustomed to their surroundings.

These methods were used for the larvae of *Platyura nigricornis, P. fasciatus,* and *P. discoloria* and, with slight modifications, were also used for rearing other species of these subfamilies.

The larvae quickly responded to any movement in their web and have not been found to fail to attack anything alive and moving, from the larvae of large chafer beetles to small Collembola. In the field the remains of the following prey have been found in webs of *Platyura spp.*: Enchytraeus, Myriapoda, Achorutes, other Collembola, Coleoptera, and Miastor. In the laboratory the following prey was offered and accepted, as well as the prey recorded from webs in the field: larvae of *Piophila casei* and of *Scolytus intricatus;* ½″ larvae of Scarabaeidae; Anurida; and free-living nematodes ¼″ long.

Cannibalism was the invariable result of overcrowding. A space of 5 square inches was the least in which 2 larvae were kept without fighting, and then cannibalism often occurred.

The pupal stage was found to be a critical period in the life cycle. About half the pupae in the laboratory were attacked by fungus on pupation and died. Pupae which were disturbed or taken from their webs usually died.

M. E. D.

*Abstracted from a paper in *Trans. Ent. Soc. London* 81:75, 1933, by G. H. MANSBRIDGE, *Imperial College of Science and Technology.*

Family SCIARIDAE

CULTURE METHODS USED FOR SCIARA

HELEN B. SMITH, *Johns Hopkins University*

Methods of collecting. Sciara is collected most easily in greenhouses. The flies are usually found on the window panes, not in the sun. They may be captured by inverting a glass vial over them and then gradually inserting a piece of paper or cardboard between the window pane and the vial, so as to force them into the vial. Cotton may be used to stopper the vial.

Culture medium. Sciara is usually cultivated in pair matings in glass vials 1 inch wide and 4 inches high. Mass-cultures may be grown in half pint milk bottles. The vials or bottles are sterilized and filled to a depth of about 1 inch with plain agar medium made by heating approximately 2 parts of agar in 3 of tap water, by measure. When the agar has solidified, finely ground sterilized straw is sprinkled into the vials to insure a dry surface. The vials are plugged with cotton. Frequently small quantities of ground straw are added to the agar medium before it is poured into the vials; this serves to make the substratum more porous, but is not essential.

Feeding. Many different types of food have been tried with varying degrees of success. The most satisfactory one thus far used is a mixture of equal parts of poultry yeast, powdered mushroom, and ground straw. The latter serves to prevent the formation of an impervious surface layer on the cultures. When small larvae are visible (usually 10 days after the parent flies have been placed in the vial) a small quantity of food mixture is sprinkled on the surface. This is soon eaten up and the supply must be replenished about every second day until pupation begins. Practice alone will demonstrate what quantity of food is required. In general it is better to feed sparingly rather than abundantly, for if cultures are given too much food, the larvae fail to eat all of it, and the excess remains on top of the culture as a loose mixture to drop out when one attempts to remove the flies that have hatched. Although this culture method is by no means perfect as yet, it is adequate and reliable for present purposes.

Temperature and moisture conditions. Sciara is resistant to cold; the only effect of low temperatures is to retard the rate of development. The larvae are very susceptible to heat, however, and 29° C. is lethal if maintained more than a short time. Higher temperatures are immediately lethal. In the laboratory the cultures are kept in an incubator with a temperature range of 22°-24° C. Moisture conditions are regulated by placing a large flat pan of water on the lowest shelf of the incubator in front of an electric fan which is in continuous operation. Under these conditions, the life cycle of *S. coprophila* occupies about a month, divided approximately as follows: egg stage, 5-6 days; larva, 14-15 days; pupa, 3-4 days; adult, 5-8 days. Thus 12 to 14 successive generations may be grown in the course of a year.

Breeding Technique. The type of inheritance found in *Sciara coprophila* necessitates a technique somewhat different from that employed with other organisms. In this species individual females typically give "unisexual" progenies. Occasionally there will be one or more "exceptional" males in a female progeny, or "exceptional" females in a male progeny, in which case sib matings may be made; but usually such inbreeding is not possible. It is advisable to cross the various strains with each other frequently to keep the stocks in good condition.

The technique outlined above has been found reasonably satisfactory for a few other species of Sciara, but since different species may differ both in respect to food habits and to sex ratios it is necessary to modify the methods to fit the needs of individual cases. *S. pauciseta* and *S. impatiens* are both vigorous species and may probably be reared satisfactorily by this same method.

CULTURE OF SCIARA

F. H. BUTT, *Cornell University*

SCIARA females were caught from cabbages, corn, potatoes, and onions, and placed in quart-size wide-mouthed Mason fruit jars containing 1 inch of agar covered with ¼ inch of bran, wheat flakes, or other such breakfast food; ½ inch of sheep manure; and 2 inches of wet sphagnum that had been sterilized by heating for 20 minutes to rid it of mites. The flies laid eggs readily in the sphagnum, the next generation multiplying in enormous numbers. The life cycle on the average was 26 days at room temperature, although it lengthened during the winter months. The food contained in the medium was sufficient for one generation only. Another generation of larvae, if allowed to develop in the same jar as the first, always appeared stunted and greatly depleted in numbers. Therefore new jars should be made up for each generation.

To obtain eggs for embryological work, 50 to 100 females were collected from the breeding jar and put in a cage which consisted of a lantern chimney covered with a piece of muslin, resting on a piece of cheesecloth placed on black paper. The whole cage was placed on damp sand which kept the paper and cheesecloth moist. This method prevented the eggs from drying out. Eggs were collected at intervals and placed in salve boxes in the bottom of which had been placed pieces of damp blotting paper with black paper coverings. As many as 600 eggs were taken from the cage at one time.

These methods proved successful for *S. coprophila* and *S. pauciseta*.

REFERENCE

For the culture of *Neosciara* (=*Sciara*) *pauciseta* see also p. 266.

A LABORATORY METHOD FOR REARING SCIARA AND PHORID FLIES*

REARINGS have been carried on of certain dipterous pests of cultivated mushrooms, mainly *Sciara spp.* and some Phoridae. The method described below has been used successfully over a long period of time with Sciara, notably *S. fenestralis.* These comparatively small flies were collected as pairs *in copulo* from an infested mushroom house.

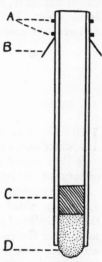

The rearing tubes consist of convenient lengths of glass tubing (about 8 cm.) with a diameter of 10 mm., open at both ends. (Fig. 70.) At one end sterilized stable manure is introduced and packed from the other end by means of a glass rod, care being taken to avoid soiling the inner surface of the tube. It is important to obtain a level surface on the manure, in order to ensure that the female, when ovipositing, will lay her eggs on the surface of the manure and not too deeply within it. The manure is packed to a depth of about 1 cm. and, from below, a plug of cotton is inserted and the manure plug is then pushed up so that its surface is now at a distance of 2 cm. from the base of the tube. The tube is then ready for the introduction of the pair of flies.

FIG. 70.—Rearing tube for Sciara and phorid flies. A, rubber bands; B, cellophane cap; C, manure; D, cotton.

The tube, manure plug downwards, is placed in a convenient receptacle in a darkened situation. With Sciara oviposition usually takes place on the manure. About a week elapses between copulation and the death of the female following oviposition. During this period it is sometimes necessary to add moisture, and this is easily done by damping the manure from below after removing the cotton-wool plug, or by wetting this plug itself. Placed with the plug end in a shallow film of water, the manure may take up moisture. If this happens, a vigorous growth of molds may appear, which inhibits development of the ova.

*Abstracted from an article in *Ent. Mo. Mag.* 72:12, 1936, by M. D. Austin and R. S. Pitcher.

In order to facilitate the study of ecdysis, individual larvae are isolated in circular glass cells of approximately 11 mm. internal diameter and 3 mm. height. These are cemented to 3″ x 1″ microscope slides with Canada balsam. They are covered at the top with a circular cover glass which is secured in place with vaseline. To maintain humidity within, a circle of filter paper is cut to fit the cell, and on this a minute pellet of the moistened powdered sterilized manure is placed. It has been found that unless additional precautions are taken, excessive drying out may result when the slides are kept in an incubator. To overcome this, numbers of the slides are placed in a flat tin (tobacco tins are commonly used) in which is placed a layer of damp sand, covered with blotting paper. Both this and the filter paper in the cells require periodical, if not daily, moistening to maintain suitable conditions for larval development. Providing that the food is renewed as required, larvae of *S. fenestralis* pass through readily to adults in these cells.

J. G. N.

Family SIMULIIDAE

SIMULIUM ORNATUM*

LARVAE of all stages were collected by rapidly removing from the water weeds or stones on which they are wont to congregate. They were then placed in jars containing water and transported to the laboratory for rearing.

Larvae were maintained alive for considerable periods of time in vessels containing water through which a jet of compressed air, delivered through a plug of porous wood, was passed. It was found, however, that in spite of the provision of algal food, most of the larvae died. The exceptions were mature larvae that were ready to pupate. Adult flies have been reared from larval and pupal stages by Edwards (1920), Cameron (1922), and others, and Puri (1925) states that he successfully reared *S. aureum* and *S. erythrocephalum* from egg to adult in bell jars filled with rain water, in which there was a growth of algae and through which a jet of compressed air was passed. This method failed to give the required results with *S. ornatum* and eventually the apparatus shown diagrammatically (Fig. 71) was designed, in which *S. ornatum* was successfully reared from the egg to the adult.

The apparatus consisted of a large cylinder about 20 inches high and 5 inches in diameter, containing water with algal food in suspension. Submerged in the water was a large-bore glass tube, up which the water

---

* Abstracted from an article in *Proc. Roy. Physical Soc.* 22:217, 1934, by JOHN SMART, *University of Edinburgh*.

was induced to circulate by the action of a jet of compressed air released from a glass jet introduced at the lower end of the wide-bore tube. The wide-bore tube had an internal diameter of 1 to 2 cm., a tube of this size being adopted after a number of trials with tubes of various diameters as the one in which the most suitable current could be produced. The capacity of the cylinders was about 5 liters and the compressed air served to aerate the water as well as to create the current. The length of the wide-bore tube varied, but this appeared to be immaterial provided the opening at the bottom was kept free of the débris that eventually accumulated at the foot of the cylinder, and the open end at the top was sufficiently submerged to ensure effective circulation of the water up the tube. The tube for introducing the compressed air into the system had an external diameter of 4 mm., the actual jet being drawn out and slightly slanted so as to project the stream of air bubbles against the wall of the wide-bore tube. The two tubes were held firmly together by means of rubber bands, and pieces of rubber tubing were slipped over those parts which were susceptible to injury and seemed to require protection.

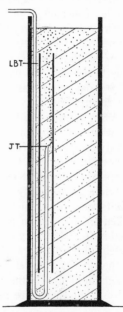

FIG. 71.—Diagrammatic section of rearing apparatus for *Simulium ornatum*. (After Smart.) (x ¼). LBT, large bore tube; JT, glass jet.

The cylinders were first filled with tap water and a culture of algae introduced by the addition of about 250 cc. of water containing a dense algal growth. This addition tinged the water in the cylinder green, and all that was subsequently necessary was to replenish the stock of algae, when the green tinge showed signs of disappearing. Some of the water in the cylinder was then removed and replaced by an equal amount of water containing the dense algal culture. It was necessary that the jet should deliver a considerable and steady quantity of air as it was found by experience that any but a momentary interruption of the air supply served to disturb the conditions in the cylinder to such an extent as to cause results fatal to the larval population.

Newly hatched first stage larvae were placed in the cylinder in large numbers, and those which were carried by the current into the wide-bore tube and contrived to secure a hold on the inner surface of the tube, survived. On the average, about 20 imagines were reared in each from about 200 first stage larvae. The main objection to the rearing apparatus was that it did not solve the difficulty of making a series of continuous observations of individual larvae at regular intervals. This fact was due to the frequent changes of location of the larvae over the inner surface of the large-bore tube in their constant search for optimum conditions for feeding. The intervention of 3 glass surfaces in contact with water between the larvae and the observer also increased the difficulties of making accurate observations.

Eggs collected immediately after oviposition took 5 to 6 days to develop in the laboratory, at a temperature of about 16° C. in water aerated and circulated by means of a jet of compressed air. Eggs kept on moist blotting paper and in a very humid atmosphere took a similar time to develop. It may be noted that non-viable eggs, after the 2nd or 3rd day, may easily be distinguished by their opacity from their normal neighbors.

When mature, the larva of *S. ornatum* forms its cocoon and pupates on whatever substratum it may happen to occupy at the time. The duration of pupal life varies according to temperature. At a constant temperature of 21° C. it was as short as 3.75 days, while at lower temperature it might extend to 12 days.

While no difficulty was experienced in obtaining large numbers of adults from pupae in the laboratory, the occasions on which they were taken on the wing in nature were few. Attempts to induce the flies to feed in the laboratory on human and rabbit hosts failed both with those caught in the open and those reared in the laboratory. Cattle and sheep in the vicinity of the stream did not appear to be molested by any species of simuliid flies. In the laboratory flies were offered moistened sugar and raisins, but they were not observed to feed on these.

M. E. D.

BIBLIOGRAPHY

CAMERON, A. E. 1922. The morphology and biology of a Canadian cattle-infesting black fly, *Simulium simile,* Mall. *Canad. Dept. Agric. Bull.,* n.s. No. 5.

EDWARDS, F. W. 1920. On the British species of Simulium. II. The early stages. *Bull. Ent. Res.* 11:211.

PURI, I. M. 1925. On the life-history and structure of the early stages of the Simuliidae (Diptera, Nematocera). *Paras.* 17:295.

Family TABANIDAE

METHODS FOR COLLECTING AND REARING HORSEFLIES

H. H. SCHWARDT, *University of Arkansas*

COLLECTING ADULT TABANIDAE

CATTLE in a partly wooded pasture near a pond or sluggish water course are likely to be annoyed by horseflies during the appropriate season. An afternoon of collecting from animals so located is usually fruitful. Small isolated ponds, especially if full of aquatic vegetation, attract adult horseflies which come to drink or to oviposit. Such places are frequented by males as well as females, the former often perching in numbers on the vegetation. Sweeping of grasses, sedges, or flags about such ponds often results in the capture of male specimens. Light colored surfaces such as the sides of concrete culverts, or small isolated white buildings, often attract numbers of adult Tabanidae. Horseflies are seen in greatest numbers on hot sunny days when there is little motion of the air.

COLLECTING IMMATURE STAGES

Horsefly larvae inhabit a wide variety of situations. They may be found in greatest number in the mud banks of ponds or slow-flowing streams. They are usually within two feet of the water and seldom deeper in the mud than four inches. Banks composed of loose soil containing some fine gravel or sand usually yield more larvae than those composed of clay. Larvae of *Tabanus annulatus* apparently live only in decaying logs or in decayed portions of living trees. They have been collected in numbers from such places. Larvae of *T. fronto* and *T. lineola* have been taken in soil of average moisture content and well removed from water. Larvae of *T. sulcifrons, T. melanocerous,* and *T. trimaculatus* have been taken under logs on marshy ground. Since egg masses of *T. lasiophthalmus* and *T. benedictus* have been found over fairly dry ground it is possible that larvae of these species are partially terrestrial. Larvae of *T. atratus* and *T. lineola* have been found in large numbers among floating algae in swamps, stagnant ponds, and the irrigation ditches serving rice fields. Larvae of *Goniops chrysocoma* inhabit the top inch of soil under a heavy blanket of leaves. Occasional individuals are found under rocks or logs. For collecting various species of larvae from mud, a sieve 1 ft. square and 2 in. deep made of a wooden frame, covered on one side with 16 mesh screen wire, has been found the most efficient equipment. A handful of mud from the larval habitat is placed in the sieve and spread out in a thin layer. The sieve is then moved up and down slowly in the water until the mud is washed through, leaving the larvae. Where quantitative collection is unnecessary, many larvae may be located by turning the mud with a fork or trowel. In the latitude of northwest Arkansas larvae are most easily found and collected in numbers during March and April.

Pupae occupy the same habitat as the larvae from which they develop and may be collected by the same means. Larvae of those species which live in mud near water usually move 6 inches or a foot farther back from the edge of the water before pupating. Pupae usually are difficult to find, probably because the stage is short, and it seldom happens that many individuals of a given species are in the pupal stage at the same time. There are a few exceptions to this among the species of Chrysops.

Eggs of the Tabanidae also occur in very diverse situations. Vegetation, especially grasses, sedges, and flags, growing in the water or on the banks within 6 feet of the water are favorite oviposition sites for several species. Sticks or other debris similarly located are also frequently used. Hundreds of egg masses of *Chrysops flavidus* and *Tabanus lineola* have been seen on rice plants in flooded fields. *T. vivax* places its egg masses on rocks or debris protruding above the surface of very rapidly flowing water. The same site is frequently chosen by several females of this species so that great compound egg masses containing over 100,000 eggs are sometimes found. *T. sulcifrons* often places its eggs on the under sides of small tree limbs growing 6 to 10 feet from the ground, and not necessarily near water. *Goniops chrysocoma* places its eggs on the under sides of leaves of trees, frequently using maple. The eggs may be on a seedling only 2 feet high, or 30 feet up in a large tree. Large numbers of egg masses of various species have often been found on the under surface of concrete bridge arches. Ovipositing females of both Tabanus and Chrysops have been taken under bridges.

REARING METHODS

Engorged female flies collected from animals will usually oviposit within a week after capture if kept in a suitable cage. A cage which has proven successful for several species consists of a 1-gallon stone jar, into the top of which is closely fitted a cylinder of screen wire about 18 inches long and the diameter of the inside of the stone jar. This cylinder is provided with a muslin cover held in place by a rubber band. The stone jar is filled ¾ full of soil and a medium-sized plant of some tall grass set into it. A large or bushy plant makes it difficult to find the egg masses. A small wad of cotton soaked in very dilute honey is fastened in the cage. Some species will oviposit more readily if the cage is flooded so that water stands above the soil. The cage should be kept in the sun for most species. It is possible that smaller cages may be used, since oviposition was once secured accidentally in a glass vial in which the fly could scarcely turn. Larger cages are impracticable because the flies spend their time flying from side to side in an effort to escape.

Jelly glasses approximately 3 inches in diameter, 2 inches deep, and provided with finely perforated tin lids, have been found satisfactory for incubation and rearing cages. Fine sand is placed in these glasses to a depth of ½ inch and saturated with water. There should be no standing water in the glasses. The correct moisture content for the sand may best be obtained by adding a slight excess of water and then removing as much as possible with a pipette, pushing the pipette under the sand and slowly taking up water till bubbles begin to appear in the tube.

For incubation the eggs, still fastened to a fragment of the plant on which they were deposited, are fastened to the side of a large cork by a pin through the plant fragment. The cork is then set in the cage in such a manner that the eggs do not touch the damp sand and so that the larvae, upon hatching, will fall directly into the sand.

Newly hatched larvae to be reared are separated immediately after hatching and placed in jelly glasses prepared as for incubation. The glasses, however, are set with one edge slightly elevated so that a moisture gradient is established in the sand. Where large scale rearing work is contemplated it will be convenient to nail strips of lath across the top of the table used. Rows of cages may then be set with one edge on a lath so that their bottoms form an angle of about 15 degrees with the table top.

Very young larvae should be fed daily. They probably will eat a variety of insects, annelids, Crustacea, or Mollusca, but Crustacea have been found most convenient to use. Crayfish are easily obtained in quantity. The white meat from the abdomen is cut from the shell and divided into pieces the size of wheat kernels. One piece is placed in each cage and the newly hatched larva *placed on the meat* with a camel's hair brush. If not actually placed on the food the small larva is unlikely ever to find it. To find the larva a slight excess of water is poured into the cage and shaken. The larva and its cast skin, if present, and any residual food will float out. The cage may then be drained by decantation and with the pipette. The first few molted skins are very small and are difficult to find unless the sand is very fine and free from small bits of trash.

A few species, notably *T. costalis* and *T. lasiophthalmus*, progress more satisfactorily and with lower mortality if kept in damp soil instead of wet sand. It is much more difficult to maintain soil at the correct moisture content, and to find small larvae in it. The soil must be fairly damp but dry enough to prevent lumping or becoming muddy. To locate small larvae in soil-filled cages, the soil must be dumped out on a black surface and spread out thinly. Under these conditions it is practically impossible to find the early molted skins.

Among the horsefly larvae which have been studied, the majority require a year or longer for development, and must, therefore, be properly cared for during the winter months. They will live if kept in a warm room and fed during the winter, but certain species, notably *Tabanus atratus,* will pupate and emerge during mid winter if so treated, resulting in a strictly abnormal life history. Overwintering in a nearly normal manner may be accomplished by keeping the larvae about 4 feet underground. The overwintering chamber which the writer has used successfully for many species and over a period of eight years consists of a hole of which the floor is 4 feet beneath the soil surface and measures 4 x 6 feet. It has brick reinforced walls and a concrete cover 6 inches thick. The cover is 1 foot below the soil surface and covered with a foot of soil. The entrance is an opening at one end measuring 2 x 4 feet and provided with two doors, one at the level of the concrete cover, and one at the surface. The top door is made water tight. The hole necessarily must be located on high ground so that water will not seep in. Larvae should be placed in such winter quarters by the average date for the first killing frost in the locality, and left until after danger of frost has passed in the spring. The writer has repeatedly overwintered hundreds of larvae in such a chamber, leaving them there from October 15 to April 1. During that period the mortality has averaged about 2%. There is practically no evaporation from the sand in the jelly glass cages and the temperature (at Fayetteville, Arkansas) remains between 50° and 60° F., even though temperatures as low as -10° occur above the surface. Such an underground chamber incidentally is ideal for rearing many species of subterranean insects, and for overwintering reptiles and other animals which normally hibernate during the cold season.

For most species no special care is required at the time of pupation. Almost invariably the larvae crawl completely out of the sand to pupate, the pupa, after the pupal molt, lying on top of the sand. Species reared in soil usually pupate beneath the surface. Larvae of *T. atratus* apparently pupate more readily if moved into soil-filled cages when nearly full grown.

Adult flies to be mounted should be removed from the rearing cages as soon after emergence as they are dry and firm. If left an extra hour they are likely to beat their wings off, and injure other parts, by buzzing about in the sand. Those to be kept alive should be transferred to the oviposition cages already described.

Feeding caged flies on blood is difficult and only a very small percentage may be induced to feed. Cylindrical screen wire cages 5 inches long and 2 inches in diameter, capped with muslin at both ends, have been found most convenient for feeding cages. The cage is held against the host animal, the fly biting through the meshes of the wire. Flies reluctant to feed may do so if the muslin cap is removed from one end of the cage and the open end set on the host. However, this procedure greatly increases the hazard of losing the fly if the host becomes nervous. The chances of success are much greater if the host is kept in full sunlight during the feeding attempt.

A few reared flies will feed in captivity and deposit eggs, but so far as the writer's experience has gone, these eggs are never fertile. Mating has never been observed by the writer either in cages or in the field.

REFERENCE

Family Phoridae
  For culture see pp. 401 and 402.

Family SYRPHIDAE

THE CULTURE OF APHIDOPHAGOUS SYRPHID FLIES*

C. L. FLUKE, JR., *University of Wisconsin*

THE culture of predacious syrphid flies has not been very successful, although the securing of ova from the adults may be accomplished by proper moisture, food, and lighting conditions. No substitute food for the larvae has been developed. This statement refers to the forms preying upon aphids and other soft-bodied insects.

The adults need water, which is best taken from a wick; light, such as sunshine or light from an incandescent bulb; and a diet of dried yeast 50% mixed with sterilized honey 50%. The yeast should be dried, sterilized, and pulverized before mixing with the honey. This forms a thick paste which may be smeared near the top of screen cages. The water wick should be placed near the top of the cage to take advantage of the flies' habits of crawling and flying upwards. Small cages are preferred to large ones and the plant leaves on which syrphid flies prefer to lay their eggs should also be near the top of the cage. Moist sand placed in the bottoms of the cages will maintain sufficient moisture for the flies.

Aphidophagous syrphid flies will lay eggs more readily on leaves infested with plant lice than on uninfested leaves. Certain species are apparently stimulated to lay when fed, in addition to the honey yeast formula, a thin syrup of dextrose and levulose.

The use of a sun ray lamp is not recommended as preliminary tests have indicated that, while the adults appeared to be stimulated, all ova secured at the time were sterile.

*Unpublished results of a project sponsored by *Wisconsin Alumni Research Foundation.*

The larvae must be fed their favorite aphid hosts and may be reared in almost any type of cage. When they are full grown they must be placed in a moist environment exposed to light. Glass tumblers or jars covered with cheesecloth, half full of moist sand, the surface of which is covered with leaves and sticks, are the most convenient types of pupal cages. The sand must be kept moist and the jars placed near windows or electric light. Sunshine does not seem to be necessary.

CULTURE OF THE DRONE FLY, ERISTALIS TENAX*

WILLIAM L. DOLLEY, JR., C. C. HASSETT, W. B. BOWEN, GEORGE PHILLIES, *University of Buffalo*

ERISTALIS tenax has been shown to be especially valuable for the study of its reactions to light, because it is uniformly positive and orients accurately in light, is of large size, and is hardy in captivity. It is also valuable for many other types of work.

Previous attempts to rear it have proved unsuccessful. This organism has now been successfully reared for over 3 years. In December 1931, a female collected in the open the previous month laid eggs, and from these a strain has been reared continuously since.

The flies are kept in wire cages, 15 x 15 x 15 cm., containing watch glasses filled with cheesecloth moistened with tap water. In these cages are also small wooden feeding troughs filled with a mixture consisting of equal parts of dry poppy, *Eschscholtzia californica,* pollen and dry powdered cane sugar. On this food the flies live perfectly and lay many fertile eggs.

The cages are kept before a laboratory window but are not exposed to the direct rays of the sun.

The eggs are collected and placed on human feces in a vessel also containing moist earth. Fresh feces are added daily. The larvae pupate in the soil.

At a temperature of between 20° and 25° C., a typical female began laying eggs 10 days after emergence and laid about 3,000 eggs in about 60 days. The eggs hatch about 36 hours after they are laid. The duration of the larval and pupal stages is about 2 weeks and 8 days, respectively, at about 22° C. Oviposition has been observed at various temperatures between 20.5 and 30.5° C.

The pollen may be purchased from Knapp and Knapp Pollen Gardens, North Hollywood, California, or it may be raised. The poppy blossoms are collected each day. The anthers are clipped off with scissors and dried in the sun for 12 hours. The pollen, separated from the dried anthers by means of a sieve with a fine mesh, is placed in a desiccator

*Reprinted with slight changes by the senior author from *Science* 78:313, 1933.

over calcium chloride for from 24 to 48 hours. It is then kept in darkness in glass bottles in which air has been replaced by nitrogen or carbon dioxide. Poppy pollen rapidly deteriorates on exposure to light, air, or moisture.

Since these methods of culturing it are comparatively simple, *Eristalis tenax* is now available for work throughout the year.

Family TACHINIDAE

METHODS USED IN REARING LESCHENAULTIA EXUL

HENRY A. BESS, *Ohio State University*

A TACHINID fly, *Leschenaultia exul*, deposits microtype eggs upon foliage fed upon by its host larvae. Rearings of this parasite were made from larvae of *Malacosoma americana* (tent caterpillars) which had ingested foliage on which females of *Leschenaultia exul* had been induced to deposit eggs.

The oviposition chambers used in the laboratory were glass-covered wooden boxes 5.9 x 7.9 x 3.9 inches. The boxes were supplied with block cane sugar, honey water on a piece of sponge, and cherry foliage, with the basal ends of the twigs in a bottle of water. Care was taken to keep the food and foliage fresh at all times. To obtain oviposition in the field flies were confined in bags made of cheesecloth and cellophane. These bags were about 5 feet in length and 16 inches in diameter. Only the middle third of each bag was cellophane and the cloth ends were open so that the bag could be slipped over a branch and tied in place.

Oviposition was not obtained readily from freshly collected flies without either cutting the leaves or placing host larvae within the containers. The effect produced by host larvae feeding on the leaves would be similar to cutting the leaves with shears.

Parasitism was obtained by feeding pieces of foliage on which eggs had been deposited to individual host larvae in metal boxes 2 inches in diameter and 1½ inches in depth. The turgidity of the foliage was maintained by placing a piece of moistened paper toweling in the bottom of each box. In many instances to insure early ingestion of the eggs the host larvae were starved for 1 day previous to their entry into the experiment.

Each day the caterpillars which had eaten the infected foliage were removed from the individual metal boxes (except a number for special study) and placed in one gallon glass jars which contained about two inches of loam soil. Over the soil was placed a piece of paper toweling which was removed with the frass daily. The jars were covered with paper toweling held in place with a rubber band. By moistening the paper covers once or twice daily the foliage within did not dry out appreciably.

This season I have been able to get females of *Leschenaultia exul* mated in the laboratory and to produce fertile eggs. There is only one generation each year. The adults emerge from the overwintering puparia (normally in the soil but held in the laboratory in moist sawdust or peat moss) in April and May. The males emerge at least three days earlier than the females. The gestation period was about two weeks for the adults held this spring but it might be shorter normally since it was an unusually cool spring in eastern Massachusetts where the work was done. The reared females deposited eggs on foliage placed in the containers just as the collected females did. Although I have not reared adults from reared adults I have obtained fertile eggs as mentioned above and have had host larvae parasitized by the maggots from such eggs.

Family SARCOPHAGIDAE

A NEW TECHNIQUE FOR REARING DIPTEROUS LARVAE*

IN rearing larvae of the Sarcophagidae and also of other Diptera such as the Phoridae, Borboridae, *etc.*, a nutritive medium commonly used in bacteriological technique has been used with success. It consists of 10 parts of nutritive agar and 1 part of normal horse serum. This medium has the great advantage of being sufficiently transparent to allow the observation of all stages of development under a binocular microscope. The medium may be kept in ampules of 50 cc., dated and labeled, and thus may be kept for months, always ready for use. When eggs or larvae of the larger species, or a fertilized female when one is dealing with small species, are placed within the ampules or in other tubes with the medium, the open end may be plugged with cotton or covered with a fine piece of cloth which permits entrance of air.

The puparia are formed on the surface of the medium or on the walls of the tube, and generally one can see the segmentation in the adult under the microscope by transmitted light.

M. E. D.

SARCOPHAGA BULLATA

ROY MELVIN, *U. S. Bureau of Entomology and Plant Quarantine*

EIGHT generations of this species were reared at a temperature of 86° to 90° F. during the winter of 1934-35.

The adults are handled in the same way as are those of *Cochliomyia*

*Slightly condensed from a translation by JULIO GARCIA-DIAZ, *University of Puerto Rico*, of an article by H. DE SOUZA LOPES in *Rev. de Entomologia* 5:502, 1935.

americana [see p. 416], except that the meat is changed daily. During copulation many of the pairs fall to the floor of the cage, and if the meat is slightly decomposed the flies that fall on it become stuck and die.

Larvae are deposited on the meat, but since each female deposits only a few larvae per day it has been found advisable, especially when a large culture is desired, to catch the females individually and squeeze the larvae out. By the squeezing method 50 or more larvae are obtained from each female, whereas if allowed to deposit normally from 9 to 15 larvae are obtained per female per day. The objections to squeezing the females are that the larvae vary slightly in size and that the females are killed.

Once the larvae are obtained, the method of handling is the same as that for larvae of *Cochliomyia macellaria.*

Family CALLIPHORIDAE

COCHLIOMYIA AMERICANA AND C. MACELLARIA

ROY MELVIN, *U. S. Bureau of Entomology and Plant Quarantine*

THE fly, *Cochliomyia americana,* has been reared in captivity for 12 consecutive generations by the following method.

Feeding and care of adults. The cage for the adults is constructed as follows: The bottom consists of a 1″ x 12″ board 17½ inches long and is nailed to a 1″ x 12″ board 11 inches long, which forms one end. The upper corners of this end are rounded to prevent the wire from breaking. A small angle-iron is used to add rigidity. The end and bottom are then painted to prevent warping. A piece of 16-mesh galvanized screen wire 18 inches wide is tacked along one edge of the bottom and stretched completely around and tacked to the wooden end, to form the 2 sides and top. A cloth sleeve is sewed into the other end.

Water is supplied by means of a fountain consisting of a jar, with a small groove filed in the lip, filled with water and inverted in a saucer containing a small cloth disk. Bananas are halved and placed in the cage. A small piece of lean beef, to which a few cc. of water are added, is placed in a saucer in the cage during the pre-oviposition period. Once daily honey is strung along the cage by means of a straw. Since the adults of this species are very clumsy, care should be taken to prevent the honey from dropping to the floor of the cage where the flies are likely to become stuck in it.

Feeding and care of immature stages. The eggs are obtained by placing gravid females in vials containing small strips of lean beef and plugged with dry cotton. The optimum temperature for oviposition is around 95° F. The eggs are removed from the meat and placed on small squares of wet black cloth and incubated in the laboratory. The incubation period ranges from 9.2 hours at 99° to 25.2 hours at 74° F. Stock cultures are reared on rabbits. From 30 to 40 larvae will mature and drop normally from a 5-pound rabbit. The rabbit, however, usually dies a day or two after the larvae have dropped. Since partly developed larvae will continue their development in the carcass, especially if the carcass is kept at a fairly high temperature, say 90° F. or above, 700 to 800 normal sized adults may be reared on a 5-pound rabbit. To implant the newly hatched larvae, a fold of skin on the rump of the rabbit is pulled up and a plug about 1 inch in diameter is cut out with a pair of scissors, care being taken not to cut the blood vessels. The larvae are placed in the wound and covered with a small piece of moist cotton which is held in place with adhesive tape. The rabbits are placed in cages 20 inches long and 4½ inches wide. The sides and ends are made of 1″ x 8″ boards, the bottom is ¼-inch-mesh hardware cloth, and the top consists of a 1″ x 3″ board hinged to one end. The width of the cage is very important and should be such that the rabbit cannot get its head to the wound to destroy the larvae.

The cages are placed over shallow trays of sand from which the larvae are removed and placed in jars partly filled with half-saturated sand, where pupation and emergence take place. As they emerge, the adults are liberated in the cage described above under care of adults.

Cochliomyia macellaria is very easy to rear in captivity. The adults are caged and fed in the same manner as that described for *Cochliomyia americana*. Eggs are obtained by placing strips of lean beef in a saucer in the cage with gravid females.

The larvae are reared as follows: Into a No. 2 galvanized tub containing 1 inch of dry sand is placed a 6-quart enameled pan half filled with rather moist sand. Three pounds of lean beef are placed on the moist sand and 4,000 to 5,000 eggs are added. The tub is covered with sheeting to prevent contamination. The mature larvae migrate from the wet sand in the pan and are trapped in the dry sand in the tub, where pupation occurs. The pupae are buried in quarter-saturated sand in a 1-gallon bucket. At time of emergence the bucket is placed in a breeding cage.

THE CULTURE OF BLOWFLIES

DWIGHT ELMER MINNICH, *University of Minnesota*

VARIOUS species of blowflies have long been favorite forms for a wide variety of experimental problems. Methods of culture, however, have not always been satisfactory, and, while much remains to be done in this field, it is the purpose of this paper to describe such of our

experience as may be helpful to other workers. Some of this technique
has already been described by us (Minnich, 1929). The procedure to be
described has been successful in the culture of the following species:
Calliphora erythrocephala, Cynomyia cadaverina, Lucilia sericata, and
Phormia regina.

The above species will mate and oviposit, and their larvae will mature
successfully, at temperatures between 21° and 27° C. At temperatures
much below or above these limits oviposition is greatly reduced or completely inhibited. A suitable breeding cage housing 50-100 adult flies
is a cubicle measuring approximately 25 cm. on each side and consisting
of a readily constructed light wooden frame covered with mosquito netting
except on the bottom. Cotton tape
is used where the gauze is tacked to
the frame to insure firmer construction. The wood stock is about
2 x 0.5 cm. and is smooth. When the
mosquito netting has become soiled
with the feces and regurgitation of
the flies, it may readily be removed
and the frame scraped and recovered. Since the flies are more
or less strongly positive to light the
door of the cage should be placed
away from the windows of the culture room. To provide additional
light and heat we have kept an
electric lamp provided with an ordinary desk lamp reflector burning

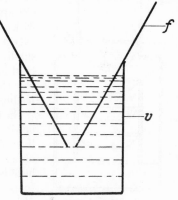

Fig. 72.—Water feeder
for blowflies. f, fun-
nel; v, vial or beaker.

close to the lighted side of the cage. A 40-watt frosted bulb is entirely
adequate for the purpose. A further device permitting access to the
cage and at the same time preventing escape of the flies is provided by a
loose curtain of mosquito netting immediately within the door. Paper
toweling is a convenient cover for the table on which the cage is placed.

Water may be supplied in a funnel (f) from which the delivery tube
has been cut and which is inserted into a vial or beaker (v) of the appropriate size (Fig. 72). If a beaker is used, the spout should be removed by heating and reshaping the glass to the general contour of the
lip to prevent the flies from creeping in and drowning. The inner surface
of the funnel should also be etched to afford a suitable creeping surface.
While some flies drown in the funnel, it is our experience that these are
old and decrepit individuals. Haub and Miller (1932) have described
an even simpler device for supplying water which eliminates the pos-

sibility of drowning. It consists of a small beaker of water inverted over a semicircle of filter paper in a petri dish. [See p. 413.]

As a food, cane sugar will support the flies indefinitely. In supplying sugar we have abandoned our earlier use of a molar solution in favor of lumps of domino sugar as suggested by Haub and Miller (*loc. cit.*).

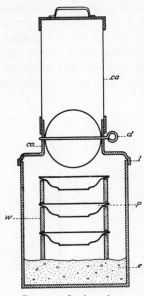

This is a vastly superior method. While cane sugar alone will support the flies, the production of eggs requires protein. This we have supplied with fresh beef liver which also provides a favorable medium for oviposition. Every second day a small porcelain dish 16 x 12 x 3.5 cm. loosely filled with liver, cut into approximately 2 cm. cubes and moistened with a few drops of water, is placed in the cage and left for 24 hours. The amount and subdivision of the liver insure moist surfaces in at least some crevices of the mass throughout the 24 hour interval, thus permitting feeding and oviposition.*

Once the egg masses are laid, the eggs or newly hatched larvae are removed from the liver and placed in the gills of fish heads obtained from the fish market. The fish head is then placed in a wide-lipped porcelain soup plate and placed in the rearing can (Fig. 73).

FIG. 73.—Section of can for rearing blowfly larvae. ca, removable screen cage; co, collar over which screen cage slips; d, damper; e, earth; 1, lid of can; p, soup plate culture dish; w, wooden supports between plates.

The rearing can consists of a galvanized pail in the lid (l) of which a circular opening is cut. Into the opening a metal collar (co) is soldered containing a simple damper (d). Over the collar a removable cylindrical screen cage (ca) is fitted. The damper permits the regulation of moisture which is very important in the successful rearing of larvae. If conditions are too moist the larvae leave the food and migrate in all directions, a fact which must be familiar to all who have tried to rear these animals extensively.

*The species above enumerated readily oviposit under the conditions described. Another closely related species, however, *Calliphora vomitoria*, has failed to breed. Several years ago we bred this form successfully at the Zoological Institute in Munich, Germany, (Minnich, *loc. cit.*). Either or both of two conditions probably account for the discrepancy. First, the culture room was cooler than our present culture room. Second, fresh deer heads were readily available and these were the only medium on which the flies oviposited. Half a deer head, split lengthwise, never failed to induce egg laying. Unable to obtain these at will in Minneapolis, we have tried various types of vertebrate flesh but invariably without success.

Several culture dishes (p) may be stacked in the same can by using square wooden frames between (w). Food should be added as needed, care being taken that no great amount of liquified material accumulates in the dishes. As the larvae mature they creep out on the flat edges of the plate (p) and fall to the damp earth (e) which fills the bottom of the can to a depth of 7-10 cm. Here the larvae pupate. When the flies emerge they creep up the walls of the can and into the cage. The damper may then be closed; the cage may be removed, and the flies delivered where desired. When all the flies have emerged, the can is ready for immediate use again for the earth in the bottom may be used for a number of months without change.

Much remains to be done to make the technique of blowfly culture more precise. Conditions of temperature and humidity, oviposition media, and larval foods all require additional investigation. A rather detailed study of this sort has been made on *Lucilia sericata* by Cousin (1929). Additional work is needed, however, on the requirements of different species, and it is to be hoped that one result of the present account may be the publication of useful experiences of other investigators working with these forms.

BIBLIOGRAPHY

COUSIN, G. 1929. Sur les conditions indispensables à la nutrition et à la ponte de *Lucilia sericata* Meig. *C. R. Soc. Biol.* 100:570.

———1929. L'alimentation de *Lucilia sericata* Meig. et ses relations avec la ponte. *Ibid.* 100:648.

———1929. Sur le mode de ponte de *Lucilia sericata* Meig. *Ibid.* 100:731.

———1929. Sur les relations entre l'accouplement et le réflexe de ponte de *Lucilia sericata* Meig. *Ibid.* 100:818.

———1929. Sur les conditions extérieures déterminant le lieu de ponte de *Lucilia sericata* Meig. *Ibid.* 100:820.

———1929. Remarques sur la vie larvaire de *Lucilia sericata* Meig. *Ibid.* 101:653.

——— Conditions externes nécessaires pour obtenir un dévelopement normal des larves de *Lucilia sericata* Meig. *Ibid.* 101:788.

———1929. Influence de l'état hygrométrique du mileu sur 'l'evolution larvaire de *Lucilia sericata* Meig. *Ibid.* 101:913.

———1929. Influence de l'alimentation, des gaz toxiques et de la température sur la diapause de *Lucilia sericata* Meig. *Ibid.* 101:1115.

———1929. Les facteurs externes qui déterminent la reprise de l'évolution larvaire de *Lucilia sericata* Meig. et leur relation avec les influences extérieures qui out provoqué la diapause. *Ibid.* 101:1117.

HAUB, J. G., and MILLER, D. F. 1932. Food requirements of blowfly cultures used in the treatment of osteomyelitis. *J. Exper. Zool.* 64:51.

MINNICH, D. E. 1929. The chemical sensitivity of the legs of the blowfly, *Calliphora vomitoria* Linn., to various sugars. *Zeitschr. vergl. Physiol.* 11: 1.

REARING MAGGOTS FOR SURGICAL USE

G. F. WHITE, *U. S. Bureau of Entomology and Plant Quarantine*

THE epoch-making observation made by the late Dr. William S. Baer, and confirmed by many other surgeons, that sterile living blowfly larvae are a tremendously useful adjunct in the post-operative treatment of chronic osteomyelitis and other suppurative conditions has created an urgent need for maggots suitable for surgical use.

If the maximum benefits are to be experienced by the greatest number of patients, the maggots not only must be sterile but also must be readily obtainable the year round, must be available in ample numbers at low cost, and must be ready for the surgeon any hour of the day throughout the year. A method for the production of surgical maggots by which these objectives may be closely approached is outlined here.

APPARATUS

Fly Cages. The fly cages (Fig. 74) have a frame of wood with a solid

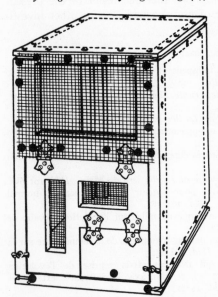

board bottom and measure 10 inches wide by 15 inches high by 18 inches deep. The sides, top, and one end are of cheesecloth fastened to the frame by thumbtacks aided by a cord fitting in grooves in the top and the bottom pieces. Galvanized iron wire screen and a door in which is cut a smaller one enclose the front end.

Larval Pans. Circular, covered pans 8.5 inches in diameter by 4 inches high (Fig. 75 A, B,) are used for rearing larvae for stock flies. A smaller pan or crystallizing dish within rests on a handful of fine wood shavings. Openings in the lids are covered with cheesecloth and cotton in rearing larvae on autoclaved food. Cheesecloth alone covers the openings in growing

FIG. 74.—Cage for blowflies. The frame is of wood with a solid bottom and is enclosed on four sides with cheesecloth.

them on unheated food.

Strainer for Eggs. A strainer (Fig. 76) for removing eggs from the disinfecting solution and for washing them consists of a bottle with a

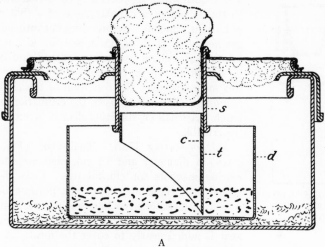

A

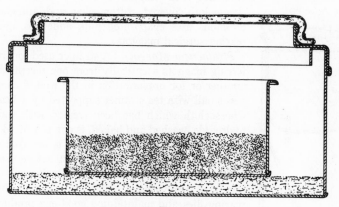

B

FIG. 75.—Pans for rearing maggots on autoclaved food. (Sectional drawings.) The lid of pan A has large perforations, the center one being fitted with a metal sleeve (s) into which is inserted a metal tube (t); the sleeve is plugged with cotton covered with cheesecloth, and the other perforations are covered with cotton and cheesecloth; d is a crystallizing dish containing the maggots and their food, c. Pan A is preferred in rearing larvae on autoclaved food. The lid of pan B has a large opening covered with cotton and cheesecloth. In growing larvae on raw meat the openings are covered with cheesecloth only. Pan B is then preferred.

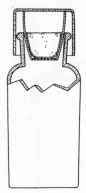

FIG. 76.—Strainer for eggs. (Section removed.)

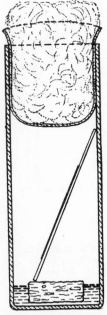

FIG. 77.—Shell vial for rearing clinical maggots.

wide mouth which supports a 25 cc. Gooch crucible. In this is placed a circular piece of a thin grade of bleached muslin. Before being cut into suitable patches, the cloth is immersed in a hot 2% solution of sodium hydroxide, washed and baked to a light brown in the hot air sterilizer. This treatment improves the condition of the cloth for straining. The color aids in the estimation of the hatch. A small crystallizing dish is inverted over the crucible.

Maggot-rearing Vials. Shell vials (Fig. 77) 4 cm. in diameter and 12 cm. high are used in rearing maggots for clinical use. Vials slightly larger than these may serve the purpose better. A section of autoclaved lung about 1 cm. thick is placed in each vial and 1.5% peptonized glucose agar is added nearly to cover the meat. A glass slide within the vial rests upon the meat. The vials are then stoppered with a snugly fitting, cheesecloth-covered cotton plug and autoclaved. Simmons uses evaporated milk added to agar in rearing surgical maggots.

Strainer for Maggots. A strainer used for transferring maggots aseptically from one receptacle to another or for implantation in the wound consists of a small wire tea strainer supported by a beaker. Cheesecloth which has been treated with sodium hydroxide, washed and baked, is cut and fitted into the strainer. A crystallizing dish is inverted over it and the whole is autoclaved just before use.

Fly Cabinet. A cabinet (Fig. 78) providing regulated temperature and humidity is useful in rearing flies and maintaining good egg production the year round. During the cooler months the temperature is raised to approximately 26° C. During the warmer months it is sometimes better to remove the cabinet to a cool room in the basement or elsewhere.

Brood Larval Cabinet. When larvae for stock flies are grown on unheated meat a cabinet providing a draft to outdoors is needed to remove offensive odors. One similar to the fly cabinet equipped with an exhaust fan is suitable. An

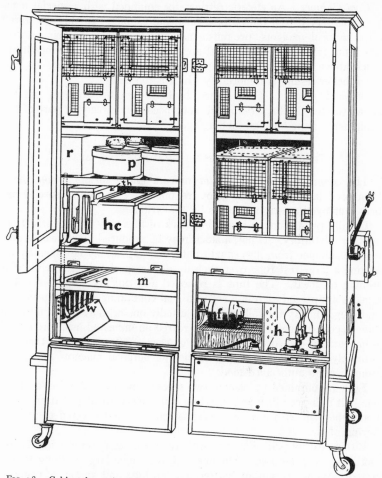

FIG. 78.—Cabinet for maintaining flies the year round. (Lower doors are open to show content and construction.) By means of an electric fan (f) air is drawn through cotton at the intake (i), over a heating unit (h) of electric light bulbs, and is blown past moist wicks (w) and through cotton (c) into the middle chamber (m). From here it passes through cotton covered holes in the floor of the fly chamber and out through cotton protected slits on the top. r, water reservoir of the humidifying unit; p, larval pans; hc, humid chambers for hatching eggs.

unused furnace has answered the purpose. No disagreeable odors are formed in growing larvae on autoclaved food. The rearing may be done, therefore, in the fly cabinet or out in the room.

Cool Cabinet. An electric refrigerator equipped with a special regulator has served well the purpose of a cool cabinet. In this are stored eggs, surgical maggots, pre-pupae and pupae to retard their growth. The temperature is maintained at approximately 10° C. A temperature much above this permits too rapid development of the fly stages, and much below results in a mortality which is too high.

Other Apparatus. Petri dishes, beakers, pipettes, forceps, and the apparatus for the bacteriological work needed is already a part of the equipment of the hospital laboratory.

PRODUCING STOCK FLIES ON UNHEATED MEAT

The common blowflies, *Lucilia sericata* and *Phormia regina,* have been used largely in the maggot treatment. The former species has been employed mostly in studies by the writer.

Usually pupae for the beginning stock of flies may be procured from another laboratory. If not, a stock may be produced rather easily during the summer from flies caught outdoors. Flies may be taken by inverting a large test tube over each fly of the species desired while it is feeding on meat. The tube is removed and quickly stoppered. The females are placed each in a separate vial containing a bit of fresh beef and plugged. By the following day usually one or more of ten flies will have deposited eggs. Flies are then reared on unheated meat preferably from each of two or more layings of eggs. After emerging they are definitely identified and stocks of flies for surgical maggots are reared from them on autoclaved food.

Eggs are obtained by placing two slices of meat about 1 cm. apart in one half of a petri dish and inserting it in cage with flies. After 2 or 3 hours the dish with meat and eggs is removed and covered to prevent drying of the eggs.

Either rearing pan (Fig. 75) with the openings covered with cheese-cloth only may be used. The one with the single large opening is preferred. About 250 gm. of coarsely ground lung and 50 gm. of chopped liver is placed within the inner container of the larval rearing pan. About 700 eggs are placed on the meat and put into a rearing cabinet having a forced draft to outdoors. The larvae, when full grown, migrate to the shavings and pupate. The residue of larval food is burned or emptied into the sewer. The pupae with the shavings are put in shallow pans, inserted into empty fly cages (Fig. 74) and placed in the fly cabinet (Fig. 78). If flies are not needed at once late pre-pupae and early pupae may be stored in the cool cabinet at 10° C. for 2 weeks or more. If desired they may be shipped conveniently in a mailing tube.

CARE OF FLIES

As the flies begin to emerge a water fountain consisting of a filled beaker inverted on filter paper in the half of a petri dish is placed within the cage. The water supply must be available at all times. On the day following emergence the flies are given slices of ripe banana and lumps of sugar each in halves of a petri dish. On each succeeding day they are fed fresh sliced liver until egg laying begins. When eggs are desired fresh beef is placed in the cages.

ESTIMATING THE NUMBER OF EGGS

A calibrated pipette is useful in estimating the number of eggs that are used. In calibrating it the eggs are separated in 2% sodium hydroxide. A number are drawn into the pipette and the volume is noted. They are discharged into 20 cc. of 20% aqueous solution of glycerin. A fractional portion of the suspension is pipetted into water in a petri dish. A portion of the eggs are counted over a bacteria colony counting plate and the number drawn into the pipette is computed. This is repeated until the volume is determined for the number of eggs desired.

DISINFECTANTS

In rearing maggots for surgical use, the eggs are disinfected and the larvae hatching from them are grown on autoclaved food. Sodium hydroxide, formaldehyde, or mercuric chloride may be used for the disinfection.

Sodium Hydroxide. Sodium hydroxide is preferred by the writer for its efficiency in destroying spores as well as vegetative forms of pathogenic species, for the resistance of eggs to it, for the readiness with which the eggs are separated by it, and for the ease with which the disinfection may be done. The solution consists of 5 gms. of the (commercial) hydroxide added to 95 cc. of distilled water. Should eggs not settle readily in it, slightly more water is added. This will not reduce the absolute sodium hydroxide below 4%.

Formaldehyde. The disinfecting efficiency of formaldehyde is generally known and eggs resist it well. Favorable results may be obtained with a solution containing 6.25% formalin (approximately 2.5% formaldehyde).

Mercuric Chloride. The following solution may be employed: Mercuric chloride, 0.5 gm.; sodium chloride, 6 gm.; hydrochloric acid (commercial), 1.25 cc.; ethyl alcohol, 250 cc.; and distilled water, 750 cc. If preferred the sodium chloride may be omitted. Mercuric chloride of ½ the strength in the formula is followed by favorable results also.

DISINFECTION OF EGGS

In disinfecting eggs and rearing larvae for stock flies on autoclaved food and maggots for surgical use, the following equipment is made ready and autoclaved: Short 10 cc. shell vials; medicine droppers; pipettes, 10 or 20 cc. capacity; Gooch strainers; rearing pans (Fig. 75) and maggot rearing vials (Fig. 77) with food in them; 0.02% hydrochloric acid; 0.02% formic acid; and distilled water. A bit of alcoholic solution of phenolphthalein is added to each of the acid solutions and the water, and these are then distributed in large test tubes preferably with lip and plugged. Bacteriological technique is used throughout.

PRODUCING LARVAE FOR STOCK FLIES USING AUTOCLAVED FOOD

Approximate 150 gm. of autoclaved lung and 50 gm. of autoclaved liver are coarsely ground and placed within the inner container of the larval pan. The one (Fig. 75, A) with a metal sleeve plugged with cotton is preferred. Liquified agar, 1.5%, containing ¼ to ½ of a hen's egg, and ¼ of a yeast cake or 1 gm. of dry yeast, is added nearly to cover the meat. The lid is replaced, the metal tube inserted and the whole autoclaved for a few minutes at 15 lbs. pressure and repeated the following day.

Eggs are removed with curved forceps and placed in a small shell vial containing 2% sodium hydroxide. They are readily separated by slight agitation with a dropper pipette.* The hydroxide is decanted and a 5% solution of it is poured on and allowed to remain for ½ hour or more at room temperature. Approximately 700 eggs are pipetted to the gauze of the Gooch strainer and washed by pouring or pipetting about 20 cc. of 0.02% hydrochloric acid over them. The cloth with the eggs attached is transferred with forceps to the inner surface of the metal tube of the larvae rearing pan and incubated in the fly cabinet. On the following day the metal tube with the cloth and unhatched eggs and eggshells are removed.

REARING MAGGOTS FOR CLINICAL USE

Eggs used for rearing clinical maggots are from flies obtained from larvae grown on autoclaved food. Any one of the following methods may be employed for disinfection of the eggs.

Disinfection with Sodium Hydroxide. Eggs are disinfected, strained, and washed as outlined above with the exception that they are allowed to remain in the 5% hydroxide for 1½ hours at 32° C. They are transferred from the Gooch strainer to the slide in the larval rearing vials

*Simmons moistens eggs by means of a cloth wet with water and separates them mechanically.

(Fig. 77) and incubated in a moist chamber in the fly cabinet. On the following day the slide and the cloth with unhatched eggs and eggshells are removed from the vial. When the larvae approach the size desired by the surgeon microscopic examination and cultures are made of the partially liquified maggot food and the vials are placed in the cool cabinet at 10° C. When bacteriological tests warrant it, the maggots are ready for the surgeon. If not needed at once, they may remain in the cool cabinet for a week or more before they are implanted.

Disinfection with Formaldehyde. After decanting the 2% hydroxide from the separated eggs they are washed by pouring on 0.02% formic acid, decanting and repeating the washing until the egg suspension is neutralized as indicated by phenolphthalein. The eggs are then immersed in 6.25% formalin and allowed to remain for 20 minutes at room temperature. They are strained, washed with water, transferred to larval vials, incubated, and the maggots are tested for sterility.

Disinfection with Mercuric Chloride. After the hydroxide is decanted from the separated eggs they are washed with 0.02% hydrochloric acid, and immersed in the mercuric chloride solution at room temperature for 15 minutes. The technique used after formaldehyde disinfection is then followed.

Disinfection with Sodium Hydroxide Followed by Other Disinfectants. The efficiency of sodium hydroxide is less generally known than that of some other disinfectants. Therefore further to assure sterility of the clinical maggots the eggs may be treated with another disinfectant following the hydroxide. If formaldehyde or mercuric chloride is chosen, the eggs are first disinfected with 5% sodium hydroxide. They are then washed and treated with either of these disinfectants as is done when it is used alone, with the exception that the immersion in the disinfectant is for 10 minutes.

STERILITY OF CLINICAL MAGGOTS

The chief danger in the maggot treatment lies in the possibility that disease producing agents might be introduced into the wound with the maggots. In routine rearing of maggots no laboratory method is available by which absolute sterility may be determined. This limitation makes it imperative that every reasonable precaution be taken which will tend to insure sterility.

Sterility is judged from the technique used in producing the maggots rather than from tests made afterwards. Tests are made, however, of all vials of maggots used. Each worker should choose for himself those tests which he deems sufficient. Microscopic examination of partially liquified food and inoculation of glucose bouillion and deep glucose agar with it are probably sufficient for routine rearing in most instances.

Clinical maggots reared from eggs disinfected with sodium hydroxide are probably free from filterable viruses, from the pathogenic spore-producing organisms, and from most of the non-spore-producing ones. While freedom from the tubercle bacillus cannot be assured altogether, it seems most unlikely that this bacterium would be present with the maggots reared by this method.

COST OF MAGGOTS

The apparatus needed for rearing clinical maggots in addition to that already in a hospital laboratory is inexpensive. The trained staff of the laboratory can supervise the work. The small cost of producing suitable maggots for surgical use is, therefore, no longer a valid objection to the maggot treatment.

DISCUSSION

Lucilia sericata is a favorable blowfly species for laboratory use. It may be reared much of the year at the temperature and humidity of the room. The fly cabinet and cool cabinet for controlling these factors are useful in speeding up production.

Eggs are susceptible to injury from drying. Feeding larvae on the other hand are not dependent on high atmospheric humidity. They may be grown well at temperatures of the room up to 32° C. or somewhat more. They leave the food when adequate ventilation is not maintained. The amount of air exchange required in the rearing containers varies with the number of maggots present and the rapidity of their growth. In growing larvae on autoclaved food it is sometimes necessary to remove or partially remove the lid of the larval rearing pan to permit additional ventilation. With experience numerous variations in technique for rearing and care of maggots and adult flies will be apparent.

BIBLIOGRAPHY

BAER, W. S. 1931. The treatment of chronic osteomyelitis with the maggot (larvae of the blowfly). *J. Bone and Joint Surg.* 13:438.

BUCHMAN, J., and BLAIR, J. E. 1932. Maggots and their use in the treatment of chronic osteomyelitis. *Surg. Gyn. Obst.* 55:177.

CHILD, F. S. and ROBERTS, E. F. 1931. The treatment of chronic osteomyelitis with live maggots. *N. Y. State J. Med.* 31:937.

MCKEEVER, D. C. 1933. Maggots in treatment of osteomyelitis. *J. Bone and Joint Surg.* 15:85.

MILLER, D. F., DOAN, C. A., and WILSON, E. H. 1932. The treatment of osteomyelitis with fly larvae. *Ohio J. Sci.* 32:1.

MURDOCH, F. F., and SMART, T. L. 1931. A method of producing sterile blowfly larvae for surgical use. *U. S. Naval Med. Bull.* 29:406.

ROBINSON, W. 1934. Literature relating to the use of maggots in the treatment of suppurative infections. *Circ. E-310* (multigraphed) *Bur. of Ent., U. S. D. A.*

Robinson, W., and Simmons, S. W. 1934. Effects of low temperature retardation in the culture of sterile maggots for surgical use. *J. Lab. and Clin. Med.* 19:683.

Simmons, S. W. 1934. Sterilization of blowfly eggs. *Amer. J. Surg.* n. s. 25:140.

Weil, G. C., Henry, J. P., Nettrour, S., and Sweadner, W. R. 1931. The cultivation and sterilization of fly larva or maggot. *W. Va. Med. J.* 27:458.

REARING LARVAE OF THE CLUSTER FLY, POLLENIA RUDIS

R. M. DeCoursey, *Connecticut State College*

THE larvae of the cluster fly feed upon certain species of earthworms such as *Allolobophora chloroticus, A. caliginosa,* or *Eisenia rosea.*

Copulation of adults occurs in the latter part of February at Urbana, Ill., and during the early part of March at Storrs, Conn. After copulation females may be collected by hand on the sunny side of buildings by placing a test tube over the flies, or they may be caught in traps designed for catching houseflies. The best bait for cluster flies is banana.

Females kept in cages over soil will usually lay eggs on or in the soil. Cages made from lantern globes are convenient. Flies caught early in the spring will often delay ovipositing for two or three weeks. It is necessary to supply food and water during this period. Pieces of banana or apple may be used for food.

One method of rearing consists of permitting the flies to oviposit on soil in cages known to contain certain species of earthworms. The 1st instar larvae enter the soil, presumably attack the earthworms, and in about 30 days a few may emerge as adults. This method does not enable one to learn much about the habits of the larvae during the various instars.

Another method is to collect the eggs, placing them on moist blotting paper in a low stender dish with a cover to preserve moisture. The eggs hatch in about three days. A few larvae are transferred to earthworms which are kept on moist filter paper in other stenders with covers. The species of earthworm most commonly used is *Allolobophora chloroticus.* After the 1st instar larvae attack the earthworm a small amount of rich soil is added to keep the earthworm alive. The larvae usually penetrate through the cuticula at the anterior end of the worm from about the 10th segment to a few segments posterior to the clitellum. The clitellum seems to be a favorite point of entry. Most larvae enter from the dorsal side of the earthworm. Under a microscope they may be observed feeding with their posterior spiracles exposed.

As the larvae grow and pass into later instars they cause greater damage to their hosts. The effect of the larval feeding combined with the unnatural environment often causes the earthworm to die; so several earthworms are ordinarily used in rearing a single larva. Temperatures approaching that of the natural habitat of the earthworm in the soil are more favorable for the earthworms and probably for the dipterous larvae. Both must be kept moist.

Pupation occurs in the soil. The pupa should be removed to drier soil. The life cycle is about 30 days.

The best and most abundant generation with which to work is the hibernating generation, but there is a summer generation appearing the latter part of May at Urbana, after which the flies gradually become more common until the large hibernating generation appears toward the latter part of September.

BIBLIOGRAPHY

DeCoursey, R. M. 1927. A bionomical study of the cluster fly, *Pollenia rudis* Fab. *Ann. Ent. Soc. Amer.* 20:368.

——— 1932. The feeding habits of the first instar larvae of the cluster fly. *Science* 75:287.

Garrison, G. L. 1924. Rearing records of *Pollenia rudis* Fab. *Ent. News.* 35:135.

Keilin, D. 1911. On the parasitism of the larvae of *Pollenia rudis* Fab. in *Allolobophora chlorotica* Savigny. *Proc. Ent. Soc. Wash.* 13:182.

——— 1915. Recherches sur les larves de Dipteres Cyclorhaphes. *Bull. Sci. France Belgique* 49:15.

Webb, J. L., and Hutchinson, H. H. 1916. A preliminary note on the bionomics of *Pollenia rudis* Fab. in America. *Proc. Ent. Soc. Wash.* 18:197.

Family MUSCIDAE

STOMOXYS CALCITRANS

Roy Melvin, *U. S. Bureau of Entomology and Plant Quarantine*

THE stable fly, *Stomoxys calcitrans*, has been reared in captivity through many successive generations by the following method.

Feeding and care of adults. The cage is 2 x 3 feet and 2 feet high. Both sides, the top, and one end are made of 16-mesh galvanized screening. The bottom and one end are made of 1-inch pine. A hole 10 inches in diameter is cut in the solid end of the cage, in which a cloth sleeve is attached.

The adults are fed water by means of a fountain [see p. 432], honey every other day, [see p. 409], and guinea pig blood once a day. The guinea pig is fastened to a board 6 inches wide and 12 inches long by means of four soft strings, one around each foot, which pass through ¼-inch holes in the board and fasten to a binding post at the end of the board. By this method the guinea pig can stand or recline but cannot kill or dislodge the engorging flies. It has been found that if a guinea pig is allowed to remain in the cage for 2 hours each day the flies will obtain enough blood to carry on normal life processes; that is, to mate and lay fertile eggs.

Feeding and care of immature stages. The larvae are reared in a No. 2 galvanized tub on a mash consisting of 100 cc. cheap molasses, ¼ cake yeast, 5 pounds crushed oats, and 1 gallon water. The mash is allowed to ferment for 4 days at a temperature of 30° C. (86° F.) before the eggs are added. Three or four thousand normal-sized flies may be reared on a tub of the mash. Two methods are employed in obtaining eggs. The first, used when stock cultures are desired, is to place a small pan of fermented mash in the cage for 5 to 10 hours. The second method, employed when large numbers of eggs are desired within a comparatively short period, consists in confining the gravid females in vials plugged with cotton which has been moistened with 0.1% ammonia water.

The eggs are placed in the fermented mash and the tub is covered with cloth to prevent contamination. By the time the larvae reach maturity the upper layer of the mash will be sufficiently dry to permit pupation.

Just before emergence begins a special cover is placed over the tub. This cover consists of a piece of cloth fastened between two pieces of 1" x 4", one slightly shorter than the diameter of the tub and the other slightly longer than the diameter of the tub to support the weight of the cage. There is a 2-inch hole in the center of the 1" x 4" boards, and a similar hole in the bottom of the cage. If the cage is placed on the tub so that the two holes match, and if the edge of the tub is darkened, the flies will go directly into the cage.

If the flies are to be used for experimental purposes, the cage is inverted and darkened, causing the flies to come back out the same hole by which they entered.

Temperature and light. Although sunlight is not essential for the completion of the life cycle, it shortens materially the length of the pre-oviposition period. High temperatures are fatal to the eggs, only a small percentage hatching at 99° F. The larvae will continue to feed at 99° F., but at 104° F. they discontinue feeding and concentrate on the upper surface of the media. At 99° F. the mortality of caged adults is high, even though plenty of water is available. A temperature of 86° F. has been found very satisfactory for rearing all stages.

REARING THE HOUSE FLY, MUSCA DOMESTICA, THROUGHOUT THE YEAR

HENRY H. RICHARDSON, *U. S. Bureau of Entomology and Plant Quarantine*

THE rearing of house flies throughout the year for use in various lines of biological research has developed largely in the last decade. Formerly they could be reared in the northern states only from April to December (Glaser, 1923, 1924) as horse manure, which was used as the larval medium, was found deficient in nutritive value during the winter months. R. W. Glaser (1927) found that the addition of small amounts of baker's yeast to horse manure made it possible to rear the flies during the winter. Grady (1928) developed the technique of rearing large numbers of flies for daily insecticidal tests and by use of Glaser's method was able to rear flies continuously throughout the year. However the use of horse manure or mixtures of it with hog manure (Hockenyos, 1931) as a rearing medium has several disadvantages. It is not always available to most laboratories and also it is rather disagreeable to use. Most important is the fact that frequently a species of red mite parasitic on the house fly (probably of the genus Trombidium) is brought in on horse manure. As many as 40 or more mites will attack one house fly and the presence of these mites of course precludes the use of such parasitized flies for experimental work. The writer (1932) developed a medium of wheat bran and alfalfa meal which was found suitable for rearing the larvae throughout the year. The materials needed are readily available to most laboratories; they are free from parasitic mites; and are clean and easy to handle. The preparation of the medium is as follows:

Wheat bran ....3-¼ lbs.	} Mix thoroughly
Alfalfa meal ....1-¾ lbs.	

Water ....5000 cc.	
Yeast suspension* ....300 cc.	} Mix thoroughly
Diamalt** .... 25 cc.	

Add the water mixture to the bran mixture and stir thoroughly. The amount of water used in the medium is of considerable importance and depends to some extent on the type of rearing jar used and the tightness of the cover. Tall narrow-mouthed containers need less water as evaporation from such jars is less. The amount of water should be such that the medium will dry out on top as incubation progresses, as the mature maggots pupate here. If too much water is used the top of the medium remains wet and the larvae will tend to migrate out of the jar in their effort to find a dry place for pupation. Trouble with fungous growths may also be experienced. The medium may be used as soon as prepared.

The equipment needed for rearing a large steady supply of house flies throughout the year includes: A room in which temperature may be kept approximately constant near 80°-85° F. to be used as the insectary or breeding room; a supply of small wire-screened cages in which to keep the adult flies; and a number of rearing jars or pails. A room 8 x 12 ft. should be sufficiently large in which to raise 2000 or

*Prepared from 1 lb. baker's yeast to 2 liters of water. This stock suspension should be kept on ice and used as needed.
**A malt sugar concentrate made by the Fleischmann Yeast Co.

more flies daily. The walls should be lined with suitable shelves on which to place the cages and jars. Electric heaters thermostatically controlled or temperature regulators for radiators may be used for holding the temperature fairly constant. A basement room is quite suitable as temperature variations are usually less, and if well insulated, cooling units will not be needed in hot summer weather. Relative humidity should be kept above 50 per cent.

In starting a culture it is important to obtain large, healthy, unparasitized flies. These are placed in a screen breeding cage where mating and oviposition take place. A cage of approximately 12″ x 12″ x 12″ with one sliding glass side and a wooden bottom is quite suitable. Egg laying usually starts when the flies are 3 days old. A dish containing a small amount of the bran mixture just described should be placed in the cage for egg deposition and should be replaced each day. Food consisting of milk diluted with equal parts of water should also be placed in the cage in a small dish and renewed daily. Glass battery jars approximately 6 inches in diameter by 8-12 inches high may be conveniently used as rearing jars or where larger numbers of flies are desired galvanized iron pails (12 qt. capacity) are suitable and are not as easily broken. The rearing jars are filled about ¾ full of the alfalfa meal-wheat bran mixture and the eggs dropped on top. For a battery jar of the size mentioned about 600 eggs are sufficient. For larger or smaller jars a proportional number should be used. It is well to make an approximate count of the number of eggs used so that overcrowding will not occur else a population of undersized flies will emerge. The tops of the jars are covered with cheesecloth held on with a rubber band and the jars then placed on a shelf and incubated for 9-11 days at which time the adult flies should be emerging. The house fly is positively phototropic and advantage is taken of this for transferring the flies to stock cages by means of a cone shaped top made to fit the jar or container. Stock cages of the same size as breeding cages may be used to keep the emerging flies in until needed for experimental work. As many as 1000 or more flies may be kept in a cage of this size but it is probably advisable not to overcrowd. Diluted milk should of course be supplied daily as food. The flies vary in resistance to insecticides at different ages being of low resistance in the writer's experiments, just after emerging and of greatest resistance at about 48 hours of age after which resistance decreases as they grow older. The resistance of the flies varies from day to day and season to season but is fairly uniform on any one day. For this reason in a series of comparative tests it is well to use flies all of the same age and to finish the series as soon as possible, preferably in 2 to 4 hours.

By shrouding the cage in black cloth except for a hole at the top which connects with a milk bottle or other glass container samples of flies from the stock cages for use in experimental work may easily be taken by taking advantage of the positive phototropism of the fly. In some types of experimental work, it might be more suitable to use the method developed by F. L. Campbell and W. N. Sullivan (1934) where all the flies are chilled at 30° F. for 15 minutes. These paralyzed flies are then mixed and the number to be used in the experiment rapidly counted into petri dishes or other enclosed cages which are then brought back to the constant temperature room where the flies all revive to normal activity in about 10 minutes. Such a treatment has not appeared to effect the resistance or subsequent activity of the flies.

BIBLIOGRAPHY

CAMPBELL, F. L., and SULLIVAN, W. N. 1934. *Soap* (Sanitary Products Section) 10, No. 3:81, 82, 83, 85, 87, 103, 107.

GLASER, R. W. 1923. The effect of foods on longevity and reproduction in flies. *J. Exper. Zool.* 38:383.

———— 1924. Rearing flies for experimental purposes with biological notes. *J. Econ. Ent.* 17:486.

———— 1927. Note on the continuous breeding of *Musca domestica. Ibid.* 20:432.

GRADY, A. G. 1928. Studies in breeding insects throughout the year for insecticide tests. I. House flies (*Musca domestica*). *Ibid.* 21:598.

HOCKENYOS, GEORGE L. 1931. Rearing house flies for testing contact insecticides. *Ibid.* 24:717.

RICHARDSON, H. H. 1932. An efficient medium for rearing house flies throughout the year. *Science* 76:350.

THE CULTURE OF MUSCINA STABULANS *

EVELYN GEORGE GRIEVE, *Cornell University*

FLIES were reared through numerous generations, the year round, using very simple methods.

The adult flies need to be kept in a warm room, 76° to 80° F., and preferably near a window, although direct sunlight should be avoided. A spacious cage is recommended as overcrowding may have a tendency to retard oviposition. A satisfactory size is 18 x 18 x 72 inches and is suitable for about 250 flies. The type of cage used in this rearing work was made of cheesecloth, with top and bottom (18″ x 18″) of beaverboard, the two fastened together by means of gummed paper. A celluloid window about 16″ x 16″, in one side near the bottom, is very useful, and may be sewed into the cheesecloth on a sewing machine. The opening to the cage may be provided with a cheesecloth sleeve for convenient closing.

The flies require a constant supply of water; a convenient arrange-

—————
*Project carried out for the N. Y. State Conservation Commission, rearing larvae as food for young grouse.

ment for providing it is a wide-mouthed bottle filled and inverted over a petri dish lined with filter paper. The only food which is essential is sugar. But if oviposition is desired some protein should be fed. A cake of Fleischmann's yeast, moistened occasionally, will last for several weeks. Boiled egg, chopped fine, is also recommended twice a week.

In order to secure Muscina eggs, place a pan containing a suitable larval food in the fly cage after the flies are 12 days old. A satisfactory larval diet may be prepared as follows:

Alfalfa leaf meal	6 parts
Soybean meal	1 part
Water	11 parts
Boil all together 10 minutes. Add dried skim milk	1 part

(All of these materials may be purchased at a feed store; cost for large scale production, about 5 cents for 4000 maggots.)

A pan containing 3 to 4 cups of this ration, placed in a fly cage for 2 days, should secure enough oviposition to produce several hundred full grown larvae in 8 to 10 days under summer conditions. (If the larvae are too abundant for the quantity of food they will not develop to maturity, and more food should be added.) The larval medium should be kept moist while the larvae are growing, but when ready to pupate they require a semi-dry medium, and sometimes additional space—not more than 300 in a pan 6 inches in diameter, so that all pupation chambers may be in one layer at the surface.

The temperature recommended for larval development is 72° to 76° F.

If it is desired to remove full grown larvae from the food substance, for laboratory purposes, place the culture in a basket made from screening, 8 meshes to the inch, and wash in running water or in a basin of water.

There are many other combinations of meals and vegetable products that are satisfactory for larval diets, but the following requirements should be considered: The mixture should be sufficiently porous to allow escape of noxious gases, and to provide air for respiration. The protein concentration should be relatively low, to minimize disagreeable odor. The ration should be sufficiently nutritive to promote rapid growth, in order that the flies may escape infestation by mites. The consistency should not be glutinous, so that the particles will separate readily in water, if the maggots are to be removed from the media by washing.

Very frequently a thick growth of mold appears on the surface of the larval medium after 3 or 4 days; but a healthy crop of maggots will soon demolish it, and no harm seems to be done.

Certain extraneous dipterous species were occasionally present in the cultures, but had no apparent detrimental effect.

Two species of mites, whose adults were ectoparasitic on the adult flies, were sometimes present in the medium, but only attacked the emerging adult flies in those cases where larval development was retarded, giving the mites time to mature.

When flies were due to emerge (7 to 12 days after pupation), the pans containing them were placed under the emergence cages. These were more or less funnel shaped cages, made of screening, 8 meshes to the inch. They were left open at the wide end, to be placed on a flat table, and had a screen cap fitted over the small end. By placing a black cloth around the cage the flies were induced to ascend to the light and were removed *via* the screen cap.

A factor to be considered in winter rearing was the tendency of the adult females to develop enlarged fat bodies for hibernation, and to cease oviposition. Hence it is advisable to secure eggs from young females and to rear other generations as soon as possible. In summer, females may continue to oviposit for 6 weeks.

Family BORBORIDAE

BORBORIDAE *

INTEREST attaches to forms easily reared throughout their life cycles in the laboratory because of their possible value both in the classroom and in research work. During a study of certain insects found about sheep manure, the ease was noted with which two species of Leptocera (Limosina) were carried through from generation to generation in milk bottles or shell vials, when sheep dung was used as food.

The two species studied, *Leptocera longicosta* and *L. ordinaria,* belong to the family Borboridae and are not distantly related to the Drosophilidae. In size also they approximate the smaller fruit flies. At Princeton summer temperatures the former completes a life cycle in 11 to 14 days, the modal period being 12 days, while that of the latter is shorter at 9 to 10 days. They are handled in transferring after the manner familiar with fruit flies, being positively phototropic and withstanding etherization well. It is probable from our observations on nearly a dozen generations that they may be maintained indefinitely by successive transfers. While only two species are here discussed, additional species of the same family were encountered in our catches out-of-doors,

*Reprinted with slight changes from an article in *Science* 69:577, 1929, by J. W. Wilson and Norman R. Stoll, *Rockefeller Institute for Medical Research.*

viz., L. frontenalis, Borborus equinus, and *Sphaerocerus subsultans,* and they are probably susceptible to similar handling.

These small flies of the genus Leptocera are numerous about dung, especially sheep dung, during apparently the whole of the summer season. They are easily captured in the field with a sweeping net, or at windows of barns, where they gather in large numbers at the top of the window panes, and may be collected by taking advantage of their positive phototropism.

Sexes are easily determined with the aid of a hand lens or dissecting microscope. Occasionally the anal plates of the female are not visible. Slight pressure on the abdomen of an etherized individual with a camel's hair brush will force the anal plates beyond the edge of the last segment, if the individual be a female.

In breeding the flies we have used sheep dung, although it appears probable that other food materials ("decomposing organic matter," Williston, 1908) may be used. Our method was to collect sheep pellets, preferably fresh samples, which were first crushed in water and then boiled. This procedure resulted in sterilizing the dung to a large extent as well as permitting it to be brought to a certain desirable consistency. After cooling, pint milk bottles were about ¼ filled with the cooked dung and were plugged with cotton, after which newly emerged flies were transferred to them. Flies for breeding were allowed to remain in the bottles 7 or 8 days, by which time the females have laid most of their eggs.

It seems to us possible that *Leptocera spp.* as representatives of a fly family, the Borboridae, which are wide-spread if not cosmopolitan in nature upon the dung of mammalia (Howard, 1900), with their small convenient size, short life cycle, easily satisfied food conditions, capability of continuing their life histories in the now familiar laboratory milk bottle, and apparent hardihood in withstanding repeated etherization, combine a group of characteristics which might well make them utilizable material for investigations in insect physiology, genetics, *etc.* It may be mentioned in addition that members of the Borboridae, both larvae and adults, are reported as hosts of herpetomonads (Patton and Cragg, 1913).

REFERENCE

For the culture of Borboridae see also p. 412.

BIBLIOGRAPHY

HOWARD, L. O. 1900. A contribution to the study of the insect fauna of human excrement. *Proc. Wash. Acad. Sci.* 2:541.

PATTON, W. S., and CRAGG, F. W. 1913. A Textbook of *Medical Entomology.* P. 311.

WILLISTON, S. 1908. *North American Diptera,* 3rd edit. P. 316.

M. E. D.

Family TRYPETIDAE

NOTES ON BREEDING THE APPLE MAGGOT, RHAGOLETIS POMONELLA

PHILIP GARMAN, *Connecticut Agricultural Experiment Station*

CONTINUOUS breeding of the apple maggot has until the last few years been regarded as difficult and unsatisfactory. Fluke, however, demonstrated that flies might be reared successfully and, with proper feeding, kept for a considerable length of time. Following this work, an attempt was made at the Connecticut Agricultural Experiment Station to rear the insect for experimental use, with the result that it was bred continuously from August, 1934, to June, 1935, and many flies were secured for experiment during the winter.

Flies emerging in field cages are brought to the laboratory as soon as they appear and are placed in $5\frac{1}{2}$ x $11\frac{1}{2}$ x 7 inch cages with a glass front and a cloth back. Honey and powdered yeast (4 parts honey to 1 part yeast) are smeared on the upper parts of the cage. After mating, which takes place within a week (4 to 10 days), apples are placed in the cage for oviposition. Green apple thinnings from commercial orchards are used for this purpose, the stock being placed in cold storage during July and removed from storage as needed. Apples in which eggs are deposited are removed from cages frequently to pans or battery jars for emergence of the larvae, which are then placed in smaller glass jars and layered with sand for emergence of the adults. On removal of the apples from oviposition cages they are put in a dry place to prevent excessive rotting. The sand within emergence jars must be kept moist during the pupal period, usually about one month, and the flies removed promptly on emergence to cages, where they may secure water and food. Much seems to depend on the quality of the apples offered for oviposition, since green fruit appears to be much more attractive to the flies than ripe or partly ripe fruit. Apples used in spring after long storage are relatively unattractive, though more attractive than fully ripe apples. The most difficult breeding period is in spring before new apples can be obtained, and after the green fruit reaches the point where it rots rapidly when taken from storage. The ratio of increase in fall is likewise much better than during the winter or spring, and has varied from 3 to 17 per individual in successful work. Furthermore, it appears that flies from puparia hibernated in insectary and refrigerators are much less vigorous and shorter lived than those from fall-bred laboratory stock.

The following table gives some of the data from fall breeding work at the Connecticut Agricultural Experiment Station during 1934 in a room varying from 75° to 80° F.; humidity 60-70%; food, yeast 1 part, honey 4 parts; light, daylight from a north window.

Pre-oviposition period ....7 to 10 days
Oviposition period (average)....................... 71 days
Pre-mating ....4 to 10 days
Mating period (average)............................ 52 days
Larval emergence from apples
    Time to first emergence* (average).............. 21 days
    Period of emergence (average)................... 12 days
Fly emergence from soil
    Time to first emergence* (average).............. 63 days
    Period of emergence (average)................... 107 days
Maximum life of flies.............................. 103 days
Average life .... 41 days
Sex ratio of flies bred in laboratory.................45% males, 55% females

BIBLIOGRAPHY

FLUKE, C. L. 1933. *J. Econ. Ent.* 26:1111.

Family PIOPHILIDAE

PIOPHILA CASEI

DON C. MOTE, *Oregon State Agricultural College*

I USED battery jars with some sand in them, and a piece of cured ham as the medium in which the cheese skipper was raised. Cheesecloth was placed over the top of the battery jar. Once the infestation was started, little or no attention was required, the cheese skippers multiplying continuously for over a year.

Family DROSOPHILIDAE

CULTURE METHODS FOR DROSOPHILA

A. H. STURTEVANT, *California Institute of Technology*

THE cultivation of Drosophila in the laboratory is simple, rapid, and may be carried out with little or no special equipment. The technique has been elaborated for special purposes—for quantity production, for the maintenance of relatively constant conditions, and for the reduction of mortality of weak types—but for many purposes these elaborations remain unnecessary. It is proposed here to describe the simple techniques, together with certain of the more complicated developments.

*From date of egg deposition.

MEDIA

As shown by Guyenot (1917), Baumberger (1919), and others, Drosophila larvae feed principally on yeast. The technique of rearing them consists, then, essentially in producing satisfactory media for rearing yeasts that are also convenient in other respects. The usual breeding place for wild specimens is decaying fruit (in the case of *D. melanogaster*, the most used species), and this forms the most easily used laboratory medium. Various kinds of fruit may be used, but banana is the most satisfactory. Fresh, ripe bananas are peeled, placed in a yeast suspension, and allowed to stand for about a day, then drained and about 25 grams placed in a bottle; pint or half-pint milk bottles are convenient. A folded square of filter paper (paper toweling is less expensive and equally good) is added to soak up surplus moisture, and the bottle stoppered firmly but not too tightly with cotton. Adult flies are introduced, and should produce a new generation without further attention in 8 days or more, the time depending upon temperature.

The yeast suspension used may be started with ordinary commercial yeast cakes, but it is better not to make a new suspension each day. Routine procedure is as follows, where bottles are being made up frequently. Each day the banana is removed from the jar, and new banana for use the next day is added. The container (unwashed) is filled with water and shaken, so as to wet all the surface of the banana. Nearly all the water is then drained off, and the jar set aside. Banana so treated is at its best after about 24 hours, and rapidly becomes less satisfactory after two days.

One of the early modifications of this technique was the stiffening of the medium by the use of agar. This method was described in detail by Bridges (1921); it is still preferred by many workers. Fresh ripe bananas are peeled and pressed through a "potato-ricer" or coarse sieve. For each 100 grams of peeled banana use 100 cc. of water and 2 grams of agar-agar. Add agar to the water and heat until the agar is dissolved (the solution may be hastened by stirring in fresh water after boiling begins). Remove from flame, and at once stir in the banana pulp. Pour about 50 cc. of hot medium into each half pint bottle. Add commercial yeast (either sprinkle a small pinch of dry yeast, or add a drop of a water suspension of fresh yeast cake). Add paper toweling and stopper with cotton. Such bottles are ready to use as soon as they are cool; they should not be used after two days. Before flies are added it is desirable to remove a plug of material entirely to the bottom at one edge; otherwise fermentation may cause gas to accumulate under the food and force it out of the neck of the bottle. A corner of the paper may be pushed into this hole to prevent the formation of a well of liquid in which adults might drown.

This medium is much more convenient to prepare in large quantities than is the fermented banana described above; cultures containing it are more convenient to handle owing to the solid nature of the food; there is less free moisture in which the adults may be drowned; and its nature is less dependent on the ripeness of the banana and therefore more uniform.

The banana agar is, however, rather expensive when hundreds of cultures per day are needed; and it does vary with the condition of the bananas used. These facts have led to the development of the cornmeal-molasses-agar that is now the standard medium in this laboratory and in several others. This medium has been described, together with a history of its development and a discussion of its properties and of several variations, by Bridges and Darby (1933). The usual formula is as follows:

Water	75	cc.
Cornmeal	10	gm.
Molasses	13.5	cc.
Agar	1.5	gm.

The cornmeal is first wet thoroughly with some of the water. Of the remaining water, about two thirds is heated with the agar in it. As this water begins to boil, more water is added and stirred in to hasten solution. The cornmeal and molasses are then added, and the mixture boiled for 5 to 10 minutes. The remaining water is then added, to increase the ease of pouring the hot medium into the culture bottles. With this medium also it is necessary to remove a "plug" to prevent gas accumulation under the block of food.

In the interests of economy it is usual to employ a low grade of cornmeal that is sold as poultry feed ("fround maize" in England). Bridges recommends cane molasses free of SO_2; I am not convinced that SO_2 is a serious drawback, but it is at least as well to avoid it. Corn syrup may be used, and I have had good results from unrefined sugar substituted for molasses. The exact proportions may be varied within rather wide limits without materially affecting the results produced. Many workers prefer to measure, rather than weigh, the cornmeal since this may be done more rapidly.

Winchester (1933) recommends the addition of an extra supply of dead brewer's yeast. This method enables more larvae to develop in a small space, and also appears to help in the production of large, well-grown specimens. For most purposes its advantages over well prepared food supplied in sufficient amounts (*i.e.*, in cultures in which relatively few eggs are to be deposited) do not seem great. Similar results may be obtained by adding a fresh supply of yeast after the larvae have begun to develop.

Pearl (1926) has recommended a synthetic medium, made up as follows:

Solution A		Solution B	
Cane sugar	500 gm.	Agar	135 gm.
K Na $C_4H_4O_6$ $4H_2O$	50 gm.	Tartaric Acid	30 gm.
(NH_4) SO_4	12 gm.	KH_2 PO_4	6 gm.
Mg SO_4 $7H_2O$	3 gm.	Water to make 3000 cc.	
Ca Cl_2	15 gm.		
Water to make 3000 cc.			

Dissolve the agar in solution B by heating; mix equal parts of solutions A and B; use 50 cc. per culture bottle.

The advantage claimed for this medium is that it is constant. Other workers have failed to find it satisfactory, and real constancy may hardly be attained without accurate control of the yeast supply.

Several workers have used different materials, when bananas or cornmeal were difficult to obtain, as in certain foreign countries. Bridges and Darby (1933) describe several of these media; Komai (1927) and Gershenson (1928) are original references for two of them. None of these media have proven as generally satisfactory as the three described above.

As shown by Baumberger (1919), dead yeast may be substituted for live as food for Drosophila larvae. This is the basis for the usual technique for keeping bacteriologically sterile cultures, though these may also be maintained by seeding with bacteria-free yeast cultures. For the methods used in these studies, see the papers of Delcourt and Guyenot (1911), Guyenot (1917), Baumberger (1919) and Northrop (1917).

EQUIPMENT AND PROCEDURE

Half-pint milk bottles are very satisfactory for breeding-jars. Pints or quarter pints may be used, but for most purposes are less convenient. Bridges (1932) has developed a special bottle (that may be purchased from the Illinois Pacific Coast Company, Los Angeles, California) which has side walls that converge from the bottom, thus helping to prevent the block of agar medium from shaking loose. My own opinion is that this is a minor advantage; but workers who depend less on the phototropism of the flies for emptying the bottles do not agree with me (see below, under etherizing bottles).

Paper toweling is usually placed on the medium, in folded squares about 3 inches broad. This serves to absorb surplus moisture and decrease the danger of drowning the adults. Filter paper or toilet paper may be substituted; even newspaper has been used. Many workers prefer not to make use of any paper at all, since it makes it very much more difficult to be certain that all adults have been removed from a bottle.

The cotton plugs are more convenient to handle and have a longer life if they are wrapped in cheesecloth. They may be used repeatedly, if sterilized. A dry air sterilizer is useful for this purpose, or fumes of formalin or of carbon tetrachloride may be used if plugs are thoroughly aired before being used again. In cases of serious infection with molds or mites (see below) it is perhaps safest to destroy all old plugs. Some workers use the cardboard caps that dairymen employ, instead of cotton plugs. These must have pin-holes pricked in them to allow air exchange; they have been discarded in this laboratory because the pinholes make the spread of mite infections too easy.

Culture bottles may be kept at a wide range of temperatures, but between 18° and 26° C. is best for most purposes. Above this range breeding is possible, with most strains, up to about 31° (Plough and Strauss, 1923); but above 27° is definitely suboptimal. The results of Young and Plough (1926) show that the most marked effect of unfavorably high temperatures is that of sterilizing the males. At low temperatures oviposition is greatly reduced (practically ceasing below 15°) and the development rate is slowed down markedly, though it is possible for the whole development to be completed at temperatures at least as low as 12°. For many purposes it is necessary to control the temperature, since the development rate and many of the structural characters of the adult vary with temperature. Bridges (1932) has described an incubator adapted to Drosophila work. The design of such an incubator is outside the scope of the present account, but two points may be mentioned. Firstly, it is desirable to arrange, so far as possible, that when the thermostatic control goes wrong the heating unit will go off, not on, since too high a temperature is more harmful than too low. Second, it must not be assumed that the temperature in the bottles is the same as that in the incubator, since the fermentation of the medium makes some heat. This source of error has not usually been taken into account in the published results on temperature experiments with Drosophila.

In many regions summer temperatures are likely to reach the danger-point. If the heat is not prolonged cultures may survive, but it is often necessary to place the bottles in a cold-room or otherwise protect them. Setting their bases in running tap water is often adequate. For routine genetic experiments incubators set at 25° are usually employed; in this laboratory stock cultures are kept at 19°, since the resulting decrease in development rate saves labor by making it unnecessary to make up new cultures so often. Molds are often worse at temperatures below 25°, but may usually be controlled (see below).

When the adults emerge they may be anesthetized with ether for examination. If the etherization is done with reasonable care it does not damage the flies in any way; neither their length of life nor their fertility is reduced. I use a wide-mouthed specimen bottle, the mouth of which will just fit inside the collar of the milk bottle, in the space intended for the pasteboard top. The culture bottle is turned with its mouth away from the light, and tapped until the plug may be removed without flies coming out. The etherizing bottle is then applied to the mouth; the two may easily be held in one hand. They are reversed, and tapping the culture bottle disturbs the flies, which then react positively to the light. The process may be hastened by holding the pair of bottles at an angle, so that shaking makes the flies drop into the etherizing bottle. Into the etherizing bottle is now inserted a cork, to which is wired a piece of cotton that is moistened with ether. The flies are watched until they no longer move, and are then emptied out for examination. They should remain anesthetized for several minutes. The first sign of an over dose is that the wings are held erect, over the thorax; such flies may recover, but in general they should be removed before this reaction occurs.

Bridges (1932) has described a more elaborate etherizing bottle which is preferred by many workers. It consists of a metal funnel, of a size to fit the culture bottle, cemented to a glass chamber, with a corked opening opposite the end of the funnel, through which the flies are removed. There is a collar, filled with asbestos, and having a separate corked opening; the asbestos is saturated with ether. This bottle has the advantages that it anesthetizes more quickly than the simpler one, and that it uses less ether and lets less escape into the room to be absorbed by the experimenter. It has the disadvantage that is is largely opaque, and prevents taking advantage of the phototropism of the flies in emptying culture bottles. Those who use it depend wholly on shaking the flies out by gravity, usually pounding the bottle on a pad of soft rubber.

For examination of the etherized flies a hand lens may be used, but a wide-field binocular microscope is much more efficient. For ordinary genetic work a magnification of about 16 diameters is used. Under this power it is easy to work rapidly for long hours without eye strain or undue loss of efficiency from the smallness of the field that comes with greater magnifications.

A plate of white glass resting on the microscope stage furnishes a good and convenient background for examining the flies. An ordinary desk light, with a frosted 100-Watt lamp, makes a satisfactory source of light. A spherical flask of water should be placed in front of it, to serve as a heat screen; otherwise the flies will not remain etherized so long and may even be killed by heat. The water in the flask may be colored by any of the methods usual with microscopists. The flies are manipulated on the plate by various instruments: a fine brush, blunt forceps, or a special instrument known as a "fly-pusher." This is simply a pointed blade of soft metal with at least one straight edge, usually curved to suit the taste of the worker. This may be used for manipulating individual flies, and also for raking whole groups of them into rows or off the plate.

When the flies are discarded they are killed, since to release them into the room increases the dangers of contaminating the cultures and also favors the spread of mites. This is done by pouring them into a bottle filled with waste alcohol, kerosene, or some heavy oil (Muller recommends crank-case oil drained from an automobile).

In making up new cultures it is, for many purposes, desirable to cross known individuals. This involves the procuring of unmated females. Mating may occur before the females are 24 hours old, especially if old males are present. The usual procedure is to select pale large females, which can with a little practice be easily identified as newly emerged ones. There is a chance of error in this method, since such females occasionally will be found to contain sperm. Greater certainty may be obtained by removing all the flies in the evening and then selecting young females the next morning, since under these conditions no old males will be present. The reason for suggesting these times of day is that, under usual conditions, most of the emergence of the adults from the puparia occurs in the early morning hours. Some workers prefer to isolate pupae; but the labor involved here is disproportionate to the added certainty of virginity.

Oviposition may occur on the first day of adult life, but is commonly deferred to the second; it continues at a high rate for about a week, and then gradually decreases for a longer period, perhaps a month or more. It follows that flies may be put into the culture bottles as soon as they recover from ether; but my own practice is to keep them for 24 hours in vials. Ordinary shell vials are in any case commonly used to keep them until they recover from ether, though they may be placed in a paper cornucopia and put directly into the culture bottle. If they are to be left in the vial for a day it is necessary to feed them. I use a small piece of the "plug" taken from a culture bottle to prevent gas accumulation, as described above. In transferring flies from vials to culture bottles it is desirable to avoid rough handling, since this delays oviposition somewhat. It is better to "pour" the flies toward the light, rather than to shake them out.

PESTS

Wild flies, and their immediate descendants, sometimes have tangled whitish masses of soil nematodes about the bases of their legs and wings; these impede their movements and lead to death. This condition is, however, too rare to be a serious difficulty. There are also hymenopteran parasites and fungi of the Empusa group that attack wild Drosophila; but these have never been encountered as laboratory pests.

There are only two serious laboratory enemies to be dealt with: molds and tyroglyphid mites. The remedy for molds is to prevent infection, by sterilizing bottles thoroughly, sterilizing or replacing cotton plugs, and watching the yeast supply. The infection from spores attached to the parent flies themselves may be decreased by repeated transfers (at one or two day intervals) to new culture bottles. In general, molds are not serious pests for vigorous strains of flies kept at optimum temperatures on satisfactory media, since under these conditions the activity of the larvae keeps the hyphae from developing many spores. There is a German proprietary substance sold under the name of "Nipagin" that is stated to inhibit mold growth without harming yeasts or flies. Several workers have reported success with its use. Parker ("Drosophila Information Service" 4) reports more satisfactory control with less expense from the use of "Moldex-A," obtainable from the Glyco Products Company, 949 Broadway, New York, New York.

The tyroglyphid mite (genus and species not determined) that makes trouble is a more serious enemy. The adults and early nymphal stages feed in the more moist parts of the culture bottle; so far as known they do no damage. There is however a facultative last nymphal stage, known as the hypopus, that does not feed and wanders to the drier parts of the bottle, often becoming attached to the adult flies. Such enormous numbers often cling to a single fly that the latter becomes scarcely able to move and soon dies. The hypopi also crawl out of the bottle and may travel many feet and into a fresh bottle. Sometimes whole laboratories seem to be over-run with them. The best remedy is prevention; at the first sign of their presence the infected bottle should be quarantined—discarded and quickly sterilized if possible. Carbon tetrachloride should be poured into all suspected bottles as soon as they are discarded. Painting shelves and outside of bottles with kerosene is helpful. Since wild flies in the room may be carriers, they should be destroyed as far as possible. Lightly infected individuals, if it is important to keep them, may be "deloused" under the microscope, or repeatedly transferred to fresh vials, when the hypopi will gradually drop off of their own accord. In badly infected laboratories it may be necessary to keep the culture bottles on a water-table, in a solution of creosote. Soapy water has been tried for this purpose; it is apparently effective.

TECHNIQUE FOR SPECIES OTHER THAN D. MELANOGASTER

The foregoing account is intended to apply to *Drosophila melanogaster*, the most used species. With one or two modifications, however, the same technique may be used successfully for many other species of the genus. Most of these species are more sensitive to high temperature; 25° is satisfactory for *D. simulans, D. funebris, D. virilis, D. busckii,* or *D. repleta.* For the members of the *D. affinis* or *D. obscura* groups it is best to use 24° or less. For other forms experiment will show what is optimum.

The other modification often necessary arises from the fact that many of the other species require to be aged longer before they are ready to lay. In the case of *D. simulans* one day in the vial is adequate, but all the other forms that I have bred extensively require more than this. For *D. pseudobscura* three days, or better four, is usual; for *D. affinis* or *D. repleta* a week is desirable. *D. funebris* and *D. virilis* need nearly as long a period. In these cases, if the females are put into the culture bottle too soon they usually fail to lay any eggs, though they may survive and may produce offspring if transferred to fresh medium later. My experience has been, however, that females of these species are much more likely to breed if they have been given fresh food about 24 hours before they are transferred to the culture bottle.

In dealing with the more difficult species it is especially necessary to avoid rough treatment, as this usually interferes with egg laying even more markedly than it does in *D. melanogaster.*

REFERENCE

For the culture of Drosophila see also p. 305.

BIBLIOGRAPHY

BAUMBERGER, J. P. 1919. A nutritional study of insects with special reference to microorganisms and their substrata. *J. Exper. Zool.* 28:1.

BRIDGES, C. B. 1921. Gametic and observed ratios in Drosophila. *Amer. Nat.* 55:52.

——— 1932. Apparatus and methods for Drosophila culture. *Ibid.* 66:250.

BRIDGES, C. B., and DARBY, H. H. 1933. Culture media for Drosophila and the pH of media. *Ibid.* 57:437.

DELCOURT, A., and GUYENOT, E. 1911. Génétique et milieu. Nécessité de la détermination des conditions; sa possibilité chez les Drosophiles. *Bull. Sci. France Belg.* 45:249.

GERSHENSON, S. 1928. A new sex-ratio abnormality in *Drosophila obscura.* *Genetics* 13:48.

GUYENOT, E. 1917. Recherches sur la vie aseptique et le developpement d'un organisme en fonction du milieu. Thesis, Paris, 330 pp.

KOMAI, T. 1927. The culture medium for Drosophila. *Science* 65:42.

NORTHROP, J. H. 1917. The rôle of yeast in the nutrition of an insect (Drosophila). *J. Biol. Chem.* 32:123.

PEARL, R. 1926. A synthetic food medium for the cultivation of Drosophila. *J. Gen. Physiol.* 9:513.

PLOUGH, H. H., and STRAUSS, M. B. 1923. Experiments on toleration of temperature by Drosophila. *Ibid.* 6:167.

WINCHESTER, A. M. 1933. A method of increasing the yield of Drosophila. *Science* 78:483.

YOUNG, W. C., and PLOUGH, H. H. 1926. On the sterilization of Drosophila by high temperature. *Biol. Bull.* 51:189.

Family HIPPOBOSCIDAE

PSEUDOLYNCHIA MAURA

CLAY G. HUFF, *University of Chicago*

THIS fly is parasitic on birds during its entire life cycle except the pupal stage. It can live for only very short periods of time off the host. Flies may usually be obtained from pigeon farms in the Southern states. They may be shipped in the pupal stage by mail or the adults may be placed upon the living pigeon and shipped along with it. To be successful in growing these flies in the laboratory one needs to observe

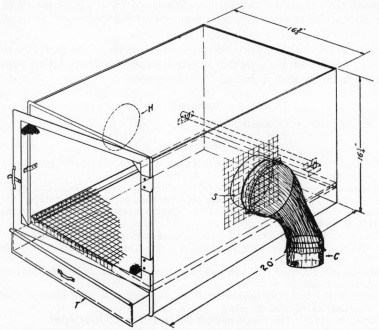

FIG. 79.—Fly-tight bird cage for rearing *Pseudolynchia maura.* C, emergence chamber; H, hole for connecting cages; S, metal sleeve with screen; T, removable tray.

the following precautions. The temperature and humidity should be high, the puparia should be collected frequently and kept in a warm place until eclosion, and they should be kept in fly-tight cages. The cage illustrated (Fig. 79) has been found to be satisfactory for growing these flies.

These cages are constructed of solid sheet metal on all sides except the front which is screened. This arrangement maintains the more humid condition required by the flies. They are provided with a metal sleeve (S) on one side and a hole (H) on the other, so that they may be connected, two or more, together. A coarse screen covers the inside of the opening (at S) which prevents the pigeons from going, but allows the flies to go, from cage to cage. On one end of such a battery of cages an emergence chamber (C) may be attached into which the collected puparia are placed. Upon emergence, the flies readily enter the cage and infest the birds. The tray (T) provided with sawdust provides a place for pupiposition.

The colony requires little attention beyond the daily care of the birds and weekly gathering of the puparia from the tray. Infections of Haemoproteus [see p. 98] are maintained by the frequent bloodsucking of the flies. It is advisable to introduce a new bird at intervals of 3 to 4 months in order to keep the infections going well.

Order COLEOPTERA

FAMILY CICINDELIDAE

For the feeding of *Cicindela sexguttata* and *C. dorsalis* see p. 242.

Family CARABIDAE

THE CALOSOMA BEETLE (CALOSOMA SYCOPHANTA)*

THIS European beetle, a natural enemy of the gipsy moth, has been reared with fair success in the laboratory and in large numbers in an outdoor insectary in the New England territory infested by that moth.

Adult beetles were kept in screened-in cages. Pairs were isolated in battery jars containing 3 inches of earth for oviposition, caterpillars for food, cover for hiding, and supports for climbing; a ventilated cover was used for closing each jar. Daily cleaning of the jars and removal of waste food was necessary. When eggs were found the adults were removed to other cages.

*Abstracted from *U. S. D. A. Bull.* 251, 1915, by A. F. BURGESS and C. W. COLLINS. For further details of methods and equipment see the original publication.

The cannibalistic larvae were isolated for rearing in jelly tumblers or smaller wire cages with moist earth and supplied with caterpillars or pupae for food. The larvae prey on various caterpillars, but the life history of Calosoma is particularly well adapted to that of the gipsy moth.

There is but one brood a year. The eggs hatch in June or July. There are three larval instars and growth is attained by midsummer, after which they enter the soil to pupate. Adults emerge the following spring. Cages of wire cloth buried in the soil have served as suitable containers for hibernation.

Adult beetles as a rule live two years and frequently three, hibernating in the soil during the intervening winter. After emerging from hibernation and feeding several days, mating takes place and eggs are laid by the females. It is necessary for a female to mate several times during the season or a large percentage of infertile eggs will be laid. The adults will feed upon beef for a short time if caterpillars are not available, but after a week they refuse to eat it.

J. G. N.

REFERENCES

For the feeding of *Calosoma calidum* and *C. scrutator* see p. 242.
For the feeding of *Tachyura incurva* see p. 455.
For the feeding of *Harpalus caliginosus* see p. 242.

Family HALIPLIDAE

BREEDING AND REARING HALIPLIDAE*

AFTER considerable experimentation, methods were found by which it was possible to maintain these insects in the laboratory the year around. Beetles collected in the field were separated, according to species, into finger bowls containing water, with not more than 12 individuals in one bowl. Cistern water was used for the culture of all stages, although from experiments it appeared to have no particular advantage over tap, pond, or distilled water. A little muck was placed in the bottom of the bowls in order that the beetles might hide in it when disturbed. Branches of Elodea, Chara, or Ceratophyllum were also introduced so that they might have a place to oviposit. The plants mentioned were never changed during the winter. Water was added about every month to replace that which had evaporated. During the summer, changes were made whenever the water became foul, at times as often as once a week.

*Abstracted from an article in *Ann. Ent. Soc. Amer.* 24:129, 1931, by JENNINGS R. HICKMAN, *Michigan State Normal School.*

Temperatures up to about 75° F. had no detrimental effects, winter or summer, but much higher temperatures were destructive. Food was furnished not oftener than once a month during the winter since the beetles require little at this season, and the food will remain in good condition for a long time. During the summer, these conditions are reversed. The beetles require more food because they are more active and the food will soon deteriorate. As often as every other day a little food was added.

When eggs appeared, they were usually removed to separate finger bowls which contained water. The temperature was maintained at about 70° F. No particular attention was paid them until hatching time. Very few eggs failed to hatch.

The larvae were very easy to rear in the laboratory when a few essential factors such as food, temperature, and condition of the water, remained about constant. They were isolated in stender dishes which contained water to a depth of about one inch. During the warm days of summer when the temperature was much above 75° F., the water was changed daily and all unconsumed food was removed. Either the water was removed by means of a large pipette or the larvae were removed to new culture dishes. In order that the condition of the culture dishes might be observed easily, they were arranged on a shelf one row deep. Covers were placed on the dishes to check evaporation. They were never exposed to direct sunlight.

The pupa is the most difficult stage to obtain because the larvae will not pupate unless conditions are just right. Instead, they will remain larvae or will die. Nevertheless, the pupae of all species studied were secured. When the larvae had reached the 3rd instar they were transferred to a smaller stender dish containing a little water and food. A branch of a water plant was so arranged that it extended over the top of the dish in order that the larvae could crawl out to pupate. This small dish was placed inside a larger stender dish which contained a small amount of earth. This earth had been taken from the shore of the lake in the vicinity of the place where the larvae would naturally pupate.

Before they will enter this earth it must have the right moisture content. This seems to be the most important factor. If it is too wet or too dry they will not construct the pupal chambers. It was found that if the earth was just damp enough to hold together, the larvae would pupate. A few drops of water were added from time to time to prevent undue drying. Fungous growths must be watched for and eliminated. They were largely avoided at the outset by moistening rather large quantities of this shore material, allowing it to stand for a few days before using, and selecting those samples which showed no fungous growth.

Spirogyra proved to be the only kind of food that gave satisfactory results for *Peltodytes edentulus, P. sexmaculatus, P. lengi,* and *Haliplus immaculicollis.* Beetles of these species have been kept living on this kind of food for 18 months. During this time, they have laid eggs that hatched. Nitella was the only food that gave successful results for *Haliplus cribrarius* and *H. triopsis.* They have been kept alive for about 9 months.

The larval food without a doubt is algae. The species of Peltodytes and *Haliplus immaculicollis* feed exclusively on filamentous algae. *H. cribrarius* and *H. triopsis* feed upon Chara and Nitella.

The larvae are free from cannibalism, and any number may be kept together.

M. E. D.

REFERENCE

Family Dytiscidae
For the feeding of Dytiscus see p. 242.*

Family GYRINIDAE

REARING GYRINIDAE**

THE food of adult Gyrinidae consists of animal matter that has fallen on the surface of the water. Captive Dineutes have been induced to feed on dead flies and on bits of raw beef that were made to float by spearing them on toothpicks. Never would they feed unless the meat was at the surface.

The eggs are laid on submerged vegetation or submerged portions of emergent vegetation. In captivity in June and July eggs of both Dineutes (*D. nigrior, D. hornii,* and *D. discolor*) and Gyrinus were laid on aquarium plants and on the sides of the container both above and below the water line. Those laid in the air dessicated. When females were brought from the field and placed in aquaria most of them laid eggs within the first 12 or 18 hours. From 20 to 50 eggs were usually laid by a single Dineutes.

Young Dineutes larvae feed by sucking. They were fed on small tubificid worms. The larvae will also attack and suck their fellows. The larvae come to shore to build their pupal cases, whence they emerge in a few days.

M. E. D.

*Editor's Note: Several members of the family Dytiscidae have been kept alive for some months in a balanced aquarium on a prepared fish food consisting of "a mixture of cereal, powdered shrimp, and ground ant 'eggs.'" Particles of this food were seized and devoured with apparent eagerness. M. E. D.

**Abstracted from an article in the *Bull. Brooklyn Ent. Soc.* 20:101, 1925, by MELVILLE H. HATCH, *University of Washington.*

Family HYDROPHILIDAE

HYDROPHILIDAE*

METHODS OF COLLECTING

THE majority of these beetles live at the water's edge and, if the soil, grass, or other vegetation is stirred rapidly or washed briskly with the water, the Hydrophilidae will soon be released and will come to the surface. They may then easily be gathered by the hand. They do not become submerged immediately as do the Dytiscidae, but swim about on the surface until they regain shore or find some plant to aid them in descending. An examination of the banks adjacent to the collecting grounds at the time of transformation will offer good collecting because often the larval skin, pupal skin, and the adult may be procured in the pupal cell at one time. Some of the species are attracted by arc lights during warm nights and, in fact, it is there that Hydrous is most frequently obtained.

METHODS OF REARING

The isolation, according to species, of adults, which readily lay eggs in captivity, proved the best method of acquainting oneself with the immature stages. Newly hatched larvae are thus easily obtained. The most advisable temporary aquarium for such work seems to be a small stender dish. A small stone, half submerged in the water and draped with Cladophora gave excellent conditions for egg laying, especially for smaller beetles which, as a rule, lay their eggs in moist places and not directly in the water.

For larvae, larger containers produce better results. Moreover, they should be arranged as aquaria-terraria, for many of the adults and larvae spend most of their time on shore. In preparing this, it is best to get some mud from the bottom or edge of a pool and, after placing it in the container to the depth of about an inch, slope it up gradually so that it forms a miniature bank. The bank end should normally be high enough so as to be a little dry on the surface. Cladophora and money-wort make the best plant materials because of their cleanness and lasting qualities. As a rule, the container should be filled so that the bank is covered and then placed in the sun. In a few days, the time depending on the conditions in the pool where the mud was obtained, numerous entomostracans destined to be food for the future larvae will be present. The vegetation is then added.

The larvae, when fully grown, seem restless and try to crawl out. If

---

*Abstracted from an article in *Bull. Amer. Mus. Nat. Hist.* 42:1, 1920, by E. AVERY RICHMOND, *Pennsylvania State College.*

the time for transforming has arrived, they rapidly burrow down and form their pupal cells. Some, however, pupate on the surface of the terrarium, evidently not liking the conditions below. Slightly moist earth seems to be the most natural substance for the terrarium and an inch or so of depth will suffice. If not too deep, they will often make their cell next to the glass container, where it is favorably placed for observation.

The adult is chiefly herbivorous. It feeds mostly on the lower forms, such as algae, but does not seem to be restricted to this diet. Decaying vegetation is its favorite food. It feeds also on dead animal tissue (earthworms, insect larvae, *etc.*).

The principal egg laying months are May and August, although the egg cases of some species may be found during the entire summer.

The larvae are carnivorous and cannibalistic, the different genera varying in their greed. The young larvae feed upon small organisms (entomostracans, Tubifex, leeches, *etc.*) and they capture larger prey as they themselves increase in size. Helophorus was observed feeding on Simocephalus, Cypris, Cyridopsis, Cyclops, and Canthocampus. The full grown larva feeds readily on tadpoles, annelids, fish, and, in fact, almost anything that it can overcome or that is fed to it.

M. E. D.

REFERENCE

For rearing Hydrophilidae see also p. 453.

Family SILPHIDAE

SILPHA INAEQUALIS*

A FEW live specimens of *Silpha inaequalis* were secured from the carcass of a cat and placed in wide-mouthed tobacco jars containing several inches of fresh, moist soil, a few dry leaves beneath which they might hide, a shallow vessel of water, and a small piece of beef. The jars were then covered with a tin cover, the center of which had been cut away and a piece of cheesecloth glued over the opening so as to admit plenty of air.

Freshly killed flies were often thrown into the jar and were eaten by the beetles in preference to the stale meat. They sometimes dug themselves into the soil but remained on top most of the time, often hiding under the leaves. They were frequently found drinking. Close watch was kept for eggs and the first were found in the soil late in July. These Silphas, without exception, deposited their eggs in the soil.

*Abstracted from an article in *Ent. News* 30:253, 1919, by MILTON T. GOE, Portland, Oregon.

The eggs were buried in some moist soil in a jar and hatched six days later. The larvae were quick of motion and fed freely on the stale beef. They rarely entered the soil, but could usually be found close together under the dry leaves. Molting occurred twice before they entered the soil to pupate. The adults emerged about the last of August.

The young beetles ate very little at any time and during the winter months took no food at all. They spent most of their time in the soil, seldom being seen on top. About the last of March a piece of liver was placed in the jar and a few hours later one of the beetles was found clinging to it; this was the first evidence of their eating anything since November.

M. E. D.

Family STAPHYLINIDAE

STAPHYLINIDAE*

DURING the summer a large number of rove beetles appeared in decaying vegetable matter in which flies were being bred. Plants of various kinds were ground up in a clover cutter and the material placed in cake tins. To induce flies to lay their eggs on this pulpy mass, it was baited with ground-up apple, hawthorn, grape, or cantaloup and exposed to the air. The upper layers soon became black, although in several cases the lower surfaces remained green indefinitely. Exposed to the air and to changes of weather, some of the pans became wet and soggy, while those that were sheltered remained comparatively dry. Within a few days the mass was teeming with life. Dipterous larvae of many kinds were most numerous, but Coleoptera of several families were fairly abundant. Small Hydrophilidae were found in the wettest of the pans; one or two of the Nitidulidae were frequently found in the decaying fruit; but by far the commonest beetles were the Staphylinidae.

The first beetles were taken July 2 and others were collected at intervals of a few days until the latter part of August. Pans of vegetable substance in which they were found ranged from nine days to two months old. The amount of decomposition in the plant material appeared to make no difference in the number of beetles, but the amount of moisture was of the greatest importance. The kind of plant used had some effect on the appearance of the beetles, although that may have been mainly a question of moisture also. The largest numbers were found in a combination of alder and touch-me-not, and in sweet clover. Where rain had fallen into the pans until they had become a wet, slimy mass, few

---

*Abstracted from an article in *Ann. Ent. Soc. Amer.* 16:220, 1923, by HELEN G. MANK, Lawrence, Massachusetts.

beetles appeared although there was an abundance of fly larvae. Mold, also, seemed to produce an unfavorable environment. Rather dry material, on the other hand, practically always showed a large number of Staphylinidae.

The beetles, both larvae and adults, were usually securely hidden in the material and when a pan of it was suddenly overturned they would scamper away in all directions.

Both larvae and adults were hardy and were easily kept in small tin salve boxes which were half filled with moist sand. A bit of the disintegrating vegetable material from the pans was added to give the same general environment as that in which they had been found. This vegetable substance was full of dipterous larvae and mites and from time to time more larvae were added. The Staphylinidae were so easily raised that in about six weeks over 20 were reared from the larval to the adult stage in these little boxes.

The larvae have a wide range in their food habits. Larvae of the muscids and other Diptera were eaten readily. In two cases they were fed entirely on mites and they grew well. The larvae will eat other larvae or pupae of the same species. They thrive on a variety of food, both as to kind and as to amount. The amount of food that was definitely put in was no true estimate, however, for whenever vegetable matter was introduced it was full of minute forms of life.

In a period of about two months *Philonthus brunneus, P. longicornis, P. cyannipennis, Tachinus flavipennis,* and *Belonuchus formosis* were raised, the first named of these from the egg stage.

M. E. D.

Family PSELAPHIDAE

BATRISODES GLOBOSUS*

A COLONY of the ant, *Lasius alienus americanus,* was found in a broad dry board in the sunlit margin of a hemlock forest. It yielded workers in abundance, eggs, larvae, many pupae and freshly pupated "callows." With the ants were taken four males and four females of the myrmecocole, *Batrisodes globosus.*

Since the exact food of this species appears to be in doubt, the beetles and a part of the colony were studied to determine this point if possible. The general method of observing the nest inhabitants was that previously used (Park, 1929).

B. globosus has been reported previously by Schwartz (1890) with

---

*Abstracted from an article in *J. N. Y. Ent. Soc.* 40: 377, 1932, by ORLANDO PARK, *Northwestern University.*

Lasius alienus, Crematogaster lineolatus, and *Camponotus pennsylvanicus.* It has also been found in numbers with *Formica ulkei* (Holmquist, 1928; Park, 1929), so that it appears to have a wide range of formicid hosts.

It is now certain that *B. globosus,* sharing the protection of the host's nest and unmolested by the latter, feeds upon their brood.

Living host larvae, dead and discolored larvae, and larvae which were experimentally crushed and mangled were offered to the pselaphids. All were attacked eventually, although the beetles did not show a tendency to eat every day. Occasionally they fed on two consecutive days, but more often feeding occurred every other day. The mangled larvae with gaping wounds and exuded body fluid were most stimulating to the beetles. In general *B. globosus* fed less often, less voraciously, and there were fewer beetles eating jointly, than was the case for the carabid, *Tachyura incurva.*

M. E. D.

BIBLIOGRAPHY

HOLMQUIST, A. M. 1928. Notes on the life history and habits of the mound-building ant, *Formica ulkei* Emery. *Ecol.* 9:70.

PARK, ORLANDO. 1929. Ecological observations upon the myrmecocoles of *Formica ulkei* Emery, especially *Leptinus testaceus* Mueller. *Psyche* 36:195.

SCHWARZ, E. A. 1890. Myrmecophilus Coleoptera found in temperate North America. *Proc. Ent. Soc. Wash.* 1:237.

Family ELATERIDAE

REARING METHODS FOR WIREWORMS

W. A. RAWLINS, *Cornell University*

WIREWORM rearing methods with a few minor modifications are similar to those used for rearing other underground insects. In the laboratory, salve boxes, petri dishes and moist chambers are usually used as breeding cages for obtaining records of behavior and oviposition of adults, and as rearing cages for growth studies of wireworm larvae. Under outdoor conditions, clay pots, drain tiles, galvanized cylinders, and barrels sunk into the soil have been recommended for wireworm life history work. Caves and cellars as described by McColloch (1917) and Lane (1924) make excellent underground laboratories. Temperature and humidity in these chambers were similar to outdoor conditions of the normal habitats of wireworm larvae. Bryson (1929) stated, however, that the cave method has not been as successful in the case of wireworm rearing as in white grub studies. He recommended unglazed drain tiles for outdoor work and described the technique for their use.*

Adults of many wireworm species may be collected from the foliage and flowers of shrubs and trees in woodlands or on meadow grasses and weeds during the warm days of spring. Other species, particularly *Agriotes mancus,* are attracted to clover. foliage baits placed on cultivated fields in previously infested areas and may easily be collected in this way. Since beetles collected in the spring may have mated and laid eggs previous to capture, accurate records on the pre-oviposition periods and total oviposition cannot be obtained. This difficulty may be overcome (Lane, 1924) by rearing larvae taken from the field in outdoor cages and collecting the beetles early in the spring before they emerge from their pupal cells.

Beetles collected in the field are placed in oviposition cages, either salve boxes or petri dishes, with moist previously sterilized soil and food such as honey, sugar syrup, or molasses. Beetles removed from pupal cells are placed, *en masse,* in a moist chamber or similar receptacle with moist soil and food and allowed to remain in a warm room. In a few days mating will take place. After mating, pairs are transferred to individual salve boxes or petri dishes prepared in the usual way. Eggs laid in the cages are separated from the soil particles by washing the soil mass through a fine sieve of 60 to 80 meshes to the inch. Stone (1935) described a very simple and convenient apparatus for this operation. The bottom was cut from the lower half of a 2-ounce salve box leaving only the rim which was soldered to the lower end of a funnel of the same size. The flat surface of the salve box top was replaced with fine mesh wire cloth soldered to the rim. In operation the sieve was attached to the funnel and the soil containing the eggs was washed into the funnel and through the sieve using a gentle stream of water. The sieve then containing the eggs was detached from the rest of the apparatus and the eggs recovered.

Eggs are immediately placed in moist soil to avoid desiccation. Under moist conditions molds grow rapidly and destroy egg cultures unless the eggs are buried or mixed with the soil. For best results the soil should be moderately moist. During the past summer the writer was successful in preventing fungous growth from killing eggs by placing the eggs on a piece of cellophane cut to fit the inside of salve boxes. The circular pieces of cellophane were placed on a layer of moist soil in the lower halves of the boxes. Water was added to the soil from time to time.

Newly hatched larvae are removed from the salve boxes to rearing cages containing moist soil and sprouting seeds of grain or clover. Salve boxes and drain tile are generally recommended (Bryson, 1929;

*Rearing cages and equipment used in underground insect studies are described and illustrated in Peterson, 1934.

Lane, 1924; Stone, 1935) but the writer has obtained higher survivals of young *A. mancus* larvae by using 6-inch moist chambers than by the use of drain tiles or clay pots. Young larvae require sprouting seeds or living plant roots as food. The food requirements of young wireworm larvae needs further investigation, for our present knowledge is contradictory and incomplete.

Cast skins, particularly of the first instars, are difficult to find in the soil because of their small size. Stone has suggested a method whereby the exuviae are easily located. Cells 1 inch in diameter and 3 inches deep were made in a plaster of paris block. A newly hatched larva was placed in each cell containing starchy material from corn grains and the block was then placed in the dark. Moisture was provided by adding water to the block from time to time. After the 3rd or 4th instar the larvae were transferred to salve boxes. An abundance of food was provided at intervals.

Pupae are difficult to handle and high mortalities generally occur. Observations on this stage are successfully made by transferring larvae in the prepupal stage to individual cages. They are placed on the bottom of small vials and the vials then filled with moist soil. Larvae form pupal cells near the glass sides of the vials and the progress of pupation may be easily followed. When salve boxes are used the prepupae are placed in depressions made in the moist soil by the tip of the forefinger or thumb (Stone, 1935).

BIBLIOGRAPHY

BRYSON, H. R. 1929. A method for rearing wireworms. *J. Kans. Ent. Soc.* 2:15.
LANE, M. C. 1924. Simple methods of rearing wireworms (Elateridae). *J. Econ. Ent.* 17:578.
McCOLLOCH, J. W. 1917. A method for the study of underground insects. *Ibid.* 10:183-188.
PETERSON, ALVAH. 1934. A manual of entomological equipment and methods. Part I. Pls. 37-42; 72-73.
STONE, M. W. 1935. Technique for life-history studies of wireworms. *J. Econ. Ent.* 28:817-824.

Family HELODIDAE

SCIRTES TIBIALIS*

ALTHOUGH aquatic, the larva is not an open water swimmer. It has a distribution restricted to that of the duckweed, *Lemna minor*, its one food plant. The larvae are usually found resting on the lower surfaces of the Lemna leaves.

*Abstracted from an article in *Ann. Ent. Soc. Amer.* 11:393, 1918, by WALTER C. KRAATZ, *University of Wisconsin.*

The adult beetle is never aquatic, but is commonly found on grasses and other plants along the shores and the exposed portions of aquatic vegetation.

Many eggs were laid under laboratory conditions by both reared and captured beetles. Whether eggs are normally laid submerged could not be determined. All eggs secured were laid by beetles on dry objects, directly on the glass surface, or on bits of leaves in small vials (without water) in which many of the beetles were isolated for observation. Young larvae were obtained from these egg masses in the laboratory. There is an incubation period of about 10 days, a larval life of about 11 months, a pupal period of 3 days, and there is but one brood a year.

M. E. D.

Family DERMESTIDAE

BREEDING DERMESTES VULPINUS THROUGHOUT THE YEAR*

Dermestes vulpinus has proved a satisfactory standard insect for biological experiments, since it is prolific, has a short life cycle, is easily handled, and may be raised successfully in quantity throughout the year.

Cultures are formed in tin cans 10 inches in diameter by 8 inches high and equipped with tightly fitting covers. Holes punched in the centers of the covers admit air and keep down the humidity. By thus rearing the insects in separate containers little difficulty is experienced with parasites or diseases because if the larvae in one unit become infected the condition is easily checked before it can spread throughout the rest of the cultures.

As the adults and larvae require foods high in protein content a diet consisting of fish-scrap, salmon, cheese, and bacon was fed. A layer of oily fish-scrap about ½ inch deep is spread over the bottom of the rearing chamber and serves both as a food and as a carpet in which the larvae move about. The other foods are added as needed, *i.e.*, salmon is fed to the larvae first and when that is consumed, cheese is added and so on in an effort to give some variety to the diet. The foods are not allowed to dry out, being kept in a fairly moist condition by adding water when needed. The beetles thrive on this diet.

In starting a culture about thirty adult insects, equally divided as to sex, are placed in a container in which food has been placed. Over a period of 10 days about 150 to 200 eggs are laid. As this is about the maximum number satisfactorily reared in each container, the adults are then removed. With the exception of feeding the larvae little at-

*Abstracted from an article in *J. Econ. Ent.* 21:604, 1928, by A. G. GRADY, *Research Laboratories, Rohm and Haas Co., Inc.*, Bristol, Penna.

tention is paid to the culture. The containers are cleaned about once a month. This is accomplished by sifting the fish-scrap with a No. 10 mesh sieve, which keeps back the larvae. The tin cans are then thoroughly cleaned, a fresh layer of fish-scrap and other food added, and the larvae put back in the containers. Otherwise cultures are not disturbed, except when food is added, until the adults emerge. In practice about three cultures are started a week, assuring an ample supply of adults at all times. Adult insects are kept in separate containers with the exception of those used for starting new cultures.

M. E. D.

REFERENCE

For rearing *Dermestes lardarius* and other dermestids see p. 242.

CARPET BEETLES

GRACE H. GRISWOLD, *Cornell University*

SEVERAL species of carpet beetles (*Anthrenus scrophulariae*, *A. verbasci*, *A. vorax*, *Attagenus piceus*, and *Trogoderma versicolor**) have been reared successfully at the Cornell Insectary on a varied diet consisting of woolen cloth, rat fur, chicken feathers, and fish meal. Since many carpet beetles like cereals, a small amount of 3-minute oat flakes has usually been provided in addition to the other foods mentioned. Cultures may be kept going in large tin salve boxes or in ½-pint cylindrical cardboard cartons such as are commonly used for cottage cheese. Where large colonies are desired, the gallon-size "Seal-right" cartons will be found very useful. Adults of two of the common carpet beetles (*Anthrenus scrophulariae* and *A. verbasci*) will usually be found feeding on blossoms of Van Houtte's Spiraea during late May and early June. If some of these beetles are collected and placed in small tin salve boxes with bits of woolen cloth, the females will probably lay eggs and colonies may thus be started with little effort.

REFERENCE

Family Nitidulidae
For rearing of members of this family see p. 453.

* Editor's Note: J. E. Wodsedalek says (*Ann. Ent. Soc. Amer.* 5:367, 1912) that *Trogoderma tarsalis* may be found in all stages of development throughout the year in well heated buildings. Under favorable conditions with ordinary room temperature and plenty of food two and a partial third generation have been obtained in one year. There is a wide variety of substances on which this species can subsist. The pests seem to thrive best on dried insects and fish.

Adolph A. Beyer says (*Kan. Univ. Sci. Bull.* 14:373, 1922) that adults of *T. inclusa* [=*versicolor*] mated a day or two after emergence. Eggs, varying in number from 10 to 50, were placed indiscriminately on the bottoms of the petri dish containers from 4 to 6 days after copulation. The young larvae hatched from 8 to 12 days later at ordinary room temperature. The young larvae were reared entirely on rye grain. This species apparently thrives best on cereals. M. E. D.

Family EROTYLIDAE

MYCOTRETUS PULCHRA*

THIS member of the family Erotylidae was found breeding in *Polyporus chioneus* early in September. At this time larvae, pupae, and several adults were present, with the larvae most plentiful. The infested fungus was moved to the laboratory and kept moist by being placed close to a wet sponge. The larvae continued to feed in the fungus until they were full grown, when they entered the pores of the sponge and pupated, the sponge being rather dry at the time. From this it appears likely that pupation in the field takes place in the wood to which the fungus is attached. Under laboratory conditions the pupal stage required from 10 to 12 days during the last half of September.

M. E. D.

Family COCCINELLIDAE

HYPERASPIS LATERALIS**

THE ladybird beetle, *Hyperaspis lateralis*, is a predator on the redwood mealybug, *Pseudococcus sequoiae*, on Monterey cypress. It also feeds voraciously on the golden mealybug, *Pseudococcus aurilanatus*, and upon other species of coccids or mealybugs. The adults prefer to eat the eggs and young of the mealybugs, but when these are gone they will eat the adults.

Small twigs infested with mealybugs were placed in separate petri dishes to serve as food for each pair of beetles. *P. aurilanatus* was used as food for the fall brood, while *P. sequoiae* was used in the spring. Moistened filter paper was put in the bottom of the petri dishes so as to provide moisture for the insects, but this procedure proved unsatisfactory because of the development of fungi on the twigs, which eventually enveloped the foliage as well as egg masses of the mealybugs. Not only were the latter destroyed, but the fungi also prevented the hatching of the ladybird beetle eggs. Later, fresh green leaves were successfully used to supply moisture for the insects.

Just as soon as the eggs of the beetle were laid on the twigs or underneath the mealybugs, the twigs were removed and replaced by fresh ones.

*Abstracted from an article in *Canad. Ent.* 52:18, 1920, by HARRY B. WEISS, *New Jersey State Experiment Station.*

**Abstracted from an article in *Univ. of Calif. Publ. in Ent.* 6:9, 1932, by H. L. McKENZIE.

Under starving conditions as carried out in the laboratory, *Hyperaspis lateralis* may attack aphids.*

M. E. D.

HIPPODAMIA 13-PUNCTATA**

INDIVIDUAL larvae and beetles were successfully reared under the inverted halves of petri dishes placed on a smooth surface. Aphids were fed to them daily, either attached to leaves or stems, or free from any plant tissue.

The eggs are found on the under side of leaves. In confinement, the females attach their eggs usually to the most convenient surface, but utilize shaded locations if these are available. Under usual summer temperatures eggs hatch in 3 days.

After females have been fertilized, fertile eggs will be laid for about 3 weeks; at the end of this time the eggs become sterile. If a male is again introduced the fertility of the eggs will be restored in from 3 to 6 days.

There was a definite effect on egg production due to varying amounts of food. When only 5 to 10 aphids were available daily, neither copulation nor egg laying occurred. If 50 or more aphids were at hand, egg laying proceeded at the maximum rate.

M. E. D.

BREEDING AND REARING THE MEXICAN BEAN BEETLE, EPILACHNA CORRUPTA

S. MARCOVITCH, *University of Tennessee*

FOR mass production or life history studies of *Epilachna corrupta*, this insect may easily be bred on bean plants covered with 16-mesh screen wire cages. A constant temperature of 77° F. and a relative humidity of 70% offers the optimum requirements for survival. Temperatures above 90° F. are unfavorable for the very small larvae and especially for hatching of the eggs.

For exact temperature studies or records of individual larvae, 1-ounce

---

*Editor's Note: W. M. Davidson, U. S. Bureau of Entomology and Plant Quarantine, reported in *Ent. News* 32:83, 1921, that all stages of *Psyllobora taedata* are to be found associated with fungous infestations of the mildew type and appear to be especially attracted to rose and apple powdery mildew (*Sphaerotheca pannosa* and *Podosphaera oxyacanthae* respectively). Glass vials with cotton stoppers were used as containers. The adult female commenced oviposition about 10 days after emergence. The cycle from egg deposition to adult emergence is passed in July in about 20 days, towards the end of September in about 33 days, and a month later in about 50 days. In no instance was cannibalism displayed by either adults or larvae. M. E. D.

** Abstracted from an article in *Ann. Ent. Soc. Amer.* 17:188, 1924, by CLIFFORD R. CUTRIGHT, *Ohio Agricultural Experiment Station.*

tin salve boxes are well suited. The bottom of these boxes are covered with two pieces of blotting paper that is moistened each day to maintain the proper relative humidity.

A fresh bean leaf is then placed in the box, and one newly hatched larva is carefully laid on the leaf. Examination should be made each day and fresh food or moisture added. For temperature studies, the salve boxes are placed in constant temperature cabinets regulated to any degree of heat required.

At a constant temperature of 60° F. the total length of time for development from egg to adult will be about 83 days, while at 86° F. only 27 days are required. Ordinarily the larvae are bright yellow in color, but at the lower temperatures the larvae assume a dark appearance.

LINDORUS LOPHANTHAE*

A common coccinellid predator of red scale is *Lindorus lophanthae*. If fruit heavily infested with red scale is placed in a container the larvae of Lindorus appear in numbers as soon as the minute scale insects, which are usually present, increase in size. That larger larvae are not found to be so plentiful on the fruit is probably due to the fact that the young larvae are active and have a tendency to drop off or crawl on to the limbs.

When black scale eggs were glued to the fruit the larvae in the 3rd and 4th instars seemed to prefer them to red scale. In order to obtain oviposition records it was necessary to use black scale as a stimulus for egg deposition.

Mating occurs readily in confinement. When paired and placed in a vial with an abundance of black scale eggs one female deposited among the black scale eggs as many as 144 pearly white or yellowish eggs.

Although Lindorus exhibited a fondness for black scale eggs it may be reared successfully on them only after the second ecdysis. Newly hatched larvae placed on black scale eggs suffered a heavy mortality and the length of the 1st instar was three times that of those feeding on red scale. Moreover, all of the 2nd stage larvae died with an abundance of black scale present.

Many larvae may be reared in a small container such as a petri dish 4 inches in diameter without a high degree of cannibalism. The writer placed 120 larvae of all stages in such a container and reared all but 5%. The pupal stage is most subject to injury by the larvae.

M. E. D.

* Abstracted from an article in *Ann. Ent. Soc. Amer.* 23:594, 1930, by STANLEY E. FLANDERS, *University of California.*

Family TENEBRIONIDAE

MEALWORMS, BLAPSTINUS MOESTUS AND TENEBRIO MOLITOR

WILLIAM LeRAY and NORMA FORD, *University of Toronto*

IN addition to the common meal worm (*Tenebrio molitor*), used quite generally as food for fish, frogs, birds, *etc.*, we are finding it most profitable to have a supply of the smaller and more delicate larvae of *Blapstinus moestus*. The latter are especially suitable as food for the smaller animals, such as the swamp tree frog (*Pseudacris feriarum*) and the Spring Peeper (*Hyla crucifer*). Moreover these larvae can withstand moisture better than *T. molitor* and do not die as quickly if dropped into a damp jar with Amphibia. Another point in their favor is their more rapid development.

In rearing either of these larvae, boxes of smooth galvanized iron are set up. The smoothness of the sides of the container is important to prevent the escape of the larvae, since it is preferable to leave the boxes open. Each box should be about 2 x 1¼ feet and have a depth of 1 foot. Over the bottom is spread chick-growing mash to a depth of ¼ inch and this is covered by 4 or 5 layers of burlap, with a sprinkling of mash under each layer of cloth. If possible several hundred worms should be placed in the box. Each day the box is sprinkled with water. In about 3 months it will be seething with larvae. In our department six boxes in various stages of development are kept running.

An old box, in which the mash has been reduced to a powder, may contain many eggs. If this powder is left as a foundation, over which fresh mash and burlap are laid, a rich growth of larvae may result.

THE CULTURE OF TRIBOLIUM CONFUSUM

THOMAS PARK, *School of Hygiene and Public Health*

THIS beetle is easy to culture and requires neither expensive apparatus nor elaborate technique for its maintenance. The eggs are about 0.4 mm. wide and 0.6 mm. long. The larvae are active, burrowing forms which pass through from 6 to 11 instars in their metamorphosis, depending upon the temperature and type of culture medium. The pupal stage is the earliest in which the sex of individuals may be determined on the basis of external characteristics. The sexes may readily be differentiated by examining the ventral, posterior end of the pupa under low magnification (preferably binocular dissecting microscope). On the terminal segment the female has a pair of small appendages which are reduced to indistinct elevations in the male. (Fig. 80.)

The pupae hatch into small, brownish beetles having a mean length, according to Brindley (1930) of 3.4 mm., mean width across the thorax of 1.02 mm., mean male weight of 1.48 mg., and mean female weight of 1.78 mg. Although adult Tribolium may live two or three years it is probable that their usual life span runs from six months to a year. The time required from oviposition to emergence of the imago varies with the ecological conditions. At 28° C., 75% relative humidity and in whole wheat flour, Chapman and Baird (1933) found that metamorphosis took approximately 40 days.

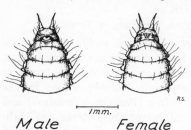

Male   Female

Fig. 80.—Terminal view of male and female Tribolium pupae showing sexual characteristics. (From the *Quart. Rev. Biol.,* with permission.)

Tribolium lives in many types of grain and grain-like habitats. It has been reported from whole wheat flour, patent flour, patent breakfast cereals, bran, rice flour, rye flour, corn meal, barley flour, oat meal, chocolate, spices, certain nuts, and sometimes as predacious on specimens in insect collections. The requirements of the investigator, however, usually rule out most of these substances as suitable culture media. Here, it is necessary to have a medium which may be passed through a sieve fine enough to separate eggs, larvae, pupae, and imagos from the flour and still be nutritious enough to sustain the population. At the present moment it is impossible to state what type of medium best fulfils these requirements. Chapman, who first developed an experimental culture technique for Tribolium, has used finely ground whole wheat flour. Park has used an unbleached patent flour (Ceresota). Either may be recommended at this time. Of course, if the culturist is not interested in obtaining the smaller stages of the beetle (eggs and early instar larvae) for study and count, whole wheat flour, with the bran left in, will make an excellent medium.

The following specific program in developing and maintaining Tribolium stock cultures may be suggested as a working scheme.

1. Into each of a number (depending on the stock desired) of pint milk bottles put about 200 gm. of whole wheat or patent flour.

2. To each bottle add 10 males and 10 females and stopper with a cotton plug.

3. Place in an incubator or a constant temperature room with the temperature at 28°C. The humidity may be allowed to vary between 25% and 75% or may be controlled. These beetles may be reared at room temperature but it is preferable to culture them in an incubator.

4. The bottles should be examined by sifting (method to be described

later) after about 20 days. Pupae, if present, should be isolated by sexes
into new and separate containers. This should be kept up until the desired
number of pupae have been obtained from each bottle.

5. It is preferable at this point to select some of these isolated pupae and
put them back into new stock bottles with fresh flour, thus completely
renewing the stocks. It is important that the flour be changed, as Park
(1934a, 1935) has shown that old or "conditioned" flour reduces the
fecundity and adversely affects the metamorphosis of the beetles.

Flour infested with Tribolium may be sifted in such a way as to
separate the beetles in all instars from it provided finely ground flour
has been used. Chapman (1918, 1928) used standard meshes of silk
bolting cloth and found that mesh number 9 would not pass any of the
stages but would pass finely milled flour; number 3 segregated eggs and
larger larval instars from the flour, and number 000 passed all eggs and

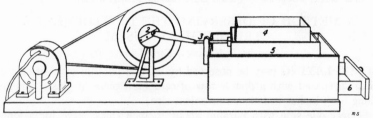

FIG. 81.—Diagram of the automatic flour sifter. 1, belt wheel; 2, driving wheel; 3,
driving rod; 4, flour sieve; 5, flour sieve holder; 6, removable collecting tray. (From
Quart. Rev. Biol., with permission.)

larvae except the largest instar. Thus, by using appropriate meshed
sieves, all stages may be obtained as desired. To aid in this somewhat
laborious sieving the author uses a mechanical device (Fig. 81) which
automatically shakes the flour through the cloth and collects it in a removable tray below. The beetles are retained in the sieve.

In handling the beetles it is well to be as gentle as possible; the author
has found that both brush and small spatula are useful in this regard.
In experimental work the adults should be removed from infected flour
where possible before sifting since there is some evidence to the effect
that too rough handling diminishes the fecundity of the females.
(Stanley, 1932).

In the accompanying bibliography the references have been chosen
with the culturist in mind. Most of the material on the biology of
Tribolium has been reviewed recently by Park (1934).

BIBLIOGRAPHY

BRINDLEY, T. A. 1930. The growth and development of *Ephestia kuehniella*
Zeller and *Tribolium confusum* Duval under controlled conditions of temperature
and relative humidity. *Ann. Ent. Soc. Amer.* 23:741.

CHAPMAN, R. N. 1918. The confused flour beetle (*Tribolium confusum* Duval). *Minn. State Ent. Rept.* 17:73.

—— 1928. Quantitative analysis of environmental factors. *Ecol.* 9:111.

CHAPMAN, R. N., and BAIRD, LILLIAN. 1933. The biotic constants of *Tribolium confusum* Duval. *J. Exper. Zool.* 68:293.

GOOD, NEWELL E. 1933. Biology of the flour beetles, *Tribolium confusum* Duv. and *T. ferrugineum* Fab. *J. Agric. Res.* 46:327.

PARK, THOMAS. 1934. Observations on the general biology of the flour beetle, *Tribolium confusum*. *Quart. Rev. Biol.* 9:36.

—— 1934a. Studies in population physiology III. The effect of conditioned flour upon the productivity and population decline of *Tribolium confusum*. *J. Exper. Zool.* 68:167.

—— 1935. Studies in population physiology IV. Some physiological effects of conditioned flour upon *Tribolium confusum* Duval and its populations. *Physiol. Zool.* 8:91.

STANLEY, JOHN. 1932. A mathematical theory of the growth of populations of the flour beetle, *Tribolium confusum* Duv. *Canad. J. Res.* 6:632.

A METHOD OF OBSERVING THE DEVELOPMENT OF TRIBOLIUM CONFUSUM

HERBERT S. HURLBUT, *Cornell University*

EGG LAYING may be observed by using a paraffin oviposition tray prepared with a double row of cells on a piece of glass (6 inches long by 3 inches wide is a convenient size).

Cover one side with paraffin about ⅛ inch thick, save for a longitudinal strip ¾ inch wide on one edge. In the paraffin two longitudinal, parallel rows of cells are made, by rotating on it with pressure the warmed mouth of a 6 drachm homeopathic vial. The cells should then be excavated down to the glass. Cover the cells with individual squares of ordinary glass. To close a cell, warm a square of glass and press it down with forceps.

Use only one row of cells at a time, changing each day. Number each pair of cells on the bare glass at the side. Prepare the cells for the beetles by dusting very lightly with the food material. Whole wheat flour or whole milk powder may be used. After two beetles (a pair) have been in a cell for a day, remove them to the opposite cell and examine the cell they have occupied for eggs. The eggs may be identified by their ovoid shape and yellowish color. They may be removed with a needle, the end of which has been ground flat and bent at an angle of a little less than 90 degrees.

The larvae may be reared in petri dishes dusted with the food material. Dust very lightly at first, so that the small larvae may not be hidden. Neither larvae nor adults will escape from uncovered dishes if the sides are clean.

REFERENCE

For the culture of *Tribolium ferrugineum* and mealworms see p. 242.

TENEBRIO CULTURE

WILLIAM M. MANN, *National Zoological Park*

AT the National Zoological Park Tenebrio larvae are cultivated in shallow trays which have an overhang at the top to prevent the insects from crawling out, and a mesh cover also to keep the beetles from flying.

The boxes are kept half filled with bran; an occasional bit of potato, carrot, and vegetables added for the adult beetles. Under these simple conditions we are raising all that is necessary as food for our Zoo animals.

REFERENCE

For the culture of *Tenebrio molitor* see also pp. 479 and 480.

TENEBRIO OBSCURUS*

UNDER favorable conditions, larvae of the dark meal worm, that hatch in the spring or early summer months, become apparently full grown by the middle of August. They do not transform at that time but normally remain as larvae, with but little change in size or outward appearance, until the following spring. If the larvae are kept in a heated room, development is hastened and a certain percentage may begin to pupate in November or December.

During the course of a study of the biology of the dark meal worm it was noted that light had a marked effect upon the larvae, so much so that, when well grown worms were kept continuously in light they quickly began to pupate regardless of the season.

By holding the meal worm larvae at temperatures below normal they may be prevented from transforming at the regular period, and by the use of light and warmth they may be induced to transform without passing through the normal hibernation period; hence, with the proper use of these three agents, a supply of all stages of the dark meal worm may be obtained at all times of the year.

M. E. D.

Family CISIDAE

CISIDAE**

"IN confinement many species of Cisidae will continue feeding and breeding in dry *Polyporous versicolor* until the fungus has been practically all consumed."

* Abstracted from an article in *Proc. Ent. Soc. Wash.* 32:58, 1930, by RICHARD T. COTTON, *U. S. Bureau of Entomology and Plant Quarantine.*

** From *Bull. Brooklyn Ent. Soc.* 15:110, 1920, by HARRY B. WEISS, *New Jersey State Experiment Station.*

Family SCARABAEIDAE

METHODS OF BREEDING AND REARING SCARABAEIDAE

HENRY FOX, *U. S. Bureau of Entomology and Plant Quarantine,* and DANIEL LUDWIG, *University College, New York University*

THE methods employed in the breeding and rearing of Scarabaeidae are largely modifications of those described by Davis (1915). It is evident from his account that they need to vary, depending largely on whether the rearing is to be done out-of-doors, under essentially natural conditions, or in the laboratory under controlled conditions. The following procedure has reference to the needs of controlled experimentation, but it could be easily adapted to the ordinarily less exacting needs of out-of-door work.

COLLECTION OF MATERIAL AND METHODS OF INDUCING OVIPOSITION

To obtain a supply of eggs with which to begin rearing experiments, adult beetles are collected and confined under conditions that will lead to oviposition. In most cases, little difficulty is experienced in bringing this about. The beetles are gathered off the foliage, transferred to the laboratory, and confined in suitable cages. Even if the females are not already impregnated when collected, mating usually takes place readily once the two sexes are brought together. There are, however, some Scarabaeidae, particularly those with a highly elaborate copulatory apparatus, like that existing in the larger May beetles of the genus *Phyllophaga* Harris (*Lachnosterna* Hope), which do not readily mate in confinement. In these instances, it is best to secure material already mated. Mating pairs can be readily obtained at night on the foliage of trees and bushes by the aid of a flashlight.

In transporting beetles from the field to the laboratory, it is very important to protect them against crowding, excessive heat, and desiccation. Overcrowding may be prevented by placing not more than 50 to 100 beetles to a pint jar and including some twigs of a food plant bearing foliage to enable the beetles to crawl about. The injurious effects of direct exposure to sunlight may be prevented by covering the jars with a thick cloth or other suitable device. To protect the beetles against desiccation, the use of containers which permit a ready escape of moisture should by all means be avoided. Glass jars or metal boxes, with firmly fitted lids, are satisfactory, provided enough air space is left for respiratory needs. Even in such containers it is often desirable to place a sprig of moistened foliage or to add a few slices of some highly succulent fruit such as apple.

For securing eggs under ordinary conditions, 12-inch standard size flower pots may be used. These are filled with finely sifted soil and each covered with a cylindrical wire screen cage (Tower type), as shown by Davis (1915, plate 3, fig. 4). In filling the pots, it is desirable to add enough water to the soil to make it moderately moist. It is also necessary to avoid an excess of moisture, as a wet soil is not favorable for oviposition and is likely to make sifting for eggs difficult. Before placing the beetles in the cage, it is advisable to introduce an ample supply of food. The usual procedure is to sink a milk bottle or mason jar deep enough in the soil to hold it upright, add water, and insert in it the cut ends of stalks of such food plants as are preferred by the insect for food. In the case of the Japanese beetle, the food commonly preferred consists of the foliage of smartweed (*Polygonum*), rose, grape, sassafras, linden, *etc.** In addition, fruit such as apple is relished and, if cut into thick slices or if peeled to expose some of the pulp, it supplies an easily accessible source of moisture as well as food. When feeding normally takes place underground, as in *Euetheola, Ligyrus,* or *Dyscinetus,* food should be buried in the soil. Thus, young tender plants or soaked kernels of corn pushed well down into the soil are readily eaten by the adults of *Euetheola* (Phillips and Fox, 1924).

Frequently it is possible to secure a supply of eggs with much less trouble than is imposed by the use of a commodious breeding cage like that just considered. It is a relatively easy matter, for example, to get many beetles to deposit eggs in quart milk bottles if enough sifted soil, properly moistened, is introduced to fill them one-fourth to one-third full and slices of apple or other suitable food added. This method is particularly advantageous in winter, as the bottles can be placed in an incubator at summer temperatures, thereby stimulating the deposition of eggs.

In the case of beetles reared from larvae kept indoors during the winter, it is often difficult to induce them to mate as long as they are permitted to bury themselves in the soil of the jars. This difficulty may be overcome by temporarily transferring them to a test tube containing no soil, which, after adding a slice or two of apple, is placed in an incubator at a temperature of about 25° C. (77° F.)

---

* Editor's Note: William P. Hayes, of the University of Illinois, reported in *Canad. Ent.* 53:121, 1921, the feeding of adults of *Strigoderma arboricola* on various blossoms, including roses, while confining them in covered tin pails containing damp soil. The young grubs were fed bran until the second molt, when wheat grains were substituted. Lachnosterna grubs were reared on the same substances.

The feeding of adult *Osmoderma eremicola* on flowers, such as dandelion and Spiraea, was reported in *Bull. Brooklyn Ent. Soc.* by Harvey L. Sweetman, Massachusetts State College, and Melville H. Hatch, University of Washington. Eggs were laid and hatched in the wetter portions of decayed wood in the cages. M. E. D.

CARE AND HATCHING OF THE EGGS

The eggs are removed from the soil by sifting it at intervals. They are considerably smaller when freshly laid than later when they increase considerably in size by absorption of water. Their white color, however, makes it relatively easy to detect them and pick them out of the darker soil irrespective of whether they do or do not pass through the sieve. Eggs are transferred to the hatching boxes by means of a slightly moistened camel's hair brush. The hatching boxes are each about three-fourths filled with finely sifted soil, previously sterilized and moistened by kneading with tap water. One-ounce or two-ounce metal salve boxes are satisfactory for this purpose. The soil is packed down in the box until its surface is firm enough to enable crater-like pits to be made in it which retain their shape. One egg is placed in each of these pits. To prevent the larvae, as they hatch, from crawling out of their pits and straying into others, the pits are made about one-fourth inch deep with vertical sides. The soil may be sterilized by heating it in an oven for several hours at a temperature of 100° to 150° C. (212° to 301° F.), or by fumigation with carbon bisulphide or chloroform for a period of about 24 hours.

The boxes containing the eggs should be placed in an incubator at the desired temperature. Ludwig (1928) found that at 30° C. (86° F.) development of the eggs of the Japanese beetle occurred most rapidly. The eggs of this species are not likely to hatch at constant temperatures above 33° C. or below 15° C. (59° F.). Furthermore, in 1930 he demonstrated that long exposures to a temperature as low as 10° C. (50° F.) will delay the hatching of the larvae when they are subsequently placed at higher temperatures.

The eggs should be examined daily to make certain that moisture conditions are favorable and to note the progress of development. When needed, water can be added from a pipette, but care must be taken to avoid an excess, which might prove detrimental since it favors the growth of parasitic molds that kill the eggs. Hatching may be anticipated by noting the appearance of the brown jaws of the developing larvae, which can be seen through the egg membrane.

CARE AND FEEDING OF THE LARVAE

For the general rearing of scarabaeid larvae, the one-ounce metal salve boxes recommended by Davis (1915, plate 5, figs. 10-12) are satisfactory. On account of the pugnacious habits of the larvae, it is unsafe to place more than one individual in a box.

The medium used in the rearing boxes should be sifted and sterilized. It may be quite varied in nature and composition, the main considerations being the capacity to hold moisture and supply food. For this double purpose a vegetable mold is used. This consists of the thoroughly rotted and disintegrated vegetable debris which accumulates beneath tufts of various grasses, sedges, rushes, and similar vegetation growing luxuriantly in meadows and other low-lying tracts of sluggishly draining land. Forest leaf mold has not been found satisfactory. Vegetable mold has a high water-holding capacity. This gives it a distinct advantage over mineral soils because it loses moisture more slowly and does not become wet so readily when water is added to it.

As a food, vegetable mold is readily consumed by larvae of Euetheola and Cotinus,* often to the neglect of other food, while other forms, as the larvae of the Japanese beetle, consume it more sparingly. It has been possible to rear larvae of the Japanese beetle from egg to adult on vegetable mold alone, although in such instances development is somewhat retarded as compared with that of larvae also supplied with other food, such as grains of wheat. In the case of the Japanese beetle, best results have been obtained when several grains of wheat were added to the plant mold at intervals of about a week during the growing period. These soon soften and germinate, and the larvae feed not only on the grain itself but also on the growing rootlets. In the case of newly hatched larvae, mortality may be considerably reduced by moistening the plant mold with a mixture of equal parts, by volume, of water and milk previous to transferring it to the rearing boxes. This provides the larvae with a highly nourishing food. Freshly hatched larvae treated in this manner not only survive in greater numbers but, even when deprived of wheat, have been found to pass through the earlier instars as rapidly as other larvae, that were provided in addition with grains of wheat. The use of a diluted milk is necessary to prevent the liberation of too much ammonia due to the decomposition of the protein. Survival may also be favored by burying the larvae in the vegetable mold instead of merely placing them on the surface and allowing them to burrow down into it on their own volition.

The rearing boxes should be made about one-half full of plant mold in the case of young larvae and two-thirds full for older larvae. In either case a cushion of air is left between the surface of the plant mold and the lid which is normally sufficient to meet the respiratory needs of the larvae.

In the case of sluggish larvae, like those of the Japanese beetle, the

---

* Editor's Note: The late Anna Laura Hintze of Goucher College reported in *Ann. Ent. Soc. Amer.* 18:31, 1925, the rearing of grubs of *Cotinis nitida* on the following foods, listed in the order of preference: sweet potatoes, Irish potatoes (if the skin was broken), turnips, and carrots. The larvae showed a preference for a soil temperature as high as 40° C. M. E. D.

same supply of plant mold, moistened at suitable intervals, normally serves to carry them through the first and second instars. Subsequently, as more food is consumed and as fecal material accumulates, it is necessary to renew the vegetable mold. Vigorous larvae, like those of Euetheola, Cotinus, *etc.*, consume vegetable mold very rapidly. This necessitates frequent renewal, and as this material cannot always be obtained in quantity, it becomes advisable, as the larvae increase in size, to place them in boxes with soil and to add food in the form of wheat grains or corn kernels as needed. In rearing Euetheola, Phillips and Fox (1924) failed to get larvae of the earliest instar to feed on wheat or corn, but these larvae readily consumed the vegetable mold. In later instars, it was found that they fed on corn previously soaked in water. Larvae fed in this double way were carried in considerable numbers from the egg to the pupal and adult stages, which appeared at the same time that these stages appeared in the field. Baerg and Palm (1932) experienced difficulty in rearing Euetheola larvae on vegetable mold alone, but succeeded in rearing them through the first instar in a sandy loam containing humus and other plant debris, to which in later instars sprouted kernels of corn were added. Hayes (1929) found that the larvae of such Scarabaeidae as Ligyrodes and Euphoria, which normally live in manure and other decaying matter, could be successfully reared by mixing the soil in which they were placed with an equal quantity of manure.

The temperature range for the normal development of the larva seems to be more restricted than for the egg stage. Ludwig (1928) found that 25° C. (77° F.) was optimum for complete larval development of the Japanese beetle. Considering the entire larval stage, complete development was obtained only at temperatures between 20° and 27.5° C. (68° and 81.5° F.). Above and below these points the larvae did not transform to pupae. In his experiments, each instar was able to tolerate a greater range of temperatures. For instance, the first instar larva was successfully reared at temperatures ranging from 15° to 30° C. (59° to 86° F.). However, it has been found that larvae, particularly of the second and third instars can be kept at temperatures as low as 10° C. (50° F.) for months without injury. When these larvae are later placed at high temperatures, development occurs normally. Since 10° C. (50° F.) is too low for development, it is possible, in this way, to keep larvae in any desired stage of development until needed for experimentation.

Since the pupal stage is non-feeding, the essential requirements for its development are proper moisture and temperature. Pupae can be successfully carried through to the adult stage in a medium of moist sterile soil or plant mold. Adults of the Japanese beetle have been obtained from pupae kept at constant temperatures ranging from 15° to 35° C. (59° to 95° F.).

BIBLIOGRAPHY

BAERG, W. J., and PALM, C. E. 1932. Rearing the rough-headed corn stalk beetle. *J. Econ. Ent.* 25:207.

DAVIS, J. J. 1915. Cages and methods of studying underground insects. *Ibid.* 8:135.

HAYES, W. P. 1929. Morphology, taxonomy, and biology of larval Scarabaeoidea. *Ill. Biol. Monographs,* 12, No. 2.

LUDWIG, D. 1928. The effects of temperature on the development of an insect (*Popillia japonica* Newman). *Physiol. Zool.* 1:358.

———— 1930. The effects of exposure to cold on the embryonic development of the Japanese beetle (*Popillia japonica* Newman). *Ibid.* 3:291.

PHILLIPS, W. J., and FOX, H. 1924. The rough-headed corn stalk beetle. *U. S. Dept. Agric. Bull. No.* 1267.

A SUCCESSFUL METHOD OF REARING TRICHIOTINUS

C. H. HOFFMANN, *U. S. Bureau of Entomology and Plant Quarantine*

IN ORDER to obtain eggs of Trichiotinus mated pairs were confined in 3-ounce salve boxes partially filled with small particles of damp wood. The wood was carefully examined for eggs every other day and moisture added if necessary. To avoid desiccation, the eggs obtained were quickly transferred to cavities in dampened soil within 2-ounce salve boxes, and covered with soil to conserve moisture and prevent losses due to the attacks of parasitic fungi. Even though it consumed much time, the soil was changed every second day until hatching occurred. Not over 10 eggs were isolated in each box, and often a perfect hatch was obtained. Upon hatching, each grub was carefully transferred to a 2-ounce salve box, which had been previously supplied with relatively small particles of moist decaying wood. Here the larva remained until maturity or death. These salve tins were kept in a basement which maintained a rather uniform temperature of 23° C. The boxes were examined every other day and new food or a few drops of water from an eye dropper were added if needed. Moisture is undoubtedly the most difficult factor to control properly in the rearing of wood-inhabiting forms. The usual tendency is to over-water, which is far more injurious than under-watering.

Other scarabaeids and lucanids, which develop in decaying wood, were also reared to maturity in salve boxes containing small particles of moist wood. One species of Trichiotinus has been reared through consecutive generations in the laboratory.

Family PASSALIDAE

PASSALUS CORNUTUS*

THE social reactions of *Passalus cornutus* are of particular interest in that it is one of the few social Coleoptera.

The life cycle of this particular beetle is normally passed within decaying wood where it is safely hidden from light and observation. One of the difficulties encountered in rearing these insects was the lack of a method whereby normal reactions could be carefully observed. It was finally discovered that by using decaying sawdust of the right degree as a medium for galleries, and feeding the proper kind of decaying wood in amounts too small for the adults to burrow in and conceal themselves, the actions of both adults and larvae might be satisfactorily observed.

Enameled cake plates approximately 2 inches deep were used for brood dishes. Pieces of window glass were used to cover the plates, and pieces of cardboard were then placed on the glass to exclude the light. Great care was necessary to prevent the accumulation of refuse in the brood dishes as the adults showed a tendency to plaster over the glass covers and thus prevent observation of their activities. It was found that the greatest activity occurred at night, and that artificial light did not interfere with their activities if it was not too intense. By placing a binocular microscope on the window glass covering the brood dish, and adjusting it to focus through the glass, one could get a very interesting picture of the actions of any specimen. Great care was necessary, however, in moving the microscope in order not to jar the dish and thus disturb the individuals to be observed.

For purposes of observation several pupa cases were opened and glass tops inserted. These were immediately plastered over. An artificial pupa case was finally devised out of wet blotting paper and fitted with a removable glass cover. This might be placed on a binocular platform and the interior of the case subjected to magnification. Larvae transferred to this type of case went through the pupal changes without injury.

Cannibalism is very prevalent and forms one of the greatest difficulties in carrying out observations on any particular larvae.

Although clumsy and awkward in many of its movements, Passalus is readily adaptable to the laboratory when provided with the proper food and humidity.

M. E. D.

* Abstracted from an article in *Ann. Ent. Soc. Amer.* 25:709, 1932, by WARREN C. MILLER, *Bedford High School*, Bedford, Ohio.

Family CERAMBYCIDAE

THE PAINTED HICKORY BORER, CYLLENE CARYAE*

THE hickory borer is a sun-loving insect. On bright, sunny days during May and June adults may be found on the trunks and branches of recently killed trees or on felled timber, running rapidly back and forth. Rarely are they found on such material when it is well shaded.

Like many of the Cerambycidae, the adults of this species are pollen feeders. For some time the writer was puzzled as to what the food plants of the beetles could be, for while males and females copulated freely when confined in cages, oviposition did not occur, and both sexes died in three or four days when no food was supplied. Finally, the beetles were found actively feeding on the pollen of the flowers of hawthorn (*Crataegus sp.*). From then on no difficulty was experienced in breeding the insects in captivity. With a supply of these blossoms in the cages, copulation took place and eggs were promptly deposited.

Mating occurs shortly after emergence. Adults which emerged June 6 were found copulating the following day. Oviposition takes place very soon after copulation. Females which were observed mating on June 13 deposited eggs the following day. The eggs are always placed in crevices or under scales of the bark.

In branches with very smooth bark slits were cut which provided favorable places for the deposition of eggs. The branches were placed in cages, each of which contained a single fertilized female. In the insectary the number of eggs placed in a single crevice varied from 1 to 14.

The eggs hatch in from 6 to 10 days. When a large number are laid in a single crevice there is not room enough for all to get started. Accordingly, when two or more penetrate a single burrow, one is punctured by the mouthparts of the other and killed. Out of 52 larvae hatching in a single piece of hickory, only 12 were able to survive and complete their burrows. Moreover, when the bark is smooth and no crevices or scales are present to serve as braces for the larvae in beginning their burrows, they are unable to penetrate the bark and soon die. In like manner, the larvae are unable to burrow into material from which the bark has been removed.

The larva becomes full grown in from 10 to 12 weeks. At the end of that time it gnaws a large, oval-shaped hole through the bark to the

---

*Abstracted from *Cornell Univ. Agric. Exper. Sta. Bull.* 407:175, 1921, by E. H. DUSHAM, *Pennsylvania State College.*

exterior, and begins construction of the pupal cell. The duration of the prepupal stage varies with the temperature and humidity. In the laboratory, where it was warm and dry, this period lasted, on an average of 15 days, while in the insectary, under normal conditions, it was much longer, lasting from 23 to 63 days. In the laboratory, pupation began as early as August 23, while in the field the first pupae were found on September 11.

In the laboratory the pupa began to show the characteristic markings of the adult by the middle of October. However, they did not transform to adults until the following February. In the field the winter is passed in the pupal stage.

M. E. D.

BIBLIOGRAPHY

GARMAN, H. 1916. The locust borer (*Cyllene robiniae*) and other insect enemies of the black locust. *Ky. Agric. Exper. Sta. Bull.* 200:99.

Family CHRYSOMELIDAE

CALLIGRAPHA PNIRSA*

TWENTY adults, captured late in May, were placed in a cage with freshly gathered basswood leaves on which they began to feed almost at once.

The next morning after the introduction of the adults, several egg masses were found, attached to the leaves in the cage. They were placed on end in the same fashion as those of the well known *Leptinotarsa decemlineata*.

These eggs began to hatch in just 7 days. The young, almost as soon as they were out of the egg, fed eagerly and continuously on the basswood leaves and grew rapidly. They were confined in glass covered plant crocks partly filled with moist earth and were supplied with fresh basswood leaves. The larvae readily accepted the situation and throve in confinement.**

*Abstracted from an article in *Canad. Ent.* 57:209, 1925, by the late C. N. AINSLIE, U. S. Bureau of Entomology and Plant Quarantine.

** Editor's Note: As reported by Milton T. Goe in *Ent. News* 29:224, 1918, plants of the dock species, *Rumex crispus* and *R. obtusifolius* are the favorite hosts of both adults and larvae of *Gastroidea caesia*. Rhubarb was the only cultivated plant on which they would feed in confinement, though they were tested on many, and they would readily leave it if supplied with dock. Eggs found in masses on the under side of leaves hatched in about 10 days. The larvae were kept as above described and provided with fresh dock leaves daily. They entered the soil to pupate and emerged as adults about 2 weeks later.

M. E. D.

METHOD OF REARING DIABROTICA DUODECIMPUNCTATA, THE SOUTHERN CORN ROOT WORM

D. L. WRAY, *North Carolina State College*

AFTER collecting the adults in the field each pair is placed for egg laying in a 4-ounce tin salve box with a piece of slightly moist blotting paper covering the entire bottom. Small sections of very young corn stems, or clover leaves, or leaves of other food plants are put in the boxes with the beetles. The female will lay her eggs in the moist spot of the blotting paper in most cases. However, some eggs are laid on the under side of the clover leaves or on the cornstalk. The food should be watched carefully and changed daily if egg laying records are to be kept. The moisture in the blotting paper should be kept at a minimum.

The eggs may be removed from the blotting paper by means of a moistened camel's hair brush and transferred to an incubation cage which consists of a $\frac{1}{4}$ ounce tin salve box lined with a moist piece of blotting paper. The moisture content must be carefully watched as too much water will cause molds to develop and too little will cause desiccation of the eggs. The happy medium must be judged by the surrounding temperature and humidity.

After the eggs hatch the young larvae may be transferred to a 4-ounce tin salve box on the bottom of which is a thin layer of coarse sand covered by a piece of blotting paper. On the paper are placed the small sections of very young, tender cornstalk, in which the larva will begin eating out a cavity; or else the larva may be placed in a small cavity dug out with a scalpel to accommodate it. For food for young larvae it is best to keep on hand several small plats of seedling corn in order to have sufficient tender food. They may be planted at weekly intervals. When the larvae become older, very young cornstalks may be obtained from the field. The food must be kept fresh and will need to be changed every 3 or 4 days.

After the last larval molt the larva and its food (generally it is inside the section of cornstalk at this time) may be transferred to a jelly glass or small-sized battery jar, the bottom of which is covered with about $1\frac{1}{2}$ inches of soil, preferably loam. The larva and its food is placed on this and a cheesecloth cover put on. The soil in the jelly glass should be just barely moist. It is well to have small pieces of blotting paper directly under the food if the soil is too wet. The larva will generally go into the soil to pupate or may form a pupal cell in the section of cornstalk. The moisture content must be watched carefully in order to get the best percentage of emerging adults. These adults may then be used for egg laying if successive generations are to be reared.

Family MYLABRIDAE

REARING STORED FOOD INSECTS FOR EXPERIMENTAL USE

L. PYENSON and H. MENUSAN, JR., *Cornell University*

IN REARING insects for experimental use it is of great importance to have a large and constant supply of the different stages available. The insects should also remain constant in their reactions to changes in the environment for successive generations. To obtain insects which constantly react in the same way it is necessary to rear them on a uniformly balanced food in an environment that is maintained constant. The food used should give the greatest growth in the shortest possible time, and the environment (temperature and humidity) should be readily maintained and should allow maximum development in the shortest possible time of the greatest number of individuals.

The food to use will depend entirely on the species of insect. The optimum environment for stored food insects is a temperature of approximately 30° C. with a relative humidity of from 80% to above 90%. The difficulty of maintaining the humidity above 90% without occasional condensation of water on the food (either because of temperature fluctuations or because of metabolic water given off by the insects), with a consequent growth of fungi, renders the higher humidities impracticable.

Control of temperature and humidity* is essential since it has been found that these environmental factors affect the rate of growth, size of resulting adults, rate of oviposition, death rate, *etc.* Other environmental factors such as light, air movement, *etc.*, may easily be controlled.

The control of temperature is satisfactorily handled by a bimetallic thermo-regulator in connection with heating elements made with wire of the desired resistance. The constant temperature box will operate best when placed in a room the temperature of which is about 10° C. below the temperature required. An 8-inch electric fan circulating air maintains the same temperature throughout the box in addition to permitting a more accurate control.

The control of the relative humidity depends on accurate control of the temperature. For most rearing work the humidity may be approximately controlled by placing large shallow dishes of the appropriate supersaturated salt solutions in the constant temperature box. A more

---

* For further details of this technique the following references are suggested:

SHELFORD, VICTOR E. 1929. Laboratory and Field Ecology (Williams and Wilkins Company, Publishers, Baltimore).

SPENCER, H. M. 1926. Laboratory methods for maintaining constant humidity. *International Critical Tables* 1:67. New York & London.

accurate and preferable method is to pass air through gas washing bottles containing either salt or sulphuric acid solutions. In this case the insects are reared in more or less close contact with an air stream of known humidity. The rate at which the air should be passed through the solutions will depend on many factors, such as the size of the rearing box, the number of insects per container, and the facilities for controlling the temperature of the air.

All rearing should be done in shallow containers with a comparatively thin layer (½ to 1 inch) of food in the bottom of each. A thin food layer allows the food to come into equilibrium with the environment quickly and to remain so. During their growth and development insects liberate relatively large quantities of water which alter the relative humidity of the environment unless removed as rapidly as liberated.

The following methods have been used by the writers for rearing large numbers of bean weevils (*Bruchus* [=*Mylabris*] *obtectus*) and mealworms (*Tenebrio molitor*). The same general methods are applicable for other stored food insects with minor modifications.

Bean weevils were reared on red kidney beans since it has been found* that this bean variety apparently furnished the optimum food as measured by the most rapid growth with the least mortality. The cultures were started at weekly intervals by placing 500-1000 eggs in pint jars containing about an inch of red kidney beans and covered with cheesecloth or wire screening of 20- or 24-mesh. These containers were placed at a temperature of 25° C. and a relative humidity of 75-80%. In this way new batches of adults were obtained each week. The bean weevils, upon emerging, were separated from the beans by sifting through an 8-mesh wire screen. The weevils were then placed in special oviposition cages. These cages consisted of pint cardboard containers with the bottoms pushed out and replaced by 20-mesh wire screening. This size allowed the eggs to drop through readily, but kept the bean weevils in the cage. The cover of the cage was also made of wire screening to provide proper aeration. Another cover on the bottom of the cage served to collect the eggs. The cage contained about a dozen red kidney beans as a stimulus for oviposition. Large numbers of clean eggs may be obtained in this way with relatively little trouble. The eggs may be removed at definite intervals, thus providing a source of eggs of known age.

Under the conditions described above, one generation of bean weevils will require about 40 days from egg to egg stage at 25° C. and 80% relative humidity. If the relative humidity is the same and the temperature is raised to 30° C. only 30 days will be required.

* L. HILL and F. B. MAUGHAN. Unpublished work of the Dept. of Entomology, *Cornell University*.

Mealworms were reared under environmental conditions similar to those of the bean weevil. The optimum food for this species is not definitely known. Excellent results have been obtained by rearing them on a prepared dog meal containing dried vegetables, cereals, and meat, or in dog biscuits containing the same general ingredients.

Cultures were started in pint jars with about 100 eggs per culture. When the larvae reached a moderate size the culture was divided so that only 40-50 larvae were reared in one culture. When the larvae are small they require little attention but in late larval instars the food should be changed at least twice a month.

When ready to pupate the larvae come to the top of the meal and pass into a quiescent state. This prepupal state may be readily recognized and such individuals may be removed from the culture if desired or the pupae may be removed at definite intervals.

After emergence the adults were placed in ovipositing cages similar to those of the bean weevil. The false bottom in the case of the meal worm adults contained whole wheat flour sifted through a 72-mesh silk screen. The adults oviposited in the flour through the wire screen and the eggs were readily separated from it by sifting through a 30-mesh silk screen. The mealworm adults feed, and the rate and amount of oviposition depends to a great extent on the food that the adults receive.

Dog biscuits and canned dog meat were used as food for the ovipositing adults. The moist dog meat should be suspended by a wire basket from the top of the ovipositing cage so it does not come in contact with the flour in the bottom; otherwise the flour will lump and become difficult to sift. Fresh food was supplied at least once a week. Whenever moist food such as meat or portions of banana was supplied the rate of oviposition increased remarkably. The increase in oviposition may be due to an increased amount of water present since relatively dry dog meat did not give an increase.

With the food described and the environment maintained at 30° C. and 80% relative humidity *Tenebrio molitor* may be reared from egg to adult stage in less than 4 months.

Family CURCULIONIDAE

THE DUCK-WEED WEEVIL, TANYSPHYRUS LEMNAE

MINNIE B. SCOTLAND, *New York State College for Teachers*

THIS very minute, widely distributed weevil is easily reared wherever a culture of the common duckweed, *Lemna minor*, may be maintained.* It is easy to collect, but often hard to find, being but

* As in a greenhouse tank or trough filled with pond water.

little more than 1 mm. long and of obscure coloration. Its presence is indicated by feeding punctures (deep round holes) in the thalli of the duck-weed and by the mines of its larvae. These mines are long and very irregular tunnels through the thalli. The damage that they do to the plants is often conspicuous. Adults are most easily obtained by rearing them from infested thalli.

Sphagnum is excellent material on which to place the larvae just before pupation. As they become ready to pupate they leave the floating plant and move about on the open water, evidently in search of a suitable place. When removed to a small handful of moist sphagnum they crawl into the cup-like leaves and pupate there.

The moss should be placed in a shallow dish and covered with a tumbler. Thus as the adult forms emerge they can not escape.

BOLL WEEVIL CULTURE*

F. A. FENTON, *Oklahoma A. and M. College*

1. *Storage of material.* No adequate information. Weevils are susceptible to temperature exposures of 10° F. for short periods. Probably the best storage temperature is 50° F. Only adult weevils will store for any length of time.

2. *Food.* Cotton fruits in following order of preference: Square, bloom, young boll, medium-sized boll, mature unopened green boll.

3. *Oviposition.* Immature anthers are necessary for egg development, but some oviposition will occur when bolls are fed upon.

4. *Cages.* Large lantern globes over pans filled with moist sand are first choice; jelly tumblers second.

5. *Rearing.* To keep strong stock, fresh unpicked cotton squares are needed for oviposition. These must not be picked but left on the plant until normal shedding time which will occur in approximately 6 to 7 days. Some weevils will develop in picked squares, but stock will die out about F_2 generation. Optimum temperature 80° to 84° F. (variable).

6. *Adult recovery.* Place shed squares in pàrtitioned cages over dampened sphagnum moss. Each compartment of cage equipped with glass vial for recovery of weevils upon emergence from pupae.

GRAIN WEEVILS

D. L. LINDGREN, *University of Minnesota*

TWO species of grain weevils, *Sitophilus granarius* and *S. oryzae,* are common pests of stored grain. The former, the granary weevil, is more abundant in the north, and the latter, the rice weevil, in the south.

* See *U. S. D. A. Tech. Bull.* 112 for further details. It is practically necessary to have growing cotton. For technique see pp. 9-11, 41, 46-48.

They are very similar in their habits and look very much alike. The granary weevil is the larger of the two species, is chestnut brown or blackish in color, and has no functional wings. The rice weevil is smaller, brownish in color with four light spots on the wing covers, and is an active flier.

The larvae of both the rice and the granary weevils live throughout their entire life within the kernel, and are not ordinarily capable of a free existence outside the kernel. The adult female, before laying her eggs, bores a small hole in the grain berry with her mandibles, then turns about and lays in it an egg which she covers with a gelatinous fluid that seals the hole. In warm weather the granary weevil requires about 4 to 5 weeks to complete its development from egg to the adult weevil, while the rice weevil may complete its development in 26 to 30 days.

Granary or rice weevils may be raised in large quantities, with but little care, in large-mouthed glass containers of about a gallon capacity. This type of jar has a diameter slightly less than the height. A screen wire cover or heavy muslin is used to keep the beetles in while allowing a certain amount of air circulation.

The jar is filled about ⅓ full of wheat, or wheat and corn, of a moisture content of 14 to 15%, the optimum moisture level for weevil infestation. It is often necessary to moisten wheat somewhat for culture purposes because, when well dried for storage, wheat has a moisture content of only 11 to 13%. When exposed in a dry laboratory the moisture content may go as low as 9%. A culture of adult weevils is placed with the grain and the jar allowed to remain at a temperature of about 23° to 26° C. Eggs will be laid in the grain, and in about 4 to 6 weeks adults of the first generation of beetles will appear. After the culture is strong enough, hundreds of weevils may be removed every day with no decided reduction in population. The beetles may be removed by scraping them off the inside of the glass jar or sifting them through a No. 10 wire sieve, which allows the weevils to pass through, but retains most of the wheat.

After a time all the wheat will be riddled, with nothing but the husk left, and much finely ground powder will collect on the bottom of the jar; also, if the culture becomes too densely populated, much metabolic water accumulates within the jar, whereby the contents may become a soggy mass. Before this happens the weevils should be separated from the grain and placed in a jar containing fresh clean grain, thus starting the culture over again. By keeping 3 or 4 jars going at the same time a continuous supply of beetles will always be on hand in the laboratory.

If beetles of a certain age are required, a large number of adults may be placed in clean grain for 2 or 3 days and then removed. The eggs laid by the adults will hatch and after a time, depending upon the temperature at which the culture is held, adults will appear. If the weevils are removed daily the exact age of the adults will be known.

BIBLIOGRAPHY

BACK, E. A., and COTTON, R. T. 1926. The Granary Weevil. *U. S. Dept. Agric. Dept. Bull.* 1393.

———— 1922. Stored Grain Pests. *U. S. Dept. Agric. Farmer's Bull.* 1260. (Revised 1931.)

METHOD OF REARING CALANDRA* CALLOSA, THE SOUTHERN CORN BILL BUG

D. L. WRAY, *North Carolina State College*

AFTER the adult beetles are collected in the field the following simple method may be used to obtain and study the different life stages. The adults are sorted into pairs, each of which is placed in an ordinary large-sized jelly glass or in a small-sized bell jar if records of mass rearings are to be made. This is covered with a double thickness of closely woven cheesecloth. Pieces of young, tender cornstalks are put in the containers daily or whenever the food becomes stale. The adults will feed on and lay eggs in these sections of cornstalk, which also furnish sufficient moisture. If a daily egg record is to be obtained the sections of cornstalk should be removed at a definite time each day as the beetle has two main periods of egg laying activity, one from about 4-8 A.M. and one from 4-8 P.M. The pieces of cornstalk are removed from the jelly glasses and the eggs may be picked out.

For an incubation chamber, the ordinary 2-ounce tin salve box will suffice. Place a piece of blotting paper in the bottom and place the eggs upon it. The paper should be kept moist and the box kept in an insectary. They should be watched daily to maintain the proper degree of moisture. Great care should be exercised not to have any excess water as this will be conducive to mold. The eggs will hatch in about 96-100 hours under favorable temperature conditions which average about 80°-85° F.

When the young larvae hatch they should be removed to rearing boxes. The 4-ounce tin salve box will give very satisfactory results. Split longitudinally small sections of cornstalk; in the center of each half hollow out a cavity large enough to contain a young larva; place it in this cavity and then bind the halves of the cornstalk section together with a rubber band or a piece of string. Place the section of cornstalk in the tin box and cover tightly with the lid. The moisture of the stalk will be sufficient for the larva and the tin box will help preserve the food. The cornstalk should be changed when it begins to dry out or when the larva has completely hollowed out the center.

*[=Sitophilus.]

The larva will develop and molt inside the piece of cornstalk within the tin box, and will pupate also within the stalk. Or, as the time for pupation approaches, the pieces of stalk may be removed to a small bell jar on the bottom of which is a layer of heavy loam. The larvae will go into the soil to make an earthen pupal cell. The most satisfactory method, however, is to keep them through the pupal stage in the tin boxes where their development may be observed more easily. When the adults emerge they may be placed in jelly glasses or small bell jars and the life cycle begun again.

Family SCOLYTIDAE

METHOD FOR REARING SCOLYTUS MULTISTRIATUS

PHILIP A. READIO, *Cornell University*

THE following method of rearing *Scolytus multistriatus* in numbers is that followed by the Cornell University entomologists, working in conjunction with members of the Plant Pathology Department, in their investigations of insect transmission of the Dutch elm disease organism, *Ceratostomella ulmi*.

Wood from recently felled elms is cut into convenient lengths (we use sticks about 2 feet long, and from 4 to 8 inches in diameter), paraffined thoroughly on the cut surfaces, and placed in suitable cages. Our cages are 1 foot wide, 1 foot high, and 2 feet long, of wooden frame and wire screen construction. Into this cage newly emerged beetles are introduced; they start almost immediately to tunnel into the elm wood provided. We have found that the providing of fresh elm twigs, for the so-called "maturation feeding" of newly emerged adults before reëntrance into fresh wood for oviposition, is unnecessary, and is taken advantage of by very few beetles. From cultures of this type we harvest a good yield of vigorous, off-spring beetles, after a period of $1\frac{1}{2}$ to 2 months, depending on the temperature. Furthermore, it is possible to obtain a second off spring generation from the same wood if it is not too thoroughly used up by the first generation larvae.

PITYOGENES HOPKINSI*

IN ORDER to secure large numbers of the specimens in each of the stages in which growth and development occur, adult beetles were collected from dead pine limbs in the field, placed on freshly cut green pine in breeding jars, and kept at a constant temperature of approxi-

* Abstracted from an article in *Ann. Ent. Soc. Amer.* 20:522, 1927, by JAMES A. BEAL.

mately 80° F. This was accomplished by the use of a large pasteboard box in which was placed an electric bulb of sufficient voltage to keep the temperature within at about that temperature, thus serving as an incubator in which the breeding jars were kept at all times. Moist sand was placed in the jars and the bottom ends of the pine sticks were imbedded in the sand; the upper ends were coated with paraffin. This method of handling the breeding material conserved the moisture long enough, under high temperature, to allow the broods to develop successfully.

As this species usually breeds only in the smooth bark of pine it was necessary to select pine limbs from ½ to 2 inches in diameter. It was possible to get larger-sized limbs having smooth bark but they were not so easily handled in the breeding jars.

Order HYMENOPTERA, Family CEPHIDAE

A METHOD FOR BREEDING CEPHIDAE

Donald T. Ries, *Ithaca, N. Y.*

IN ORDER to obtain data on the life history and habits of the wheat-stem sawflies, *Cephus pygmaeus* and *Trachelus tabidus,* the writer developed the following method for the former species and later used approximately the same method for the latter species. It is probable that this method would also be satisfactory for other related herbaceous stem-borers.

At first a large cage 6 ft. long by 4 ft. square was constructed and covered with cheesecloth. Late in the fall infested stubble was collected and planted in the cage. In this same cage winter wheat was sown and allowed to develop, the cage being covered with cheesecloth until all danger from Hessian fly infestation was past. The covering was then removed to give as nearly natural conditions as possible and replaced in the spring before time for emergence of the adult insects.

Later these cages as well as the small Hadley cage (12″ x 12″ x 24″) were used indoors with excellent results. In these the wheat was grown in large 12″ flower pots and the adults introduced. By this method parasitism of the sawfly larvae by adult parasites which emerge from stubble was eliminated. When one female was introduced in each, the large cages served for making egg counts, as a single female usually deposits only one egg in each stem. Inasmuch as a large cage may contain as many as 1,000 stalks of wheat it is easy to obtain a fairly accurate egg count.

Because adults in the field were noted feeding on the pollen of wild mustard, *Brassica vulgaris,* plants of this species were introduced into the cages or grown with the wheat. Mating took place in the cage and the females oviposited freely on the growing wheat stems. The female usually chooses the largest and healthiest stems in which to oviposit.

BIBLIOGRAPHY

RIES, D. T. 1926. *J. Agric. Res.* 32:277.

REFERENCE

Family Crabronidae
For the rearing of Crabro see p. 517.

Families DIPRIONIDAE and TENTHREDINIDAE

A METHOD OF BREEDING SOME DEFOLIATORS

S. A. GRAHAM, *University of Michigan*

IN REARING various species of defoliating insects, it has been found that the greatest success has almost always been attained by placing the insects under as nearly natural conditions as possible. Rearing on the living tree, in such a manner that an adequate supply of suitable food is always available, usually works out well for the feeding stages. When, however, it is necessary to use cut foliage, it is essential that it be kept green by placing the cut ends of the branches in water, and by providing fresh foliage every day or two. If kept under cover, the insects should be provided with necessary water by sprinkling a little on the food each day. In the open this need is usually satisfied automatically by rain and dew. Many adult insects require drinking water even though they do not eat. Therefore it is always best to sprinkle a little water daily in all cages kept in the laboratory or insectary.

THE LARCH SAWFLY, LYGEONEMATUS ERICSONII

This technic for handling the larch sawfly has proved very satisfactory and has made possible the maintenance of the insect for generation after generation.

Oviposition. Because this insect will oviposit only on newly expanding shoots of larch, it is necessary to confine the females on such suitable developing shoots. The best results were obtained when they were caged on living trees. For this purpose wire cylinders about $1\frac{1}{2}$ inches in diameter and 6 or 8 inches in length were used. After the shoot to be enclosed was inserted in the cylinder the proximal end was closed with a split cork, appropriately notched on the split surfaces to admit the stem.

The insects were then placed in the cage, and the distal end closed with a piece of cloth fastened with a string and made doubly safe by inserting pins through both wire and cloth. One female was placed in each cage. In some instances males were confined with the females for certain experiments, but this is unnecessary because the species is parthenogenetic. In the cages the females oviposit freely and the eggs develop normally.

In using these cages two important points should be remembered: first, that the females in ovipositing always rest with the head toward the end of the shoot and therefore require that the new growth be at least ½ inch in length and preferably longer; and, second, that in placing the cage on the branch allowance must be made for the growth of the shoot.

Larvae. The larvae of the larch sawfly are gregarious and move about very little. Therefore they are very easily handled. They must, however, be provided with a continuous supply of fresh food. This is very important because even a short period of starvation of the larvae may result in the sterility of the adult females. For this reason it was usually most convenient to rear them on living trees, although they were also successfully reared in cages where they were fed on cut branches set in water to keep them fresh. When they were fed on cut branches it was necessary to change the branches every day or two.

When rearing was conducted on the living tree the oviposition cages were removed before the eggs hatched. Adjacent branches were cut away so that none were in direct contact with the branch on which the rearing was conducted. In order to prevent the larvae from making their way to other branches a tanglefoot band was placed around the branch. Beneath the rearing branch a tray with muslin bottom and tanglefoot around the edges was fastened, usually on a post set in the ground and sufficiently high to bring the tray within a foot of the branch. The rearing branch was then fastened to the tray by wires so as to prevent the wind from moving it away from the tray. Thus any larvae that dropped from the branch were caught and confined in the tray until they could be cared for.

Ordinarily the larvae remained on the tree until they were fully fed and ready to make cocoons. They were then removed and placed in woven wire cages. Fresh food was provided in these cages for larvae that might have fallen into the tray by accident before they completed feeding.

Cocoons. The cages mentioned above were cylinders of wire cloth about ten inches in diameter and a foot high with a wire bottom and removable cloth top. Three inches of moist sphagnum moss was placed in the bottom. After the larvae had made their way into the moss and spun their cocoons the cloth tops were replaced with wire and the cages were placed in a nearby swamp where they were sunk in the moss so that the top of the surrounding moss was at the same level as that in the cage. There they remained over the winter, and until the insects pupated and finally emerged as adults in the early summer following. Similar treatment, differing only in that the cages were set in the ground on high land, was unsuccessful, due primarily to the invasion of ants that found their way into the cages and destroyed the sawflies.

As the adults emerged they were removed from the cages and, if the rearing of a second generation was desired, they were placed in the oviposition cages described above.

THE JACK PINE SAWFLY, Neodiprion banksianae

The jack pine sawfly was reared by using practically the same technique as that described for the larch sawfly except that the larvae were confined during the feeding stage in muslin bags fastened on branch ends of living trees. In the bottom of the cages for cocooning was placed a layer of mineral soil about an inch thick, over which a layer of needle litter from under jack pine trees was placed. These cages were set in the ground under jack pine trees instead of in the swamp.

The bags mentioned above were muslin cylinders large enough in diameter to slip over the branch ends easily. Each was tied tightly around the branch at the basal end and the outer end was closed with a string which might easily be removed when it became necessary to examine the cages.

THE SPRUCE BUDWORM, Harmologa fumiferana *

Considerable difficulty has been experienced in rearing the spruce budworm because of the exacting requirements of this insect at certain stages. The method described here is of such recent development that there has not as yet been time to carry individual insects of this species through a complete cycle. We have, however, successfully handled different sets of these moths in every stage and therefore it seems logical to assume that the method described will prove to be a successful culture procedure.

Oviposition. In early experiments, attempts were made to obtain eggs of this insect by confining pairs in large cages enclosing trees six feet or even more in height. All of these attempts were unsuccessful. It was found, however, that mating and oviposition occurred regularly if the pairs were placed in a shell vial with a shoot of their food plant, jack pine for the pine form and fir for the fir-spruce form. A large proportion of the eggs obtained in this manner proved to be fertile.

Hibernation. Numerous attempts were made to carry the larvae

* Order Lepidoptera.

through the winter without success. After hatching from the eggs the larvae spin hibernacula in sheltered locations in which they pass the winter. Apparently the winter mortality is very high even under natural conditions. Under the abnormal experimental conditions devised total losses occurred, until it was found that a favorite location for hibernating is under the thin bark scales on branches of jack pine, and that if branches on which the insects were hibernating were kept out of doors, in a place where the sun did not strike them, a considerable number of larvae survived.

Feeding Period. In the spring, when the larvae emerge from hibernation, they must be provided with a supply of expanding buds and young foliage. It was found that the easiest way to supply satisfactory food for them was to confine them on the tree in muslin bags similar to those described for the jack pine sawfly. The less the larvae are handled the lower the losses. Therefore it was found desirable to place only a few larvae in each bag so that enough food would be available for their complete development without transferring them to new branches. About five larvae to the branch end proved satisfactory.

Pupation and Emergence. Pupation occurs on the branches where the larvae feed. Therefore it was found that the most satisfactory way of handling this stage was to leave pupae in position within the bags until the moths emerged. At this stage, it was necessary to watch their development carefully so that the moths might be removed as soon as possible after emergence.

REFERENCE

For the rearing of sawflies see p. 517.

Family BRACONIDAE

TECHNIQUE OF CULTURING HABROBRACON JUGLANDIS

P. W. WHITING, *University of Pennsylvania*

THE first requisite is a large number of well developed caterpillars of the mediterranean flour moth, *Ephestia kuehniella* [see p. 355]. It will take at least 5 weeks to obtain these if a good supply of moths is available immediately. If only a small culture of Ephestia is available, 7 or 8 weeks should be allowed for obtaining a good supply of moths. Six to ten wasps may be obtained from one caterpillar. Fifty to 300 caterpillars may be obtained from one pair of moths.

Equipment Needed. Shell vials (70 x 20 mm.) plugged with cotton wrapped in fine meshed cheesecloth. The plugs may be conveniently made by cutting cheesecloth in 2.5 in. squares, fitting cotton into end of vials, removing, covering with cheesecloth, and replacing. The plugs should be tight and closely fitting on all sides without wrinkling of cheesecloth. Vials are best cleaned by soaking in hot water without soap and then rinsing.

Egg boxes with square compartments in two rows of six each. Four vials stand upright in each compartment; thus 48 cultures occupy the space taken by a dozen eggs. Egg boxes are placed side by side on shelves of the incubator so that the ends are visible and may be marked according to convenience.

Tweezers for handling wasps and caterpillars.

Gelatine capsules for isolating pupae for virgin females.

Petri dishes (inside measurements, 9 cm. wide, 1 cm. deep) with circular paper cut to fit inside.

Incubator regulated to 30° C. (This is for the maximum speed consistent with safety and normal development. Wasps will stand three or four degrees higher temperature, but do not develop as well. At lower temperatures development is normal but retarded. Body coloration is black at lower temperatures, yellow at higher.) The incubator may be made of ⅝″ board. Shelves should be frames covered with wire netting (½″ mesh), and 17″ deep to allow space in front of 12-inch egg boxes for petri dishes. There should be about a 4-inch clearance space between the shelves for 70 mm. vials plus the protruding ends of cotton plugs. There should be 6.5 inches above the upper shelf for a thermostat which is screwed to the top and regulated through a small hole made in the top. The heating unit is placed beneath the lowest shelf. Be sure to place a pan or piece of asbestos directly over the heating unit to distribute the heat. Test various regions with a thermometer. The incubator may be 36 inches wide and as high as convenient. If much space is not needed a chicken incubator may be used, heated from above by several small carbon bulbs which should be arranged at least in part in parallel. If they are all in series, burning out of one will cause the temperature to drop. Regulate the incubator for temperature at the level of the cultures.

Technique. Adult wasps may be kept for several months in the refrigerator but will not live unless they have been reared at low temperatures, 20° to 25° C. This is the best way to keep stock. Place adult females in shell vials. Feed with honey water by dipping a wire into honey, then into water, and then touching to the inside of the vial, thus leaving a drop. In new vials the drop is likely to spread, but after they are once used and washed in warm water without soap, an invisible coating of grease causes the drop to stay in one place. Set vials of stock wasps in a tight tin box in which has been placed one or more vials of water plugged with cotton and standing upright. Diffusion of water vapor prevents desiccation. Stock wasps should be removed from the refrigerator every three months and fed with honey water.

Males at room temperature may be kept alive for many days by feeding with honey water. They become sterile after two or three weeks. Several matings may be made with one male which may be transferred after mating is observed with a hand lens. Matings are ordinarily made in vials but gelatine capsules may be used if the males are weak or fail to react toward females in the vials.

A female to be set for culturing is placed in a vial with three or four full grown caterpillars. The vial is set in an egg box in the incubator. Caterpillars should soon be paralyzed, eggs laid within two days, and maggots pupating after three or four days.

Virgin females are obtained by placing caterpillars covered with maggots on paper in petri dishes. Caterpillars may be removed from vials with tweezers. Maggots will spin on the paper which may be cut in order to separate the cocoons. These are then placed in gelatine capsules. Adults will eclose in capsules after five days and females may be transferred to vials for mating or setting.

Caterpillars may be collected with tweezers from top or sides of breeding box or from the cereal. They will congregate especially in contact with the box about the edge of the cereal. If the cereal is disturbed they will crawl about and rest on the inside of the cover or escape from the box and crawl on the outside. Cereal may be removed and placed on a table or sheet of paper for greater convenience in collecting caterpillars.

Virgin heterozygous females may be set for linkage tests. Wasps may be etherized for examination.

REARING CHELONUS ANNULIPES

ARLO M. VANCE, *U. S. Bureau of Entomology and Plant Quarantine*

THIS parasite of the European corn borer *Pyrausta nubilalis* in Europe was handled in small quantities for laboratory studies as follows: Under warm room conditions each adult parasite was confined in a small glass globe cage having a diameter of about 3 inches at the middle and an opening 2 inches in diameter at each end. The top opening was provided with a removable tin cover while the bottom was set upon a piece of strong white cloth tightly stretched across a 5-inch square wooden frame about an inch in height. The arrangement of the cage on the cloth frame permitted a constant interchange of air with the outside atmosphere and at the same time provided a suitable base to which the cage could be attached by means of a strong rubber band.

The most satisfactory food used was a half lump of dry sugar placed on a small 1-inch square of paraffined cardboard at the bottom of the cage. Water was supplied with a pipette to the sides of the cage, usually only once a day. Mating of Chelonus adults was obtained in the lighted end of 4-inch vials, in globe cages, and in a square box cage, but none of these methods was very certain. Oviposition was secured by exposing a mass of Pyrausta eggs on the floor of the female's cage for a period varying from a few up to 24 hours. The parasitized egg mass was then removed and placed in a small glass-covered tin box with a few leaves of green dock. When the hatched borer larvae reached the 4th instar, they were isolated in 3-inch glass vials plugged with cotton, and given a more substantial diet of small pieces of green cornstalk, fennel plant, or string beans. Chelonus cocoons spun in the vials were left undisturbed for pupation and adult emergence. Both parasitized host larvae and immature parasites were reared at a constant temperature of either 68° or 77°F. with varying relative humidity.

BIBLIOGRAPHY

VANCE, ARLO M. 1932. The biology and morphology of the Braconid *Chelonus annulipes* Wesm., a parasite of the European corn borer. *U. S. Dept. Agric. Tech. Bull.* No. 294.

REARING APANTELES THOMPSONI

ARLO M. VANCE, *U. S. Bureau of Entomology and Plant Quarantine*

ADULTS of this parasite of the European corn borer *Pyrausta nubilalis* were handled in small numbers for experimental use in a wooden box cage 2 feet square and 6 inches deep, covered at one end with cheesecloth and closed at the other end by a sliding glass plate. Such a cage containing Apanteles was placed with the cheesecloth toward a window and the opposite side partly opened. Borer larvae of the 1st to 4th instar were placed on the cage floor and each one removed after having been stung by the female. Immediately after being parasitized, the young borer larvae, in lots of 20 or 25, were put into small round tin boxes and supplied with leaves of dock for food. They were kept under such conditions at various temperatures until about the 4th instar, when each was put into a glass vial and fed with stems of dock until the issuance and spinning of the mature parasite larvae. The colonies of parasite cocoons placed in similar vials, each containing moist blotting paper or a bit of green vegetable matter, were then kept at a constant temperature of either 68° or 77° F. until the adults emerged. Water and drops of sugar solution were supplied the caged females. Prolongation of the life of *A. thompsoni* was best accomplished by the method used by other workers of keeping the adults in a box cage in a cool dark closet and bringing them out into light and warmth for only a short time each day to allow them to feed and oviposit.

BIBLIOGRAPHY

VANCE, ARLO M. 1931. *Apanteles thompsoni*, Lyle, a braconid parasite of the European corn borer. *U. S. Dept. Agric. Tech. Bull.* No. 233.

METHODS OF PRODUCING MACROCENTRUS ANCYLIVORUS IN LARGE NUMBERS FOR COLONIZATION IN PEACH ORCHARDS

PHILIP GARMAN, *Connecticut Agricultural Experiment Station*

PRODUCTION of Macrocentrus in large numbers for colonization may be accomplished by laboratory breeding or field collection. In regions where Macrocentrus is abundant on such hosts as the strawberry leaf roller (*Ancylis comptana*), collection from commercial plantings is probably the simplest and most economical method. In regions where field collection is difficult or commercial plantings widely separated, it may prove simpler and less expensive to rear Macrocentrus by laboratory or other means than to collect from the field. In some localities alternate hosts are scarce and the first generation of fruit moth (*Grapholitha molesta*) larvae is so small that recolonization from these sources is impractical.

(1) Field collection as practised in New Jersey by the U. S. Bureau of Entomology and Plant Quarantine and others consists of assembling crews of men who visit commercial plantings and remove folded leaves with leaf roller larvae. The leaves are fastened together in bundles of convenient size and placed with the stems in water. Before emergence of the parasites they are put in a large, darkened, emergence cage with a light screen at one end. In some cases the leaves have been shipped to distant points and there placed in cages to obtain the parasites. It appears more desirable, however, to ship the adult parasites after they emerge, but in order to transport them without undue mortality it is advisable to refrigerate by some means during shipment. In handling field-collected leaves it is necessary to prevent them from becoming too moist because of the danger of mold, and to provide occasional lots of fresh leaves in which the smaller larvae may complete development. After the parasites have spun their cocoons, the leaves should be spread out in trays in the emergence room.

(2) A second method designed for breeding Macrocentrus throughout the winter consists of obtaining Oriental fruit moth eggs in large numbers (see p. 345) and placing these on green apples sliced part way through. The apples are then incubated at 80° F. and five to six days after the fruit moth larvae have hatched the slices are separated,

strung on wires and exposed in cages with Macrocentrus adults. The temperature in the parasite cages should be about 75° F. and the humidity kept down to 70%. A room held at 76° F. and 60% relative humidity is satisfactory. Light is important. This should be neither too strong nor too weak. About 10 foot candles illumination from blue daylight bulbs provides suitable working conditions for the parasites. The cages used are covered with cloth, and moisture for the insects is provided by a wick extending from a pan of water to the top of the cage. Infested apple slices are exposed to parasite action for 24 hours, but if the cage is well stocked they may be removed at shorter intervals. It is not advisable to leave the slices longer than 24 hours. After exposure, the slices are placed in a dry incubator kept at 80° F. and 50% relative humidity or lower to prevent rot and to allow the larvae to develop. After several days, new apples are placed over the slices to give additional food. If it is necessary to hold the material for any length of time it should be reared in a cool place (60° F.) instead of the 80° F. incubator, and as soon as the larvae have spun they should be placed in a still cooler atmosphere, between 32° and 45° F., humidity 80% to 95%. A common storage cellar has been used by us for this purpose, and material may be kept there until June. If removed from the breeding rooms and placed at outside temperatures during cold weather (below 20° F.), a large percentage of the larvae and their parasites may be killed.

In order to maintain a favorable sex ratio, males at the rate of two or three to one female should be used in the cages. Both sexes are put in the cage immediately after emergence and the males removed after 24 hours. Large numbers of males kept in the oviposition cages during the oviposition period are undesirable with this insect. The normal ratio appears to be about 60% males and 40% females, and it is possible with care to obtain this ratio in laboratory breeding.

The main problems that arise in continuous Macrocentrus breeding consist (1) of difficulties in securing abundant host material, as discussed by Mr. Brigham [see p. 348]; (2) in maintaining a satisfactory sex ratio and ratio of increase; and (3) in hibernating the reared parasites without excessive loss. It should be mentioned that proper temperature, moisture, and light are important items especially in handling the adult parasites, and maintenance of these conditions requires considerable equipment and knowledge of air conditioning. Without them satisfactory increases are difficult to obtain.

(3) A third method of production consists of using strawberry plants artificially infested with strawberry leaf roller larvae. A large outdoor cage placed over a number of growing strawberry plants is employed. Macrocentrus adults are introduced at the proper time and the leaves

collected and placed in an emergence cage, just before the adults emerge.

(4) Peach twigs infested with fruit moth larvae and then exposed to Macrocentrus for oviposition have also been used. When young fresh twigs are not available, slits are made in older twigs, fruit moth larvae inserted and frass placed on the outside to incite oviposition. Larvae are removed from the cages as soon as parasitized, and reared to maturity.

The last two methods have been used successfully at the New York Agricultural Station.

BIBLIOGRAPHY

ALLEN, H. W. 1931. The mass production of *Macrocentrus ancylivorus* a parasite of the Oriental fruit moth and its distribution from southern New Jersey. *J. Econ. Ent.,* 24:309.

DANIEL, D. W. 1932. *Macrocentrus ancylivorus* Rohwer, a polyembryonic braconid parasite of the Oriental fruit moth. *N. Y. State Agric. Exper. Sta. Tech. Bull.* 187.

GARMAN, PHILIP, and BRIGHAM, W. T. 1933. Studies on parasites of the Oriental fruit moth. II. Macrocentrus. *Conn. Agric. Exper. Sta. Bull.* 356.

REARING APHIDIINAE

ESTHER W. WHEELER, *University of North Dakota*

DURING the winter and spring, roomy lamp chimneys were placed over potted plants in a small greenhouse. Lawn cloth stretched tightly over the top of the chimney and held in place by a rubber band gave free circulation of air and prevented the insects from escaping. The aphids were allowed to grow at least two weeks to exclude any possibility of undetected previous parasitism. Then an aphidiine female was introduced and allowed to oviposit. Various stages of the Aphidiinae were obtained by dissecting aphids at intervals. Moisture condensing on the glass caused trouble occasionally, but the chimney might be removed and wiped out quickly without losing the insects. In summer the greenhouse was too hot for them.

Another method which was more satisfactory, and absolutely necessary in the case of a plant too large for a lamp chimney, required petri dishes. This procedure was carried out in a large, dry laboratory, steam-heated in winter and cool in summer. The bottom of the dish was lined with slightly moistened coarse filter paper, upon which were placed clean leaves of the host plant. Finally unparasitized apterous aphids and a female parasite were introduced. The leaves were changed every day; the insects were transferred with a fine, dry camel's hair brush; and every two days, or oftener if signs of condensation appeared, the dish and paper were changed. In spite of the fact that the Aphidiinae are agile they rarely escaped. In these few cases their positive phototropism would lead them to the nearest window where they were easily recaptured. The females copulated readily in captivity but, failing this, reproduced parthenogenetically. In some cases, the adult parasites were fed with small drops of diluted honey in a separate dish so that the aphids would not become entangled in the food. This was not necessary when material was abundant as they can live without food for 5 days. The above methods were employed with the following Aphidiinae and hosts:

PARASITE	APHID HOSTS	PLANT
Aphidius ribis	*Macrosiphum sp.*	*Helianthus tuberosus*
Aphidius phorodontis	*Myzus persicae*	Radish
Lysiphlebus testaceipes	*Macrosiphum tanaceti*	*Tanacetum vulgare*
Praon simulans	*Myzus persicae*	Radish
Ephedrus incompletus	*Aphis pseudobrassicae* *Myzus persicae*	Radish Radish
Diaeretus rapae	*Myzus persicae*	Cabbage

BIBLIOGRAPHY

WHEELER, ESTHER W. 1923. Some braconids parasitic on Aphids and their life-history. *Ann. Ent. Soc. Amer.* 16:1.

Family ICHNEUMONIDAE

HYMENOPTEROUS PARASITES OF GYRINIDAE*

ADULTS of several species of Hemiteles were obtained by rearing from cocoons of Gyrinus which were placed in small vials with cellucotton stoppers. Later in the season the parasites were reared successfully in small paraffin cells made by sinking a heated nail-head into a paraffin block. The parasitized host larva was removed from its pupal case and placed in the paraffin cell. Then a small cover glass was heated and placed on the cell, a small air hole being made by means of a "minute nadel." By this method the development of the insects, which feed externally upon the host larvae, could be observed carefully under the binocular.

Oviposition was first observed in the laboratory with females which had been reared from host cocoons and kept isolated. Newly constructed host cocoons were placed in isolation vials with adult females to permit oviposition. Eggs deposited by these females developed into adults, demonstrating that these insects can reproduce parthenogenetically. Later in the season the two sexes were mated.

* Abstracted from an article in *Ann. Ent. Soc. Amer.* 26:76, 1933, by F. GRAY BUTCHER, *N. Dakota College of Agriculture.*

In isolation vials the adults lived about 36 hours without food. By feeding the wasps a mixture of 40% honey and 60% water they were kept alive for more than 3 weeks.

Hemiteles hungerfordi, H. cushmani, H. cheboyganensis, and *H. pimplae* were reared by these methods. By the same technique *Cyrtogaster dineutes* was successfully reared through two generations and a partial third.

REFERENCE

For the rearing of ichneumonids see also p. 517.

REARING PANISCUS

ARLO M. VANCE, *U. S. Bureau of Entomology and Plant Quarantine*

OVIPOSITION by females of *Paniscus spinipes* and *P. geminatus* var. *sayi* on larvae of the corn ear-worm *Heliothis obsoleta,* and on several cutworm and army worm larvae, was obtained within a cheesecloth-covered glass cylinder 20 inches in height and 10 inches in diameter under laboratory conditions, temperature varying from about 60° to 70° F. In the cage a nearly full grown ear-worm larva was isolated on each of a number of sections of corn ear impaled on small spikes driven at intervals in an upright block of wood 16 inches high and 2 inches square. Food in the form of a hanging drop of thick honey and a 17% sugar solution in a watch glass was supplied the parasites. Each ear-worm larva parasitized with eggs of Paniscus was removed from the cage, placed on a few inches of sterile soil in a jelly glass, and fed with corn kernels until it entered the soil to pupate. Within the pupal cell made by the ear-worm, one of the parasitic larvae destroyed its host and constructed its cocoon. Usually the Paniscus cocoon was removed about three weeks later and buried about an inch deep in soil in a glass vial where it remained until the adult insect emerged. Mating of *P. spinipes* was secured in the type of cage above described.

BIBLIOGRAPHY

VANCE, ARLO M. 1927. On the biology of some ichneumonids of the genus Paniscus Schrk. *Ann. Ent. Soc. Amer.* 20:405.

CULTURE OF HABROCYTUS CEREALELLAE, PARASITE OF THE ANGOUMOIS GRAIN MOTH

B. B. FULTON, *North Carolina State College*

THE technique used for rearing the parasites under observation was different from that employed by Noble, who succeeded in getting oviposition on host larvae removed from the grain and confined with the female parasites in small tubes. The writer made a few unsuccessful attempts to induce the parasites to oviposit on free-moving larvae and then adopted the scheme of confining the host larvae in small glass cells made in the following manner: A glass tube just large enough to hold a full grown Angoumois larva was cut into sections about 1 cm. long. One end of the tube was touched on a smear of glue and then pressed against a piece of tissue paper. After drying, the edges of the paper were trimmed off, leaving a circular cap over the end of the tube. Host larvae were pushed into the other end of the tube head first, and held there by a small cotton plug. Several such cells were placed in holes in a card so that they would stand with the paper cap uppermost, and the whole card was then pushed under a large inverted petri dish used for confining the adult parasites. A cotton wad saturated with sugar water was kept under each dish. The female Habrocytus would climb to the top of such a cell and oviposit through the tissue paper cap the same as through the seed coat of an infested grain. If the cell was placed close to the side of a glass dish the whole process of oviposition could be watched with a binocular microscope. The number of eggs in each cell might be counted easily through the glass and further observation made on the development of the parasite without disturbing it.

The life cycle of *Habrocytus cerealellae* was run at two constant temperatures, 25° C. and 30° C. The time required for a complete life cycle of the Angoumois moth at a favorable temperature is a little over a month. Considering the short life cycle of Habrocytus (10 to 15 days), the number of eggs laid and the fact that a large proportion of the offspring are females, the reproductive capacity of the parasite must be close to three times as great as that of the host.

Large stock cultures of Habrocytus were maintained in Angoumois infested corn. The ear corn was kept in a large garbage can to protect it from mice. Both the Angoumois moth and its parasite continued to breed in the closed can and seemed to maintain a fairly constant balance.

REFERENCES

Family Calliceratidae
  For the culture of Calliceras (Ceraphron) see p. 266.
Family Cynipidae
  For the rearing of gall insects see p. 517.
Family Chalcididae
  For the rearing of members of this family see p. 517.
Family Pteromalidae
  For the culture of *Asaphes americana* see p. 500.
  For the culture of *Cyrtogaster dineutes* see p. 497.

BIBLIOGRAPHY

FULTON, B. B. 1933. Notes on *Habrocytus cerealellae,* parasite of the Angoumois grain moth. *Ann. Ent. Soc. Amer.* 26:536.

NOBLE, N. S. 1932. Studies of *Habrocytus cerealellae* (Ashmead), a pteromalid parasite of the Angoumois grain moth. *Univ. Calif. Publ. Ent.* 5:311.

Family APHELINIDAE

BREEDING A PRIMARY PARASITE AND TWO HYPERPARASITES OF THE GERANIUM APHID

GRACE H. GRISWOLD, *Cornell University*

THE geranium aphid, *Macrosiphum cornelli*, has proved an ideal host for the breeding of parasites. Unlike many other greenhouse aphids it is present at all times of the year and may easily be propagated.

Before breeding the parasites might be attempted it was necessary to devise some method of caging that would make conditions entirely satisfactory to the aphids. Geraniums are very susceptible to mildew if the plants are kept under too moist conditions. On the other hand, if a geranium gets too dry, the aphids soon become restless and crawl from the plant. Rearing the insects on growing plants, therefore, did not seem to be feasible. Leaves of the common Lady Washington geranium (*Pelargonium domesticum*) will keep fresh for days in water and on leaves so kept the aphids were found to thrive. Although the development of the aphid is somewhat hastened by this method it is not probable that the development of the parasites is abnormally affected.

The rearing cage finally adopted consists of a glass lamp chimney covered at the top with cheesecloth and set in an earthenware saucer. Although the glass cylinder comes in close contact with the saucer, a strip of cotton batting was kept about the bottom of each cage as an added precaution against the entrance of undesirable animal life. Not only has this cage proved satisfactory to the aphids but it appears to be equally satisfactory to the parasites, which are able to move and fly about in an almost normal manner. A large supply of aphids, free from parasites, was kept on hand in separate rearing cages.

A certain number of parasite-free aphid nymphs of early instars were exposed each day to the primary parasite for a period of 24 hours or less. Later, if desired, these same aphids were exposed to the hyperparasites for another and similar period. As soon as the aphids turned black they were removed to small shell vials and carefully labeled.

Aphelinus jucundus is an internal primary parasite which has been commonly reared from the geranium aphid. It has also been bred from the green peach aphid, *Myzus persicae,* and from an aphid on rose, *Macrosiphum pseudodirhodum.* Aphelinus will oviposit in aphids of any stage of development, though the earlier instars seem to be preferred. Hatching occurs in slightly less than 3 days and *A. jucundus* reaches maturity about 4 weeks after the eggs have been laid.

Aphidencyrtus inquisitor is an internal secondary parasite. The egg of this hyperparasite is laid within the body of the larva of the primary parasite which is living in the host aphid. *A. inquisitor* will not oviposit until at least 2 days after the egg of *Aphelinus jucundus* has hatched. If the temperature is lower than usual an even longer time must elapse. The life cycle covers a period of about 3 weeks.

Asaphes americana has proved to be both a secondary and a tertiary parasite. It will not oviposit in parasite-free aphids, nor in parasitized individuals until the latter are dead and have turned black. The life cycle extends over a period of approximately 3 weeks.

As far as could be observed *Aphelinus jucundus* reproduces only parthenogenetically and all individuals are females. *Aphidencyrtus inquisitor* and *Asaphes americana* reproduce both sexually and parthenogenetically; in the latter case all progeny are males. No more than one parasite has been known to emerge from a single aphid although in the breeding cages more than one egg might frequently be found in one individual.

Family TRICHOGRAMMIDAE

PRODUCTION OF TRICHOGRAMMA

STANLEY E. FLANDERS, *University of California*

THE parasitic wasp *Trichogramma minutum* will develop from egg to adult within the eggs of individuals of other species of insects representing six different orders and many families and genera.* Hence it is not surprising that it should develop in the eggs of Sitotroga, a form that it probably never attacks under natural conditions. The first attempt to use this insect as a host was made by the writer in 1926. Because it proved adaptable, unlimited quantities of a suitable medium for rearing Trichogramma became available. Sitotroga eggs may be held in refrigeration for several weeks without becoming unsuitable. [See P. 345.]

The eggs are most easily handled and parasitized when fastened to cardboards of convenient size. This is accomplished by pouring the eggs on freshly shellacked cards and shaking off all of the eggs not adhering. The shellac at the moment of applying the eggs should be just sticky enough to hold them, but should not engulf them. The preparation of these egg cards is facilitated by giving the cards a primary coating of shellac and allowing it to dry thoroughly. Owing to a soluble coating on the surface of Sitotroga eggs, water may also be used in fastening the eggs to almost any surface.

*Editor's Note: M. F. Bowen reports (*Ann. Ent. Soc. Amer.* 29:119, 1936) using eggs of the bagworm *Thyridopteryx ephemeraeformis* as host material for Trichogramma and putting a fresh seedless raisin on a pin in the cork of each breeding container. The raisin was moistened daily to help in maintaining a favorable relative humidity. M. E. D.

Only a single generation of Trichogramma may be reared on one card of eggs, unless fresh eggs are added at the time the adult Trichogramma are about to emerge. It is more convenient to use separate, freshly prepared cards for each generation.

Some strains reproduce readily in complete darkness, but as a rule the maximum oviposition occurs in diffused daylight. At certain times the adults are strongly positively phototropic and tend to leave the vicinity of host eggs. Light is not necessary for oviposition, for the writer has obtained tenfold reproduction in complete darkness. Under certain conditions light may result in a decrease in reproduction.

The life cycle of Trichogramma varies with the temperature, ranging from 6 days at 90° F., to 80 days at 50° F.

Glass vials, petri dishes inverted on plate glass, or mailing tubes may be used as rearing containers. To obtain parasitization a fresh egg card and ⅓ of a card from which adults are beginning to emerge should be placed in a container. On the second day another fresh egg card may be placed in with the inoculation card and the first one removed. Thus a sixfold reproduction is obtained. The emergence of the parasites may be concentrated within a short period of time by keeping the parasitized eggs in darkness until emergence begins and then placing them in the light.

M. E. D.

REFERENCES

Family Psammocharidae
For the rearing of Psammochares, Anoplius, and Ceropales see p. 517.
Family Chrysididae
For the rearing of members of this family see p. 517.
Family Sapygidae
For the rearing of Sapyga see p. 517.

BIBLIOGRAPHY

FLANDERS, S. E. 1930. Recent developments in Trichogramma production. *J. Econ. Ent.* 23:837.

———— 1931. The life cycles of *Trichogramma minutum* in relation to temperature. *Science* 73:458.

HASE, A. 1925. Beiträge zur Lebensgeschichte der Schlupfwespe *Trichogramma evanescens* Westwood. *Arbeit. Biol. Reichsanstalt fur Land-und Forstwirtschaft* 1925, 14. Band, Heft 2.

WISEHART, G. 1929. Large scale production of the egg parasite *Trichogramma minutum. Canad. Ent.* 61:73.

Families TIPHIIDAE and SCOLIIDAE

METHODS FOR REARING TIPHIIDS AND SCOLIIDS

J. L. KING, Division of Fruit Insect Investigations, *Bureau of Entomology and Plant Quarantine,* United States Department of Agriculture

THE members of the families Tiphiidae and Scoliidae are preëminently parasites of the larval stages of the Scarabaeidae. While the life cycles of these two groups are similar in many respects, several points of difference occur which must be considered if these wasps are to be reared in captivity.

The female tiphiid or scoliid wasp seeks out its host by digging in the soil. The wasps of both families sting the host, causing paralysis prior to oviposition. With tiphiids, paralysis is temporary, of 20 to 30 minutes' duration, and during this time the parasite attaches its egg firmly to the host. When the period of paralysis is over the host larva becomes normally active, and feeds until after the parasite egg has hatched and the parasite larva has grown to about one-third of its full size. By this time the host has become weakened and it now remains quiet within its earthen cell and is completely consumed by the parasite. The parasite larva then spins its cocoon within the cell formed by the host.

With the scoliids, the paralysis of the host is permanent and the wasp removes the host from the original cell to another, which is constructed by the parasite, usually at a greater depth than where the host was first located. The scoliid then deposits a single egg on the host, and this is attached so slightly at one end that it may be easily dislodged if the host is not handled carefully. Hatching of the parasite egg and all subsequent development take place in the cell formed by the parent wasp.

As both groups of parasites undergo their development within the soil, it is evident that two common requirements should be met when rearing them, namely, a fairly high constant relative humidity and uniform temperatures or at least protection from sudden and extreme temperature changes.

REARING METHODS FOR TIPHIIDS

In general the methods discussed here are those already described in the literature. There are certain refinements, however, that have been developed by other workers,* and these have been included in this discussion.

In order to rear either tiphiids or scoliids one must be familiar with the larval stages of the true host, and if these are not known, experimental

---

* The writer is indebted to his associates for many improvements herein included, and special credit should be given to J. K. Holloway, T. R. Gardner, M. H. Brunson, and R. W. Burrell for improving rearing methods in this group. Other necessary acknowledgments are indicated through the literature cited.

rearings will have to be conducted to supply the information needed for their recognition. If larvae are used that are not true hosts, the oviposition of the parasite will usually be slow and intermittent, or there will be no oviposition. Eggs that remain attached in such cases may hatch and a few larvae may reach maturity, but ordinarily the subsequent development of the parasite is not completed. In the tiphiids the position of the egg on the host is constant for each species but varies with the different species. The number of eggs per female usually ranges between 50 and 100.

A propagation container that has proved satisfactory consists of a tin salve box, of 6-ounce capacity, that is 2¾ inches in diameter and 2 inches in depth. The box should be fitted with a wire screen separator which divides the box into four or more equal compartments, to prevent host mortality through injury and cannibalism. One host larva is placed in each compartment.

The separators are made of wire screen sufficiently coarse to allow the passage of the parasite from one compartment to another but fine enough to prevent such movement by the host. The size of the mesh used should therefore be gauged according to the size of the parasite and its host. Separators may be constructed by placing together two or more strips of wire screen of the desired mesh, the length of these being about the diameter of the propagation container and the width slightly less than the depth of the container. These strips are fastened together in the center by means of a brass paper fastener of the split-pin type and are then bent apart so that when they are placed inside the box it is divided into equal compartments. From 4 to 6 compartments have been used successfully.

When the grubs are placed in the compartments of the propagation tins they are covered with soil that has been sifted through a 3- or 4-mesh screen. This soil should be sufficiently moist so that when a handful is pressed together it will form a ball that is easily friable. The container should be filled level and the soil then pressed down firmly so as to be about one-half inch below the edge of the tin. The pressure of the soil will not injure the host grub, which is at the bottom of the tin. Compression of the soil is necessary so that the grub may form in it an earthen cell that will not collapse. A convenient tool for compressing soil in the tins consists of a circular wooden disk with a handle attached at the center, the disk being slightly less in diameter than the circular opening of the propagation tin.

When the box has been prepared as just described, food for the parasite is provided. This may consist of a 10 per cent solution of honey and water, or candy. A convenient candy is made by mixing honey and pulverized sugar. To an ounce of honey add enough sugar to make a thick dough. Keep adding sugar and kneading until the dough becomes "dry" and will not take up more sugar. Either a drop of honey solution or a pellet of candy half the size of a pea is enough per tin. This is placed on a 1-inch square of heavy waxed paper, together with a separate drop of clear water. The waxed paper food retainer is allowed to rest on the surface of the soil.

The propagation container is then ready to receive the female parasite, which must be inserted quickly and covered with the lid. For each female parasite, one container should be prepared as described, and then set aside for 24 hours, after which it should be emptied and the parasite transferred to a freshly prepared tin, with fresh host larvae that have not been used previously, and with food. The tins may be kept at room temperature, but if large numbers of parasites are to be reared, a constant temperature of about 70° F. is best.

The host larvae that have been so exposed to the parasite should be examined both dorsally and ventrally for the parasite egg. Tiphiid eggs are small, usually creamy white in color, and may easily be overlooked if the examination is not thorough.

Larvae bearing parasite eggs are then ready for transfer to the cross section rearing trays. These trays, made of heavy galvanized iron, provide a single compartment for each grub as a further precaution against injury and cannibalism. Trays may be made to contain any desired number of compartments, but a convenient size for mass rearing is 18 inches by 18 inches by 2¼ inches. The edges should be rolled or folded for strength and to prevent cutting of the hands, and the corners folded and riveted. The inside of the tray is divided into 196 compartments each 1 inch square by 2 inches deep. The cross partitions forming these compartments are 3/16-inch wooden strips cut so as to fit together like the sections in an egg crate and are best made by machine. (If only a few parasites are to be reared, the host larvae may be kept individually in tin salve boxes filled with soil and the cross section trays will not be necessary.)

One host grub bearing the parasite egg is then placed in each compartment and fine, moist soil is sifted into the compartments and pressed lightly into place. Just before the cross sections are completely filled, 5 or 6 grains of wheat or rye are placed in each compartment and then covered with soil. The sprouting grain in the compartments furnishes food for the host until it finally succumbs to the parasite. (If tins are used, they too should be provided with grain.) The trays should be moistened slightly at this time and then stacked and allowed to remain undisturbed for about 1 month, at the end of which time cocoons should be formed. For species inhabiting temperate regions, the optimum temperature for development to the cocoon stage is about 70° F.

While in nature normal hibernation is within the cocoon in the soil, it has been found best in rearing to remove the cocoons from the soil soon after their formation so as to avoid the high mortality caused by the disease organisms so prevalent in soil. The cocoons are therefore removed from the cross section trays by lifting out the cross partitions, shaking out the soil, and sifting.

The cocoons are then placed individually in 2-dram homeopathic vials and these are capped with fine copper wire screen. These individual containers further prevent the spread of disease. A large number of these vials may be stored in trays the bottoms of which are covered with ordinary copper wire screen that allows ample air circulation when the trays are stacked or held in racks. Racks so constructed as to hold the trays and allow them to slide in and out are most satisfactory.

The cocoons are held in the vials until emergence of the adults. As the maintenance of large numbers of living cocoons—40,000 to 50,000—in healthy condition through the long period of development and hibernation is not easy, for they should be kept at a fairly even temperature and in a relative humidity of between 80 and 90 per cent. For this purpose specially designed cellar rooms with controlled temperature and humidity are best. These are refrigerated by means of special machines such as are used in commercial cold storage plants. As the cocoons pass from summer soil temperatures to hibernation the temperature is lowered at 15-day intervals to correspond with the average mean soil temperature at a 3-inch depth for the particular period under consideration. It has been found, however, that 38° F. is sufficiently low for hibernation and that with insects of this group lower temperatures such as occur during January and February need not be considered. As the hibernation period passes, temperatures are again increased at 15-day intervals until the prevailing temperatures of summer are reached. Since a detailed account of an ice-chilled cellar for hibernation has been published by Allen and Burrell,* the reader is referred to those authors for further details.

As little has been published on soil temperatures with reference to soil-inhabiting insects, a table has been prepared which may be of use to workers in this and other fields.

---

* ALLEN, H. W., and BURRELL, R. W. Methods of obtaining emergence of *Tiphia* adults from imported cocoons for use against the Japanese beetle. *J. Agr. Res.* 49:909-922, illus. 1934.

AVERAGE OF MEAN SOIL TEMPERATURES AS TAKEN AT A 3-INCH DEPTH IN
THE PHILADELPHIA AREA, BASED ON A 9-YEAR PERIOD

		°F.			°F.
Jan.	1-15	35.6	July	1-15	76.0
	16-31	34.7		16-31	77.6
Feb.	1-15	33.6	Aug.	1-15	76.8
	16-28	35.5		16-31	72.5
Mar.	1-15	36.9	Sept.	1-15	71.7
	16-31	43.1		16-30	67.6
Apr.	1-15	47.3	Oct.	1-15	61.8
	15-30	51.2		16-31	53.3
May	1-15	59.8	Nov.	1-15	48.5
	16-31	63.4		16-30	46.8
June	1-15	68.8	Dec.	1-15	38.8
	16-30	72.6		16-31	37.2

While it is realized that the equipment and methods herein described and referred to are somewhat expensive and elaborate, they are recommended where mass production of parasites is to be undertaken. For small numbers of cocoons when these are not practical, storage for hibernation in smaller containers is recommended. These can be stored in an ordinary cool cellar, and humidity can be kept fairly constant by the use of moist sphagnum moss. In any case, however, the cocoons keep best if stored in individual vials. Frequent examination is recommended, to check on the moisture of the moss and to curtail any fungous growth that might appear. The writer has reared *Tiphia* successfully in the tin salve boxes already referred to, but mortality in the cocoons is usually high when these are allowed to remain in moist soil.

The conditions under which the different species of *Tiphia* mate are not uniform for the groups. Some species mate readily in captivity under almost any conditions, whereas with others it is difficult to induce mating. In general, the more difficult species seem to require heat and strong light or even full sunlight for mating; even starving such females for 2 to 3 days prior to mating is advantageous. The females appear ready to mate very shortly after emergence, but in some instances the males have to be 4 to 5 days old. Females should therefore be subjected to males of different ages in numbers considerably in excess of the females.

A box of convenient size in which to mate *Tiphia* may be made of ½-inch soft pine 11 inches by 7 inches by 6½ inches deep. The cover of the box is of glass and slides in a snug-fitting groove, or the lid may be made as a separate unit which rests on the edge of the box and is prevented from slipping laterally by fitting over metal pins. If a lid of the latter type is used it is well to line its edge with felt to insure tight fitting, as *Tiphia* wasps are capable of making escape through small openings. Each end of the box has a 1-inch hole in the center, fitted with a cork, for the convenient entry of the parasites. In each side of the box along the central line two 1-inch holes are drilled, one about 3 inches from each end. These are covered with fine wire cloth and serve as vents. When the boxes are in use they are provided with a small water bottle fitted with a lamp wick that terminates in a ball of cotton wrapped in gauze. This furnishes water and humidity. Food for the adult consists of the candy which has been described, but for convenience it may be placed in small wooden blocks that have been drilled so as to contain several thimble-like depressions. The block fits conveniently in one corner. Often it is found desirable to cover the floor of the box with fine moist soil ¾ inch deep, into which the *Tiphia* may retire if the heat becomes too great. Care must be exerted to keep this soil moist. Small twigs with leaves may also be furnished for the *Tiphia* to rest upon. Paired couples may be removed to other containers with a suction pipette.

REARING METHODS FOR SCOLIIDS

The adults of *Scolia, Campsomeris,* and other allied genera require larger containers while being held during the oviposition period. Tins or jelly jars capable of holding about a half pint of soil are desirable. The soil used should be moistened as previously described for the tiphiids. The sifted soil is then pressed firmly in the containers after one host grub has been placed in each. A square of waxed paper bearing a pellet of candy and a drop of water to serve as food and drink for the adult, is placed in the container. The parasite is then quickly inserted and held in with a snug-fitting lid. The temperature required is the same as that used in rearing *Tiphia*. After the containers have been filled and provisioned they may be set aside until examined the following day. Illingworth,* however, states that two to three eggs per day may be procured by examining the containers twice daily, removing the parasitized grubs, and supplying new host larvae. The removal of the soil from the tins or jars should be done with care, for if simply dumped in a heap the egg may be dislodged from the host.

After the paralyzed host has been removed from the soil with the parasite egg attached, the grubs may be held in smaller tin boxes until the cocoons are formed; in this case, however, the box is half filled with moist soil which is pressed down flat, and in the middle of this flat surface an elliptical depression is made just large enough to hold the host grub. Over the top of this depression a sheet of paper or cellophane

* ILLINGWORTH, J. F.   A successful method of breeding parasites of white grubs. *J. Econ. Ent.* 12:455-457, illus. 1919.

should be placed so that when the parasite starts to spin its cocoon it can have a ceiling for the attachment of its silk when spinning, otherwise no cocoon will be formed. If large numbers of parasitized grubs are to be reared, greenhouse flats or trays filled with smoothly pressed soil in which numbers of depressions are made serve the purpose very well, but they too must be covered with paper or cellophane. The boxes may be stacked so as to preserve moisture.

The cocoons when formed may be removed and stored in the manner described for the maintenance of *Tiphia* during the winter. If they are formed at the beginning of the summer season, care must be taken to observe the cocoons at intervals, as many of this group have more than one generation a year. Illingworth advises leaving the cocoons in the flats and collecting the emerging adults by inserting a glass tube or vial in one side of each flat or tray. This being the only source of light, the adults enter the tube in an attempt to escape.

While the writer has had no experience in mating scoliids in captivity, he believes that this could be accomplished by using boxes similar to those described for tiphiids.

Other important papers* deal with the rearing of these parasites and should be consulted if work of this kind is to be undertaken.

REFERENCE

Family Mutillidae
For the rearing of members of this family see p. 517.

Family FORMICIDAE

LABORATORY MAINTENANCE AND CARE OF THE MOUND-BUILDING ANT, FORMICA ULKEI

A. M. HOLMQUIST, *St. Olaf College, Northfield, Minnesota*

IN KEEPING ants for observation and experimentation in the laboratory it is necessary to put them in containers that will prevent not only their escape but also their destruction by drowning or other means. The following description of methods used in maintaining *Formica ulkei* may also be applied to other species of soil-inhabiting ants.

Stock nests. For maintaining stock colonies of ants in the laboratory, a galvanized tin container, constructed with a space in the center for a

* CLAUSEN, C. P., KING, J. L., and TERANISHI, CHO. The parasites of *Popillia japonica* in Japan and Chosen (Korea) and their introduction into the United States. *U. S. Dept. Agr. Bull.* 1429, pp. 34-36, illus. 1927.

CLAUSEN, C. P., JAYNES, H. A., and GARDNER, T. R. Further investigations of the parasites of *Popillia japonica* in the Far East. *U. S. Dept. Agr. Tech. Bull.* 366, p. 29, illus. 1933.

nest and a water moat around it to prevent the escape of the ants, has proven very successful (Fig. 82).

A water-tight pan, 12″ x 12″ x 2″ deep, is used. In the center is placed a water-tight enclosure, 6″ x 6″ x 2½″ or 3″ deep, in which moist, black soil is provided for nest building. Over each edge of this center nest section is hung a strip of tin, bent at an angle and reaching down to the surface of the water. This bent strip prevents the ants from drowning as they rush precipitately over the edge of the nest to attack the disturber whenever the cover is lifted or the nest is otherwise disturbed. It also provides easy access to the water and might even be used for feeding. The surrounding space, 3 inches in width, is kept filled with water to prevent the escape of the ants. The nest is kept covered with a piece of tin or other opaque material, or may be covered with a glass plate if closer observation is desired; the cover prevents too rapid

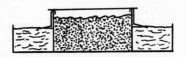

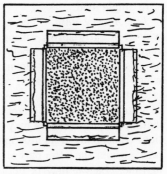

Fig. 82.—Diagram of stock nest for *Formica ulkei* in the laboratory.

evaporation from the soil, which must be kept moist at all times.

Feeding may be done in small tin covers, or other small, shallow receptacles, placed in the nest on the surface of the soil.

The accumulating excavated soil in the moat may be flushed out with water from a rubber tube attached to a faucet. A small hole in each corner of the moat as close to the bottom as possible, is convenient for cleaning purposes. The holes may be kept stoppered with small corks when the moat is not being cleaned. The water in the moat must be changed from time to time, as a thick film soon covers it and this may become strong enough to allow the ants to escape by walking on it.

Observation nest. Several observation nests are available at biological supply houses. These are often elaborate and more expensive than necessary. A simple, inexpensive way to observe ants is to establish colonies in glass finger bowls. The ants are confined to the bowl by a glass plate over the top of the bowl. Moist filter paper or blotting paper covers the bottom. An extra folded piece of filter paper provides a place for hiding and for storage of the young.

When feeding the ants or cleaning these nests, the finger bowl is placed in a shallow pan of water to prevent the escape of the ants.

This type of nest is best adapted to the study of the life history of the ant and such other studies as require only one or two examinations per day. The material in the bottom may easily be searched for young. Black or other dark colored paper is preferable, as the eggs and larvae are white.

Feeding. The food required for this species of ant is of the usual kind: Apples, bananas, honey, syrup, sugar solution, and fresh insect bodies (preferably cut into small pieces). Ants are cannibalistic and eat their own eggs and young. It is therefore necessary to provide them with ample food.

Life history data. The ants are most easily obtained in late fall, winter, or early spring during the period of hibernation. At this time, they form dense clusters below the frost line. They are also so sluggish at this time that they do not eject the little droplets of formic acid which is so pungent that it may kill them during transportation to the laboratory. They should, however, be handled gently, even at this time of year to prevent the secretion of formic acid. Workers and sexually mature wingless females may be obtained during the period of hibernation. Emergence from hibernation begins about the middle of April. Egg laying begins the latter part of April and continues up to the first few days of June. Larvae may be obtained in the field from the middle of June until the middle of August. Worker pupae are obtainable from the middle of June to the latter part of October. The large pupae of the reproducing males and females are obtained in July and the winged males and females appear about the middle of that month when mating occurs. In the laboratory, eggs appear in the nests as early as January.

These data are based on observations made in the Chicago region. Allowance must be made for differences in the life history periods with different localities.

SOME AIDS TO THE STUDY OF MOUND-BUILDING ANTS

E. A. ANDREWS, *Johns Hopkins University*

FOR breeding ants in captivity a compromise must be made between the need of the observer to see the ants and the need of the ants to be screened from some of the rays of light and to be supplied with food and moisture at certain temperatures. When large ants such as the mound-building ant, *Formica exsectoides*, are to be studied in regard to feeding, direction-finding and the like, some special adaptations of the usual formicaries are advisable.

Transplanting of mounds may be done in winter or summer. In each case much of the old mound may be transported for quicker rebuilding of the new one. In the winter the semi-dormant ants, far below the earth's surface, may be dug out and placed in a correspondingly deep hole in a new locality and covered with fragments of the old mound. In the summer the material of the mound may be carried off in grain sacks with such ants as stay with it, while most of the population may be concentrated in jars or old milk cans by taking advantage of the habit of the ant to seize hold of any new object. That is, bits of rags are thrown on the mound and when attacked by ants, shaken over the mouth of an open can or paper bag and again used until most of the visible ants are captured. After that, digging in the mound reveals the young, which should be carefully taken up by means of a spoon and placed in preserve jars without crushing. In the winter time, the queens are rather readily found jammed with workers in some deep-lying galleries beneath the mound, but in summer they readily escape capture. In order to study these ants in the laboratory itself, various modifications of formicaries in use for smaller ants may be made. Large horizontal and also vertical formicaries are made with large sheets of glass (old windshields will serve) separated by rather thick strips of wood or by plaster of Paris, with holes and plugs for access to the interior.

To supply somewhat natural conditions for the ants in the laboratory three-dimensional formicaries were made from old tubs, alcohol barrels sawed in two, or even packing boxes, filled with clay at bottom and friable earth on top. When the colony is placed in such a tub the ants dig in and become established, but wander out and are lost or destroyed unless restrained. They are kept in by supporting the tub on bricks in a shallow metal-lined box containing water. Even then ants fall into the moat about the tub and after they have thrown various fragments onto the water, will eventually make a bridge across the moat unless the water surface is kept clean. Vaseline may be smeared over the outer wall of the moat to diminish the loss of prisoners. Such a tub colony survived several years, fed with earthworms, insects, and honey, and watered with occasional rains from a watering pot. On the surface of the earth, which the ants raised into a mound, twigs with honey-dew insects were placed for observation and various frames were erected with contrivances to present food to wandering ants which could be marked with colored shellac before returning to the mound for the reinforcements needed to manage large masses of food.

A large mound was established in a dark room designed for experiments. Placed on the floor, this populous mound was surrounded by a water moat 3 inches wide made by soldering zinc strips to form a rectangular trough 6 feet long and wide, 3 inches high and broad, filled with water. Within the enclosed 36 square feet of area, the ants carried on their architectural work, their feeding, and their disposal of the dead for more than a year without sunshine and with no regular alternation of light and dark, but with many days and nights of complete darkness followed by brief lighting with a search light, or with other intense electric light. Various frames erected in the enclosure served for feeding and other experiments. Water was supplied both by basal tunnel under the mound and by occasional showers over the mound surface to bring out the building reactions that follow when the surface is wet after long dry periods in which material is accumulated; the activities after rain being essentially a turning of the roof upside down by carrying the inner part onto the outer part through turrets built up over the surface.

To simulate the sunshine in which ants may bask, a suspended source of dark heat called out masses of ants to bask in a small local area of warm darkness. As a cheap source of dark heat the flat metal heaters used for poultry proved efficient.

In a room of nearly uniform temperature and general darkness, ants thus existed without sunlight and carried on, both day and night, as they do normally in warm nights out of doors.

REFERENCE

For the feeding of ants see note on p. 49.

Family BETHYLIDAE

METHODS OF BREEDING PERISIEROLA ANGULATA, A COCOON PARASITE OF THE ORIENTAL FRUIT MOTH

J. C. Schread, *Connecticut Agricultural Experiment Station*

THE Australian bethylid parasite, *Perisierola angulata*, has been reared for two consecutive seasons at the Connecticut Agricultural Experiment Station. It is a cocoon parasite of some promise, having been recovered from succeeding fruit moth generations subsequent to field colonization during the first season of handling. Because it presents several discouraging features in artificial breeding as a result of its peculiar habits (the females require a prohibitive amount of individual handling and attention), only a limited number may be reared in any one season with the present technique employed in breeding.

Three-dram homeopathic vials are used as rearing containers. The bottom of the vial is removed and replaced with ⅓ of a straight-sided wine cork into which a small nail with an impaled raisin is inserted. The opposite end of the vial is fitted with finely woven absorbent cloth forced into the neck of the vial and held in place by an 8 x 14 x 2 mm. washer.

Host material used for mass production of the parasite is confined to freshly spun larvae of the fruit moth. [see p. 345.] Several other hosts were tried, none of which gave desirable results. One pair of parasites is placed in each vial without host material for a period of 5 days in order to permit mating and to complete the pre-oviposition period. Finally, a single fruit moth larva, spun in corrugated cardboard, is exposed to each female for 24 hours at a controlled temperature of 76° F. and 60% relative humidity. Parasitized larvae, when removed from the parasite containers, are placed in vials similar to those employed for rearing purposes except that there is no raisin present. These vials are held at the foregoing temperature and humidity until the adult parasites emerge. The latter are then refrigerated at 50° F. and 80% relative humidity to await colonization.

The immature or larval development of the parasites is passed concealed in the cocoon of its host. Likewise, the pupal stage is completed in this matter. However, occasionally a larva may, during its prepupal stage, work its way to the exterior of the host cocoon before forming its own cocoon in preparation for pupation. Males complete their development in slightly less than 12 days, whereas females require a few additional hours, extending their emergence into the twelfth day. The optimum period for both sexes is from $12\frac{1}{2}$ to 14 days. Adult Perisierolas may remain in their cocoons for some time following the appearance of exit holes. Notwithstanding, males manifest a proclivity for visiting females before the latter leave their cocoons. Occasionally these visits result in successful mating prior to cocoon evacuation. The initial fertilization is sufficient to fecundate females for the entire period of reproduction which generally extends intermittently throughout their life. Males survive for a much shorter period than females, the average being from 12 to 16 days. Female longevity averages 40 days with a maximum of four months.

The parasite paralyzes its host by stinging prior to parasitizing. The number of eggs deposited on a single host of the size of the fruit moth larvae varies from 1 to 14, averaging about 4 to 6. The incubation period of the eggs under controlled conditions is from 36 hours to two days and the larvae feed from the exterior of the host for 3 to 4 days before pupating. Thus the cocoon and pupal stage of the parasite includes more than half the life cycle of the species. The sex ratio is approximately one to one.

REARING LAELIUS ANTHRENIVORUS

ARLO M. VANCE, *U. S. Bureau of Entomology and Plant Quarantine*

THIS parasite was handled in a warm laboratory room. Each female was placed in a small glass globe cage containing some dry insect material upon which Anthrenus larvae of different stages were feeding.

[see p. 459.] Oviposition by the parasite on this host was readily obtained and the resulting progeny were reared to the adult stage in small glass vials. Although small lumps of dry sugar and occasional drops of water were provided some of the female parasites, neither food nor moisture of this nature appeared to be essential.

REFERENCE

Family Vespidae
For the rearing of Eumenes, Odynerus, and Polistes see p. 517.

BIBLIOGRAPHY

VANCE, A. M., and PARKER, H. L. 1932. *Laelius anthrenivorus* Trani, an interesting bethylid parasite of *Anthrenus verbasci* L. in France. *Proc. Ent. Soc. Wash.* 34:1.

Family DRYINIDAE

CULTURE OF APHELOPUS THELIAE

S. I. KORNHAUSER, *University of Louisville Medical School*

Aphelopus theliae (Gahan, 1918) is a polyembryonic dryinid, parasitic on the membracid, *Thelia bimaculata.*

The eggs of Thelia are laid in the smaller branches of the black locust tree, *Robinia pseudo-acacia* (Funkhouser, 1915). They hatch in late spring or early summer and the nymphs are tended by ants and transported to the bases of the locust trees where they feed, staying fairly quietly in the cracks of the bark. Aphelopus females were first found in early June running over the bark hunting the nymphs. They attack and lay small, transparent, oval eggs in the body cavity of the nymphs, piercing the chitinous exoskeleton with their sharp ovipositors. One egg is generally laid in each nymph. This act of oviposition may be demonstrated in the laboratory in a test tube, one nymph after another being put into the tube with a female Aphelopus. Thelia nymphs of the 2nd or 3rd instar are best.

The stung nymphs are then placed on a locust tree out of doors to feed and grow. Around the trunk is sewed a cylinder of mosquito netting which may be tied to the trunk near the ground and with a removable loop above. One can examine the nymphs from time to time in this way and protect them from enemies and also from escaping. When the stung nymphs have reached the 6th instar their abdomens show the effects of the parasites. The sclerites are poorly chitinized, the segments distended by the fifty to seventy larval Aphelopus, and the nymphal genital appendages greatly reduced (Kornhauser, 1919). When the larvae are about to emerge, the nymph becomes restless and crawls up on the bark.

At this stage nymphs should be transferred to freshly cut branches of Robinia in laboratory cages. These branches are kept in water to keep them fresh. The nymph, when the parasites are ready to emerge (August and early September), crawls out on a small branch and fixes its tarsi tightly. One then sees rows of elevations, four or five to a segment, appear across the abdominal sternal plates. Place a flower pot with soft earth beneath the Thelia nymph. The Aphelopus eruciform larvae emerge head first from holes in the abdomen of the host and drop into the flower pot. They burrow into the soil and spin little, peanut-shaped cocoons in which they overwinter.

Some of the pots were kept outside over the winter and others were kept in the laboratory and sprinkled occasionally. Those in the laboratory matured much more quickly than those kept outside. *Aphelopus theliae* was first described from specimens reared in this way.

BIBLIOGRAPHY

FUNKHOUSER, W. D. 1915. Life history of *Thelia bimaculata* Fab. (Membracidae). *Ann. Ent. Soc. Amer.* 8:140.

GAHAN, A. B. 1918. An interesting new hymenopterous parasite. *Canad. Ent.* 50:151.

KORNHAUSER, S. I. 1919. The sexual characteristics of the membracid, *Thelia bimaculata* (Fabr.). *J. Morph.* 32:531.

ANTEONINE PARASITES OF LEAFHOPPERS*

THE Anteoninae confine their attacks to the Fulgoridae, Cicadellidae, and Membracidae. Adults of both sexes feed readily on water sweetened with sugar.

Leafhoppers captured in the field were kept alive and the parasitized ones isolated in shell vials provided with a layer of damp soil and a cotton plug. Fresh leaves were added every day until the host had been killed by the parasite. The cocoons are spun either beneath the soil or above it on leaves or other objects.

By this method life histories were obtained for *Gonatopus erythrodes, G. contortulus, Haplogonatopus americanus, Chelogynus osborni, Phorbas mirabilis,* and *Aphelopus dikraneuri.*

M. E. D.

* Abstracted from an article in the *Ohio J. of Sci.* 18:177, 1918, by F. A. FENTON Oklahoma A. and M. College.

Families SPHECIDAE, ANDRENIDAE, and

MEGACHILIDAE

METHODS FOR REARING WILD BEES, WASPS, AND THEIR PARASITES

CHARLES H. HICKS, *University of Colorado*

THE writer has successfully reared a large number of bees, wasps, their parasites, and other insects, during the past ten years. Insects from ground nests, as well as those from exposed nests attached to stones or other objects, or those found in stems and in hard wood (such as in logs, stumps, sawed blocks, and the like) have, with few exceptions, yielded a total and maximum number of the possible and expected adults. The following is an abbreviated account of the methods used and of the results attained.

It is not the purpose to point out here the detailed methods of locating insect nests except to indicate a few general and fruitful sources. Probably the easiest one involves the finding of nests of bees and wasps in wood. These may be obtained during any month of the year in almost any region from old stems or from pith-bearing plants. Especially favorable for nest sites are the stems of sumac, blackberry, raspberry, rose, elder, mullein and various weed stems. These are usually stems which have been cut off in one way or another or which have been broken by wind or other agent leaving the pith exposed and easily accessible to the insects. The stems containing possible nests have visible openings or tunnels in the exposed end. If plugged flush across this end or slightly below it, the characteristic plug or outer barricade reveals the builder. The cap may be of resin and pebbles, cotton, mud or other materials, depending on the species building it. Usually, the cancavity in the pith reveals the presence of a nest beneath or beyond. When a stem is suspected of containing insects, it may be split open with a jackknife and further investigated. The old or empty ones may be discarded; the others brought to the laboratory for further study.

It has been found that test tubes of sizes varying to meet the specific measurements of particular stems, may be used as containers and the insects reared or the adults obtained. A plug of cotton, packed sufficiently tight to prevent the insects from working their way out, prevents escape even of the smallest forms and at the same time allows for exchanges of gases in respiration.

My plan has been to give each tube containing a nest, a number which corresponds to the like number on a filing card. This card holds pertinent data. The practice has been to stick a label with a number on the outside of the tube and to place the same number on a loose label inside. This is a double check to accuracy. The emerging insects are given the same number and are distinguished one from another by the date or time of emergence.

When the insects are in the late stages of development, there has been little need for supplying moisture. When one has pollen and eggs, or young bee larvae and pollen, a piece of a live plant leaf inserted in the tube has supplied sufficient moisture. The amount of moisture may be regulated easily and successfully by varying the size of the leaf surface. The leaf does not require changing oftener than every day and may be left longer. The period during which this attention is required is comparatively short, being only until feeding is over. The same treatment applies to wasps, although there is no need for adding moisture except in a few cases, as for example in the case of the pollen-using wasps, *Pseudomasaris spp.* The temperature does not need to be constant and may be increased somewhat above ordinary room temperature. This increase hastens development and, by regulating it, one may have insects emerging any month of the fall, winter, or spring. The emergence may easily be "timed" to meet the need of the individual or the needs of general or special classes in entomology.

The nests of insects taken from the ground, especially of those insects nesting near the surface or in hard banks, respond readily to the methods outlined above. In a few instances, involving but a comparatively small number of species, it would seem that a careful regulation of temperature and humidity are needed. The required change should follow an attempt to approximate the normal conditions under which the species develop in nature.

Bees successfully reared have been those belonging to the following genera: Alcidamea, Andronicus, Anthidium, Anthophora, Ashmeadiella, Augochlora, Bremus, Callanthidium, Ceratina, Chelynia, Coelioxys, Dianthidium, Dioxys, Exomalopsis, Halictus, Hoplitina, Hylaeus, Lithurgus, Megachile, Mellisodes, Nomia, Osmia, Perdita, Proteriades, Pseudomelecta, Spinoliella, Stelis, Xylocopa, Zacosmia and some others.

Some of the wasps reared have been specimens belonging to these genera: Anoplius, Bembex, Cerceris, Ceropales, Chalybion, Chlorion, Crabro, Dryudella, Eucerceris, Eumenes, Eusapyga, Odynerus, Podalonia, Polistes, Psammochares, Pseudomasaris, Sapyga, Sceliphrons, Sphex, Trypoxylon and others. Many parasites and other insects, such as chalcids, chrysids, ichneumonids, parasitic beetles, mutillids, gall insects, sawflies and the like, have likewise been reared.

This method of rearing enables the investigator to obtain large numbers of various adult insects and to follow their earlier development. It supplies insects for taxonomic work, for studies involving accurate sex ratios, for the difficult matching of the sexes in sexually dimorphic species, for obtaining and having at hand living material in the winter months, and for the study of the larval and pupal stages of rare and little known species. In this way one may also rear species new to science, as well as secure a large number of insects but rarely caught in the net. This is especially true of the small insects which in field collecting are overlooked or which, because of their small size, are able if caught to crawl through the net and escape. The method outlined above may be found a valuable supplement to others now in general or current use.

Phylum XV

MOLLUSCA, CLASS *Amphineura*

CHAETOPLEURA APICULATA

BENJAMIN H. GRAVE, *De Pauw University*

Chaetopleura apiculata is a small species of chiton which occurs abundantly in Vineyard Sound near Woods Hole, Massachusetts, and is collected by dredging. The breeding season begins about June 25 and extends to September 25. It is at its height during July and the first half of August. Spawning takes place at night from 8 to 11 P.M.

METHOD OF OBTAINING EGGS

To obtain eggs and sperm, place 25 or 30 chitons in a large crystallization dish and keep in running seawater during the day. They cling to the bottom and sides of the dish and creep about more or less. Toward evening wash free of sediment and place the containing dish, half filled with seawater, on a laboratory table and allow to remain undisturbed. It is sufficient if the chitons are well covered with water. About 8 P.M. the males may be expected to begin to extrude sperm into the water and half an hour later a few of the females spawn.

For some reason many more eggs are shed during the second night after collection than the first. A few are likely to be spawned the third night, but after that a new collection of animals should be made.

It has been observed in some species of mollusk that sperm in the water stimulates the female to shed her eggs. For instance, Galtsoff showed that this is the effective stimulus in the oyster. Metcalf made the observation that when an aquarium contains both male and female chitons the sperm is always shed before the eggs and he interpreted the phenomenon as due to a chemical stimulus between the sexes. However, female chitons will spawn when isolated so that it is possible to obtain unfertilized eggs if desired.

CULTURE METHODS

After spawning is completed the eggs may be taken up in a pipette and transferred to fresh dishes of seawater. They should be washed several times by decanting the water and refilling the dishes during the next 24 hours to insure proper aeration and elimination of body fluids.

The eggs of Chaetopleura are enclosed within a bristly chorion from which they hatch as swimming trochophores in from 25 to 30 hours. The larva is well supplied with yolk and therefore requires no feeding for several days. In order to carry larvae through to metamorphosis it is necessary to transfer them daily to dishes of fresh seawater by means of a pipette. Otherwise they soon become infected with bacteria and tend to develop abnormally. After the second day of larval life the shell and foot begin to appear on the trochophore and these continue to develop during succeeding days. In from 7 to 12 days the larva metamorphoses into the adult form and becomes a dorsoventrally flattened creeping animal. It is possible to carry them through metamorphosis without feeding but it is thought that transformation is hastened if the feeding of diatoms is begun on the sixth day of larval life. This species is used regularly in the embryology course at Woods Hole and no great difficulty has been experienced in securing the complete development of the larva including metamorphosis under laboratory conditions. The young metamorphosed chitons may also be kept indefinitely by allowing seawater to flow through the dishes in which they are kept a part of each day. This supplies necessary food and ensures rapid growth. Washing them free of sediment periodically is the chief requirement for keeping the young animals in a thriving condition after metamorphosis.

BIBLIOGRAPHY

GRAVE, B. H. 1932. Embryology and life history of *Chaetopleura apiculata*. *J. Morph.* 54:153.

HEATH, H. 1899. The development of Ischnochiton. *Zool. Jhrb.* 12:567.

KOWALEVSKI, A. 1883. Embryogenic du *Chiton polii*. *Ann. Mus. Hist. Nat. Marseilles.* 5.

CLASS *Gastropoda*, ORDER PULMONATA

LYMNAEA [=PSEUDOSUCCINEA] COLUMELLA*

THE hermaphroditic snail *Lymnaea* [=*Pseudosuccinea*] *columella*, when isolated, lays fertile eggs which are self-fertilized (Colton, 1912, 1918). This observation has been confirmed by Crabb (1927). We can, therefore, establish a pure line in animals in the same way that it can be done in many plants.

A line was started in 1911 and since then the descendants of the original parent have been under controlled conditions for over 93 genera-

* Abstracted at the suggestion of the authors from an article in *Amer. Nat.* 68:129, 1934, by HAROLD S. COLTON and MIRIAM PENNYPACKER, *University of Pennsylvania.*

tions. The closest kind of inbreeding has been practiced, each young snail being isolated in a jar by itself, and a race has been established of a gametic purity rarely attained in animals. Nevertheless, the race shows remarkable hardiness and longevity.

Since *Lymnaea columella* reacts readily to slight environmental changes, a controlled environment becomes necessary. The standard medium for a single snail is 500 cc. of filtered pond water placed in a 4½" x 5" battery jar. The jar containing the snail is kept at room temperature which, between October and April, ranges from 19° to 22° C. with a mean of about 21°. In the summer months a temperature approaching 30° accelerates development.

Chemical analyses of the medium show that the water in which the snail lives is practically without oxygen. Since the snail is air-breathing, this anaerobic condition offers but slight disadvantage to the animal (Colton, 1908; Walter, 1906).

For food, dried leaves of the Carolina poplar are introduced, one at a time. Small tender leaves are chosen at first, when the snails are small, and larger, tough leaves later. It is necessary to add but few leaves at a time and to add no leaves that appear green, for these seem to form a favorable medium for bacterial growth. The bacterial scum from such leaves keeps the young snails from reaching the surface and causes them to drown. Dried leaves may be gathered in the autumn and kept indefinitely.

As the senior author pointed out some years ago (Colton, 1908), this snail has a true gizzard containing small stones. These small stones are necessary for the breaking up of plant tissue. Without stones the animal starves amid abundance. Therefore, it is necessary to introduce a pinch of soil into each jar.

Even under standard conditions there is considerable variation in the time between the laying and the hatching of the eggs. If sexual maturity is considered as the time of laying the first eggs the time of reaching this stage is also variable. In general, when a snail reaches the length of 10 mm. it usually lays eggs, but the range extends from 7 mm. to 12 mm. The first eggs are usually laid forty days after hatching. This interval is much longer in the autumn, often extending over three months, and is shortest in the spring, when it may be only five weeks. The factor prolonging the life cycle in the autumn is neither food nor temperature and at the present time is unknown and uncontrolled.

M. E. D.

BIBLIOGRAPHY

COLTON, HAROLD S. 1908. Some effects of environment on the growth of *Lymnaea columella* Say. *Proc. Acad. Nat. Sci. Phila.* July, p. 410.
—— 1912. *Lymnaea columella* and self-fertilization. *Ibid.* May, p. 173.

—— 1918. Self-fertilization in the air-breathing pond snails. *Biol. Bull.* 35:48.

CRABB, E. D. 1927. The fertilization process in the snail *Lymnaea stagnalis appressa* Say. *Ibid.* 53:67.

WALTER, HERBERT E. 1906. Behavior of the pond snail *Lymnaea elodes*. *Cold Spring Harbor Monographs* No. 4.

REARING AQUATIC PULMONATE SNAILS

ELMER PHILIP CHEATUM, *Southern Methodist University*

IN THE artificial rearing of snails one cannot ignore the natural environmental conditions to which each species is best adapted. Much better results are secured in the culture of snails if field conditions are simulated as nearly as possible in the laboratory aquaria.

In the rearing of hundreds of lake, pond, and marsh-inhabiting snails the author early discovered that conditions favorable for the growth of one species may be rather adverse for another. For example, the depth of water in rearing aquaria proves to be an important factor. The large marsh-inhabiting species such as *Lymnaea megasoma, L. palustris, Helisoma trivolvis,* and the smaller lymnaeids and physids thrive better in aquaria containing 2 or 3 inches of water than in aquaria containing 10 or 12 inches of water. Species inhabiting the more open bodies of water in a lake such as *Physa parkeri, Lymnaea emarginata angulata, L. stagnalis, Helisoma campanulatum,* and *H. antrosum* live equally well in either deep or shallow water. It is generally much better, then, to rear snails in aquaria with glass sides (for photosynthetic purposes) that are wide and shallow rather than narrow and deep.

A layer of sand and gravel about 1 inch in thickness should be placed on the bottom of each aquarium. This serves as support for the roots of aquatic plants which are grown as a source of food supply as well as for oxygenation of the water. After planting the vegetation in the aquarium it is best, if at all feasible, to use the same water in the aquarium as that from which the snails came. If it is not convenient to do this, usually it is much better to use water from some nearby pond or stream rather than to use tap water which may contain harmful substances.

Food is a very important item in snail culture. Filamentous algae and Elodea are excellent aquarium plants, since both are active photosynthetically and are fed on by snails. Thin slices of apple, lettuce leaves, small sticks, and dead leaves covered with microscopic plant life should frequently be placed in the aquaria. If the water in the aquarium is several inches deep the sticks should be so arranged that snails may use them as highways in reaching the surface for air. It is wise to remove such objects as leaves and twigs at least once each week and replace them with fresh material preferably collected from the same pond or stream from which the snails were secured.

REARING AQUATIC SNAILS

WENDELL KRULL, *U. S. Bureau of Animal Industry*

USE water which has been kept in stone jars in subdued light for several weeks; if the water becomes acid on standing, add enough calcium carbonate to cover the bottom of the container. All water should be filtered through coarse filter paper before it is used in aquaria. If these precautions are taken algae, which are a constant nuisance in most cases, are largely eliminated. Snails, apparently, thrive best in alkaline water and no success has been had in using acid water, although one species, *Pseudosuccinea columella*, has grown and matured in water having a pH of 5.5.

FEEDING, FOOD, AND ITS PREPARATION

In rearing many of the freshwater pond snails, only two kinds of food, dead leaves and lettuce, appear to be necessary. Some snails may complete their development when fed on either the dead leaves or on the lettuce, while others change from one to the other during their development; however, most of them can survive for some time on dead leaves alone. In view of this fact it is a good plan to keep a few dead leaves in the aquarium as an emergency measure. Such snails as *Fossaria modicella*, *F. m. rustica*, *Gyraulus parvus*, and *Planorbula armigera* may be raised successfully on dead leaves, and *Pseudosuccinea columella* and *Lymnaea palustris* on lettuce, while *Helisoma trivolvis* requires dead leaves when hatched and lettuce when some growth has taken place if they are to be raised without excessive mortality.

Dead leaves. Leaves from maple trees are superior to any of the numerous kinds of leaves which have been tried in snail culture. The leaves may be gathered any time during the summer and cured by placing them in a sack or screen container and hanging in the sunshine for 6 or 8 weeks. The drying of the leaves may be shortened considerably if they are collected at the time they are being shed in the fall; they may be dried on a radiator or near a stove. After the leaves have been thoroughly dried and cured they should be placed in a glass container and covered with the same kind of water which is to be used in the aquaria. The leaves should be soaked for three days, changing water twice daily, after which they should be dried by spreading them out on paper. The leaves are then ready for use in aquaria as desired; when used they should be placed on the bottom of the aquarium after they become moistened. It is desirable that the leaves be kept intact as much as possible.

Lettuce. Head lettuce is much superior to leaf lettuce because of its keeping qualities, both in the refrigerator and in aquaria, and because it may be obtained in most places the year around. The lettuce may be kept for weeks in a mechanical refrigerator in a covered tin can. Use, except in the cases discussed subsequently, only the leafy part of the lettuce whether bleached or unbleached, avoiding the central vascular, thick part of the leaf as well as any part that has been bruised. The lettuce in its preparation for the aquarium should be torn with the fingers, avoiding excessive pressure and the use of the thumb nail as a punch.

Calcium carbonate. In addition to the foods mentioned above, calcium carbonate not only is desirable but seems almost indispensible. It is not only eaten by the snails but it serves also to regulate the acidity of the water; however, it is of no value for this purpose in an over-stocked aquarium or one in which there is an excessive amount of decaying organic material. Calcium carbonate in the form of crushed lime rock or of precipitated chalk is of no value in snail culture, since these forms appear to be too finely divided and cause the snails to produce a superabundance of slime. Calcium carbonate comparable to "Baker's Analyzed" (product of the J. T. Baker Chemical Co.) is the form most suitable for both terrestrial and aquatic snails.

PREPARATION OF THE HABITAT

For a small number of snails an evaporating dish 9 inches in diameter and 3 inches high is suitable; this should be filled with approximately 2,000 cc. of water or to within about ½ inch of the top. To the water should then be added about one gram of calcium carbonate; most of the carbonate should be piled up near the center with a thin film spreading over most of the bottom of the aquarium. This may be accomplished by dropping the calcium carbonate from a piece of paper held about 3 inches above the surface of the water. Dry leaves in an amount of leaf area equal to the area of the bottom of the aquarium are introduced; the leaves should be piled up so as to cover only about a third of the bottom. After the addition of the snails and a small amount of lettuce the aquarium should be covered with a glass plate; the cover need not be propped up for air circulation unless the snails crawl out of the water and carry with them enough water to "seal" the cover.

An aquarium of this size will support about 12 *Fossaria modicella,* 6 *Helisoma trivolvis,* or 8 *Pseudosuccinea columella* for months; eggs or young snails should be removed promptly.

Species of Fossaria, Helisoma, Planorbula, Gyraulus, Physa, Stagnicola, Lymnaea, and Pseudosuccinea have been raised without difficulty by using this method. It should be noted, however, that *Fossaria modicella, F. m. rustica,* and *Pseudosuccinea columella* may normally spend much of their time out of water; this, however, should not occasion concern unless they tend to get too far away from the water and become too dry.

The principle in the foregoing example is applicable to aquaria of all sizes from finger bowls for snails kept individually to aquaria of 5 or 10 gallons capacity.

MAINTENANCE

Snails are fond of calcium carbonate in the form already mentioned and most of it will have been collected and deposited in cylinders of feces in a day or so. It is mixed subsequently with increasing amounts of organic material, since the snails eat the feces repeatedly. The snails should be given lettuce every other day and accumulation of excesses should be prevented by regulating the amount given them. In case excess lettuce remains, remove it at the subsequent feeding. Sometimes an excess of lettuce is necessary to keep the snails in the water, and in this event the portion remaining should be removed at each feeding. The dry leaves should be removed and replaced by a fresh supply when they become skeletonized.

The water in the aquarium should remain clear and be colored only slightly. Odors, cloudy conditions of water, and usually the crawling of the snails out of the water are warning signs which indicate that something is wrong with the habitat. Cloudy conditions due to protozoans are usually not serious; it is well in such cases, however, to reduce the amount of green food for several days and to introduce a culture of Cyclops into the aquarium. Cyclops are very desirable to have in any aquarium intended primarily for snails, since they tend to keep down excessive development of protozoans. Cloudy conditions of the water due to causes other than those already mentioned should be watched carefully; it is usually desirable to dispose of such abnormal appearing aquaria although before so doing air may be introduced and allowed to bubble through the water in an attempt to remedy the situation. Instead of cleaning such an aquarium and immediately using it again, it is better to transfer the snails to a new container. Before introducing the snails into the new habitat they should be rinsed and the shells wiped with a dry cloth; it may be necessary to repeat this procedure daily for 3 or 4 successive days in order to restore normal conditions. If an abnormal condition cannot be corrected in this way it is possible that the number of snails is too great for the size of the container.

Most snails, apparently, thrive best in shallow water, not over 4 inches deep, although of the ones mentioned above *Lymnaea palustris* and *Stagnicola coperata* prefer 7 or 8 inches of water; for snails requiring the greater depth of water battery jars may be used for small aquaria. Some snails, such as *Fossaria modicella, Helisoma antrosa,* and *Physa sp.*, prefer decaying to fresh lettuce. In the case of the first two species the excess need not be removed but the amount given at each additional feeding is reduced to a minimum, the pieces of fresh lettuce being reduced to the size of a pea; these pieces should soften and decay after they are in the aquarium. The vascular parts of the lettuce are the most satisfactory for this purpose; these pieces normally do not become covered with long filaments of mold and any which become moldy should be removed. Should a snail refuse dead leaves and if no decaying lettuce is available, the leafy part of fresh lettuce may be cut into narrow strips with a pair of scissors, thus insuring softening of the tissue sufficiently to afford a satisfactory food; under such conditions the snails will usually eat the lettuce at once.

When an aquarium is stocked with newly hatched snails, usually a millimeter or less in diameter, it is not necessary to start them in small aquaria in order to prevent losses. The aquarium should be prepared 24 hours prior to the introduction of the snails and food, except for the dead leaves which are introduced at the time the aquarium is set up. The lettuce, of which a very small amount is necessary, should be cut into narrow strips with scissors. When the snails are introduced it is necessary to see that they fall on the dead leaves which give them an immediate food supply. The aquarium should not be disturbed subsequently for at least 48 hours.

The food habits of snails of the same species may vary in different aquaria; this is especially noticeable in the case of *Fossaria modicella* and *F. m. rustica*. Some snails seem to be influenced by the seasons in the amount and kind of food they prefer.

Aquaria should never be kept in sunlight but in subdued light.

REARING TERRESTRIAL SNAILS

WENDELL KRULL, *U. S. Bureau of Animal Industry*

A RECTANGULAR terrarium about 18″ x 9″ x 10″ is ideal in size. Cover the bottom with an inch of gravel and then add soil to a depth of 2 inches at one end to 5 or 6 inches at the other, making a sloping contour. Cover the surface of the deeper half with several layers of dry leaves; a few small dry sticks covered with bark are desirable in a terrarium of this size or larger. Allow the terrarium to dry out thoroughly and let it stand several weeks before using. When it is ready for use cover the gravel with water, pouring it into the terrarium at one corner; a small amount of water should be kept in the gravel at at all times. The terrarium is ready for use when the soil has become moist, it should be covered with a glass plate leaving air spaces on all sides. The soil should remain moist in the aquarium subsequent to the introduction of the snails, and the leaves, except the lower layer, should remain dry; if this condition prevails molds will be reduced to a minimum. Twenty-five *Polygyra thyroides*, for example, may be kept in such a habitat unless it is used for breeding purposes, in which case it should be occupied by no more than four of these snails. The young snails should be removed to another terrarium as they make their appearance.

The snails should be fed on a mixture of dry rolled oats and calcium carbonate, the amount of the latter being all that will stick to the oats. Place the dry food on a piece of clean, dry glass at the deeper end of the terrarium. Feed the snails at least every third day and allow no excess food to accumulate. An occasional feeding of lettuce will do no harm.

A habitat such as that described above is good for more than a year and requires very little attention. The principle in the above example may be applied to terraria of any size; a single *Polygyra thyroides* will do very well in a finger bowl terrarium. Finger bowls and evaporating dishes make very good terraria for small forms such as *Zonitoides arborea*. Clean sand in this case may be substituted for the soil and gravel, and only enough water is added to moisten it. Avoid saturation. Water should not accumulate on the under side of the cover except at times when the terrarium is subjected to sudden changes of temperature. Such accumulations of water in terraria containing small snails imprison and suffocate many of those which try to walk through the drops of water. Terraria should not be kept in direct sunlight.

VIVARIUM METHODS FOR THE LAND MOLLUSCA OF NORTH AMERICA

A. F. ARCHER, *University of Michigan*

UNDER natural conditions food, shelter, and the chemical condition of the soil are very important. In laboratory cultures shelter is not so important as in nature, since it is obvious that laboratory snails will not be exposed to the same degrees of wetting and drying as those in the field. For short experiments a glass aquarium with no soil may be used. It is only necessary to provide sufficient food and moisture to keep the snails active.

The regular vivarium consists of a fairly large aquarium such as is available to those who customarily have cultures of fish and other aquatic forms. The top of the aquarium should be covered with a wire screen, since the larger species are very likely to crawl out. The bottom of the cage should be covered with a layer of soil about an inch thick. This soil should be taken from a woodland if the snails in the culture are woodland snails, or sod if they are of a type that inhabits open country. Many species are tolerant of either type of environment. Since some woodland species need only a sufficient amount of shade, a grassy substratum is satisfactory in the laboratory where shade and protection from drying are present. As a rule, however, it is best to reproduce the ecological conditions under which the snails originally lived. The soil should be kept alkaline with a sufficient amount of lime; otherwise the culture will be a failure. Fragments of dead shells may be provided for the purpose. The soil should be covered with fresh leaf mold from the woods; if sod is used, it is necessary to keep it in good condition. Two types of shelter should be furnished in addition to what the substratum affords. A few stones, preferably calcareous in composition, should be laid on the bottom of the vivarium. Since many species also seek shelter under rotten logs, a few pieces of rotten wood should be put in the cage. Moss is a very useful addition to the surface of the substratum, for it holds moisture, furnishes shelter to small species or young snails, and is a good place for the laying of eggs.

Another type of vivarium that gives good results is a flower pot in which a few ferns are planted. This arrangement is excellent for some forest-inhabiting species. It is of course necessary to build up a wall of screening on the sides of the pot to keep the snails from escaping. In this case no roofing is desirable or necessary, since the snails will not crawl up and over the rough surface of the screening. This type of cage possesses the disadvantage of furnishing only a small area in which the snails may move about, but it has the advantage that the soil has a chance to drain and therefore need not be changed for a long time. Eventually, of course, the soil will become leached and the culture is likely to die for that reason.

The food question is surprisingly simple. Fresh leaf mold furnishes the ordinary food for the forest snails. This diet may be supplemented by lettuce or bran. If the leaves of the tree-of-heaven (*Ailanthus glandulosa*) are available, they will furnish excellent food, for most snails seem to be inordinately fond of them. Burdock leaves are also very acceptable.

Moisture must be supplied, for the rooms of most buildings have a very low humidity. Water should be sprinkled lightly over the soil to wet the surface. This may be done daily if necessary. It is easy to decide by inspection whether the culture is getting too dry. It is highly important not to soak the soil. Snails from the drier areas of North America should be kept in cultures that are very seldom wet, for they die in cultures that are sufficiently wet to keep our eastern forms active. It is well to discontinue frequent wetting at times during the inactive period in order to let the snails "dig in" for a few days at a time.

It is well to test the pH of the soil after it has been in use for several months. Undrained soils in time become too acid for the continued well-being of the laboratory animals. The soil should be completely changed when it is found to be too acid. It is especially important to change the soil in the early spring before the breeding season starts. If it is done too late, clutches of eggs that have been laid in the soil will be destroyed.

While some daylight should be allowed to reach the vivarium, the rays of the sun should never strike it directly. They will heat the glass so that conditions will be suffocatingly hot and soon fatal.

CULTURE METHODS FOR LIMAX FLAVUS

EMMETT B. CARMICHAEL, *University of Alabama School of Medicine*

THIS European slug, naturalized in certain sections of this country, does not seem to be prolific enough in Alabama to become a pest in gardens, but it is always found near homes where there is access to gardens or to garbage. Being a nocturnal animal, it spends the day under shelter and comes out to feed at night. When in the field, it seems to prefer to be under rotten wood but it has been found under piles of old bricks or stones. In any case, it selects a damp, cool place that will give it protection from the rays of the sun.

Adult animals, 2 to 3 inches long, are collected in September or October and kept in quart earthenware jars on wet leaf mold. A piece of glass is used to cover the jar, which is then kept in the dark. The wet leaf mold not only keeps the slugs from being desiccated but it serves as a source of water for them. One jar furnishes ample space for a dozen adult slugs. The animals should be transferred by means of a spatula to clean jars about every two weeks, but if molds and fungi are growing on the food they should be put into clean quarters oftener.

In order to avoid contaminating the fresh quarters, it is well to transfer the slugs from the dirty jar to a wet piece of paper (wrapping- or newspaper), and allow them to move about for a few minutes before placing them in the clean jar. For observations upon individual animals, a petri dish, which contains a wet piece of filter paper, provides very satisfactory quarters.

The following foods were fed to the slugs: wheat bread (whole wheat, biscuit, *etc.*), raw Irish potatoes, raw sweet potatoes, lettuce, cauliflower, cabbage, celery, turnips, and milk. On three occasions, while collecting slugs, they were found under or near garbage cans that had holes in them or poorly fitted lids. In all three cases the slugs had access to the table scraps in the cans and they all seemed to be well fed.

In Alabama slugs usually begin to lay their eggs during the last of

September or the first of October, and the laying season lasts about six months. The number of eggs at a single laying varies widely, being from 3 to 48 in this laboratory. The usual number in a batch, however, is about two dozen. The number depends upon the size of the slug, the season, and the care that the animal has had. If they are allowed to lay their eggs in the stock jars, they often make a depression in the leaf mold and deposit the eggs in it.

The eggs are fastened together by a membrane and thus all in a batch are laid at once. The slugs do not move about while laying; hence the eggs become superimposed and are able to retain their moisture for a longer period than a single egg. The moist leaf mold serves to keep the eggs from being desiccated but some eggs have hatched after losing from 80% to 85% of their weight; or 70% to 75% in the case of eggs containing full-term embryos.

The eggs are elliptical in shape, the average diameter being about 0.5 cm. and the average length being about 0.75 cm. The weight of the individual eggs in a batch is fairly constant, but eggs from different batches have varied from 39 to 95 mg. each. They are covered with a rather tough membrane which permits them to be handled with considerable ease when they are being removed from the leaf mold.

For washing a batch of eggs it has been found convenient to put them in some water in a small beaker or petri dish for a few minutes and then remove them by means of a spatula to a dry piece of filter paper. Any mucous or dirt from the stock jar is easily removed by this process.

The time required for hatching at room temperature was found to vary from 19 to 27 days but a majority of the fertilized batches began to hatch by the 23rd day. Most of the batches were fertile in the fall but the fertility decreased within a few weeks, being much reduced by January and it was often quite low by the last of February. Occasionally a whole batch did not contain a single fertilized egg. Since the eggs are transparent it is possible at an early stage to observe the number of embryos that are developing. It is also possible to study the rate of growth. Several eggs were noted to contain twins, and these usually hatched. In the latter part of the laying season single eggs sometimes contained as many as nine embryos. They did not live long enough to hatch when an egg contained three or more.

After the embryos hatched they were placed, by means of a spatula, upon moist filter paper in a clean petri dish. Deeply pigmented embryos are especially sensitive to ultra-violet rays. For this reason and because the slugs are nocturnal animals, it is best to keep the eggs and young in a dark place.

The young slugs are fed upon white bread, raw potatoes, and lettuce for a few days and then any of the above foods may be given. If the food becomes moldy, the young slugs should be transferred to another petri dish and given fresh food.

BIBLIOGRAPHY

CARMICHAEL, E. B. 1928. Action of ultra-violet rays on *Limax flavus* Linnaeus. *Amer. J. Physiol.* 85:358.

——— 1931. The action of ultra-violet radiation on *Limax flavus* Linnaeus. I. The varying effects on non-pigmented and pigmented embryos. *Physiol. Zool.* 4:575.

CARMICHAEL, E. B., and RIVERS, T. D. 1932. The effects of dehydration upon the hatchability of *Limax flavus* eggs. *Ecol.* 13:375.

REFERENCES

Order Opisthobranchiata
For the rearing of *Tethys californicus* see p. 197.

Order PROSOBRANCHIATA

THE GENUS CREPIDULA

E. G. CONKLIN, *Princeton University*

CREPIDULA is a genus of prosobranchiate gastropods which is represented on the Atlantic coast of the United States by the species, *C. plana, C. convexa,* and *C. fornicata,* and on the Pacific coast by *C. adunca* and *C. navacelloides.* All of these species are relatively abundant and all furnish unusually favorable material for embryological research. They are all sessile or sedentary when adult and are usually found attached to shells inhabited by hermit crabs. *C. plana* is usually found on the inside of such shells, *C. convexa* and *C. fornicata* on the outside, although the latter is sometimes found on Limulus and also in chains, one on top of another, the first one frequently being attached to a stone. The shells of adult specimens take the form of the surface to which they are attached and on small surfaces or inside the shells occupied by the small hermit crab, *Eupagurus longicarpus,* the Crepidulas are dwarfed so that sexually mature individuals are sometimes only $\frac{1}{25}$ the volume of others whose growth is not so limited. Males are smaller than females and in *C. plana* and *C. convexa* they are motile; later as they grow larger they become sedentary and transform into females.

Eggs are laid in thin transparent capsules which are attached to the substrate within the mantle cavity of the female. The average number of eggs laid by each species is approximately inversely proportional to the size of the eggs and to the length of larval life, and directly proportional to the size of the female, as is shown by the following table:

Species	No. of Eggs	Diam. of Egg	Relative vol. of Female
C. plana...	9000	136″	13 1/3
C. fornicata.............	13200	182″	30
C. convexa...............	220	280″	1 ¼
C. adunca...............	180	410″	4 1/6

In both *C. convexa* and *C. adunca* there is no free larval life, the young issuing from the capsules in adult form.

The eggs are fertilized when laid, and it is generally impracticable to obtain them unfertilized for purposes of artificial fertilization or parthenogenesis. The best way of getting very early stages is to remove mature females from their substrate and to place those which have not laid in glass dishes in running seawater. After a few hours, preferably in the early morning, the water may be poured off and the under surface of the female examined through the glass. In this way one may find females in the process of laying and may obtain the earliest stages, or may fill the dish with water and may then take the eggs at any later stage desired.

Since the capsules are thin and transparent the eggs may be studied under the microscope or may be subjected to experiment while still in the capsules. For serial sections they may be fixed, stained, and sectioned while still in the capsules, but since the eggs contain a good deal of yolk and are relatively opaque, it is necessary in order to study in whole eggs the details of fertilization, cell division, *etc.*, to tease them out of the capsules with needles, and then to fix, stain, and mount them for microscopical study.

CULTURE METHODS FOR UROSALPINX CINEREA

H. Federighi, *Antioch College*

RANGE AND OCCURRENCE

THE common oyster drill, *Urosalpinx cinerea,* inhabits the marine and brackish water of the Atlantic coast from Maine to Florida. It has been collected in San Francisco Bay, in Bermuda, on the Gulf coast, and recently has been reported from England (Federighi, 1931a).

It occurs at depths ranging from between the tide levels to a maximum of approximately 25 feet. Soft mud and hard sands are not favorable for its growth and multiplication.

FEEDING HABITS

Although *U. cinerea* has been called the oyster drill because it is known to eat oysters in preference to other animals, the author has observed it feeding on clams, mussels, Crepidula, small crabs, barnacles, and even on its own kind, while other investigators report the drill as perforating scallops and chitons (Federighi, 1931a). Contrary to Colton's (1910) results with Sycotypus and Fulgur, the drill will feed on the meats of oysters, clams, fishes, crabs, *etc.**

COLLECTING

These gastropods are easily collected upon oyster and clam beds and from wharf-piles and large boulders. Several methods may be used. The following are some of the easier ways:

The trap dredge. This dredge (Fig. 83) consists of a wire cage open in front and fitted with an inclined screen. The dredge is dragged over the infested oyster bed; the oysters are picked up by the blade at the edge of the dredge, moved up over the inclined plane, and the drills automatically screened, falling into the cage below while the oysters pass over and fall back onto the oyster bed. In this way the dredge may be dragged over great areas, without involving the removal of the oysters from the bottom. The most effective time for dredging is after early spring when the animals have become active and are on the upper layers of the oyster (Federighi, 1931a).

The use of small concrete pillars. Small concrete pillars (Fig. 84), easily handled by one man, may be set out over the bottoms. These pillars, providing surfaces higher than the surrounding area of the oyster beds, act as traps because the animals congregate upon them owing to their tendency to creep upwards (Federighi, 1931a). After 3 or 4 days they are taken up, the drills removed, the pillars set out again in new places. If the area is below low water mark, lines and buoys may be attached to the concrete blocks, thus facilitating removal and replacement.

Wire Bag Trap. This consists of a wire mesh sac baited with young oysters which is lowered over the oyster bed (Nelson, 1931). These may be handled in much the same ways as the concrete pillars.

REQUIREMENTS FOR MAINTENANCE IN THE LABORATORY

Since *Urosalpinx cinera* is a marine form, it requires a laboratory with running seawater. A 10-gallon tank is sufficiently large for as many as 300 oyster drills, if kept clean of debris. The animals may be fed on any of the various bivalves but for the best results young live oysters should be used, and after these have been killed they should be removed from the tank before putrefaction begins. This, during the summer, is a very serious problem.

---

* Editor's Note: Recent investigations by the U. S. Bureau of Fisheries show that drills can be successfully fed on Carnacles and small mussels. P. S. G.

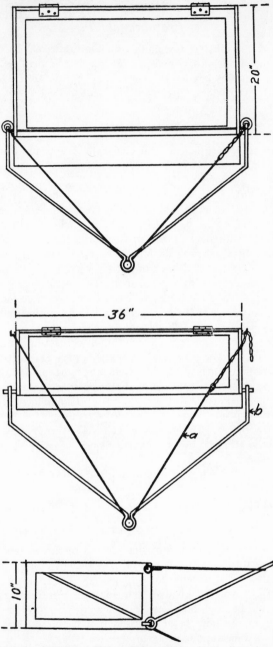

Fig. 83—Modified drill-trap dredge. Approximate dimensions are: Length, 36 inches; width, 20 inches; height, 10 inches. Sides and back to be covered with fine hardware cloth so as to prevent the escape of the trapped drills. The lid to be covered with wire screen small enough to prevent oysters from falling into trap but large enough to allow the drills to pass through easily.

BREEDING HABITS

In *Urosalpinx cinerea* as in other prosobranchs the sexes are separate, the males being distinguished by a large curved penis which lies at the right side of the head behind the eyes. The two sexes may also be separated by microscopic examination of the gonads, the male glands being whitish in appearance; those of the female yellow to orange in color. The eggs are laid in small, yellow, membranous, vaselike capsules attached to the substratum by a solid expanded foot (Fig. 85). The egg case is flattened vertically with edges marked by keel-like ridges and has, at the top, a small cap through which the fully grown larvae escape. Within the capsule is a soft jelly-like fluid in which the eggs are imbedded and which serves not only to protect them from mechanical injury but also as a source of food. Spawning begins in the early spring, the first egg cases are found after the water temperature has reached approximately 20° C. for at least one week (Federighi, 1931a; Nelson, 1931). Spawning continues throughout the summer, and during the fall gradually decreases in intensity.

The female creeps up to the higher levels to spawn. In almost all cases if oysters are present in the tank the female will climb on them to deposit the capsules in preference to the sides of the tank. While spawning the female does

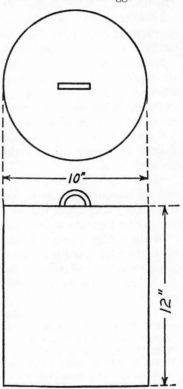

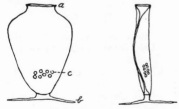

FIG. 85.—Enlarged egg case of *Urosalpinx cinerea* showing eggs within. Front and side views are given. a, Cap through which young escape; b, solid expanded foot by which capsule is attached to substratum; c, egg.

FIG. 84.—Small, concrete pillar for the trapping of oyster drills. A hook imbedded at the top facilitates handling when the pillars are to be planted below the low water mark. To the hook can be attached a line and buoy, making the trap easy to find.

not feed but remains attached to the substratum and, unless disturbed, continues until spawning is completed. Observations in the laboratory show that each snail spawns only once during the summer.

Although oviposition lasts for various lengths of time, depending on whether the animal is disturbed, the average time is approximately seven days. The rate of oviposition averages 3.9 egg cases per female per 24 hours. According to observations made at Chesapeake Bay, the average number of egg cases per female is 28; Nelson (1931) reports for Delaware Bay an average of 50 egg cases per female.

Examination of 727 capsules collected during the summer of 1927 at Hampton Roads, Virginia, gave an average of 8.8 eggs per egg case. The smallest number of eggs per capsule was 3; the largest, 22.

In order to determine the incubation period of the drill, freshly laid egg capsules were isolated and the time of hatching noted. The average incubation period obtained is approximately 40 days.

Since the period of oviposition varies greatly the period of hatching is also varied, and one finds in a single group of egg cases embryos in different stages of development. This fact undoubtedly explains the variations in the incubation period since it is impossible to tell the exact age of the embryos within the capsule at the time they are isolated.

Studies on the effect of salinity on the spawning of this species showed (Federighi, 1931a) that reproduction takes place wherever the adult lives.

At the time of hatching the larvae are approximately 1 mm. in length and are immediately able to feed themselves. These young drills will attack the young oyster spat or the thin shelled Crepidula. Before the next winter they are approximately 1 cm. long.

In the colder climates (north of and including Chesapeake Bay) where the water reaches a temperature of less than 7°-10° C. the drills become inactive and cease feeding at these temperatures. In the spring the animals again begin feeding and reach adult size the following summer.

BIBLIOGRAPHY

BROOKS, W. K. 1879. Preliminary observations upon the development of the marine prosobranchiate gastropods. *Stud. Biol. Lab., Johns Hopkins University,* 1877-78 (1879), 16 pp. Baltimore.

COLTON, HAROLD SELLERS. 1908. How Fulgur and Sycotypus eat oysters, mussels, and clams. *Proc. Acad. Nat. Sci. Phila.* 60:3.

FEDERIGHI, H. 1930. Salinity and size of *Urosalpinx cinerea* Say. *Amer. Nat.* 64:183.

—— 1931a. Studies on the oyster drill (*Urosalpinx cinerea,* Say). *Bull. U. S. Bur. Fish.* 57: 85.

—— 1931b. Further observations on the size of *Urosalpinx cinerea* Say. *J. Conchol.* 19:171.

NELSON, J. R. 1931. Trapping the oyster drill. *N. J. Agric. Exper. Sta. Bull.* 523.

Class *Pelecypoda*, Order PRIONODESMACEA

SPAWNING AND FERTILIZATION OF THE OYSTER, OSTREA VIRGINICA

PAUL S. GALTSOFF, *U. S. Bureau of Fisheries*

THE spawning season of the oyster in the North Atlantic States begins during the second half of June and ends by the 15th of August. Delayed spawning of the oysters in deep water (30-40 feet) sometimes occurs in Long Island Sound late in September. In the Middle Atlantic and South Atlantic States, and in the Gulf of Mexico the season begins earlier and extends over a longer period of time. In Texas and Louisiana, for instance, ripe oysters may be found from March until October (Hopkins, 1931).

The sexes of the oyster are separate but secondary sexual characters are wanting. The identification of sexes may easily be made by drilling* a small hole in the anterior half of the shell or by cutting a shell with a hacksaw, pinching off a small piece of gonad and examining the tissue under the microscope. This operation seems to have no ill effect on the organism.

In both males and females the well developed gonads completely embrace the visceral mass, surrounding it with a thick creamy layer. A ripe adult female may produce several hundred million eggs all of which are discharged during one spawning season (Galtsoff, 1930a). The branching genital ducts, well developed in ripe specimens, are easily noticeable on the surface of the gonad. The openings of the gonad, one on each side, may be seen by making an incision through the wall of the cloaca and exposing the posterior end of the gonad. By exerting slight pressure a small amount of sperm or eggs may be forced through it.

Spawning never takes place at temperatures below 20.5° C. and is controlled by a number of factors among which the mutual stimulation of sexes by eggs or sperm plays an important rôle (Galtsoff, 1930). Males are more responsive than females to stimulation by rise in temperature and almost always initiate spawning. Sperm discharged into water causes ovulation in the females and the presence of eggs in turn stimulates other males. The process once started spreads over the entire oyster bed. In order to prolong the use of the material for experimental purposes in the laboratory, the sexes should be separated early in the summer and males and females kept apart in different tanks.

The spawning reaction of the females is specific in the sense that it may be provoked only by the sperm of the genus Ostrea. The males are, however, entirely non-specific. Shedding of sperm may be stim-

* For drilling the shell the use of an electric "Handee Grinder" (Chicago Wheel & Manufacturing Company) is recommended.

ulated by the eggs of various mollusks (Venus, Mya, Mytilus), thyroidin, theelin, extract of thymus, various sugars, starch and other organic compounds (Galtsoff, 1935).

Naturally fertilized eggs may be obtained by the following method. Ripe females should be kept out of water for several hours or overnight, then placed in a glass tank, 15-20 liter capacity, in water of about 25°-27° C. As soon as the oyster opens the shell, which occurs almost immediately provided the organism was conditioned by being kept out of water, about 1 cc. of sperm suspension, made of 0.5 gm. of testis in 50 cc. of seawater is injected between the shells. Spawning begins after a latent period varying from 6 to 30 minutes and may last nearly an hour. The female must be removed as soon as a sufficient number of eggs is obtained. Since the eggs are fertilized in the water as they are discharged by the female, various cleavage stages become mixed together.

For embryological and cytological work it is preferable to have all the eggs fertilized simultaneously. A piece of ovary cut from the gonad is gently shaken into a finger bowl or larger jar. For insemination one or two cc. of sperm suspension is added, the water stirred and the jar set aside. All large pieces of tissues should be carefully removed.

Fertilization takes place immediately and the eggs settle to the bottom. Both polar bodies are formed within half an hour after fertilization. The rate of development is dependent on temperature. At 23°-25° C. a free-swimming stage is reached within 4½-5 hours. The larvae rise to the surface, forming easily noticeable vertical streaks in the water. They should be collected by means of a wide-mouthed pipette, transferred into fresh seawater and left undisturbed until the next day. A method of rearing them to metamorphosis is described in the following article by H. F. Prytherch.

The spawning reaction of the Japanese oyster, *O. gigas*, is similar to that of *O. virginica* with the exception that under laboratory conditions higher temperature is required. In the experiments carried out by the author at Woods Hole, the females of this species were stimulated to spawn by the sperm of either species and by raising the temperature of the water to 30° C.

Cross fertilization between the two species occurs very readily (Galtsoff and Smith, 1932). (See Editor's Note on p. 546.)

BIBLIOGRAPHY

BROOKS, W. K. 1880. Development of the American oyster. *Studies from Johns Hopkins Univ. Biol. Lab.* 4:1.

GALTSOFF, P. S. 1930. The rôle of chemical stimulation in the spawning reactions of *Ostrea virginica* and *Ostrea gigas. Proc. Nat. Acad. Sci.* 16:555.

—— 1930a. The fecundity of the oyster. *Science* 72:97.

—— 1932. Spawning reactions of the three species of oysters. *J. Wash. Acad. Sci.* 22:65.

———— 1935. Physiology of ovulation and ejaculation in the oyster. *Collecting Net* 10:261.

GALTSOFF, P. S. and SMITH, R. O. 1932. Stimulation of spawning and cross fertilization between American and Japanese oysters. *Science* 76:371.

HOPKINS, A. E. 1931. Factors influencing the spawning and setting of oysters in Galveston Bay, Texas. *Bull. U. S. Bur. Fish.* 47: 57.

THE CULTIVATION OF LAMELLIBRANCH LARVAE

HERBERT F. PRYTHERCH, *U. S. Bureau of Fisheries*

LARVAL stages of many common lamellibranchs (Ostrea, Mya, Pecten, Mytilus, Venus, Teredo, *etc.*) may be obtained from plankton collections made in inshore coastal waters during the spring, summer, and fall months. Plankton samples may be collected with a tow net or by means of a hand or power driven pump from which the seawater is passed through a net of No. 10 or No. 14 bolting silk for retention of only the larger and nearly full grown larvae or through No. 20 for all stages. The larvae are usually more abundant in surface samples collected at low slack water in proximity to the spawning beds of the desired species.

The separation of bivalve larvae from other marine forms is greatly simplified by washing the plankton sample from the net into a fish hatching jar or any tall, straight-sided glass container with funnel-shaped bottom, into the center of which the heavier, shelled forms soon collect. These are siphoned off with a glass tube, placed in Syracuse glasses, and forms other than those desired removed under the binocular by means of a fine pipette. The larvae are then placed in small piles with dissecting needles, segregated as to size and species, and may be transferred easily to other aquaria by employing a dilution pipette with 10-inch rubber tubing and mouthpiece. For identification of several representative species see Stafford (1909).

The maintenance and rearing of cultures may best be carried out in cylindrical glass vessels having a hemispherical or funnel-shaped bottom. Ordinary glass bottles, 1 to 5 gallon capacity, may be used in an inverted position provided a tube is inserted in the stopper so that air may be withdrawn from above the surface of the water. At the lowest point in the jar or bottle a very small stream of air is introduced continually, preferably through porous plugs of wood or "filtros," in order to aerate and circulate the water and stimulate the swimming (feeding) activities of the larvae. The cultures should contain not more than 200 to 500 larvae per liter as the seawater is renewed only once or twice daily and must be of sufficient quantity to provide an adequate food supply. The larvae feed on microplankton and minute particles of detritus and suspended matter, an ample supply of which may be obtained from seawater that has been passed through coarse filter paper or heavy felt. Filtration of water supply is always advisable to eliminate the larger competing or predatory forms. Oyster larvae have been successfully reared in centrifuged seawater by Wells (1926) though their development in this medium required about twice the normal time.

The chief difficulty in rearing the microscopic, free-swimming larvae of lamellibranchs is to prevent their escape in renewing the water supply. Countless millions of embryos of the previously mentioned species, and early, straight-hinge veligers (1 to 4 days old) may be obtained by artificially fertilizing the ripe eggs in jars of slowly running seawater from which the more healthy and vigorous swimmers are carried over and concentrated in large funnels containing coarse filter paper. Collections are taken from the filters for a period of 4 to 6 hours and transferred to aerated aquaria with an ample volume of water. If the embryos are not overcrowded and obtain sufficient oxygen they will develop into larvae with complete bivalve shells in 20 to 30 hours. After reaching this stage they should have a complete change of water at least every 24 hours and may be concentrated by the use of paper filters, high speed centrifuge, or No. 25 bolting silk, provided the flow of water through the latter is very gradual. The more vigorous individuals may be selected by the same procedure as that used previously following fertilization. In renewal of water, particularly in early operations, it is always advisable to discard the small amount remaining in the bottom of the aquaria in order to eliminate waste products, sediment and any weak or dead larvae. As the larvae increase in size a slow but continuous exchange of water may be maintained by filtering through No. 25 to 20 bolting silk placed over the mouth of a large glass funnel. The most critical period in development is after the larvae have completely utilized the yolk supply from the egg and begin to take in microscopic food from the water. If suitable conditions are maintained as to oxygen, water exchange, *etc.*, during this interval a fair percentage of the larvae will survive and may be reared through the succeeding stages without much difficulty.

It is a comparatively simple matter to maintain cultures of larvae that are half to full grown (approximate diameter 0.2 to 0.5 mm.) as they may easily be concentrated or retained by No. 18 to 14 bolting silk or by monel metal wire cloth or sieves of 200 to 80 mesh. Any toxic effects of the metal cloth may be prevented by a thin coating of celluloid though the author has successfully used the uncoated material after it has been "seasoned" in seawater for a few days. The essential requirements for the advanced stages are a continuous or twice daily exchange of filtered water and gradual circulation by air or a slow stirring device. The procedure outlined previously is essentially the same as that used by Prytherch (1924) and Wells (1926) in the culture of oyster larvae and related species and is applicable to virtually all free-swimming, shelled molluscan forms.

In determining the most favorable culture medium for the larvae of any particular species of lamellibranchs, consideration should be given to the natural environmental conditions under which its prolific reproduction occurs. The species mentioned thrive in inshore coastal waters where certain factors such as salinity, temperature, pH, oxygen content, *etc.*, have been found, within a certain range, to be favorable for their development. It is recommended that the seawater used for culture of these larvae conform to the following conditions,—salinity 10 to 28 per mille (1% to 2.8% salt), temperature 20° to 30° C., pH 7.8 to 8.2, oxygen 80% to 100% saturation. If the water supply is obtained from a suitable location and renewed frequently little attention need be paid to variations in these factors within the range indicated. Though the water may be pumped at any stage of tide, that obtained during the low water period has been found to be more suitable for larval growth and metamorphosis. The equipment used for pumping and storage of seawater should be constructed preferably from rubber, glass, or wood, though cast iron and lead lined material is fairly satisfactory when used with large volumes of water. Bronze or other copper alloys should be avoided.

For detailed studies of the larger and full grown larvae they may be immobilized on a glass slide by the method recently devised by the author, which is as follows: The larvae are removed from solution with a fine pipette, placed to one side of the slide and all excess water drained away with a small camel's hair brush. A drop of marine glue is placed in the center of the slide and allowed to evaporate for a minute or so until a thin sticky film has been formed. The larvae are then picked up with the tip of the brush, gently placed in the glue in the desired position and the slide transferred to seawater about five minutes later, after the glue has set. The larvae may be immobilized by either valve and should be placed with the hinge line parallel to the surface of the slide so as not to interfere with shell movements and normal functioning of the velum. This method has greatly facilitated studies of the anatomy, behavior, and reactions of oyster larvae and may be used equally well with related forms. Larvae of Mytilus, Mya, Teredo, and Ostrea that were immobilized in this manner appeared to grow and develop normally and were protected from possible injury by placing the slides in shallow, rectangular staining dishes.

The final procedure in rearing larvae is to carry them through the setting or spatting period during which they either settle to the bottom or attach to submerged objects and then undergo a rapid metamorphosis that is followed by gradual modifications in morphology to that of the adult. In the case of the oyster this developmental change is initiated by an infinitesimal amount of copper (Prytherch, 1934) and may easily be induced by placing a small piece of metallic copper 0.5 cm. square in a 10 cc. solution of seawater for an interval of 15 to 30 seconds. Other allied species, Mytilus, Mya, and Teredo, react similarly to this metal and it may also be effective for stimulating setting of other marine members of this class. Since under natural conditions many of these species are concentrated at low water tidal levels it is probable that they may be induced to set in aquaria by using water collected at this stage of tide as has been done successfully with Ostrea. River water may also be added to stimulate this reaction provided the quantity used does not reduce the salinity to less than 10 per mille.

Various devices may be employed for collection of spat, such as slides, plates and tubes of glass, porcelain, wood, *etc.*, on which the sedentary species may be grown to the adult stage. Clean shells and cement coated objects are practical for collecting spat stages of Ostrea and Anomia in aquaria or may be used effectively under natural conditions according to the methods described by Prytherch (1930) and Galtsoff, Prytherch, and McMillin (1930). Many of the larvae will attach to the sides and bottom of the aquaria and those having a byssus (Mytilus, Pecten, Mya, and Venus) may be detached from the glass with a thin, sharp blade and transferred to slides or shallow dishes for observation and to facilitate handling until they grow to a convenient size. The post larval stages should be kept in running water that has been strained through bolting silk (No. 14 to 20) or monel metal wire cloth (100 to 200 mesh) until they reach a size of 5 to 10 mm. Rapid growth may be obtained from this point on by rearing them in trays or boxes, covered with galvanized window screen, which are placed out of doors or in large tanks where there is ample exchange and circulation of water.

BIBLIOGRAPHY

GALTSOFF, P. S., PRYTHERCH, H. F., and McMILLIN, H. C. 1930. An experimental study in production and collection of seed oysters. *U. S. Bur. Fish. Doc.* 1088, Bull. 46:197-263.

PRYTHERCH, HERBERT F. 1924. Experiments in the artificial propagation of oysters. *U. S. Bur. Fish. Doc.* 961:4.

———— 1930. Improved methods for the collection of seed oysters. *U. S. Bur. Fish. Doc.* 1076:47-59.

———— 1934. The rôle of copper in the setting, metamorphosis and distribution of the American oyster, *Ostrea virginica. Ecol. Monog.*, Vol. 4, No. 1:47-107.

STAFFORD, J. 1909. On the recognition of bivalve larvae in plankton collections. *Contrib. Canad. Biol. Rept.* 14:221-242.

———— 1913. The Canadian oyster. Its development, environment, and culture. Commission of Conservation, Canada, Ottawa.

WELLS, WILLIAM F. 1926. A new chapter in shellfish culture. *Report, Conservation Commission, State of New York*, 1925 (1926): 93-126.

———— 1927. Report of experimental shellfish station. *Report, Conservation Department, State of New York*, 1926 (1927): 1-26.

Order TELEODESMACEA, Family SEMELIDAE.

CUMINGIA TELLINOIDES

BENJAMIN H. GRAVE, *De Pauw University*

Cumingia tellinoides is a small lamellibranch mollusk found abundantly in the Woods Hole region but in restricted areas only. The breeding season extends from the first or second week in June to about August 20. Eggs in small quantities may be had in September. The time of spawning by Cumingia in its natural habitat is influenced by two environmental factors. This species occurs in shallow water and when it becomes heated by a period of unusually warm days nearly all females spawn. On the other hand, if the environment remains normally uniform, heavy spawning takes place at the period of the full moon and the days immediately following. The lunar periodicity may be obscured if general spawning due to rapidly rising temperature has already occurred. It should be remarked that spawning is rarely 100% at any time, so that eggs from a few females are obtainable almost any day in the summer. However, if records of the percentage number of females spawning are kept at frequent intervals the periodic character of the spawning will be evident.*

Experiments have shown that each female spawns several times during the summer and that the gonads are again filled with eggs within a short time after spawning takes place. Eggs are not again obtainable except in very small amounts for a period of ten days after spawning has occurred. It has been shown that the germinal epithelium is active throughout the breeding season and the production of eggs and spermatozoa is a continuous process.

METHOD OF OBTAINING EGGS IN THE LABORATORY

Wash the animals free from all sediment and isolate them in small stender dishes half filled with seawater. When so placed in seawater and left undisturbed for an hour, or sometimes less, they extend their siphons and spawn if sexually mature. Eggs or sperm, as they accumulate in the supra-branchial chambers, are thrown forcibly from the dorsal siphon. The sexes are separate and may be distinguished by their color. The males are white and the females pink. The shell is not heavy so that the color of the gonads shows through more or less.

Cumingia may not be kept in the laboratory indefinitely. It is de-

*See Abstract No. 11, *Anat. Rec.* 44:198.

sirable to use them the day they are collected, although it is sometimes possible to keep them for a day or two in moist sand. They must be kept away from water if it is desirable to have them retain their eggs or sperm.

CULTURE METHODS

By the procedure just described eggs and sperm are spawned in separate dishes and the eggs may be kept several hours without fertilization. Before insemination it is good practice to change the water on the eggs and then add one or two drops of sperm. Polyspermy occurs if too much sperm is used. The fertilized egg develops into a swimming gastrula in a few hours. In the meantime it is desirable to change the water on the cleaving eggs two or three times to get rid of excess sperm and body fluids. After 12 hours all of the normal embryos, which have now reached the trochophore stage, are swimming near the surface of the water and may be poured into a fresh dish of seawater, leaving behind the debris and eggs which failed to develop. This process should be repeated once more within the next three or four hours and then the embryos may safely be left to develop undisturbed for a day or two without further care.

Under moderate summer temperatures the trochophores begin to show development of the bivalve shell within 18 or 20 hours and within 30 hours they become swimming veligers with bivalve shell covering the entire body. After the embryos (veligers) are two days old they have a tendency to settle to the bottom and lie quiescent. When this occurs they may easily be transferred to fresh dishes of seawater by means of a pipette. This change should be repeated daily as long as it is desired to keep the embryos. They remain veliger larvae, with no evident change in structure except increase in size, for three weeks. In the meantime they must be fed upon diatoms, preferably a pure culture. [See p. 36.] After a period of three or four weeks of successful culturing they lose the velum, metamorphose, and take on the form of the adult. This metamorphosis has been successfully accomplished in the laboratory at Woods Hole by keeping the veligers in a 4-gallon cylindrical aquarium jar in which a stirring device was installed, keeping the water agitated once per minute. The embryos were fed upon a pure culture of diatoms which was isolated at the Plymouth laboratory. It would no doubt be possible to carry them through metamorphosis in small dishes without aerating devices.

BIBLIOGRAPHY

GRAVE, B. H. 1927. The natural history of *Cumingia tellinoides*. *Biol. Bull.* 53:208.

———— 1928. The vitality of the gametes of *Cumingia tellinoides*. *Ibid.* 54:351.
MORGAN, T. H. 1910. A cytological study of centrifuged eggs. *J. Exper. Zool.* 9:593.

Family TEREDINIDAE

REARING TEREDO NAVALIS

BENJAMIN H. GRAVE, *De Pauw University*

THE shipworm, *Teredo navalis,* is abundant at many places on the coast of the United States. Its activities are serious everywhere but it is most destructive in the warmer waters of the south. At Woods Hole its breeding season extends from the first or second week in May to the middle of October. The first larvae of the season metamorphose and begin to burrow into exposed wooden structures about June 20. They become fully mature worms in one year and die before the end of the second summer at an age of 12 to 15 months. The largest specimens collected measure about 16 inches in length and nearly ½ inch in widest diameter. The average size attained, when grown in large timbers, is 12 to 14 inches in length but when grown in small strips of wood they often do not exceed 2½ inches in length at the end of a year's growth.

METHODS OF STUDY

It is difficult to get large numbers of Teredo for study without adopting special methods because they live normally in permanent wooden structures such as the piles of wharves. It is therefore necessary to raise them by putting out suitable timbers one summer to be studied the next. Lobster pots or cages made of lath put out early in August are found to contain sexually mature shipworms by the beginning of the breeding season the following June. For growing Teredo 2 x 4 stakes are excellent, and they may be put out as early as June or July without being completely destroyed within a year by the infesting worms. By adopting this method it is possible to obtain thousands of breeding shipworms with the expenditure of very little effort. They attack the wood at the mud-line and not to any great extent at the surface of the water.

METHODS OF EMBRYOLOGICAL STUDY

The eggs when spawned are retained in the supra-branchial chamber of the gills and during cleavage and early larval stages they will not develop normally outside the gills. In order to secure embryos of all ages it is therefore necessary to remove them from the gills of a large number of worms. It is not difficult to secure a complete series of developmental stages because the shipworm is remarkably prolific.

The embryos are retained in the gills about two weeks and are then expelled into the sea as actively swimming veliger larvae. The free-swimming larvae feed upon diatoms and grow for approximately two weeks longer, then settle upon wooden structures, metamorphose, and burrow into the wood. One month after metamorphosis the young Teredo measures ½ inch in length. In six weeks it measures 1½ inches and becomes sexually mature. The first eggs produced by these young shipworms are spawned about August 20.

It is an easy matter to collect well developed veligers from the parent worm and keep them in healthy condition in aquaria by feeding them diatoms. It is possible to study every phase of the life history of Teredo by these methods, including the rate of growth.*

*For a more complete account of the natural history of *Teredo navalis* see *Biol. Bull.* 55:260 and 65:283.

Editor's Note (see p. 538): According to recent investigation by the U. S. Bureau of Fisheries incubation period in Delaware Bay varies from 18 to 53 days.   P. S. G.

Phylum XVI

ECHINODERMATA, Class *Asteroidea*

Order FORCIPULATA

ASTERIAS FORBESI

HENRY J. FRY, *Cornell University Medical College*

AT THE Marine Biological Laboratory Asterias eggs are in optimum condition from about the middle of May to late June or early July. Thereafter they are obtainable sporadically until the middle of September.

Under natural conditions the eggs are shed at metaphase of the second polar body cycle, a fact which the writer confirmed by the cytological study of naturally shed eggs of three individuals. As Just (1928) has noted, occasionally eggs are shed naturally in the laboratory, and then usually when the moon is full. The usual method of obtaining eggs under laboratory conditions is to remove the ovaries, and the eggs are then shed in the germinal vesicle stage. Upon contact with the seawater they develop as far as the stage at which they are shed naturally, *i.e.*, metaphase of the second polar body cycle; a fact which was also confirmed by the cytological study of the eggs of three individuals. They stay in this stage unless they are fertilized. On the other hand, Professor Chambers has informed the writer that he and others have found that under laboratory conditions maturation goes to completion without fertilization.

Just's statement, "Asterias eggs are the most sensitive that I know," (1928) voices the opinion of all who work with them. This sensitivity is probably due to the abnormal conditions under which eggs are obtained in the laboratory. Just's observations (1928) concerning methods of handling them should be consulted by anyone unfamiliar with this material.

The males and females vary to an equal degree in size and color, and they may not be distinguished externally. Only those with soft skins and bulging arms have ripe gonads (Just, 1928). When obtaining gametes the animal is rinsed in tap water to kill any sperm clinging to it, and then rinsed again in seawater. The tip of one arm is cut off, and an incision made along the aboral surface to the central disc, in order that the plume-like gonads may be examined. Only if these fill a large portion of the arm is the individual usable. A male is distinguished by whitish or pale yellow gonads; those of the female are orange in color. Males are laid aside to be used later. In the case of a female, the other arms are cut as just described. The entire aboral surface of the disc, and of each arm in the region near the disc, is removed, and the sides of the arms are forced apart. Thus the entire animal is exposed aborally, and the plumes are fully visible. Throughout these operations care is used not to harm the ovaries or their gonoducts.

The dissected specimen is rinsed to wash away the body fluid. Just states (1928) that this fluid is deleterious to development, but the writer's experience indicates that small traces do not affect development adversely. Several experiments carried out with the aid of Miss Ann K. Keltch show that maturation, fertilization, and cleavage are not modified unless the concentration of body fluid is over 1%.

The ovaries are transferred to a vessel containing about 1,000 cc. of water. With a forceps each one is picked up at the blunt end, near the gonoduct. Since this is the region which contains the eggs ready to develop, it is important that all of it be removed. The narrow end contains oögonia; for this reason Just (1928) warns against cutting up the ovaries.

During development it is desirable that eggs pass through the various stages simultaneously. Since they stream forth and begin to maturate at once, the plumes should be transferred to the water as nearly at the same time as possible, and removed in a few minutes. If the plumes are allowed to shed their eggs over a long period there is a wide "spread" of mitotic stages in the developing set of eggs.

From some ovaries eggs gush out in large quantities. Those which do not shed so freely should be gently shaken to aid the release of eggs. Just (1928) warns against the harmful effects of overcrowding, but the writer's experience indicates that crowding is harmful only if continued for a relatively long time, and only if the seawater is unchanged.

Since the specific gravity of Asterias eggs is only slightly greater than that of seawater, they settle very slowly. Therefore it is important that they be disturbed as little as possible while they are being shed from the ovaries, because if they are thrown into suspension at that time it is difficult to secure samples of adequate size for experimentation until they have settled. After the plumes are removed, most of the seawater is poured off, leaving the majority of the eggs in a relatively small amount of water. Thus suitable samples are available for immediate experimentation. The usual steps are then taken to aërate the egg culture properly by changes of water. It is to be noted that fertilized eggs settle more rapidly than unfertilized ones.

Most Asterias eggs are not harmed by such physical disturbances as those involved in pouring them from dish to dish or transferring them by a wide-mouthed pipette. Some, however, are exceedingly sensitive to such manipulations between the time they are shed and the breaking down of the germinal vesicle; thereafter they are not affected.

Several cubic centimeters of eggs may be obtained from a fully ripe female. Eggs are about 110μ in diameter, yellow in color, and opaque. Cytological details may be seen only vaguely in living eggs.

The optimum percentage of normal cleavage occurs in eggs fertilized during the first ½-hour period following the formation of the first polar body, which is about the time when eggs are fertilized under natural conditions.

To obtain sperm, remove a plume of a male, rinse it in seawater to wash away body fluid, and place it in a dry vessel. The seminal fluid soon flows out.

The concentration of sperm is an important factor when fertilizing Asterias eggs, since they are unusually sensitive to polyspermy. In theory, the writer mixes one drop of "dry" sperm in 25 cc. of seawater, and uses two drops of this sperm suspension for every 250 cc. of water containing eggs. But since the consistency of dry sperm and the size of the drop differ from one experiment to another, in practice the proper suspension is determined by the eye, according to the degree of cloudiness.

Early in an experiment there are several criteria which indicate that an egg-set will cleave normally: The majority of the eggs are shed in the germinal vesicle stage, and oögonia are relatively few in number; the irregular shape of freshly shed eggs soon gives place to a rounded form; and the germinal vesicle breaks down in practically all cases. If these conditions are not satisfied the set should be discarded. When eggs in good condition are fertilized, most of them form distinct, well lifted membranes.

The temperature of the seawater at Woods Hole during late May and June varies from about 13° to 18° C.; hence much of the work is done at about 15°, unless temperature is controlled. At 15° about 4 hours are required from shedding to first cleavage. Eggs will not develop at 25°, and the lower limit is about 10°.

F. R. Lillie (1919) found that the addition of NaOH to seawater during the summer, when eggs frequently do not fertilize, aids the fertilization reaction. During May and June, however, when eggs are in optimum condition, the use of NaOH is unnecessary.

A discussion of methods of activating Asterias eggs artificially, together with a bibliography of the subject, is presented by Morgan (1927).

BIBLIOGRAPHY

JUST, E. E. 1928. Methods for experimental embryology with special reference to marine invertebrates. *The Collecting Net,* Woods Hole, Mass. Vol. 3.

LILLIE, FRANK R. 1919. Problems of fertilization. *Univ. of Chicago Press.*

MORGAN, THOMAS HUNT. 1927. Experimental embryology. *Columbia Univ. Press.* Chapter 27.

THE LABORATORY CULTURE OF THE LARVAE OF ASTERIAS FORBESI

EVERT J. LARSEN, *U. S. Bureau of Fisheries*

THERE are three accounts in the literature of the successful laboratory culture of starfish larvae through metamorphosis. The first of these is by Delage (1904) who reported the maturation of a parthenogenetically developed larvae of *Asterias glacialis*. Gemmill (1912, 1914) was able to rear *Solaster endeca* and *Asterias rubens*, the former from naturally, the latter from artificially fertilized eggs. Much earlier, Agassiz (1864) described a procedure for artificially fertilizing the eggs of *Asterias forbesi* and *A. vulgaris*. His method of caring for the larvae was insufficient, and from his accounts none of his animals metamorphosed.

Larvae of *A. forbesi* were obtained by artificial fertilization of Asterias eggs from June 5 to September 17, 1935, at the Marine Biological Station of the U. S. Bureau of Fisheries at Milford, Conn. Set was obtained from a batch begun on June 5, and later from a batch started on August 18.

The following directions include the procedures for artificially fertilizing the eggs and rearing the larvae. They differ somewhat from those of previous workers; where these differences occur the reasons for them are stated.

All the seawater used in this work must be filtered, preferably through coarse filter paper because some small forms, such as copepods, feed voraciously upon starfish larvae. It is not necessary to sterilize the glassware or to pass the seawater through a Chamberland filter according to the method used by Gemmill for *Asterias rubens*. It is impossible, and perhaps undesirable, to prevent all bacterial contamination. The water must also be fresh. The presence of adult stars is detrimental in a tank from which water is obtained for culture of larvae, as has been shown by experiments at the Milford Station. Other experiments indicate that a salinity of 27-28 parts per thousand is advantageous in the early larval development. Moreover, the evaporation from the culture jars, which is corrected daily, does not cause a rise in salinity above the normal upper limit for seawater if seawater of an initial salinity of 27-28 parts per thousand is used.

ARTIFICIAL FERTILIZATION

Fill two finger bowls with seawater. Rinse the ovaries from a ripe female in one and place them in the second (3 liter capacity). Some eggs will be lost but the amount of coelomic fluid carried over is greatly reduced. The toxic effect of the body fluids is well known. Let the ovaries stand for about five minutes. This procedure allows a large number of eggs to pass out of them without mechanical pressure. More eggs may easily be gotten out of the gonads by drawing them up into a wide mouthed medicine dropper. Agassiz advocates cutting them into small pieces; Gemmill speaks of shredding. It is very difficult to remove every piece of follicular débris after cutting or shredding, but greater damage is done by the liberation of substances from the mutilated eggs and ovarian tissues which will retard or cause abnormal development. After the gonads are removed, the eggs settle to the bottom of the dish. Decant about $\frac{4}{5}$ of the water and refill with fresh, agitating the eggs slowly in order to wash them. Repeat this procedure three times, as quickly as practicable. Meanwhile examine the eggs microscopically at intervals of ten minutes to observe the beginning of maturation. The time required for maturation varies with the stage of ripeness of the female. In May this will sometimes require two hours. Later, after the normal peak of the spawning season (from the first to the second week in July at Milford, Conn.) sperm should be added to the suspension immediately upon the liberation of the eggs, for maturation is then extremely rapid. Agassiz placed pieces of ovaries and testes in the same dish simultaneously. This adds an unnecessary amount of foreign tissue juices to the egg suspension. Gemmill did not fertilize the eggs of *Asterias rubens* until they had been liberated for two hours, which is often too late. The eggs quickly lose their power of fertilization after the liberation of the second polar body.

Use only very motile sperm to fertilize the eggs. Examine a portion of the sperm from a gonad under the microscope in a little seawater. The whole microscopic field should shimmer. Wash the examined gonad in a small finger bowl full of water and transfer to another. Press the sperm out by means of a pipette, then remove the gonad. Stir the water until a uniform suspension is obtained. Add 10 cc. of this suspension to the bowl of eggs when the germinal vesicle begins to break down and stir gently to mix the suspensions evenly.

The fertilized eggs rapidly settle to the bottom of the dish. Decant and add fresh seawater at intervals of ½ hour for two hours. There should be about seven washings altogether, so that if maturation occurs before the first three have been completed, these should be carried out after fertilization. If the eggs are very numerous separate them into two groups in 3-liter bowls. Allow only one layer of well spaced eggs on the bottom of the dish.

REARING THE LARVAE

Free swimming blastulae rise to the surface in about 20 hours. Decant these from each finger bowl into a suitable container of about 20 liters' capacity nearly filled with seawater. Be careful not to carry over unfertilized eggs or dead embryos. On the following day it is advisable to siphon half the contents of each jar into an empty one and to fill all four with seawater.

The meniscus in each jar must be carefully marked and the daily loss of water through evaporation corrected by the addition of distilled water. Stir the water gently and add the distilled water very slowly to prevent large local dilutions. In this manner a relatively stationary salinity may be maintained. This obviates the necessity for a circulation of fresh seawater through the jars. Animals have been reared in this manner without any further change of water. It is important not to have too large a number of larvae in a culture.

Aerate the cultures slowly. A glass tube with the lower end drawn out to a fine opening (0.1 mm.) is allowed to rest obliquely against the bottom of the culture jar. Clean compressed air is supplied to the glass tube so that a fine stream of very small bubbles rises through the culture medium. Rapid aeration produces swift currents which cause disintegration of larvae. Under no circumstances should rubber tubing touch the seawater. The aeration is of course more efficient if air is used to set up the circulation.

The larvae require food when the stomodaeum breaks through (second or third day). Mixed cultures of phytoplankton containing Chlorella, Nitzschia, Dunaliella [see p. 31], and phytomonads are satisfactory. The well being of the larvae is to a large measure due to the variety of food. Gemmill used Nitzschia alone at first but discovered that "Nitzschia plus a chance bacterial and flagellate infection provided even better results." Dr. P. S. Galtsoff has used a pure culture of Nitzschia [see p. 36] in raising *A. forbesi* larvae. They became large brachiolaria but never metamorphosed.

Adjust the salinity of the food culture to that of the seawater in the jars and add 5 cc. of this to each jar, three times a day. Withdraw a corresponding amount of liquid from the vessels once a day to retain the mark used in correcting the salinity.

Although the critical temperature for spawning of *A. forbesi* in Long Island Sound is 20°±0.5° C., the larvae can develop at a lower range.

When the daily temperature average is about 20° C., the larvae reach their full development in 21 days. Keep the culture jars at temperatures somewhat below 20° for best results (17°-20° C.). Higher temperatures increase the growth rate of bacteria markedly.

Direct sunlight and strong daylight are injurious to the larvae. The number of animals decreases rapidly in a culture exposed to bright light as compared to a shielded one. It is sufficient to keep the culture vessels in a dark corner of the laboratory or to place them in uncovered wooden boxes painted a dull color on the inside.

BIBLIOGRAPHY

AGASSIZ, L. 1877. North American starfishes. *Mem. Mus. Comp. Zool.* Vol. 5.

DELAGE, I. 1904. Élevage des larves parthénogénétiques d' *Asterias glacialis. Arch. de Zool. Expérimentale,* 4 Series, Vol. 2.

GEMMILL, J. F. 1912-1915. The development of the starfish *Solaster endeca. Trans. Zool. Soc. London,* Vol. 20.

———— 1914. The development and certain points in the adult structure of the starfish *Asterias rubens. Philos. Trans. Royal Soc. London,* Series B, Vol. 205.

REFERENCE

Order spinulosa
For the culture of *Solaster endeca* see p. 550.

Class *Ophiuroidea*, Order OPHIURAE

OPHIODERMA BREVISPINA

CASWELL GRAVE, *Washington University*

TO OBTAIN the eggs of *Ophioderma brevispina,* collect twenty-five or more adult animals from the grass roots or sedimentary debris on the shallow flats of their habitat (Beaufort, N. C., or Woods Hole, Mass.) during the breeding season (June and July) on the day when developing eggs are desired and place them in a large aquarium jar until sunset. To keep the animals in good physiological condition, the jar should be placed in running seawater or suspended beneath a wharf. About sunset the animals should be transferred to another aquarium jar of fresh seawater and placed on a table before a window. For a time after the transfer of the animals they may be observed to huddle together near the least illuminated side of the jar but as dusk comes on they become active, crawl about over the bottom and attempt to climb the side of the jar.

At about 8 o'clock spawning may be expected to begin. It is initiated by the males but very soon after sperm has been emitted the females begin to liberate eggs. The presence of sperm in the water, or some substance associated with sperm, seems to be a necessary stimulant to egg laying. In the presence of a greatly diluted suspension of sperm, such as may be assumed to be present under normal conditions in the sea, it is probable that mature eggs only are extruded by females but in aquaria the water becomes clouded with sperm and, thus over-stimulated, the females throw out their entire content of eggs, the immature with the mature.

A female while extruding eggs either stands upright, supported by the side of the aquarium, or with her body held horizontal to and high above the bottom by her strongly arched arms. While the body is thus elevated the eggs pass from the distal openings of the genital bursae into the water and slowly rise to the surface, having the appearance of ascending streams of minute bubbles of air. The eggs may now be taken with a pipette and placed in smaller containers of fresh seawater where development will take place and continue to a stage in which the adult structure is attained, provided daily transfers to fresh containers and seawater are made. The eggs are large, about o.3 mm. in diameter, and contain an amount of yolk sufficient for the energy requirements of complete development. The final stages are reached earlier however if a supply of diatoms or diatom-bearing sand is added to the water [see p. 31], food being thus provided for the developing stars.

BIBLIOGRAPHY

GRAVE, CASWELL. 1900. *Ophiura brevispina. Mem. Nat. Acad. Sci.*
—— 1916. *Ophiura brevispina.* II. *J. Morph.* 27:

Class *Echinoidea*, Order CENTRECHINOIDA

ARBACIA PUNCTULATA

HENRY J. FRY, *Cornell University Medical College*

AT the Woods Hole Marine Biological Laboratory the eggs of the sea urchin are used for experimental purposes probably to a greater extent than any other material. During the summer of 1935, 62,000 Arbacia were supplied to investigators. There are good reasons for this popularity: The season usually extends from the middle of June to the middle of September; one female yields about o.5 cc. of "dry eggs"; to an unusual degree these eggs withstand the abnormal conditions of various experimental procedures and yet develop like the controls (for example, fertilized eggs placed in a Warburg apparatus will cleave normally in spite of great crowding, continuous shaking, and no change of water for several hours); on the warmest days, room temperatures do not interfere with normal development; and eggs which have stood for some hours prior to fertilization develop like freshly obtained ones.* Externally the sexes are indistinguishable. Just (1928) describes several methods of obtaining gametes: (1) securing eggs shed normally; (2) slightly injuring the animal, thereby stimulating it to shed "dry" gametes; and (3) removing the gonads. The latter method is most commonly employed. Just's method is to cut through the test slightly above the equator, carefully removing the intact ovaries to seawater, and allowing the eggs to shed without stimulating the gonads. The egg suspension is then strained through cheesecloth. This is the procedure also used by Dr. Chambers and Dr. Ethel B. Harvey. If, however, it is necessary to obtain eggs in quantity from many individuals, the writer has found that they may be obtained by the following method, which does not impair their capacity for normal development in any way. The animal is rinsed in tap water in order to kill any sperm which might be on its surface, and then rinsed again with seawater; a cut is made about the peristome and the Aristotle's lantern is removed; the perivisceral fluid is poured off and replaced with seawater. The ovaries of the females, which are distinguished by their deep red color, are broken loose with a blunt instrument and poured into 250 cc. finger bowls of seawater, and are further broken up by drawing them gently in and out of a wide-mouthed pipette. The eggs are washed several times prior to the experiment.

In a few minutes, after the eggs have settled, the writer pours off the water and adds fresh water, repeating the process several times; the last time, before the eggs have settled, they are poured into another bowl, leaving any debris behind. Some workers state that ordinary physical disturbances are harmful to the eggs, but the writer has found no evidence of this.

The males are distinguished by their yellowish testes. Each male is placed, aboral side down, upon a dry Syracuse watch glass, into which it soon exudes its seminal fluid. Dr. Ethel B. Harvey removes the testes of several males to a small dish, which is kept covered to prevent their drying.

Eggs are fully maturated when shed. The polar bodies are usually absent. The location of the animal pole is indicated by the markedly eccentric position of the female pronucleus. The eggs are about 74μ in diameter. The jelly is 28 to 32μ thick, and may be demonstrated by placing the eggs in a suspension of India ink in seawater. The periviteline space is 3 to 5μ (Harvey, 1932). The presence of reddish

* Any one working with Arbacia eggs should consult Just's article (1928) concerning methods of handling them, and also E. Newton Harvey's summary of 125 investigations describing chemical and physical phenomena in the material (1932). The writer is also indebted to Dr. Robert Chambers and Dr. Ethel B. Harvey for additional suggestions.

granules renders the living egg quite opaque; cytological details during development may be seen only vaguely in most respects.

When fertilizing eggs, Just dilutes one drop of "dry" sperm with 10 cc. of seawater, and adds two drops of this suspension to the eggs in 250 cc. of seawater (1928). Dr. Ethel B. Harvey fertilizes eggs by dipping a toothpick in the "dry" sperm and stirring it in the egg-water. The exact concentration of the sperm is relatively unimportant, since Arbacia eggs are not easily subject to polyspermy. "Dry" sperm, obtained as described above, are in good condition for 6 to 8 hours, but it is the usual practice to obtain sperm from a freshly opened male each time eggs are fertilized.

As is the case with the eggs of most species, crowding should be avoided, and the water changed from time to time. However, if the experimental conditions require it, Arbacia eggs withstand the deleterious effects of crowding to an unusual degree.

The usual criteria which indicate that an egg-set is developing normally are as follows: (1) Distinct fertilization membranes are elevated within about two minutes; if some of them are wrinkled or attached to the egg at several points the set is in poor condition. (2) Practically all of the eggs cleave. From the time when about 20% of them have divided until about 80% have done so requires not more than 5 minutes at 20° C.; if this time is considerably longer, the egg-set is subnormal. (3) First-cleavage blastomeres are shaped like half-spheres which are flattened against each other and have smooth contours; if some of the blastomeres are rounded like spheres, or show occasional protuberances, the set is not normal. (4) Top-swimming plutei are produced in practically all cases; if numbers of embryos are bottom-swimmers the set is in poor condition.

Various workers (*e.g.*, Goldfarb, 1929, and Just, 1928) have demonstrated that the egg-sets of different Arbacia females differ in various respects. Fry (1936) has analyzed variation in the time when different egg-sets cleave, under various laboratory conditions, and has shown that the time when any mitotic phase is at its "peak" is a constant proportion of the cleavage time, no matter when cleavage occurs. This is of practical value in relating cytological changes to physiological ones in these eggs. If samples of an egg-set are being subjected to a given experimental treatment at intervals after fertilization, the cytological condition at each interval is easily calculated if the cleavage time is known.

Harvey (1932) summarizes previous studies of the effects of temperature upon the time of cleavage. Fry (1936) reports the time schedules of the detailed mitotic phases. Dr. Ethel B. Harvey has found that if the eggs are kept at about 8° C. they retain their capacity to be fertilized for a week or so.

In various types of investigations it is desirable to make preliminary tests of each egg-set to be used, in order to determine in advance its behavior with reference to the problem under study. Since eggs can stand for several hours without adversely affecting cleavage, as already noted, the time required for making such tests does not result in deterioration of the material—at least with reference to most factors.

During the major portion of the season, the capacity of a sample of an egg-set to raise practically 100% normal fertilization membranes indicates that it is in prime condition. But this statement does not hold true late in the season, when sets may raise 100% normal fertilization membranes but nevertheless not cleave properly. Dr. Chambers has observed that some egg-sets obtained late in the season do not have the same constancy of size as mid-season eggs; they also require heavier insemination; and the fertilization membranes lift slowly—in four to five minutes. Preliminary tests are of special value, therefore, toward the end of the season, to separate the egg-sets which are normal from the subnormal ones (Fry, 1936). (See also p. 18.)

Dr. Ethel B. Harvey stores a large number of Arbacia in laboratory aquaria in early August, when they are still in excellent condition. For some unknown reason their gonads and gametes remain normal until very late in the season, long after those of freshly collected individuals are useless.

Just uses Echinarachnius to feed Arbacia, "thus restoring the sea urchins previously in poor condition to a high degree of excellence" (1928).

Just describes various methods for removing the jelly from the eggs (1928): (1) adding HCL to the seawater; (2) shaking; (3) centrifuging; and (4) using bolting cloth. Dr. Chambers removes jelly by shaking the eggs in seawater to which isotonic NaCl has been added. A resumé of the methods for activating Arbacia eggs artificially, together with a bibliography of the subject, is presented by Morgan (1927, Chapter 27).

BIBLIOGRAPHY

FRY, HENRY J. 1936. Studies of the mitotic figure. V. The time schedule of mitotic changes in developing Arbacia eggs. *Biol. Bull.* 70:89.

GOLDFARB, A. J. 1929. Changes in agglutination of aging germ cells. *Ibid.* 57:350.

HARVEY, E. NEWTON. 1932. Physical and chemical constants of the egg of the sea urchin, *Arbacia punctulata. Ibid.* 62:141.

JUST, E. E. 1928. Methods for experimental embryology with special reference to marine invertebrates. *The Collecting Net,* Woods Hole, Mass. Vol. 3.

MORGAN, THOMAS HUNT. 1927. Experimental embryology. Columbia University Press.

NOTES ON THE CULTURE OF STRONGYLOCENTROTUS FRANCISCANUS AND ECHINARACHNIUS EXCENTRICUS

MARTIN W. JOHNSON, *Scripps Institution of Oceanography*

THE animals were usually cultured in section jars of about 500 cc. capacity. The water used was always fresh seawater carried to the laboratory in glass or enameled buckets and filtered through No. 20 silk bolting cloth. An even temperature was maintained by placing the dishes in the laboratory sink through which there circulated a stream of water previously cooled by flowing through pipes submerged in the bay. No special means of aeration was used but the specimens were never allowed to be crowded. Cultures of diatoms were added to the dishes when they were set up or shortly after. These diatoms were of mixed species but always contained a fair number of Navicula living as individual cells. A good supply of diatoms could usually be obtained in a couple of weeks by allowing a very slow stream of salt water to flow as a film over a large glass plate.

Strongylocentrotus franciscanus. The eggs and spermatozoa were obtained by breaking away a portion of the test near the genital pore of ripe adults. A few minutes after insemination the water was decanted and fresh seawater added. This operation was repeated two or three times till the water appeared clear. Each dish set up had a concentration of eggs such that an even distribution would allow the eggs to be separated by about 2 to 3 mm. The early larvae swim about in the upper portion of the water and the lower half may be siphoned away with a small rubber tube to which there is attached a glass tube which may be moved over the bottom to pick up the undeveloped eggs or weakened larvae. The whole operation should be watched closely in order to avoid removing too many of the healthy larvae. It has appeared advisable to carry on the cultures in the same dish, for the accumulation of loosely attached diatoms appears to contribute food to the larvae. A portion of the water was renewed every day for about one week and thereafter at intervals of about a week. There was always a rather high mortality and many were lost in the changing of water but a fair number of specimens were carried through to the beginning of metamorphosis, and a few specimens were well advanced at 62 days. The temperature never exceeded 12° or 13° C.

Echinarachnius excentricus. The methods were the same as for *S. franciscanus* except that the eggs and spermatozoa were obtained from spawning adults. A few specimens cultured thus completed metamorphosis in 72 to 80 days. The highest temperature was 16.1° but was usually near 11° C.

REFERENCES
For the rearing of sea urchins see also p. 197.
Order Exocycloida
  For the rearing of sand dollars see also p. 197.

Class *Holothurioidea*, Order DENDROCHIROTA

NOTES ON THE CULTURE OF CUCUMARIA

MARTIN W. JOHNSON, *Scripps Institution of Oceanography*

THE pelagic larvae of these holothurians are frequently numerous in the plankton samples collected in early spring near Scripps Institution. In the very young stages they are sufficiently large to be dipped from the water where they tend to gather in windrows at the surface. The methods for culture were much the same as for the Echinoidea (see p. 554) but the animals, being relatively large, might be removed temporarily from the culture dish while the water was being changed, and later after the tentacles and tube feet had developed, even this procedure was not necessary for they usually remained attached to the dish. The seawater used in the author's experiments was not filtered in order that the plankton organisms might contribute to the food supply. The animals grow slowly, but healthy specimens have been kept in good condition for over a year.

Phylum XVII

CHORDATA, Class *Ascidiacea*

NOTES ON THE CULTURE OF EIGHT SPECIES OF ASCIDIANS

CASWELL GRAVE, *Washington University*

AMMAROUCIUM CONSTELLATUM

THIS ascidian is viviparous. Free-swimming larvae may be secured in abundance at Woods Hole during the months of July, August, and September by placing large colonies of this ascidian in glass aquaria before a window in the laboratory. The best results have been obtained when colonies were collected the day before tadpoles were desired and kept in running seawater during the night. Care should be taken that the colonies are uninjured and are not placed in containers with other material, otherwise the sexually mature zooids are likely to die and be extruded on the surface of the gelatinous mass. Tadpoles are set free from the colonies in swarms at and just after sunrise, hence the aquaria containing the colonies should be transferred to a window table at dawn. Larvae escape from the colonies at other times in the day one by one. When liberated, the tadpoles swim immediately to the surface of the water and collect at the most illuminated edge of the container where they may be captured easily with a pipette.

Immature tadpoles and various earlier developmental stages may be secured by squeezing a colony in the hand over a culture dish of seawater. With the mass of ascidiozooids, tadpoles, embryos, and eggs thus forced from the gelatinous matrix a considerable quantity of debris is included, giving the water a milky appearance. This settles slowly and may be removed by decantation, two or more changes of water being required. Mature tadpoles may be had in small numbers in this way also. For a few seconds after having been squeezed from the colony they lie motionless on the bottom of the dish, but soon swim about, apparently being stimulated to activity by light or by contact with pure seawater. (Grave, 1921.)

SYMPLEGMA VIRIDE, POLYANDROCARPA TINCTA, AND P. GRAVEI

Wild colonies of these ascidians almost without exception are found encrusting the under side of dead coral rock, empty shells of mollusks, and especially pieces of sheet-iron and slate, that lie scattered on the sandy and rocky bottoms west and northwest of Fort Jefferson (Tortugas), over which the water at low tide has a depth varying from about 1 to 5 feet. These species incubate their eggs in the atrial cavity and give birth periodically to fully developed, free-swimming larvae.

These compound ascidians are well suited to study in that mature colonies taken from their natural habitat thrive in a live-car anchored near shore and may be transferred daily to aquaria in the laboratory for several hours without injury.

The dimensions of these larvae, which belong to the Botryllus type in structure and behavior, are as follows:

	Total length	Body length	Tail length
Symplegma viride	1.55 mm.	0.40 mm.	1.15 mm.
Polyandrocarpa tincta	1.13	0.27	0.86
Polyandrocarpa gravei	1.35	0.30	1.05

When larvae of these species were desired, a colony from the live-car was transferred to a large glass bowl of fresh seawater in the laboratory, usually between 7 and 8 o'clock in the morning, and placed on a table before a window facing west. At frequent intervals the surface of the water nearest the window was scanned for swimming larvae, for as liberated they accumulated at this most illuminated part of the bowl and were easily collected by means of a wide-mouthed pipette and transferred to beakers or shell vials.

A large colony of *Symplegma viride* might usually be relied upon to liberate larvae almost as soon as it had been placed in the bowl and to continue to set them free in a more or less constant stream throughout the day, but unfortunately this species is rare at the Tortugas. Both species of Polyandrocarpa are abundant. They tend to liberate larvae in a swarm once only during the day, usually between 11 a.m. and 12.30 p.m., but in one instance a swarm was released as early as 8:30 a.m. and in another as late as 3 p.m. A large mature colony will sometimes liberate swarms of larvae on two consecutive days but none was known to produce a swarm three days in succession. The liberation of a brood or swarm of Polyandrocarpa larvae is a continuous process covering a period varying from about 20 to 40 minutes. The number of larvae constituting a swarm varies greatly with the size and maturity of the parent colony, from less than 50 to more than 1,000, a swarm of average size numbering about 300. (Grave, 1935.)

PHALLUSIA NIGRA

The large, black *Phallusia nigra* is found sparingly on many of the bottoms in the Tortugas region attached to coral rock and to the stems of gorgonians but is abundant on the brick walls within the moat at

Fort Jefferson. Having been torn from their attachment, individuals soon die but may be kept in a live-car for a day or two without deterioration of their eggs and sperm. Fertilization of the eggs and development of the relatively small larvae take place outside the body of the parent. This larva has an average total length of about 0.93 mm. (body length 0.18 mm., tail length 0.75 mm.). Development is exceedingly rapid. At temperatures between 27° and 29° C., eggs fertilized at 5 a.m. yield free-swimming larvae at about 1 p.m., and one lot hatched after a period of development of only 6 hours and 38 minutes. By fertilizing eggs taken from several individuals early in the morning it is possible to have many thousands of free-swimming larvae available for experimentation during the afternoon.

The procedure followed with success is simple. After cutting away the projecting ends of the siphons, incisions are made in the tunic between the siphons and along one side from siphon to base of body. Spreading the opening thus made and seizing the stump of one siphon with forceps, the body is pulled away with no injury save to small blood-vessels. Removed from the tunic, washed with fresh seawater and placed separately in dry petri dishes, animals were left until the blood from severed mantle vessels had clotted. Since the long genital ducts lie close together near the surface at one side of the body and, when filled with eggs or sperm, are plainly visible, it was then possible to puncture the oviduct near its opening into the atrial cavity without rupturing the sperm duct, provided the puncture was made with a very sharp needle. As eggs flowed from the puncture they were taken up with a wide-mouthed pipette and transferred to beakers of fresh seawater and later fertilized with sperm taken either from the same or a different individual. Especial care had always to be taken that no blood was taken up with the eggs or sperm as even slight contamination results in abnormal development.

For experimental studies in which the statistical method of measuring results must be applied, it is desirable that the factors of individual variation be reduced to a minimum. This desideratum is approached in larvae of ascidians when each experimental lot is composed of individuals having the same parentage; even self-fertilization adds to the desired uniformity. But eggs of different parentage develop at rates sufficiently different to permit one lot to hatch several minutes before or after another, and undoubtedly they vary more or less in all hereditary characters.

It was often necessary to divide eggs taken from a single individual and to place them in two or more beakers, for when too many eggs were crowded together during development it was found that abnormalities appeared during the later stages, often to the extent of 100%, depending upon the extent to which they were crowded. Without attempting to ascertain just what constitutes crowding and what quantity of eggs in a 50 cc. beaker is the optimum for normal development, it was found empirically that abnormalities are likely to occur when the bottom of the beaker is covered by a layer more than one egg in thickness. To free the eggs from excess sperm and prevent the accumulation of injurious by-products of development, the surface stratum of water in each beaker was decanted and replaced with fresh seawater as soon and as frequently during the first three or four hours after fertilization as settling of the eggs would permit. After this, less frequent changes in the water were similarly made. (Grave, 1935.)

BOTRYLLUS SCHLOSSERI

To obtain free-swimming larvae of this compound ascidian, collect a considerable number of adult colonies during the early morning and place in the quiet water of a large aquarium jar before a window but not in direct sunlight. In sexually mature colonies the zooids are relatively thick and tend to mat together. Colonies in which the zooids are thin and clean do not usually liberate larvae. If the colonies contain an abundance of sexually mature zooids, swimming larvae may be expected to appear within a few minutes in the part of the jar most illuminated. When first liberated the larvae are positive in orientation to light and negative to gravity and may be collected easily with a pipette as they swarm at the most illuminated part of the water surface. There is no well marked periodicity in the liberation of larvae but light seems to be an important factor. Observations made during the summer of 1921 at Woods Hole showed that no larvae are given off in the early morning hours; that they appear in greater number as the day advances, finally reaching a maximum about or shortly after noon; that during the afternoon the number of larvae liberated decreases gradually until the evening when an occasional larvae only is set free. Botryllus larvae vary greatly in the duration of the free-swimming period. Some attach and metamorphose within ten minutes after liberation. A small percentage continue to swim intermittently and retain the tadpole form for twelve hours or more, but the greater number may be expected to metamorphose after a free-swimming period of about two hours. Under more normal conditions the larvae tend to become attached to the side or bottom of the container immediately before metamorphosis begins but under laboratory conditions in small quantities of water in small vessels, many larvae fail to attach and a small percentage do not metamorphose. Segmenting eggs and stages in development of the larvae can only be secured by dissection of sexually mature zooids and removal from the brood chamber in the atrium. (Grave and Woodbridge, 1924; Grave, 1932.)

MOLGULA CITRINA

In *Molgula citrina* fertilization and development of the egg take place within the atrial chamber of the parent. Eggs and embryos in various stages of development may usually be found together in the atrial chamber of sexually mature individuals from June 15 to September 15 at Woods Hole, Mass. Egg production and development are not affected by the transfer of sexually mature individuals from their natural habitat to aquaria in the laboratory. One lot of about 30 adults continued to liberate large numbers of active larvae daily from June 22 until discarded July 27, 1926. Adult individuals may usually be taken in considerable numbers with scrapings from piles. These, if separated from the associated debris and placed in aquaria of running water, readily and invariably re-attach themselves to the bottom or side of the container.

When larvae are desired, the aquarium containing the sexually mature adults is transferred to a table before a window. Under laboratory conditions, larvae are set free with the same frequency at one time of the day as another. As larvae escape from the atriopore, they may be easily seen as they swim to the surface where they may be taken with a pipette. This larvae lacks a light-sensitive sense organ and does not orient to light, but it has a statolith and orients negatively to gravity when first liberated by the parent. (Grave, 1926.)

BIBLIOGRAPHY

GRAVE, CASWELL. 1921. *Ammaroucium constellatum* (Verrill). II, The structure and organization of the tadpole larva. *J. Morph.* 36:71.

—— 1926. *Molgula citrina:* activities and structure of the free-swimming larva. *J. Morph. and Physiol.* 42:453.

—— 1932. The Botryllus type of Ascidian Larva. Papers from the Tortugas Laboratory, vol. 28. (Reprinted from the *Carnegie Inst. of Wash. Publ.* No. 435.)

—— 1935. Metamorphosis of Ascidian larvae. *Carnegie Publ.* No. 452. Paper IX.

——, and WOODBRIDGE, HELEN. 1924. *Botryllus schlosseri.* 39: *Ibid.* 39.

CULTURE METHODS FOR ASCIDIANS

N. J. BERRILL, *McGill University*

METHODS OF CAPTURE

ASCIDIANS are sessile, marine organisms varying considerably in habitat. Many forms are littoral, to be found in greatest quantity immediately above or below the low water spring tide level. Others may be found attached to the under surface of floating objects, while many forms are found only in deeper water attached to rocky or hard surfaces, or embedded in sand or mud without any strong attachment. In general the ideal habitat for ascidians is one in which there is a considerable natural flow of clear water, yet not sufficient water movement, such as wave action, to dislodge the animal. This habitat will vary according to the size of the animal and its relative area of attachment.

Compound ascidians as a rule tend toward a two-dimensional state with a maximum area of attachment and minimum thickness. Such forms may be found in profusion on the under surface of rocks and stones in the lower intertidal and upper littoral zones; a few species may be attached to algae and eel grass in the same region. Solitary ascidians are usually larger and possess a relatively smaller area of attachment. Their size and water requirements alone may prohibit their attachment to such surfaces as are occupied by the majority of compound forms, and they are more typically to be found attached to the sides and upper surfaces of rocks, large stones, wharf piles, and the under surface of ships and floats, *etc.*, though very rarely above and often much below the low-tide level. Mud and sand flats at some depth are typical habitats of some species of Molgula and Polycarpa, although they may become attached to rock surfaces in very sheltered positions.

The principal methods of capture are thus three-fold: turning over boulders at low-tide level, often necessitating the use of a crow-bar; scraping piles, rocks, and ship-bottoms with long-handled net-scrapers; and dredging.

BREEDING SEASONS

The breeding season for ascidians of both the Pacific and the Atlantic coasts, including the West Indian fauna typical of the Gulf of Mexico, seems to be summer. Certain forms, namely the various species of Ascidia and probably Molgula and Ciona have no definite season; individuals above a certain size are sexually mature and may breed throughout the year, although the lower temperatures of winter retard the rate of egg production. Most compound ascidians are actively budding during the winter and the individual zooids do not attain sexual maturity until early summer. Some solitary forms such as Styela and probably most species of the families Styelidae and Pyuridae have a breeding season limited to summer months. With the exception of *Styela partita,* and the polystyelids *Boltenia echinata* little is known concerning the members of these two families from this point of view.

THE COMMONER ASCIDIANS OF AMERICAN COASTAL WATERS *

Species	Distribution	Egg size in mm.	Breeding season
Ciona intestinalis	Alaska-S. Calif. Cape Cod	0.17	Depends on size
*Perophora viridis	New Eng.-Fla. Bermuda	0.24	Aug.-Sept.
*P. annectens	Vancouver-S. Calif.	0.24	July-Sept.
*P. bermudensis	Bermuda	0.24	Sept.-Oct.
*Ecteinascidia turbinata	Bermuda. Tortugas	0.72	June-Aug.
*E. conklini	Bermuda. Tortugas	0.58	July-Sept.
Ascidia prunum	New Eng. Fundy	0.18	
A. hygomiana	N. C.-Tortugas	0.17	Not seasonal; depends
A. nigra (atra)	Bermuda. Tortugas. Fla.	0.17	on size of individual.
A. curvata	Bermuda. Tortugas	0.17	
Styela partita	Mass. Bay-Fla. Bermuda	0.15	June-Sept.
S. plicata	N. C.-Fla.	0.16	June-Sept.
Polycarpa obtecta	Bermuda. Tortugas	0.18	May-Sept.
*Polyandrocarpa tincta	Bermuda. Tortugas	0.21	May-Sept.
*Symplegma viride	Bermuda. Tortugas	0.44	June-Sept.
*Botryllus schlosseri	S. New Eng.	0.42	June-Sept.
*Botrylloides niger	Bermuda. Fla.	0.26	June-Aug.
*Tethyum pyriforme	Maine-Fundy	0.26	July-Aug.
Boltenia ovifera	Maine-Fundy	0.16	July-Aug.
*B. echinata	Maine-Fundy	0.18	July-Sept.
Pyura vittata	Bermuda. N. C.-Fla.	0.16	summer
Molgula retortiformis	Maine-Fundy	0.18	Probably no definite
M. manhattensis	New Eng.-N. C.	0.11	season; individuals
*M. citrina	Fundy-L. I.	0.21	above a certain size
*M. verrucifera	California	0.13	breeding continu-
M. occidentalis	N. C.-Fla.	0.11	uously.
Eugyra pilularis	Fundy-New Eng.	0.11	
*Clavelina picta	Bermuda	0.48	July-Sept.
*C. huntsmani	Vancouver-S. Calif.	0.26	June-Sept.
*Eudistoma olivacea	Bermuda. Fla.	0.30 (?)	July-Aug.
*E. lobatum	California	0.30 (?)	summer
*Distaplia clava	New Eng.-Fundy	circa	summer
*D. bermudensis	Bermuda	0.40	June-Aug.
*Distaplia sp.	California		summer
*Aplidium pellucidum	Cape Cod-Fla.	circa	summer
*Aplidium sp.	California	0.30	summer

* Viviparous species.

PROCURING OF EGGS OR EMBRYOS

For purposes of rearing, and developmental studies in general, ascidians are to be divided into two groups according to whether they are oviparous or viviparous (see above table). Except in a very few instances oviparous ascidians are comparatively large and produce a great many small eggs, viviparous ascidians are small and produce a

---

* All these species are common shallow water forms; for further information concerning distribution, habitat, and identification, see bibliography 3, 10, 11, 13-16.

small number of comparatively large eggs. Thus in the one case rearing methods must start with the unsegmented egg, in the other with the active tadpole larva. Only after the tadpole larvae have become attached does treatment become the same for both kinds.

Oviparous forms. In Ciona and in the species of Ascidia all eggs found in the oviduct are ripe. In some species of Ascidia, especially those that tend to become exposed at low tides to the warmer temperature of the air, a large percentage of the eggs in the distal part of the oviduct may be dead (Berrill, 1929). Eggs from the middle or proximal part of the oviduct are in any case less likely to be over-ripe. To obtain the eggs and sperm the test should be removed, the wall of the oviduct or sperm duct punctured with fine scissors and the germ cells withdrawn in a pipette. This is much more satisfactory than maintaining the parents in aquaria and waiting for them to spawn naturally.

A similar procedure may be followed in the case of the oviparous species of Molgula (and Eugyra), although the oviduct is short and confined to the central part of the gonad, so that this method is likely to result in the extraction of immature as well as ripe eggs. As unripe eggs are more resistant generally than ripe eggs, fertilized or unfertilized, this is no serious drawback, as the larvae may be segregated as soon as they become active.

Such a method used with oviparous stylelids and pyurids is only occasionally successful, and it is better to maintain the adults in aquaria and collect the eggs as they are spawned and fertilized in the water. In the case of *Styela partita* spawning occurs at sundown (Conklin, 1905), and this may be so for the majority.

Viviparous forms. Viviparous species vary considerably in egg number and egg size. In some species almost all embryos will be at the same stage of development, as in Botryllus, Polyandrocarpa, *Boltenia echinata,* and *Tethyum pyriforme* (Berrill, 1935). In most species embryos at all stages of development are to be found. In both groups embryos extracted before the attainment of the tadpole stage will not continue development unless certain precautions are taken. If the developmental stages desired are those of the tadpole or later it is always safer to keep the parents alive in aquaria until the tadpoles are liberated. Or the embryos may be extracted and those tadpoles exhibiting signs of activity segregated. In the first method the risk is that the parent animals will not live long enough, in the second that they may not contain tadpole larvae sufficiently mature.

REARING OF EMBRYONIC STAGES

Until the tadpole stage is passed and metamorphosis completed to form a small ascidiozooid that is attached and has open siphons and

active stigmata, no food at all from external sources is needed.
Oviparous forms (Ciona, Ascidia, *etc.*). Eggs and sperm are extracted
from ducts after removal of test, followed by artificial fertilization. Some
species are self-fertile, others self-sterile, others, *e.g.* Ciona, vary with
locality. In any case better cultures are obtained by cross fertilizing. A
small quantity of sperm is mixed with the eggs in a finger bowl of seawater and proper mixing ensured by pouring from one bowl to another
several times. After 15 or 20 minutes the eggs should have been
fertilized and will lie at the bottom of the vessel. As much of the
supernatant water as possible should then be siphoned off and replaced
with clean water; the process of allowing the eggs to settle and replacing
the water is repeated several times to ensure complete elimination of all
surplus spermatozoa. Failure to do so leads to abnormal development.
Development up to the tadpole and beyond may take place in finger-
bowls, but vessels holding a larger volume of water are much more
satisfactory. If large cultures are desired in a limited volume of water,
bubbling air continuously through the water should ensure normal
development. In the case of Ciona such procedure is advisable in any
case, as development in this form is very prone to become abnormal
during the period of tail elongation.

If the early development of Ciona or Ascidia is to be studied, the
egg membranes may be removed in the following manner (Berrill, 1933).
Unfertilized eggs are placed in a vessel of seawater containing crustacean
stomach juice (not liver extract) in a proportion of about one part
stomach juice to 50 or 100 parts of seawater. This medium digests off
the membranes in the course of a very few hours (usually 2 or 3) and
on complete replacement of the water by clean seawater the eggs may
be fertilized.

To obtain suitable crustacean stomach juice medium-sized decapods should be
used, preferably after a day or so in an aquarium when the stomach should be empty
of food and contain only a clear reddish brown fluid. The animal may be killed
or immobilized by shallow stabbing with a scalpel along its mid-ventral surface. It
should then be placed with its ventral side downwards and the carapace cut away
with strong scissors so that the upper surface of the stomach is exposed. A small
incision is made in the upper wall of the stomach and the contents withdrawn
with a fine pipette. If digesting food is present in the fluid thus obtained it should
be allowed to settle and the clear supernatant fluid pipetted off and used.

Eggs remain viable for about 18 hours after extraction. The method
will not work with eggs that have been fertilized as it affects the surface
tension of the dividing eggs. Slight shaking, or decanting from one vessel into another, during early cleavage stages will suffice to separate
blastomeres without resort to the use of calcium-free seawater.

Viviparous forms. The embryos of viviparous ascidians extracted
before the attainment of the tadpole stage usually stop developing. A

percentage at least will continue to develop under the following conditions (Berrill, 1935). A glass T-piece is attached to the stem of a thistle funnel, the whole is immersed in seawater and air bubbled slowly through the T-piece so that a slow current of water passes into the mouth of the funnel. This is arranged so that the mouth opens downward. A piece of coarse bolting silk on which the embryos rest is attached to the mouth of the funnel. The embryos are thus kept mildly agitated in a gentle stream of water. For complete success the carbon dioxide tension of the water needs to be increased slightly (Child, 1927). Whenever possible it is better in the case of viviparous species to start cultures with the tadpole stage. It is not essential that the active stage be used, for in most forms immature tadpoles showing but a trace of sensory pigment will continue development outside the parent.

REARING POST-LARVAL AND YOUNG ADULT STAGES

In order to rear later stages of ascidians it is essential that the tadpole larvae become properly attached to some surface. Tadpoles that fail to become attached, while they may metamorphose perfectly, will not continue development and growth. Most swimming tadpoles if kept in a large vessel of seawater, such as an inverted bell jar, will become attached. It is often an advantage to lay flat pieces of glass in the vessel so that the forms which become attached to them may be studied without damage.

If tadpoles have been reared in small vessels they should be transferred while still actively swimming to the larger vessel in which they are expected to become attached and grow. An alternative method to the use of large culture vessels is to submerge glass plates to which larvae are attached in the sea in such a position that water movement will not dislodge the larvae and detritus will not accumulate on the plates (Simkins, 1924).

In large vessels the water should not be changed once the larvae show open siphons and functional stigmata. Replacement with water that presumably is in better condition is rarely tolerated, so that it is important that the water used in the first place should be of excellent quality.

Only after attachment, and when the siphons and stigmata are functioning, do ascidian larvae need food from external sources. Since mixed assortment of small diatoms and algae *etc.* has been found to be at least as satisfactory as a pure culture of Nitzschia, a coarse filtering of water to remove the larger organisms is all that is necessary. A small quantity of sodium nitrite and sodium phosphate should be added to the water from time to time in order to ensure continued multiplication of the food organisms. The ascidians will suffer if the growth, especially on the walls of the vessel, becomes too thick. This growth may be controlled by limiting with shades the amount of light that reaches the vessel. A slight circulation produced by the slow bubbling of air through the water is an advantage, but is by no means essential. Under these conditions it should be possible to rear most ascidians to a comparatively large size, even to maturity.

pH REQUIREMENTS

It is most unlikely that the pH of the water will fall to so low a value that development or growth becomes affected. Only when the pH falls to 7.0 does development tend to become abnormal and hatching in Ciona and Ascidia become inhibited (Berrill, 1929). In the other direction normal development is possible up to a pH of 9.0. There is considerable danger, however, that a luxuriant growth of algae may cause the pH to rise to even higher values, especially if small culture vessels are used. Tests should accordingly be made at intervals, and if the pH tends to become too high the light should be cut off in order to inhibit further photosynthesis.

TEMPERATURE REQUIREMENTS

As in the case of many other forms there is for ascidians a temperature range of about 15° C. within which normal development is possible. This range may be high or low, it may vary for the same species in different localities, or it may vary for the same species in summer and winter, *e.g.* Parechinus (Horstadius, 1926). Thus *Eugyra pilularis* will develop at 18° C. at Woods Hole (the southern extremity of its distribution range) but not above 12° C. if taken from the colder waters of the Bay of Fundy (Berrill, 1931).

In general, however, it is reasonably safe to assume that normal development and growth is possible when there is little difference between sea temperature and air temperature, whatever it may be, and that the temperature of the water in which development is proceeding should never exceed by more than 5° C. the temperature of the water from which the parents were taken. This margin should be reduced where sea temperatures exceed 25° C. Keeping culture vessels beneath a small tent with the walls kept saturated with water has been found to reduce the air temperature by several degrees. The distribution range of a species relative to the locality where it is taken gives some indication of its temperature tolerance. Species found near the southern end of their range are not likely to tolerate temperatures higher than that of the water in which they are found; species from the northern end of their range will tolerate temperatures considerably higher.

BIBLIOGRAPHY

1. BERRILL, N. J. 1929. Studies in tunicate development. Pt. 1. *Phil. vs. Trans. Roy. Soc.* B.218:37.
2. —— 1931. Studies in tunicate development. Pt. 2. *Phil. Ibid.* B.219:281.
3. —— 1932. Ascidians of the Bermudas. *Biol. Bull.* 62:77.
4. —— 1933. Mosaic development in ascidians. *Ibid.* 63:381.
5. —— 1935. Studies in tunicate development. Pt. 3. *Phil. vs. Trans. Roy. Soc.* B.223:1.
6. CHILD, C. M. 1927. Developmental modification and elimination of the larval stage in the ascidian, *Corella willmeriana*. *J. Morph.* 44.
7. CONKLIN, E. G. 1905. The organization and cell lineage of the ascidian egg. *J. Acad. Nat. Sci. Phila.* 13:1.
8. GRAVE, C. 1927. Studies of the activities of the larvae of ascidians. *Carnegie Inst. Yearbook* No. 26.
9. HORSTADIUS, S. 1926. Ueber die Temperaturumpassung bei den *Paracentrotus lividus* (L.). *Biologia Generalis.*
10. RITTER, W. E. 1913. The simple ascidians of the north-eastern Pacific in the collection of the United States National Museum. *Proc. U. S. Nat. Mus.* 45.
11. RITTER, W. E., and FORSYTH, R. A. 1917. Ascidians of the littoral zone of southern California. *Publ. Univ. Calif.* 16.
12. SIMKINS, C. S. 1924. Origin of germ cells in Ecteinascidia. *J. Morph.* 39:295.
13. VAN NAME, W. G. 1910. Compound ascidians of the coasts of New England and the neighboring British Provinces. *Proc. Bost. Soc. Nat. Hist.* 34:339.
14. —— 1912. Simple ascidians of the coasts of New England and the neighboring British Provinces. *Ibid.* 34:439.
15. —— 1921. Ascidians of the West Indian region and southeastern United States. *Bull. Amer. Mus. Nat. Hist.* 44:283.
16. —— 1931. New North and South American ascidians. *Ibid.* 61:207.

ADDENDA

ADDITIONS TO THE BIBLIOGRAPHY on Page 224

GIBBONS, S. G. 1933. A study of the biology of *Calanus finmarchicus* in the north-western North Sea. *Fish. Board Scotland. Sci. Invest.* No. 1, Edinburgh.

HARVEY, H. W., COOPER, L. H. N., LEBOUR, M. V., and RUSSELL, F. S. 1935. Plankton production and its control. *J. Mar. Biol. Assoc.* 20:407.

LOWNDES, A. G. 1935. The swimming and feeding of certain calanoid copepods. *Proc. Zool. Soc. London,* Pt. 3, p. 687.

INDEX

STUDIES ON THE STRUCTURE AND DEVELOPMENT OF VERTEBRATES

by Edwin S. Goodrich

This monumental work by the greatest comparative anatomist of modern times was recognized as the definitive study of the field immediately upon publication. Its wealth of factual detail plus brilliant exposition and theory have made it an indisper.sable text and reference work for anatomists, medical students, morphologists, histologists, embryologists, students of evolution, zoologists, and every person interested in biology, no matter what his field of specialization.

The skeleton, fins and limbs, head, vascular, respiratory, excretory, genital and nervous systems, and the subdivision of the body-cavity, are covered from fish to the higher mammals. Among the features of the book is the account of the structure and evolutionary history of the ossicles of the ear, extensive cranial studies, a detailed and complete classification of the vertebrate phylum including the sub-orders, the treatment of the separate divisions of the coelom and the diaphragm, the concise and lucid coverage of embryology, and the illustrations (over 300 of them by the author) which are among the very finest ever presented in a single work. The entire study is characterized by the unity and meticulous attention to detail of one man thoroughly familiar with his subject.

"For many a day this will certainly be the standard text-book," JOURNAL OF ANATOMY. "The reviewer knows of no other book in English which covers so thoroughly the more modern work on many aspects of the subject," SCIENCE PROGRESS.

Enlarged by a 69-page biographical study of his life and work by A. C. Hardy. 754 figures. Bibliography of 1186 references. Index. 2 volumes; total 906pp. 5⅜ x 8. 2 vol. set.

S449, 450 Paperbound **$0.00**

ELEMENTS OF MATHEMATICAL BIOLOGY
by Alfred J. Lotka

Formerly published as ELEMENTS OF PHYSICAL BIOLOGY, this classic work is the first major attempt to apply modern mathematics to the problems of phylogeny, ontology, ecology, physiology, endocrinology, psychology, and other branches of biology.

One of the most seminal books ever published in its field it has had enormous influence upon the later work of Norbert Wiener and N. Rashevsky. It is still of great interest to social scientists, biologists, mathematicians and engineers interested in applying mathematical concepts to social studies.

PARTIAL CONTENTS. Evolution, a system in the course of irreversible transformation. Statistical meaning of irreversibility. Evolution as redistribuition. KINETICS: Fundamental equations of kinetics of evolving systems. General, special cases. Analysis of the growth function. STATICS. General principles of equilibrium. Chemical equilibrium, interspecies equilibrium, circulation of the elements, the carbon dioxide cycle, the nitrogen cycle, the phosphorus cycle, moving equilibria, displacement of equilibrium, parameters of state. DYNAMICS. Energy transformers of nature, relation of the transformation to available sources, correlating apparatus, adjustors, consciousness, function, origin, energy relations of consciousness.

List of publications by A. J. Lotka. 36 tables. Analytical synopsis of chapters. 72 figures. xxx + 460pp. 5⅜ x 8.

Paperbound $2.95

"The only textbook on linear integral equations in the English language . . . conception and exposition are clear and easily understandable and include all fundamental questions on the subject. . . . One of its merits is that nearly half of the volume is devoted to applications . . . an excellent introduction, can be warmly recommended,"

JOURNAL OF THE ROYAL NAVAL SCIENTIFIC SERVICE.

Catalogue of Dover
SCIENCE BOOKS

DIFFERENTIAL EQUATIONS
(ORDINARY AND PARTIAL DIFFERENTIAL)

INTRODUCTION TO THE DIFFERENTIAL EQUATIONS OF PHYSICS, L. Hopf. Especially valuable to engineer with no math beyond elementary calculus. Emphasizes intuitive rather than formal aspects of concepts. Partial contents: Law of causality, energy theorem, damped oscillations, coupling by friction, cylindrical and spherical coordinates, heat source, etc. 48 figures. 160pp. 5⅜ x 8. S120 Paperbound **$1.25**

INTRODUCTION TO BESSEL FUNCTIONS, F. Bowman. Rigorous, provides all necessary material during development, includes practical applications. Bessel functions of zero order, of any real order, definite integrals, asymptotic expansion, circular membranes, Bessel's solution to Kepler's problem, much more. "Clear . . . useful not only to students of physics and engineering, but to mathematical students in general," Nature. 226 problems: Short tables of Bessel functions. 27 figures. x + 135pp. 5⅜ x 8. S462 Paperbound **$1.35**

DIFFERENTIAL EQUATIONS, F. R. Moulton. Detailed, rigorous exposition of all non-elementary processes of solving ordinary differential equations. Chapters on practical problems; more advanced than problems usually given as illustrations. Includes analytic differential equations; variations of a parameter; integrals of differential equations; analytic implicit functions; problems of elliptic motion; sine-amplitude functions; deviation of formal bodies; Cauchy-Lipshitz process; linear differential equations with periodic coefficients; much more. Historical notes. 10 figures. 222 problems. xv + 395pp. 5⅜ x 8. S451 Paperbound **$2.00**

PARTIAL DIFFERENTIAL EQUATIONS OF MATHEMATICAL PHYSICS, A. G. Webster. Valuable sections on elasticity, compression theory, potential theory, theory of sound, heat conduction, wave propagation, vibration theory. Contents include: deduction of differential equations, vibrations, normal functions, Fourier's series. Cauchy's method, boundary problems, method of Riemann-Volterra, spherical, cylindrical, ellipsoidal harmonics, applications, etc. 97 figures. vii + 440pp. 5⅜ x 8. S263 Paperbound **$2.00**

ORDINARY DIFFERENTIAL EQUATIONS, E. L. Ince. A most compendious analysis in real and complex domains. Existence and nature of solutions, continuous transformation groups, solutions in an infinite form, definite integrals, algebraic theory. Sturmian theory, boundary problems, existence theorems, 1st order, higher order, etc. "Deserves highest praise, a notable addition to mathematical literature," Bulletin, Amer. Math. Soc. Historical appendix. 18 figures. viii + 558pp. 5⅜ x 8. S349 Paperbound **$2.55**

ASYMPTOTIC EXPANSIONS, A. Erdélyi. Only modern work available in English; unabridged reproduction of monograph prepared for Office of Naval Research. Discusses various procedures for asymptotic evaluation of integrals containing a large parameter; solutions of ordinary linear differential equations. vi + 108pp. 5⅜ x 8. S318 Paperbound **$1.35**

LECTURES ON CAUCHY'S PROBLEM, J. Hadamard. Based on lectures given at Columbia, Rome, discusses work of Riemann, Kirchhoff, Volterra, and author's own research on hyperbolic case in linear partial differential equations. Extends spherical cylindrical waves to apply to all (normal) hyperbolic equations. Partial contents: Cauchy's problem, fundamental formula, equations with odd number, with even number of independent variables; method of descent. 32 figures. iii + 316pp. 5⅜ x 8. S105 Paperbound **$1.75**

NUMBER THEORY

INTRODUCTION TO THE THEORY OF NUMBERS, L. E. Dickson. Thorough, comprehensive, witn adequate coverage of classical literature. Not beyond beginners. Chapters on divisibility, congruences, quadratic residues and reciprocity, Diophantine equations, etc. Full treatment of binary quadratic forms without usual restriction to integral coefficients. Covers infinitude of primes, Fermat's theorem, Legendre's symbol, automorphs, Recent theorems of Thue, Siegal, much more. Much material not readily available elsewhere. 239 problems. 1 figure. viii + 183pp. 5⅜ x 8.   S342 Paperbound **$1.65**

ELEMENTS OF NUMBER THEORY, I. M. Vinogradov. Detailed 1st course for persons without advanced mathematics; 95% of this book can be understood by readers who have gone no farther than high school algebra. Partial contents: divisibility theory, important number theoretical functions, congruences, primitive roots and indices, etc. Solutions to problems, exercises. Tables of primes, indices, etc. Covers almost every essential formula in elementary number theory! "Welcome addition . . . reads smoothly," Bull. of the Amer. Math. Soc. 233 problems. 104 exercises. viii + 227pp. 5⅜ x 8.   S259 Paperbound **$1.60**

PROBABILITY THEORY AND INFORMATION THEORY

SELECTED PAPERS ON NOISE AND STOCHASTIC PROCESSES, edited by Prof. Nelson Wax, U. of Illinois. 6 basic papers for those whose work involves noise characteristics. Chandrasekhar, Uhlenback and Ornstein, Uhlenbeck and Ming, Rice, Doob. Included is Kac's Chauvenet-Prize winning "Random Walk." Extensive bibliography lists 200 articles, through 1953. 21 figures. 337pp. 6⅛ x 9¼.   S262 Paperbound **$2.35**

A PHILOSOPHICAL ESSAY ON PROBABILITIES, Marquis de Laplace. This famous essay explains without recourse to mathematics the principle of probability, and the application of probability to games of chance, natural philosophy, astronomy, many other fields. Translated from 6th French edition by F. W. Truscott, F. L. Emory. Intro. by E. T. Bell. 204pp. 5⅜ x 8.   S166 Paperbound **$1.25**

MATHEMATICAL FOUNDATIONS OF INFORMATION THEORY, A. I. Khinchin. For mathematicians, statisticians, physicists, cyberneticists, communications engineers, a complete, exact introduction to relatively new field. Entropy as a measure of a finite scheme, applications to coding theory, study of sources, channels and codes, detailed proofs of both Shannon theorems for any ergodic source and any stationary channel with finite memory, much more. "Presents for the first time rigorous proofs of certain fundamental theorems . . . quite complete . . . amazing expository ability," American Math. Monthly. vii + 120pp. 5⅜ x 8.   S434 Paperbound **$1.35**

VECTOR AND TENSOR ANALYSIS AND MATRIX THEORY

VECTOR AND TENSOR ANALYSIS, G. E. Hay. One of clearest introductions to increasingly important subject. Start with simple definitions, finish with sure mastery of oriented Cartesian vectors, Christoffel symbols, solenoidal tensors. Complete breakdown of plane, solid, analytical, differential geometry. Separate chapters on application. All fundamental formulae listed, demonstrated. 195 problems. 66 figures. viii + 193pp. 5⅜ x 8.   S109 Paperbound **$1.75**

APPLICATIONS OF TENSOR ANALYSIS, A. J. McConnell. Excellent text for applying tensor methods to such familiar subjects as dynamics, electricity, elasticity, hydrodynamics. Explains fundamental ideas and notation of tensor theory, geometrical treatment of tensor algebra, theory of differentiation of tensors, and a wealth of practical material. "The variety of fields treated and the presence of extremely numerous examples make this volume worth much more than its low price," Alluminio. Formerly titled "Applications of the Absolute Differential Calculus." 43 illustrations. 685 problems. xii + 381pp.   S373 Paperbound **$1.85**

VECTOR AND TENSOR ANALYSIS, A. P. Wills. Covers entire field, from dyads to non-Euclidean manifolds (especially detailed), absolute differentiation, the Riemann-Christoffel and Ricci-Einstein tensors, calculation of Gaussian curvature of a surface. Illustrations from electrical engineering, relativity theory, astro-physics, quantum mechanics. Presupposes only working knowledge of calculus. Intended for physicists, engineers, mathematicians. 44 diagrams. 114 problems. xxxii + 285pp. 5⅜ x 8.   S454 Paperbound **$1.75**

DOVER SCIENCE BOOKS

PHYSICS, ENGINEERING

MECHANICS, DYNAMICS, THERMODYNAMICS, ELASTICITY

MATHEMATICAL ANALYSIS OF ELECTRICAL AND OPTICAL WAVE-MOTION, H. Bateman. By one of century's most distinguished mathematical physicists, a practical introduction to developments of Maxwell's electromagnetic theory which directly concern the solution of partial differential equation of wave motion. Methods of solving wave-equation, polar-cylindrical coordinates, diffraction, transformation of coordinates, homogeneous solutions, electromagnetic fields with moving singularities, etc. 168pp. 5⅜ x 8.   S14 Paperbound **$1.60**

THERMODYNAMICS, Enrico Fermi. Unabridged reproduction of 1937 edition. Remarkable for clarity, organization; requires no knowledge of advanced math beyond calculus, only familiarity with fundamentals of thermometry, calorimetry. Partial Contents: Thermodynamic systems, 1st and 2nd laws, potentials; Entropy, phase rule; Reversible electric cells; Gaseous reactions: Van't Hoff reaction box, principle of LeChatelier; Thermodynamics of dilute solutions: osmotic, vapor pressures; boiling, freezing point; Entropy constant. 25 problems. 24 illustrations. x + 160pp. 5⅜ x 8.   S361 Paperbound **$1.75**

FOUNDATIONS OF POTENTIAL THEORY, O. D. Kellogg. Based on courses given at Harvard, suitable for both advanced and beginning mathematicians, Proofs rigorous, much material here not generally available elsewhere. Partial contents: gravity, fields of force, divergence theorem, properties of Newtonian potentials at points of free space, potentials as solutions of LaPlace's equation, harmonic functions, electrostatics, electric images, logarithmic potential, etc. ix + 384pp. 5⅜ x 8.   S144 Paperbound **$1.98**

DIALOGUES CONCERNING TWO NEW SCIENCES, Galileo Galilei. Classic of experimental science, mechanics, engineering, as enjoyable as it is important. Characterized by author as "superior to everything else of mine." Offers a lively exposition of dynamics, elasticity, sound, ballistics, strength of materials, scientific method. Translated by H. Grew, A. de Salvio. 126 diagrams. xxi + 288pp. 5⅜ x 8.   S99 Paperbound **$1.65**

THEORETICAL MECHANICS; AN INTRODUCTION TO MATHEMATICAL PHYSICS, J. S. Ames, F. D. Murnaghan. A mathematically rigorous development for advanced students, with constant practical applications. Used in hundreds of advanced courses. Unusually thorough coverage of gyroscopic baryscopic material, detailed analyses of Corilis acceleration, applications of Lagrange's equations, motion of double pendulum, Hamilton-Jacobi partial differential equations, group velocity, dispersion, etc. Special relativity included. 159 problems. 44 figures. ix + 462pp. 5⅜ x 8.   S461 Paperbound **$2.00**

STATICS AND THE DYNAMICS OF A PARTICLE, W. D. MacMillan. This is Part One of "Theoretical Mechanics." For over 3 decades a self-contained, extremely comprehensive advanced undergraduate text in mathematical physics, physics, astronomy, deeper foundations of engineering. Early sections require only a knowledge of geometry; later, a working knowledge of calculus. Hundreds of basic problems including projectiles to moon, harmonic motion, ballistics, transmission of power, stress and strain, elasticity, astronomical problems. 340 practice problems, many fully worked out examples. 200 figures. xvii + 430pp. 5⅜ x 8.
S467 Paperbound **$2.00**

THE THEORY OF THE POTENTIAL, W. D. MacMillan. This is Part Two of "Theoretical Mechanics." Comprehensive, well-balanced presentation, serving both as introduction and reference with regard to specific problems, for physicists and mathematicians. Assumes no prior knowledge of integral relations, all math is developed as needed. Includes: Attraction of Finite Bodies; Newtonian Potential Function; Vector Fields, Green and Gauss Theorems; Two-layer Surfaces; Spherical Harmonics; etc. "The great number of particular cases . . . should make the book valuable to geo-physicists and others actively engaged in practical applications of the potential theory," Review of Scientific Instruments. xii + 469pp. 5⅜ x 8.
S486 Paperbound **$2.25**

DYNAMICS OF A SYSTEM OF RIGID BODIES (Advanced Section), E. J. Routh. Revised 6th edition of a classic reference aid. Partial contents: moving axes, relative motion, oscillations about equilibrium, motion. Motion of a body under no forces, any forces. Nature of motion given by linear equations and conditions of stability. Free, forced vibrations, constants of integration, calculus of finite differences, variations, procession and mutation, motion of the moon, motion of string, chain, membranes. 64 figures. 498pp. 5⅜ x 8.
S229 Paperbound **$2.35**

THE DYNAMICS OF PARTICLES AND OF RIGID, ELASTIC, AND FLUID BODIES: BEING LECTURES ON MATHEMATICAL PHYSICS, A. G. Webster. Reissuing of classic fills need for comprehensive work on dynamics. Covers wide range in unusually great depth, applying ordinary, partial differential equations. Partial contents: laws of motion, methods applicable to systems of all sorts; oscillation, resonance, cyclic systems; dynamics of rigid bodies; potential theory; stress and strain; gyrostatics; wave, vortex motion; kinematics of a point; Lagrange's equations; Hamilton's principle; vectors; deformable bodies; much more not easily found together in one volume. Unabridged reprinting of 2nd edition. 20 pages on differential equations, higher analysis. 203 illustrations. xi + 588pp. 5⅜ x 8.   S522 Paperbound **$2.35**

PRINCIPLES OF MECHANICS, Heinrich Hertz. A classic of great interest in logic of science. Last work by great 19th century physicist, created new system of mechanics based upon space, time, mass; returns to axiomatic analysis, understanding of formal, structural aspects of science, taking into account logic, observation, a priori elements. Of great historical importance to Poincaré, Carnap, Einstein, Milne. 20 page introduction by R. S. Cohen, Wesleyan U., analyzes implications of Hertz's thought and logic of science. 13 page introduction by Helmholtz. xlii + 274pp. 5⅜ x 8.   S316 Clothbound **$3.50**
S317 Paperbound **$1.75**

MATHEMATICAL FOUNDATIONS OF STATISTICAL MECHANICS, A. I. Khinchin. A thoroughly up-to-date introduction, offering a precise and mathematically rigorous formulation of the problems of statistical mechanics. Provides analytical tools to replace many commonly used cumbersome concepts and devices. Partial contents: Geometry, kinematics of phase space; ergodic problem; theory of probability; central limit theorem; ideal monatomic gas; foundation of thermodynamics; dispersion, distribution of sum functions; etc. "Excellent introduction . . . clear, concise, rigorous," Quarterly of Applied Mathematics. viii + 179pp. 5⅜ x 8.   S146 Clothbound **$2.95**
S147 Paperbound **$1.35**

MECHANICS OF THE GYROSCOPE, THE DYNAMICS OF ROTATION, R. F. Deimel, Prof. of Mechanical Engineering, Stevens Inst. of Tech. Elementary, general treatment of dynamics of rotation, with special application of gyroscopic phenomena. No knowledge of vectors needed. Velocity of a moving curve, acceleration to a point, general equations of motion, gyroscopic horizon, free gyro, motion of discs, the damped gyro, 103 similar topics. Exercises. 75 figures. 208pp. 5⅜ x 8.   S66 Paperbound **$1.65**

MECHANICS VIA THE CALCULUS, P. W. Norris, W. S. Legge. Wide coverage, from linear motion to vector analysis; equations determining motion, linear methods, compounding of simple harmonic motions, Newton's laws of motion, Hooke's law, the simple pendulum, motion of a particle in 1 plane, centers of gravity, virtual work, friction, kinetic energy of rotating bodies, equilibrium of strings, hydrostatics, sheering stresses, elasticity, etc. Many worked-out examples. 550 problems. 3rd revised edition. xii + 367pp.   S207 Clothbound **$3.95**

A TREATISE ON THE MATHEMATICAL THEORY OF ELASTICITY, A. E. H. Love. An indispensable reference work for engineers, mathematicians, physicists, the most complete, authoritative treatment of classical elasticity in one volume. Proceeds from elementary notions of extension to types of strain, cubical dilatation, general theory of strains. Covers relation between mathematical theory of elasticity and technical mechanics; equilibrium of isotropic elastic solids and aelotropic solid bodies; nature of force transmission, Volterra's theory of dislocations; theory of elastic spheres in relation to tidal, rotational, gravitational effects on earth; general theory of bending; deformation of curved plates; buckling effects; much more. "The standard treatise on elasticity," American Math. Monthly. 4th revised edition. 76 figures. xviii + 643pp. 6⅛ x 9¼.   S174 Paperbound **$2.95**

NUCLEAR PHYSICS, QUANTUM THEORY, RELATIVITY

MESON PHYSICS, R. E. Marshak. Presents basic theory, and results of experiments with emphasis on theoretical significance. Phenomena involving mesons as virtual transitions avoided, eliminating some of least satisfactory predictions of meson theory. Includes production study of π mesons at nonrelativistic nucleon energies contracts between π and u, mesons, phenomena associated with nuclear interaction of π mesons, etc. Presents early evidence for new classes of particles, indicates theoretical difficulties created by discovery of heavy mesons and hyperons. viii + 378pp. 5⅜ x 8.   S500 Paperbound **$1.95**

THE FUNDAMENTAL PRINCIPLES OF QUANTUM MECHANICS, WITH ELEMENTARY APPLICATIONS, E. C. Kemble. Inductive presentation, for graduate student, specialists in other branches of physics. Apparatus necessary beyond differential equations and advanced calculus developed as needed. Though general exposition of principles, hundreds of individual problems fully treated. "Excellent book . . . of great value to every student . . . rigorous and detailed mathematical discussion . . . has succeeded in keeping his presentation clear and understandable," Dr. Linus Pauling, J. of American Chemical Society. Appendices: calculus of variations, math. notes, etc. 611pp. 5⅝ x 8⅜.   T472 Paperbound **$2.95**

WAVE PROPAGATION IN PERIODIC STRUCTURES, L. Brillouin. General method, application to different problems: pure physics—scattering of X-rays in crystals, thermal vibration in crystal lattices, electronic motion in metals; problems in electrical engineering. Partial contents: elastic waves along 1-dimensional lattices of point masses. Propagation of waves along 1-dimensional lattices. Energy flow. 2, 3 dimensional lattices. Mathieu's equation. Matrices and propagation of waves along an electric line. Continuous electric lines. 131 illustrations. xii + 253pp. 5⅜ x 8.   S34 Paperbound **$1.85**

4

DOVER SCIENCE BOOKS

THEORY OF ELECTRONS AND ITS APPLICATION TO THE PHENOMENA OF LIGHT AND RADIANT HEAT, H. Lorentz. Lectures delivered at Columbia Univ., by Nobel laureate. Unabridged, form historical coverage of theory of free electrons, motion, absorption of heat, Zeeman effect, optical phenomena in moving bodies, etc. 109 pages notes explain more advanced sections. 9 figures. 352pp. 5⅜ x 8.   S173 Paperbound **$1.85**

SELECTED PAPERS ON QUANTUM ELECTRODYNAMICS, edited by J. Schwinger. Facsimiles of papers which established quantum electrodynamics; beginning to present position as part of larger theory. First book publication in any language of collected papers of Bethe, Bloch, Dirac, Dyson, Fermi, Feynman, Heisenberg, Kusch, Lamb, Oppenheimer, Pauli, Schwinger, Tomonoga, Weisskopf, Wigner, etc. 34 papers: 29 in English, 1 in French, 3 in German, 1 in Italian. Historical commentary by editor. xvii + 423pp. 6⅛ x 9¼.
S444 Paperbound **$2.45**

FOUNDATIONS OF NUCLEAR PHYSICS, edited by R. T. Beyer. 13 of the most important papers on nuclear physics reproduced in facsimile in the original languages; the papers most often cited in footnotes, bibliographies. Anderson, Curie, Joliot, Chadwick, Fermi, Lawrence, Cockroft, Hahn, Yukawa. Unparalleled bibliography: 122 double columned pages, over 4,000 articles, books, classified. 57 figures. 288pp. 6⅛ x 9¼.   S19 Paperbound **$1.75**

THE THEORY OF GROUPS AND QUANTUM MECHANICS, H. Weyl. Schroedinger's wave equation, de Broglie's waves of a particle, Jordon-Hoelder theorem, Lie's continuous groups of transformations, Pauli exclusion principle, quantization of Mawell-Dirac field equations, etc. Unitary geometry, quantum theory, groups, application of groups to quantum mechanics, symmetry permutation group, algebra of symmetric transformations, etc. 2nd revised edition. xxii + 422pp. 5⅜ x 8.   S268 Clothbound **$4.50**
S269 Paperbound **$1.95**

PHYSICAL PRINCIPLES OF THE QUANTUM THEORY, Werner Heisenberg. Nobel laureate discusses quantum theory; his own work, Compton, Schroedinger, Wilson, Einstein, many others. For physicists, chemists, not specialists in quantum theory. Only elementary formulae considered in text; mathematical appendix for specialists. Profound without sacrificing clarity. Translated by C. Eckart, F. Hoyt. 18 figures. 192pp. 5⅜ x 8.
S113 Paperbound **$1.25**

INVESTIGATIONS ON THE THEORY OF THE BROWNIAN MOVEMENT, Albert Einstein. Reprints from rare European journals, translated into English. 5 basic papers, including Elementary Theory of the Brownian Movement, written at request of Lorentz to provide a simple explanation. Translated by A. D. Cowper. Annotated, edited by R. Fürth. 33pp. of notes elucidate, give history of previous investigations. 62 footnotes. 124pp. 5⅜ x 8.
S304 Paperbound **$1.25**

THE PRINCIPLE OF RELATIVITY, E. Einstein, H. Lorentz, M. Minkowski, H. Weyl. The 11 basic papers that founded the general and special theories of relativity, translated into English. 2 papers by Lorentz on the Michelson experiment, electromagnetic phenomena. Minkowski's "Space and Time," and Weyl's "Gravitation and Electricity." 7 epoch-making papers by Einstein: "Electromagnetics of Moving Bodies," "Influence of Gravitation in Propagation of Light," "Cosmological Considerations," "General Theory," 3 others. 7 diagrams. Special notes by A. Sommerfeld. 224pp. 5⅜ x 8.   S93 Paperbound **$1.75**

STATISTICS

ELEMENTARY STATISTICS, WITH APPLICATIONS IN MEDICINE AND THE BIOLOGICAL SCIENCES, F. E. Croxton. Based primarily on biological sciences, but can be used by anyone desiring introduction to statistics. Assumes no prior acquaintance, requires only modest knowledge of math. All basic formulas carefully explained, illustrated; all necessary reference tables included. From basic terms and concepts, proceeds to frequency distribution, linear, nonlinear, multiple correlation, etc. Contains concrete examples from medicine, biology. 101 charts. 57 tables. 14 appendices. lv + 376pp. 5⅜ x 8.   S506 Paperbound **$1.95**

ANALYSIS AND DESIGN OF EXPERIMENTS, H. B. Mann. Offers method for grasping analysis of variance, variance design quickly. Partial contents: Chi-square distribution, analysis of variance distribution, matrices, quadratic forms, likelihood ration tests, test of linear hypotheses, power of analysis, Galois fields, non-orthogonal data, interblock estimates, etc. 15pp. of useful tables. x + 195pp. 5 x 7⅜.   S180 Paperbound **$1.45**

FREQUENCY CURVES AND CORRELATION, W. P. Elderton. 4th revised edition of standard work on classical statistics. Practical, one of few books constantly referred to for clear presentation of basic material. Partial contents: Frequency Distributions; Pearsons Frequency Curves; Theoretical Distributions; Standard Errors; Correlation Ratio—Contingency; Corrections for Moments, Beta, Gamma Functions; etc. Key to terms, symbols. 25 examples. 40 tables. 16 figures. xi + 272pp. 5½ x 8½.   Clothbound **$1.49**

HYDRODYNAMICS, ETC.

HYDRODYNAMICS, Horace Lamb. Standard reference work on dynamics of liquids and gases. Fundamental theorems, equations, methods, solutions, background for classical hydrodynamics. Chapters: Equations of Motion, Integration of Equations in Special Gases, Vortex Motion, Tidal Waves, Rotating Masses of Liquids, etc. Excellently planned, arranged, Clear, lucid presentation. 6th enlarged, revised edition. Over 900 footnotes, mostly bibliographical. 119 figures. xv + 738pp. 6⅛ x 9¼.   S256 Paperbound **$2.95**

HYDRODYNAMICS, A STUDY OF LOGIC, FACT, AND SIMILITUDE, Garrett Birkhoff. A stimulating application of pure mathematics to an applied problem. Emphasis is on correlation of theory and deduction with experiment. Examines recently discovered paradoxes, theory of modelling and dimensional analysis, paradox and error in flows and free boundary theory. Classical theory of virtual mass derived from homogenous spaces; group theory applied to fluid mechanics. 20 figures, 3 plates. xiii + 186pp. 5⅜ x 8.   S22 Paperbound **$1.85**

HYDRODYNAMICS, H. Dryden, F. Murhaghan, H. Bateman. Published by National Research Council, 1932. Complete coverage of classical hydrodynamics, encyclopedic in quality. Partial contents: physics of fluids, motion, turbulent flow, compressible fluids, motion in 1, 2, 3 dimensions; laminar motion, resistance of motion through viscous fluid, eddy viscosity, discharge of gases, flow past obstacles, etc. Over 2900-item bibliography. 23 figures. 634pp. 5⅜ x 8.   S303 Paperbound **$2.75**

ACOUSTICS AND OPTICS

PRINCIPLES OF PHYSICAL OPTICS, Ernst Mach. Classical examination of propagation of light, color, polarization, etc. Historical, philosophical treatment unequalled for breadth and readability. Contents: Rectilinear propagation, reflection, refraction, dioptrics, composition of light, periodicity, theory of interference, polarization, mathematical representation of properties, etc. 279 illustrations. 10 portraits. 324pp. 5⅜ x 8.   S170 Paperbound **$1.75**

THE THEORY OF SOUND, Lord Rayleigh. Written by Nobel laureate, classical methods here will cover most vibrating systems likely to be encountered in practice. Complete coverage of experimental, mathematical aspects. Partial contents: Harmonic motions, lateral vibrations of bars, curved plates or shells, applications of Laplace's functions to acoustical problems, fluid friction, etc. First low-priced edition of this great reference-study work. Historical introduction by R. B. Lindsay. 1040pp. 97 figures. 5⅜ x 8.
S292, S293, Two volume set, paperbound **$4.00**

THEORY OF VIBRATIONS, N. W. McLachlan. Based on exceptionally successful graduate course, Brown University. Discusses linear systems having 1 degree of freedom, forced vibrations of simple linear systems, vibration of flexible strings, transverse vibrations of bars and tubes, of circular plate, sound waves of finite amplitude, etc. 99 diagrams. 160pp. 5⅜ x 8.   S190 Paperbound **$1.35**

APPLIED OPTICS AND OPTICAL DESIGN, A. E. Conrady. Thorough systematic presentation of physical and mathematical aspects, limited mostly to "real optics." Stresses practical problem of maximum aberration permissible without affecting performance. Ordinary ray tracing methods; complete theory ray tracing methods, primary aberrations; enough higher aberration to design telescopes, low powered microscopes, photographic equipment. Covers fundamental equations, extra-axial image points, transverse chromatic aberration, angular magnification, similar topics. Tables of functions of N. Over 150 diagrams. x + 518pp. 5⅜ x 8⅝.   S366 Paperbound **$2.98**

RAYLEIGH'S PRINCIPLE AND ITS APPLICATIONS TO ENGINEERING, G. Temple, W. Bickley. Rayleigh's principle developed to provide upper, lower estimates of true value of fundamental period of vibrating system, or condition of stability of elastic system. Examples, rigorous proofs. Partial contents: Energy method of discussing vibrations, stability. Perturbation theory, whirling of uniform shafts. Proof, accuracy, successive approximations, applications of Rayleigh's theory. Numerical, graphical methods. Ritz's method. 22 figures. ix + 156pp. 5⅜ x 8.   S307 Paperbound **$1.50**

OPTICKS, Sir Isaac Newton. In its discussion of light, reflection, color, refraction, theories of wave and corpuscular theories of light, this work is packed with scores of insights and discoveries. In its precise and practical discussions of construction of optical apparatus, contemporary understanding of phenomena, it is truly fascinating to modern scientists. Foreword by Albert Einstein. Preface by I. B. Cohen, Harvard. 7 pages of portraits, facsimile pages, letters, etc. cxvi + 414pp. 5⅜ x 8.   S205 Paperbound **$2.00**

ON THE SENSATIONS OF TONE, Hermann Helmholtz. Using acoustical physics, physiology, experiment, history of music, covers entire gamut of musical tone: relation of music science to acoustics, physical vs. physiological acoustics, vibration, resonance, tonality, progression of parts, etc. 33 appendixes on various aspects of sound, physics, acoustics, music, etc. Translated by A. J. Ellis. New introduction by H. Margenau, Yale. 68 figures. 43 musical passages analyzed. Over 100 tables. xix + 576pp. 6⅛ x 9¼.
S114 Clothbound **$4.95**

ELECTROMAGNETICS, ENGINEERING, TECHNOLOGY

INTRODUCTION TO RELAXATION METHODS, F. S. Shaw. Describes almost all manipulative resources of value in solution of differential equations. Treatment is mathematical rather than physical. Extends general computational process to include almost all branches of applied math and physics. Approximate numerical methods are demonstrated, although high accuracy is obtainable without undue expenditure of time. 48pp. of tables for computing irregular star first and second derivatives, irregular star coefficients for second order equations, for fourth order equations. "Useful. . . . exposition is clear, simple . . . no previous acquaintance with numerical methods is assumed," Science Progress. 253 diagrams. 72 tables. 400pp. 5⅜ x 8.
S244 Paperbound **$2.45**

THE ELECTROMAGNETIC FIELD, M. Mason, W. Weaver. Used constantly by graduate engineers. Vector methods exclusively; detailed treatment of electrostatics, expansion methods, with tables converting any quantity into absolute electromagnetic, absolute electrostatic, practical units. Discrete charges, ponderable bodies. Maxwell field equations, etc. 416pp. 5⅜ x 8.
S185 Paperbound **$2.00**

ELASTICITY, PLASTICITY AND STRUCTURE OF MATTER, R. Houwink. Standard treatise on rheological aspects of different technically important solids: crystals, resins, textiles, rubber, clay, etc. Investigates general laws for deformations; determines divergences. Covers general physical and mathematical aspects of plasticity, elasticity, viscosity. Detailed examination of deformations, internal structure of matter in relation to elastic, plastic behaviour, formation of solid matter from a fluid, etc. Treats glass, asphalt, balata, proteins, baker's dough, others. 2nd revised, enlarged edition. Extensive revised bibliography in over 500 footnotes. 214 figures. xvii + 368pp. 6 x 9¼.
S385 Paperbound **$2.45**

DESIGN AND USE OF INSTRUMENTS AND ACCURATE MECHANISM, T. N. Whitehead. For the instrument designer, engineer; how to combine necessary mathematical abstractions with independent observations of actual facts. Partial contents: instruments and their parts, theory of errors, systematic errors, probability, short period errors, erratic errors, design precision, kinematic, semikinematic design, stiffness, planning of an instrument, human factor, etc. 85 photos, diagrams. xii + 288pp. 5⅜ x 8.
S270 Paperbound **$1.95**

APPLIED HYDRO- AND AEROMECHANICS, L. Prandtl, O. G. Tietjens. Presents, for most part, methods valuable to engineers. Flow in pipes, boundary layers, airfoil theory, entry conditions, turbulent flow, boundary layer determining drag from pressure and velocity, etc. "Will be welcomed by all students of aerodynamics," Nature. Unabridged, unaltered. An Engineering Society Monograph, 1934. Index. 226 figures. 28 photographic plates illustrating flow patterns. xvi + 311pp. 5⅜ x 8.
S375 Paperbound **$1.85**

FUNDAMENTALS OF HYDRO- AND AEROMECHANICS, L. Prandtl, O. G. Tietjens. Standard work, based on Prandtl's lectures at Goettingen. Wherever possible hydrodynamics theory is referred to practical considerations in hydraulics, unifying theory and experience. Presentation extremely clear. Though primarily physical, proofs are rigorous and use vector analysis to a great extent. An Engineering Society Monograph, 1934. "Still recommended as an excellent introduction to this area," Physikalische Blätter. 186 figures. xvi + 270pp. 5⅜ x 8.
S374 Paperbound **$1.85**

GASEOUS CONDUCTORS: THEORY AND ENGINEERING APPLICATIONS, J. D. Cobine. Indispensable text, reference, to gaseous conduction phenomena, with engineering viewpoint prevailing throughout. Studies kinetic theory of gases, ionization, emission phenomena; gas breakdown, spark characteristics, glow, discharges; engineering applications in circuit interrupters, rectifiers, etc. Detailed treatment of high pressure arcs (Suits); low pressure arcs (Langmuir, Tonks). Much more. "Well organized, clear, straightforward," Tonks, Review of Scientific Instruments. 83 practice problems. Over 600 figures. 58 tables. xx + 606pp. 5⅜ x 8.
S442 Paperbound **$2.75**

PHOTOELASTICITY: PRINCIPLES AND METHODS, H. T. Jessop, F. C. Harris. For engineer, specific problems of stress analysis. Latest time-saving methods of checking calculations in 2-dimensional design problems, new techniques for stresses in 3 dimensions, lucid description of optical systems used in practical photoelectricity. Useful suggestions, hints based on on-the-job experience included. Partial contents: strain, stress-strain relations, circular disc under thrust along diameter, rectangular block with square hold under vertical thrust, simply supported rectangular beam under central concentrated load, etc. Theory held to minimum, no advanced mathematical training needed. 164 illustrations. viii + 184pp. 6⅛ x 9¼.
S137 Clothbound **$3.75**

MICROWAVE TRANSMISSION DESIGN DATA, T. Moreno. Originally classified, now rewritten, enlarged (14 new chapters) under auspices of Sperry Corp. Of immediate value or reference use to radio engineers, systems designers, applied physicists, etc. Ordinary transmission line theory; attenuation; parameters of coaxial lines; flexible cables; tuneable wave guide impedance transformers; effects of temperature, humidity; much more. "Packed with information . . . theoretical discussions are directly related to practical questions," U. of Royal Naval Scientific Service. Tables of dielectrics, flexible cable, etc. ix + 248pp. 5⅜ x 8.
S549 Paperbound **$1.50**

THE THEORY OF THE PROPERTIES OF METALS AND ALLOYS, H. F. Mott, H. Jones. Quantum methods develop mathematical models showing interrelationship of fundamental chemical phenomena wtih crystal structure, electrical, optical properties, etc. Examines electron motion in applied field, cohesion, heat capacity, refraction, noble metals, transition and di-valent metals, etc. "Exposition is as clear . . . mathematical treatment as simple and reliable as we have become used to expect of . . . Prof. Mott," Nature. 138 figures. xiii + 320pp. 5⅜ x 8.
S456 Paperbound **$1.85**

THE MEASUREMENT OF POWER SPECTRA FROM THE POINT OF VIEW OF COMMUNICATIONS ENGINEERING, R. B. Blackman, J. W. Tukey. Pathfinding work reprinted from "Bell System Technical Journal." Various ways of getting practically useful answers in power spectra measurement, using results from both transmission and statistical estimation theory. Treats: Autocovariance, Functions and Power Spectra, Distortion, Heterodyne Filtering, Smoothing, Decimation Procedures, Transversal Filtering, much more. Appendix reviews fundamental Fourier techniques. Index of notation. Glossary of terms. 24 figures. 12 tables. 192pp. 5⅝ x 8⅝.
S507 Paperbound **$1.85**

TREATISE ON ELECTRICITY AND MAGNETISM, James Clerk Maxwell. For more than 80 years a seemingly inexhaustible source of leads for physicists, mathematicians, engineers. Total of 1082pp. on such topics as Measurement of Quantities, Electrostatics, Elementary Mathematical Theory of Electricity, Electrical Work and Energy in a System of Conductors, General Theorems, Theory of Electrical Images, Electrolysis, Conduction, Polarization, Dielectrics, Resistance, much more. "The greatest mathematical physicist since Newton," Sir James Jeans. 3rd edition. 107 figures, 21 plates. 1082pp. 5⅜ x 8.
S186 Clothbound **$4.95**

CHEMISTRY AND PHYSICAL CHEMISTRY

THE PHASE RULE AND ITS APPLICATIONS, Alexander Findlay. Covers chemical phenomena of 1 to 4 multiple component systems, the "standard work on the subject" (Nature). Completely revised, brought up to date by A. N. Campbell, N. O. Smith. New material on binary, tertiary liquid equilibria, solid solutions in ternary systems, quinary systems of salts, water, etc. Completely revised to triangular coordinates in ternary systems, clarified graphic ¡representation, solid models, etc. 9th revised edition. 236 figures. 505 footnotes, mostly bibliographic. xii + 449pp. 5⅜ x 8.
S92 Paperbound **$2.45**

DYNAMICAL THEORY OF GASES, James Jeans. Divided into mathematical, physical chapters for convenience of those not expert in mathematics. Discusses mathematical theory of gas in steady state, thermodynamics, Bolzmann, Maxwell, kinetic theory, quantum theory, exponentials, etc. "One of the classics of scientific writing . . . as lucid and comprehensive an exposition of the kinetic theory as has ever been written," J. of Institute of Engineers. 4th enlarged edition, with new material on quantum theory, quantum dynamics, etc. 28 figures. 444pp. 6⅛ x 9¼.
S136 Paperbound **$2.45**

POLAR MOLECULES, Pieter Debye. Nobel laureate offers complete guide to fundamental electrostatic field relations, polarizability, molecular structure. Partial contents: electric intensity, displacement, force, polarization by orientation, molar polarization, molar refraction, halogen-hydrides, polar liquids, ionic saturation, dielectric constant, etc. Special chapter considers quantum theory. "Clear and concise . . . coordination of experimental results with theory will be readily appreciated," Electronics Industries. 172pp. 5⅜ x 8.
S63 Clothbound **$3.50**
S64 Paperbound **$1.50**

ATOMIC SPECTRA AND ATOMIC STRUCTURE, G. Herzberg. Excellent general survey for chemists, physicists specializing in other fields. Partial contents: simplest line spectra, elements of atomic theory; multiple structure of line spectra, electron spin; building-up principle, periodic system of elements; finer details of atomic spectra; hyperfine structure of spectral lines; some experimental results and applications. 80 figures. 20 tables. xiii + 257pp. 5⅜ x 8.
S115 Paperbound **$1.95**

TREATISE ON THERMODYNAMICS, Max Planck. Classic based on his original papers. Brilliant concepts of Nobel laureate make no assumptions regarding nature of heat, rejects earlier approaches of Helmholtz, Maxwell, to offer uniform point of view for entire field. Seminal work by founder of quantum theory, deducing new physical, chemical laws. A standard text, an excellent introduction to field for students with knowledge of elementary chemistry, physics, calculus. 3rd English edition. xvi + 297pp. 5⅜ x 8.
S219 Paperbound **$1.75**

8

DOVER SCIENCE BOOKS

KINETIC THEORY OF LIQUIDS, J. Frenkel. Regards kinetic theory of liquids as generalization, extension of theory of solid bodies, covers all types of arrangements of solids; thermal displacements of atoms; interstitial atoms, ions; orientational, rotational motion of molecules; transition between states of matter. Mathematical theory developed close to physical subject matter. "Discussed in a simple yet deeply penetrating fashion . . . will serve as seeds for a great many basic and applied developments in chemistry," J. of the Amer. Chemical Soc. 216 bibliographical footnotes. 55 figures. xi + 485pp. 5⅜ x 8.

S94 Clothbound **$3.95**
S95 Paperbound **$2.45**

ASTRONOMY

OUT OF THE SKY, H. H. Nininger. Non-technical, comprehensive introduction to "meteoritics" —science concerned with arrival of matter from outer space. By one of world's experts on meteorites, this book defines meteors and meteorites; studies fireball clusters and processions, meteorite composition, size, distribution, showers, explosions, origins, much more. viii + 336pp. 5⅜ x 8.

T519 Paperbound **$1.85**

AN INTRODUCTION TO THE STUDY OF STELLAR STRUCTURE, S. Chandrasekhar. Outstanding treatise on stellar dynamics by one of greatest astro-physicists. Examines relationship between loss of energy, mass, and radius of stars in steady state. Discusses thermodynamic laws from Caratheodory's axiomatic standpoint; adiabatic, polytropic laws; work of Ritter, Emden, Kelvin, etc.; Stroemgren envelopes as starter for theory of gaseous stars; Gibbs statistical mechanics (quantum); degenerate stellar configuration, theory of white dwarfs; etc. "Highest level of scientific merit," Bulletin. Amer. Math. Soc. 33 figures. 509pp. 5⅜ x 8.

S413 Paperbound **$2.75**

LES MÉTHODES NOVELLES DE LA MÉCANIQUE CÉLESTE, H. Poincaré. Complete French text of one of Poincaré's most important works. Revolutionized celestial mechanics: first use of integral invariants, first major application of linear differential equations, study of periodic orbits, lunar motion and Jupiter's satellites, three body problem, and many other important topics. "Started a new era . . . so extremely modern that even today few have mastered his weapons," E. T. Bell. 3 volumes. Total 1282pp. 6⅛ x 9¼.

Vol. 1 S401 Paperbound **$2.75**
Vol. 2 S402 Paperbound **$2.75**
Vol. 3 S403 Paperbound **$2.75**
The set **$7.50**

THE REALM OF THE NEBULAE, E. Hubble. One of the great astronomers of our time presents his concept of "island universes," and describes its effect on astronomy. Covers velocity-distance relation; classification, nature, distances, general field of nebulae; cosmological theories; nebulae in the neighborhood of the Milky way; etc. 39 photos, including velocity-distance relations shown by spectrum comparison. "One of the most progressive lines of astronomical research," The Times, London. New Introduction by A. Sandage. 55 illustrations. xxiv + 201pp. 5⅜ x 8.

S455 Paperbound **$1.50**

HOW TO MAKE A TELESCOPE, Jean Texereau. Design, build an f/6 or f/8 Newtonian type reflecting telescope, with altazimuth Couder mounting, suitable for planetary, lunar, and stellar observation. Covers every operation step-by-step, every piece of equipment. Discusses basic principles of geometric and physical optics (unnecessary to construction), comparative merits of reflectors, refractors. A thorough discussion of eyepieces, finders, grinding, installation, testing, etc. 241 figures, 38 photos, show almost every operation and tool. Potential errors are anticipated. Foreword by A. Couder. Sources of supply. xiii + 191pp. 6¼ x 10.

T464 Clothbound **$3.50**

BIOLOGICAL SCIENCES

THE BIOLOGY OF THE AMPHIBIA, G. K. Noble, Late Curator of Herpetology at Am. Mus. of Nat. Hist. Probably most used text on amphibia, most comprehensive, clear, detailed. 19 chapters, 85 page supplement: development; heredity; life history; speciation; adaptation; sex, integument, respiratory, circulatory, digestive, muscular, nervous systems; instinct, intelligence, habits, economic value classification, environment relationships, etc. "Nothing comparable to it," C. H. Pope, curator of Amphibia, Chicago Mus. of Nat. Hist. 1047 item bibliography. 174 illustrations. 600pp. 5⅜ x 8.

S206 Paperbound **$2.98**

THE ORIGIN OF LIFE, A. I. Oparin. A classic of biology. This is the first modern statement of theory of gradual evolution of life from nitrocarbon compounds. A brand-new evaluation of Oparin's theory in light of later research, by Dr. S. Margulis, University of Nebraska. xxv + 270pp. 5⅜ x 8.

S213 Paperbound **$1.75**

THE BIOLOGY OF THE LABORATORY MOUSE, edited by G. D. Snell. Prepared in 1941 by staff of Roscoe B. Jackson Memorial Laboratory, still the standard treatise on the mouse, assembling enormous amount of material for which otherwise you spend hours of research. Embryology, reproduction, histology, spontaneous neoplasms, genes and chromosomes mutations, genetics of spontaneous tumor formations, of tumor transplantation, endocrine secretion and tumor formation, milk influence and tumor formation, inbred, hybrid animals, parasites, infectious diseases, care and recording. "A wealth of information of vital concern. . . . recommended to all who could use a book on such a subject," Nature. Classified bibliography of 1122 items. 172 figures, including 128 photos. ix + 497pp. 6⅛ x 9¼.
S248 Clothbound **$6.00**

THE TRAVELS OF WILLIAM BARTRAM, edited by Mark Van Doran. Famous source-book of American anthropology, natural history, geography, is record kept by Bartram in 1770's on travels through wilderness of Florida, Georgia, Carolinas. Containing accurate, beautiful descriptions of Indians, settlers, fauna, flora, it is one of finest pieces of Americana ever written. 13 original illustrations. 448pp. 5⅜ x 8.
T13 Paperbound **$2.00**

BEHAVIOUR AND SOCIAL LIFE OF THE HONEYBEE, Ronald Ribbands. Outstanding scientific study; a compendium of practically everything known of social life of honeybee. Stresses behaviour of individual bees in field, hive. Extends von Frisch's experiments on communication among bees. Covers perception of temperature, gravity, distance, vibration; sound production; glands; structural differences; wax production; temperature regulation; recognition, communication; drifting, mating behaviour, other highly interesting topics. "This valuable work is sure of a cordial reception by laymen, beekeepers and scientists," Prof. Karl von Frisch, Brit. J. of Animal Behaviour. Bibliography of 690 references. 127 diagrams, graphs, sections of bee anatomy, fine photographs. 352pp.
S410 Clothbound **$4.50**

ELEMENTS OF MATHEMATICAL BIOLOGY, A. J. Lotka. Pioneer classic, 1st major attempt to apply modern mathematical techniques on large scale to phenomena of biology, biochemistry, psychology, ecology, similar life sciences. Partial contents: Statistical meaning of irreversibility; Evolution as redistribution; Equations of kinetics of evolving systems; Chemical, inter-species equilibrium; parameters of state; Energy transformers of nature, etc. Can be read with profit by even those having no advanced math; unsurpassed as study-reference. Formerly titled "Elements of Physical Biology." 72 figures. xxx + 460pp. 5⅜ x 8.
S346 Paperbound **$2.45**

TREES OF THE EASTERN AND CENTRAL UNITED STATES AND CANADA, W. M. Harlow. Serious middle-level text covering more than 140 native trees, important escapes, with information on general appearance, growth habit, leaf forms, flowers, fruit, bark, commercial use, distribution, habitat, woodlore, etc. Keys within text enable you to locate various species easily, to know which have edible fruit, much more useful, interesting information. "Well illustrated to make identification very easy," Standard Cat. for Public Libraries. Over 600 photographs, figures. xiii + 288pp. 5⅝ x 6½.
T395 Paperbound **$1.35**

FRUIT KEY AND TWIG KEY TO TREES AND SHRUBS (Fruit key to Northeastern Trees, Twig key to Deciduous Woody Plants of Eastern North America), W. M. Harlow. Only guides with photographs of every twig, fruit described. Especially valuable to novice. Fruit key (both deciduous trees, evergreens) has introduction on seeding, organs involved, types, habits. Twig key introduction treats growth, morphology. In keys proper, identification is almost automatic. Exceptional work, widely used in university courses, especially useful for identification in winter, or from fruit or seed only. Over 350 photos, up to 3 times natural size. Index of common, scientific names, in each key. xvii + 125pp. 5⅝ x 8⅜.
T511 Paperbound **$1.25**

INSECT LIFE AND INSECT NATURAL HISTORY, S. W. Frost. Unusual for emphasizing habits, social life, ecological relations of insects rather than more academic aspects of classification, morphology. Prof. Frost's enthusiasm and knowledge are everywhere evident as he discusses insect associations, specialized habits like leaf-rolling, leaf mining, case-making, the gall insects, boring insects, etc. Examines matters not usually covered in general works: insects as human food; insect music, musicians; insect response to radio waves; use of insects in art, literature. "Distinctly different, possesses an individuality all its own," Journal of Forestry. Over 700 illustrations. Extensive bibliography. x + 524pp. 5⅜ x 8.
T519 Paperbound **$2.49**

A WAY OF LIFE, AND OTHER SELECTED WRITING● Sir William Osler. Physician, humanist, Osler discusses brilliantly Thomas Browne, Gui Patin, Robert Burton, Michael Servetus, William Beaumont, Laennec. Includes such favorite writing as title essay, "The Old Humanities and the New Science," "Books and Men," "The Student Life," 6 more of his best discussions of philosophy, literature, religion. "The sweep of his mind and interests embraced every phase of human activity," G. L. Keynes. 5 photographs. Introduction by G. L. Keynes, M.D., F.R.C.S. xx + 278pp. 5⅜ x 8.
T488 Paperbound **$1.50**

THE GENETICAL THEORY OF NATURAL SELECTION, R. A. Fisher. 2nd revised edition of vital reviewing of Darwin's Selection Theory in terms of particulate inheritance, by one of greatest authorities on experimental, theoretical genetics. Theory stated in mathematical form. Special features of particulate inheritance are examined: evolution of dominance, maintenance of specific variability, mimicry, sexual selection, etc. 5 chapters on man's special circumstances as a social animal. 16 photographs. x + 310pp. 5⅜ x 8.
S466 Paperbound **$1.85**

DOVER SCIENCE BOOKS

THE AUTOBIOGRAPHY OF CHARLES DARWIN, AND SELECTED LETTERS, edited by Francis Darwin. Darwin's own record of early life; historic voyage aboard "Beagle;" furore surrounding evolution, his replies; reminiscences of his son. Letters to Henslow, Lyell, Hooker, Huxley, Wallace, Kingsley, etc., and thoughts on religion, vivisection. We see how he revolutionized geology with concepts of ocean subsidence; how his great books on variation of plants and animals, primitive man, expression of emotion among primates, plant fertilization, carnivorous plants, protective coloration, etc., came into being. 365pp. 5⅜ x 8.
T479 Paperbound **$1.65**

ANIMALS IN MOTION, Eadweard Muybridge. Largest, most comprehensive selection of Muybridge's famous action photos of animals, from his "Animal Locomotion." 3919 high-speed shots of 34 different animals, birds, in 123 types of action; horses, mules, oxen, pigs, goats, camels, elephants, dogs, cats guanacos, sloths, lions, tigers, jaguars, raccoons, baboons, deer, elk, gnus, kangaroos, many others, walking, running, flying, leaping. Horse alone in over 40 ways. Photos taken against ruled backgrounds; most actions taken from 3 angles at once: 90°, 60°, rear. Most plates original size. Of considerable interest to scientists as biology classic, records of actual facts of natural history, physiology. "Really marvelous series of plates," Nature. "Monumental work," Waldemar Kaempffert. Edited by L. S. Brown, 74 page introduction on mechanics of motion. 340pp. of plates. 3919 photographs. 416pp. Deluxe binding, paper. (Weight: 4½ lbs.) 7⅛ x 10⅝.
T203 Clothbound **$10.00**

THE HUMAN FIGURE IN MOTION, Eadweard Muybridge. New edition of great classic in history of science and photography, largest selection ever made from original Muybridge photos of human action: 4789 photographs, illustrating 163 types of motion: walking, running, lifting, etc. in time-exposure sequence photos at speeds up to 1/6000th of a second. Men, women, children, mostly undraped, showing bone, muscle positions against ruled backgrounds, mostly taken at 3 angles at once. Not only was this a great work of photography, acclaimed by contemporary critics as work of genius, but it was also a great 19th century landmark in biological research. Historical introduction by Prof. Robert Taft, U. of Kansas. Plates original size, full of detail. Over 500 action strips. 407pp. 7¾ x 10⅝. Deluxe edition.
7204 Clothbound **$10.00**

AN INTRODUCTION TO THE STUDY OF EXPERIMENTAL MEDICINE, Claude Bernard. 90-year old classic of medical science, only major work of Bernard available in English, records his efforts to transform physiology into exact science. Principles of scientific research illustrated by specified case histories from his work; roles of chance, error, preliminary false conclusion, in leading eventually to scientific truth; use of hypothesis. Much of modern application of mathematics to biology rests on foundation set down here. "The presentation is polished . . . reading is easy," Revue des questions scientifiques. New foreword by Prof. I. B. Cohen, Harvard U. xxv + 266pp. 5⅜ x 8.
T400 Paperbound **$1.50**

STUDIES ON THE STRUCTURE AND DEVELOPMENT OF VERTEBRATES, E. S. Goodrich. Definitive study by greatest modern comparative anatomist. Exhaustive morphological, phylogenetic expositions of skeleton, fins, limbs, skeletal visceral arches, labial cartilages, visceral clefts, gills, vascular, respiratory, excretory, periphal nervous systems, etc., from fish to higher mammals. "For many a day this will certainly be the standard textbook on Vertebrate Morphology in the English language," Journal of Anatomy. 754 illustrations. 69 page biographical study by C. C. Hardy. Bibliography of 1186 references. Two volumes, total 906pp. 5⅜ x 8.
Two vol. set S449, 450 Paperbound **$5.00**

EARTH SCIENCES

THE EVOLUTION OF IGNEOUS BOOKS, N. L. Bowen. Invaluable serious introduction applies techniques of physics, chemistry to explain igneous rock diversity in terms of chemical composition, fractional crystallization. Discusses liquid immiscibility in silicate magmas, crystal sorting, liquid lines of descent, fractional resorption of complex minerals, petrogen, etc. Of prime importance to geologists, mining engineers; physicists, chemists working with high temperature, pressures. "Most important," Times, London. 263 bibliographic notes. 82 figures. xviii + 334pp. 5⅜ x 8.
S311 Paperbound **$1.85**

GEOGRAPHICAL ESSAYS, M. Davis. Modern geography, geomorphology rest on fundamental work of this scientist. 26 famous essays present most important theories, field researches. Partial contents: Geographical Cycle; Plains of Marine, Subaerial Denudation; The Peneplain; Rivers, Valleys of Pennsylvania; Outline of Cape Cod; Sculpture of Mountains by Glaciers; etc. "Long the leader and guide," Economic Geography. "Part of the very texture of geography . . . models of clear thought," Geographic Review. 130 figures. vi + 777pp. 5⅜ x 8.
S383 Paperbound **$2.95**

URANIUM PROSPECTING, H. L. Barnes. For immediate practical use, professional geologist considers uranium ores, geological occurrences, field conditions, all aspects of highly profitable occupation. "Helpful information . . . easy-to-use, easy-to-find style," Geotimes. x + 117pp. 5⅜ x 8.
T309 Paperbound **$1.00**

DE RE METALLICA, Georgius Agricola. 400 year old classic translated, annotated by former President Herbert Hoover. 1st scientific study of mineralogy, mining, for over 200 years after its appearance in 1556 the standard treatise. 12 books, exhaustively annotated, discuss history of mining, selection of sites, types of deposits, making pits, shafts, ventilating, pumps, crushing machinery; assaying, smelting, refining metals; also salt alum, nitre, glass making. Definitive edition, with all 289 16th century woodcuts of original. Biographical, historical introductions. Bibliography, survey of ancient authors. Indexes. A fascinating book for anyone interested in art, history of science, geology, etc. Deluxe Edition. 289 illustrations. 672pp. 6¾ x 10. Library cloth. S6 Clothbound **$10.00**

INTERNAL CONSTITUTION OF THE EARTH, edited by Beno Gutenberg. Prepared for National Research Council, this is a complete, thorough coverage of earth origins, continent formation, nature and behaviour of earth's core, petrology of crust, cooling forces in core, seismic and earthquake material, gravity, elastic constants, strain characteristics, similar topics. "One is filled with admiration . . . a high standard . . . there is no reader who will not learn something from this book," London, Edinburgh, Dublin, Philosophic Magazine. Largest Bibliography in print: 1127 classified items. Table of constants. 43 diagrams. 439pp. 6⅛ x 9¼. S414 Paperbound **$2.45**

THE BIRTH AND DEVELOPMENT OF THE GEOLOGICAL SCIENCES, F. D. Adams. Most thorough history of earth sciences ever written. Geological thought from earliest times to end of 19th century, covering over 300 early thinkers and systems; fossils and their explanation, vulcanists vs. neptunists, figured stones and paleontology, generation of stones, dozens of similar topics. 91 illustrations, including Medieval, Renaissance woodcuts, etc. 632 footnotes, mostly bibliographical. 511pp. 5⅜ x 8. T5 Paperbound **$2.00**

HYDROLOGY, edited by O. E. Meinzer, prepared for the National Research Council. Detailed, complete reference library on precipitation, evaporation, snow, snow surveying, glaciers, lakes, infiltration, soil moisture, ground water, runoff, drought, physical changes produced by water hydrology of limestone terranes, etc. Practical in application, especially valuable for engineers. 24 experts have created "the most up-to-date, most complete treatment of the subject," Am. Assoc. of Petroleum Geologists. 165 illustrations. xi + 712pp. 6⅛ x 9¼. S191 Paperbound **$2.95**

LANGUAGE AND TRAVEL AIDS FOR SCIENTISTS

SAY IT language phrase books

"SAY IT" in the foreign language of your choice! We have sold over ½ million copies of these popular, useful language books. They will not make you an expert linguist overnight, but they do cover most practical matters of everyday life abroad.

Over 1000 useful phrases, expressions, additional variants, substitutions.

Modern! Useful! Hundreds of phrases not available in other texts: "Nylon," "air-conditioned," etc.

The ONLY inexpensive phrase book **completely indexed.** Everything is available at a flip of your finger, ready to use.

Prepared by native linguists, travel experts.

Based on years of travel experience abroad.

May be used by itself, or to supplement any other text or course. Provides a living element. Used by many colleges, institutions: Hunter College; Barnard College; Army Ordinance School, Aberdeen; etc.

Available, 1 book per language:

Danish (T818) 75¢
Dutch (T817) 75¢
English (for German-speaking people) (T801) 60¢
English (for Italian-speaking people) (T816) 60¢
English (for Spanish-speaking people) (T802) 60¢
Esperanto (T820) 75¢
French (T803) 60¢
German (T804) 60¢
Modern Greek (T813) 75¢
Hebrew (T805) 60¢

Italian (T806) 60¢
Japanese (T807) 75¢
Norwegian (T814) 75¢
Russian (T810) 75¢
Spanish (T811) 60¢
Turkish (T821) 75¢
Yiddish (T815) 75¢
Swedish (T812) 75¢
Polish (T808) 75¢
Portuguese (T809) 75¢

MONEY CONVERTER AND TIPPING GUIDE FOR EUROPEAN TRAVEL, C. Vomacka. Purse-size handbook crammed with information on currency regulations, tipping for every European country, including Israel, Turkey, Czechoslovakia, Rumania, Egypt, Russia, Poland. Telephone, postal rates; duty-free imports, passports, visas, health certificates; foreign clothing sizes; weather tables. What, when to tip. 5th year of publication. 128pp. 3½ x 5¼.   T260 Paperbound 60¢

NEW RUSSIAN-ENGLISH AND ENGLISH-RUSSIAN DICTIONARY, M. A. O'Brien. Unusually comprehensive guide to reading, speaking, writing Russian, for both advanced, beginning students. Over 70,000 entries in new orthography, full information on accentuation, grammatical classifications. Shades of meaning, idiomatic uses, colloquialisms, tables of irregular verbs for both languages. Individual entries indicate stems, transitiveness, perfective, imperfective aspects, conjugation, sound changes, accent, etc. Includes pronunciation instruction. Used at Harvard, Yale, Cornell, etc. 738pp. 5⅜ x 8.   T208 Paperbound $ 2.00

PHRASE AND SENTENCE DICTIONARY OF SPOKEN RUSSIAN, English-Russian, Russian-English. Based on phrases, complete sentences, not isolated words—recognized as one of best methods of learning idiomatic speech. Over 11,500 entries, indexed by single words, over 32,000 English, Russian sentences, phrases, in immediately useable form. Shows accent changes in conjugation, declension; irregular forms listed both alphabetically, under main form of word. 15,000 word introduction covers Russian sounds, writing, grammar, syntax. 15 page appendix of geographical names, money, important signs, given names, foods, special Soviet terms, etc. Originally published as U.S. Gov't Manual TM 30-944. iv + 573pp. 5⅜ x 8.   T496 Paperbound $2.75

PHRASE AND SENTENCE DICTIONARY OF SPOKEN SPANISH, Spanish-English, English-Spanish. Compiled from spoken Spanish, based on phrases, complete sentences rather than isolated words—not an ordinary dictionary. Over 16,000 entries indexed under single words, both Castilian, Latin-American. Language in immediately useable form. 25 page introduction provides rapid survey of sounds, grammar, syntax, full consideration of irregular verbs. Especially apt in modern treatment of phrases, structure. 17 page glossary gives translations of geographical names, money values, numbers, national holidays, important street signs, useful expressions of high frequency, plus unique 7 page glossary of Spanish, Spanish-American foods. Originally published as U.S. Gov't Manual TM 30-900. iv + 513pp. 5⅝ x 8⅜.   T495 Paperbound $1.75

SAY IT CORRECTLY language record sets

The best inexpensive pronunciation aids on the market. Spoken by native linguists associated with major American universities, each record contains:

14 minutes of speech—12 minutes of normal, relatively slow speech, 2 minutes of normal conversational speed.

120 basic phrases, sentences, covering nearly every aspect of everyday life, travel—introducing yourself, travel in autos, buses, taxis, etc., walking, sightseeing, hotels, restaurants, money, shopping, etc.

32 page booklet containing everything on record plus English translations easy-to-follow phonetic guide.

Clear, high-fidelity recordings.

Unique bracketing systems, selection of basic sentences enabling you to expand use of SAY IT CORRECTLY records with a dictionary, to fit thousands of additional situations.

Use this record to supplement any course or text. All sounds in each language illustrated perfectly—imitate speaker in pause which follows each foreign phrase in slow section, and be amazed at increased ease, accuracy of pronunciation. Available, one language per record for

French	**Spanish**	**German**
Italian	**Dutch**	**Modern Greek**
Japanese	**Russian**	**Portuguese**
Polish	**Swedish**	**Hebrew**
English (for German-speaking people)		**English (for Spanish-speaking people)**

7″ (33 1/3 rpm) record, album, booklet. **$1.00 each.**

SPEAK MY LANGUAGE: SPANISH FOR YOUNG BEGINNERS, M. Ahlman, Z. Gilbert. Records provide one of the best, most entertaining methods of introducing a foreign language to children. Within framework of train trip from Portugal to Spain, an English-speaking child is introduced to Spanish by native companion. (Adapted from successful radio program of N.Y. State Educational Department.) A dozen different categories of expressions, including greeting, numbers, time, weather, food, clothes, family members, etc. Drill is combined with poetry and contextual use. Authentic background music. Accompanying book enables a reader to follow records, includes vocabulary of over 350 recorded expressions. Two 10″ 33 1/3 records, total of 40 minutes. Book. 40 illustrations. 69pp. 5¼ x 10½.   T890 The set $4.95

LISTEN & LEARN language record sets

LISTEN & LEARN is the only extensive language record course designed especially to meet your travel and everyday needs. Separate sets for each language, each containing three 33 1/3 rpm long-playing records—1 1/2 hours of recorded speech by eminent native speakers who are professors at Columbia, New York U., Queens College.

Check the following features found only in LISTEN & LEARN:

Dual language recording. 812 selected phrases, sentences, over 3200 words, spoken first in English, then foreign equivalent. Pause after each foreign phrase allows time to repeat expression.

128-page manual (196 page for Russian)—everything on records, plus simple transcription. Indexed for convenience. Only set on the market completely indexed.

Practical. No time wasted on material you can find in any grammar. No dead words. Covers central core material with phrase approach. Ideal for person with limited time. Living, modern expressions, not found in other courses. Hygienic products, modern equipment, shopping, "air-conditioned," etc. Everything is immediately useable.

High-fidelity recording, equal in clarity to any costing up to $6 per record.

"Excellent . . . impress me as being among the very best on the market," Prof. Mario Pei, Dept. of Romance Languages, Columbia U. "Inexpensive and well done . . . ideal present," Chicago Sunday Tribune. "More genuinely helpful than anything of its kind," Sidney Clark, well-known author of "All the Best" travel books.

UNCONDITIONAL GUARANTEE. Try LISTEN & LEARN, then return it within 10 days for full refund, if you are not satisfied. It is guaranteed after you actually use it.

6 modern languages—FRENCH, SPANISH, GERMAN, ITALIAN, RUSSIAN, or JAPANESE *—one language to each set of 3 records (33 1/3 rpm). 128 page manual. Album.

| **Spanish** | the set $4.95 | **German** | the set $4.95 | **Japanese*** | the set $5.95 |
| **French** | the set $4.95 | **Italian** | the set $4.95 | **Russian** | the set $5.95 |

* Available Oct. 1959.

TRÜBNER COLLOQUIAL SERIES

These unusual books are members of the famous Trübner series of colloquial manuals. They have been written to provide adults with a sound colloquial knowledge of a foreign language, and are suited for either class use or self-study. Each book is a complete course in itself, with progressive, easy to follow lessons. Phonetics, grammar, and syntax are covered, while hundreds of phrases and idioms, reading texts, exercises, and vocabulary are included. These books are unusual in being neither skimpy nor overdetailed in grammatical matters, and in presenting up-to-date, colloquial, and practical phrase material. Bilingual presentation is stressed, to make thorough self-study easier for the reader.

COLLOQUIAL HINDUSTANI, A. H. Harley, formerly Nizam's Reader in Urdu, U. of London. 30 pages on phonetics and scripts (devanagari & Arabic-Persian) are followed by 29 lessons, including material on English and Arabic-Persian influences. Key to all exercises. Vocabulary. 5 x 7½. 147pp. Clothbound **$1.75**

COLLOQUIAL ARABIC, DeLacy O'Leary. Foremost Islamic scholar covers language of Egypt, Syria, Palestine, & Northern Arabia. Extremely clear coverage of complex Arabic verbs & noun plurals; also cultural aspects of language. Vocabulary. xviii + 192pp. 5 x 7½. Clothbound **$1.75**

COLLOQUIAL GERMAN, P. F. Doring. Intensive thorough coverage of grammar in easily-followed form. Excellent for brush-up, with hundreds of colloquial phrases. 34 pages of bilingual texts. 224pp. 5 x 7½. Clothbound **$1.75**

COLLOQUIAL SPANISH, W. R. Patterson. Castilian grammar and colloquial language, loaded with bilingual phrases and colloquialisms. Excellent for review or self-study. 164pp. 5 x 7½. Clothbound **$1.75**

COLLOQUIAL FRENCH, W. R. Patterson. 16th revised edition of this extremely popular manual. Grammar explained with model clarity, and hundreds of useful expressions and phrases; exercises, reading texts, etc. Appendixes of new and useful words and phrases. 223pp. 5 x 7½. Clothbound **$1.75**

COLLOQUIAL PERSIAN, L. P. Elwell-Sutton. Best introduction to modern Persian, with 90 page grammatical section followed by conversations, 35 page vocabulary. 139pp.   Clothbound **$1.75**

COLLOQUIAL CZECH, J. Schwarz, former headmaster of Lingua Institute, Prague. Full easily followed coverage of grammar, hundreds of immediately useable phrases, texts. Perhaps the best Czech grammar in print. "An absolutely successful textbook," JOURNAL OF CZECHO-SLOVAK FORCES IN GREAT BRITAIN. 252pp. 5 x 7½.   Clothbound **$2.50**

COLLOQUIAL RUMANIAN, G. Nandris, Professor of University of London. Extremely thorough coverage of phonetics, grammar, syntax; also included 70 page reader, and 70 page vocabulary. Probably the best grammar for this increasingly important language. 340pp. 5 x 7½.
Clothbound **$2.50**

COLLOQUIAL ITALIAN, A. L. Hayward. Excellent self-study course in grammar, vocabulary, idioms, and reading. Easy progressive lessons will give a good working knowledge of Italian in the shortest possible time. 5 x 7½.   Clothbound **$1.75**

MISCELLANEOUS

TREASURY OF THE WORLD'S COINS, Fred Reinfeld. Finest general introduction to numismatics; non-technical, thorough, always fascinating. Coins of Greece, Rome, modern countries of every continent, primitive societies, such oddities as 200-lb stone money of Yap, nail coinage of New England; all mirror man's economy, customs, religion, politics, philosophy, art. Entertaining, absorbing study; novel view of history. Over 750 illustrations. Table of value of coins illustrated. List of U.S. coin clubs. 224pp. 6½ x 9¼.
T433 Paperbound **$1.75**

ILLUSIONS AND DELUSIONS OF THE SUPERNATURAL AND THE OCCULT, D. H. Rawcliffe. Rationally examines hundreds of persistent delusions including witchcraft, trances, mental healing, peyotl, poltergeists, stigmata, lycanthropy, live burial, auras, Indian rope trick, spiritualism, dowsing, telepathy, ghosts, ESP, etc. Explains, exposes mental, physical deceptions involved, making this not only an exposé of supernatural phenomena, but a valuable exposition of characteristic types of abnormal psychology. Originally "The Psychology of the Occult." Introduction by Julian Huxley. 14 illustrations. 551pp. 5⅜ x 8.
T503 Paperbound **$2.00**

HOAXES, C. D. MacDougall. Shows how art, science, history, journalism can be perverted for private purposes. Hours of delightful entertainment, a work of scholarly value, often shocking. Examines nonsense news, Cardiff giant, Shakespeare forgeries, Loch Ness monster, biblical frauds, political schemes, literary hoaxers like Chatterton, Ossian, disumbrationist school of painting, lady in black at Valentino's tomb, over 250 others. Will probably reveal truth about few things you've believed, will help you spot more easily the editorial "gander" or planted publicity release. "A stupendous collection . . . and shrewd analysis," New Yorker. New revised edition. 54 photographs. 320pp. 5⅜ x 8.   T465 Paperbound **$1.75**

YOGA: A SCIENTIFIC EVALUATION, Kovoor T. Behanan. Book that for first time gave Western readers a sane, scientific explanation, analysis of yoga. Author draws on laboratory experiments, personal records of year as disciple of yoga, to investigate yoga psychology, physiology, "supernatural" phenomena, ability to plumb deepest human powers. In this study under auspices of Yale University Institute of Human Relations, strictest principles of physiological, psychological inquiry are followed. Foreword by W. A. Miles, Yale University. 17 photographs. xx + 270pp. 5⅜ x 8.   T505 Paperbound **$1.65**

Write for free catalogs!

Indicate your field of interest. Dover publishes books on physics, earth sciences, mathematics, engineering, chemistry, astronomy, anthropology, biology, psychology, philosophy, religion, history, literature, mathematical recreations, languages, crafts, art, graphic arts, etc.

Write to Dept. catr
Dover Publications, Inc.
Science B   *180 Varick St., N. Y. 14, N. Y.*

15